REARRANGEMENTS IN GROUND AND EXCITED STATES

Volume 3

This is Volume 42 of
ORGANIC CHEMISTRY
A series of monographs
Editor: HARRY H. WASSERMAN

A complete list of the books in this series appears at the end of the volume.

REARRANGEMENTS IN GROUND AND EXCITED STATES

edited by
Paul de Mayo
Photochemistry Unit
Department of Chemistry
The University of Western Ontario
London, Ontario, Canada

3

1980

ACADEMIC PRESS
A Subsidiary of Harcourt Brace Jovanovich, Publishers
New York   London   Toronto   Sydney   San Francisco

ACADEMIC PRESS, INC.
111 Fifth Avenue, New York, New York 10003

United Kingdom Edition published by
ACADEMIC PRESS, INC. (LONDON) LTD.
24/28 Oval Road, London NW1 7DX

Library of Congress Cataloging in Publication Data

Main entry under title:

Rearrangements in ground and excited states.

    (Organic chemistry series ;)
    Includes bibliographical references and index.
    1. Rearrangements (Chemistry)––Addresses, essays,
lectures. I. Mayo, Paul de. II. Series: Organic
chemistry series (New York) ;
QD281.R35R42   547.1'39   79–51675
ISBN 0–12–481303–8 (v. 3)

PRINTED IN THE UNITED STATES OF AMERICA

80 81 82 83   9 8 7 6 5 4 3 2 1

CONTENTS

v

Essay 17   Photochemical Rearrangements of Enones
DAVID I. SCHUSTER

Essay 18   Photochemical Rearrangements of Conjugated Cyclic Dienones
KURT SCHAFFNER AND MARTIN DEMUTH

Essay 19   Rearrangements of the Benzene Ring
D. BRYCE-SMITH AND A. GILBERT

Essay 20   Photorearrangements Via Biradicals of Simple Carbonyl Compounds
PETER J. WAGNER

LIST OF CONTRIBUTORS

Numbers in parentheses indicate the pages on which the authors' contributions begin.

D. Bryce-Smith (349)   Department of Chemistry, University of Reading, Whiteknights, Reading RG6 2 AD, England

J. L. Charlton (25)   Department of Chemistry, University of Manitoba, Winnipeg, Manitoba, Canada

W. G. Dauben (91)   Department of Chemistry, University of California, Berkeley, California 94720

Martin Demuth (281)   Institut für Strahlenchemie im Max-Planck-Institut für Kohlenforschung, D-4330 Mülheim a. d. Ruhr, Federal Republic of Germany

A. Gilbert (349)   Department of Chemistry, University of Reading, Whiteknights, Reading, RG6 2AD, England

E. L. McInnis (91)   Department of Chemistry, University of California, Berkeley, California 94720

D. M. Michno (91)   Department of Chemistry, University of California, Berkeley, California 94720

Michel Nastasi (445)   École Nationale Superièure de Chimie, Université de Haute Alsace, 68093 Mulhouse Cedex, France

Albert Padwa (501)   Department of Chemistry, Emory University, Atlanta, Georgia 30322

V. Ramamurthy* (1)   Chemistry Department, Columbia University, New York, New York 10027

J. Saltiel (25)   Department of Chemistry, Florida State University, Tallahassee, Florida 32306

* *Present Address:* Department of Organic Chemistry, Indian Institute of Science, Bangalore, India

Franco Scandola (549)   Centro di Studio sulla Fotochimica e Reattivita degli Stati Eccitati dei Composti di Coordinazione del C.N.R., Ferrara, Italy

Kurt Schaffner (281)   Institut für Strahlenschemie im Max-Planck-Institut für Kohlenforschung, D-4330 Mülheim a. d. Ruhr, Federal Republic of Germany

David I. Schuster (167)   Department of Chemistry, New York University, New York, New York 10003

Jacques Streith (445)   École Nationale Superièure de Chimie, Université de Haute Alsace, 68093 Mulhouse Cedex, France

N. J. Turro (1)   Chemistry Department, Columbia University, New York, New York 10027

Peter J. Wagner (381)   Chemistry Department, Michigan State University, East Lansing, Michigan 48824

Howard E. Zimmerman (131)   Chemistry Department, University of Wisconsin, Madison, Wisconsin 53706

CONTENTS OF OTHER VOLUMES

VOLUME 1

VOLUME 2

ESSAY **13** | # CHEMICAL GENERATION OF EXCITED STATES

N. J. TURRO and
V. RAMAMURTHY‡

I. INTRODUCTION

The chemical generation of an excited state occurs when a sizable fraction of the exothermicity of a chemical reaction is converted to electronic excitation energy in a reaction product. The latter may then emit a photon of light (chemiluminescence) or undergo further photochemical processes (1). The heart of the matter is the chemiexcitation since the subsequent step is the molecule's normal luminescence. Since chemiluminescence can be divided into a chemiexcitation and a luminescent or photoreaction stage, two major experimental tasks are (a) identification of the key chemiexcitation step and (b) identification of the luminescent or photoactive species.

In terms of potential energy surfaces a chemiluminescent organic reaction can be classified as a nonadiabatic thermal process wherein there is a change from one electronic energy surface to another (2). It is easily seen that the chemiexcitation step is, in general, a nonadiabatic reaction because while the reactant R is in its ground state the product P* is in an electronically excited state (Fig. 1).

---

‡ *Present Address:* Department of Organic Chemistry, Indian Institute of Science, Bangalore, India.

REARRANGEMENTS IN GROUND AND EXCITED STATES, VOL. 3

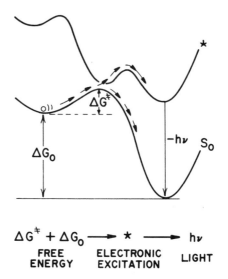

$$\Delta G^{\ddagger} + \Delta G_0 \longrightarrow \star \longrightarrow h\nu$$

FREE   ELECTRONIC
ENERGY   EXCITATION   LIGHT

Fig. 1 Schematic of a chemiluminescent organic reaction.

The known examples of organic chemiluminescence in solution can be placed under four general headings: (a) peroxide decomposition, (b) electron-transfer reactions, (c) formation of excited oxygen, and (d) pericyclic rearrangements.

The oxidation of luminol represents a classic example of a chemiluminescent organic reaction [Eq. (1)] (3). The famous example of firefly luminescence is also believed to involve an oxidative key step [Eq. (2)] (4). The reaction of the radical anions of organic hydrocarbons with organic cations produces chemiluminescence corresponding spectrally to

$$\text{1} + O_2 + 2OH^- \longrightarrow \text{2} + N_2 + 2H_2O + h\nu \qquad (1)$$

$$\text{3} + O_2 \xrightarrow{\text{enzymes}} \text{4} + CO_2 \qquad (2)$$

the fluorescence of an aromatic hydrocarbon. A typical example is the reaction of anthracene radical anion and cation of aromatic amines [Eq.

(3)] to yield anthracene, an amine, and light (5). Reports of chemiluminescent pericyclic rearrangements or reactions that do not involve oxygen in some form are very rare, an exceptional example being the electrocyclic rearrangement of Dewar benzene to benzene [Eq. (4)] (6) (Section IV).

$$\text{[structure 5]}^{\overline{\cdot}} \; + \; \overset{+}{N}Ar_3 \longrightarrow \text{[structure 6]}^* \; + \; NAr_3 \qquad (3)$$

$$\quad\quad\quad 5 \quad\quad\quad\quad\quad\quad\quad\quad\quad\quad\quad\quad 6$$

$$\text{[structure 7]} \longrightarrow \text{[structure 8]}^* \qquad\qquad (4)$$

$$\quad\quad\quad\quad 7 \quad\quad\quad\quad 8$$

There are several excellent general review articles on chemiluminescent processes, to which the reader is referred for details of specific systems (7–9). The systems of interest here are peroxide decomposition (or rearrangement) and pericyclic rearrangements.

For the chemical generation of excited states a reaction must provide (a) sufficient excitation energy, (b) at least one species capable of transforming into an electronically excited state, and (c) a reaction coordinate allowing the production of excited states.

Many energy-sufficient organic reactions are not measurably chemiluminescent. If a reaction proceeds via an elementary step for which formation of an excited state product is energetically feasible but for which chemiexcitation does not occur, one may conclude that the transition state structure for the step does not correspond to the one which brings surfaces together or that, if it does bring surfaces together, the jump to the excited surface is improbable because of electronic, vibrational, or spin prohibition. Although energetics determine the *feasibility* of producing an efficient chemiluminescent reaction, surface dynamics determine the observed *efficiency* of an energy-sufficient chemiluminescent reaction. In general, it appears that the ability to achieve a diradicaloid geometry enhances the efficiency of surface jumps corresponding to chemiexcitation (Fig. 2). In terms of energy surfaces, the diradicaloid geometry corresponds to a structure for which two or more electronic surfaces are tending to merge to a common point (zero-order surface crossing or surface touching) (10). It is precisely such a convergence of surfaces that is most favorable to jumps between surfaces. Conversely, the zero-order crossing must not be strongly avoided because such a situation would push the two surfaces far apart and reduce the probability of a surface jump (11). Although the efficiency of light emission is important in chemiluminescence,

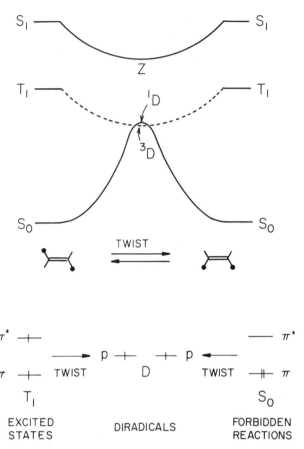

Fig. 2 Prototype surface diagram for an orbitally forbidden ground state reaction. The cis–trans isomerization of ethylenes represents the simplest reaction of this type.

the quantity of interest in this essay is the efficiency of the chemical production of excited states ϕ_{es}. The overall efficiency of chemiluminescence is a product of three efficiencies, as shown in Eq. (5),

$$\phi_{cl} = \phi_r \phi_{es} \phi_{fl} \tag{5}$$

where ϕ_r is the fraction of reacting molecules that pursue the correct chemical pathway, ϕ_{es} is the efficiency of chemical production of excited states, and ϕ_{fl} is the efficiency of fluorescence of the ultimate light emitter in the reaction. The measurement of absolute quantum yields presents many problems, but relative quantum yields are more easily obtained (12). Kinetic investigations of chemiluminescent reactions can be carried out by monitoring the concentration of the reactant or the product or by monitoring the decay of product luminescence. Any disagreement between rates obtained by different methods signals complications, such as induced decomposition or catalytic side reactions.

II. THERMAL GENERATION OF EXCITED CARBONYLS: THERMAL FRAGMENTATION OF DIOXETANES

Numerous dioxetanes and dioxetanones, once believed to be only fleeting intermediates and too unstable to be isolated, have now been prepared (13). Many are quite stable at room temperature (14). When heated in

TABLE 1

Activation Parameters of Some 1,2-Dioxetanes

Dioxetane	E_a (kcal/mol)	log A	ΔH (kcal/mol)	Φ^{*3}	Φ^{*1}	Ref.
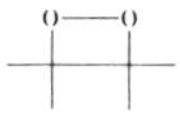 (dioxetane structure)	28	14.1	~70	~0.5–0.3	10^{-3}	a
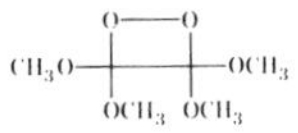 CH_3O—(dioxetane)—OCH_3, OCH_3 OCH_3	29	12.9	—	~0.3	10^{-4}	a
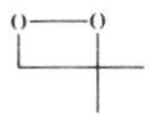 (dioxetane structure)	23	12.2	—	—	—	b
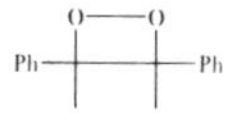 Ph—(dioxetane)—Ph	~25	~13	—	0.3	—	c
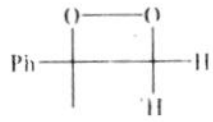 Ph—(dioxetane)—H, H	~23	~12	—	—	—	b,c
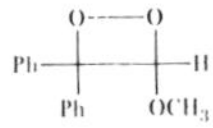 Ph—(dioxetane)—H, Ph OCH_3	26	13.5	—	—	—	d
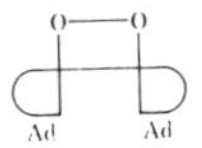 (adamantyl dioxetane) Ad Ad	~35	14	~75	0.15	0.02	e

(Ad = adamantyl)

(a) T. Wilson et al., J. Am. Chem. Soc. 98, 1086 (1976).
(b) W. H. Richardson et al., J. Am. Chem. Soc. 94, 1619 (1972).
(c) M. A. Umbreit and E. H. White, J. Org. Chem. 41, 479 (1976).
(d) A. L. Barumstart et al., Tetrahedron Lett. p. 2397 (1976).
(e) G. B. Schuster et al., J. Am. Chem. Soc. 97, 7110 (1975).

solution, dioxetanes smoothly decompose to give two carbonyl compounds [Eq. (6)], whereas dioxetanones give a carbonyl compound and carbon dioxide [Eq. (7)]. The activation energies for thermolysis of a number of dioxetanes are in the range of 25 ± 5 kcal/mol (Table 1). Since many examples have now been studied, one can draw the following general conclusions about the decomposition of dioxetanes: (a) They cleave quantitatively into two carbonyl fragments, one of which is electronically excited ($\phi^* \sim 1$–100%), and (b) the directly produced excited fragment is predominantly triplet rather than singlet ($\phi_T^*/\phi_S^* \sim 10$–1000). Surveys of

$$R_1 \underset{R_2 \quad R_3}{\overset{O—O}{\boxed{}}} R_4 \longrightarrow R_1 \overset{O}{\overset{\|}{C}} R_2 \; + \; R_3 \overset{O}{\overset{\|}{C}} R_4 \; + \; h\nu \qquad (6)$$

$$ 9 10$$

$$R_1 \underset{R_2}{\overset{O—O}{\boxed{}}}{\overset{}{O}} \longrightarrow R_1 \overset{O}{\overset{\|}{C}} R_2 \; + \; CO_2 \; + \; h\nu \qquad (7)$$

$$ 11$$

detailed experimental studies of dioxetanes have been presented in several excellent reviews (8), and only the mechanistic aspects of thermal decomposition will be discussed below. Furthermore, although the majority of studies have been concerned with tetramethyldioxetane (TMD), the general features are expected to be common for all dioxetane decompositions.

One can ask the following questions with respect to a reaction involving chemiexcitation: At what point does electronic excitation occur? What are the nuclear geometries to which chemiexcitation is possible? What determines the efficiency of chemiexcitation when these geometries are achieved? Two extreme limiting mechanisms have been proposed for TMD decomposition: the stepwise diradical path proposed by Richardson (15) and the concerted retrocyclic path suggested by McCapra (16), Kearns (17), and Turro (18).

The stepwise diradical path involves a discrete 1,4 diradical intermediate formed by cleavage of the oxygen–oxygen bond of the strained four-membered ring. The species thus formed is then said to partition between the excited carbonyl products of both singlet and triplet multiplicity and ground state carbonyl products (Scheme 1). This mechanism is consistent with thermochemical calculations (19) and with an isotopic substitution study (20). Observed high yields of triplet carbonyl formation can be

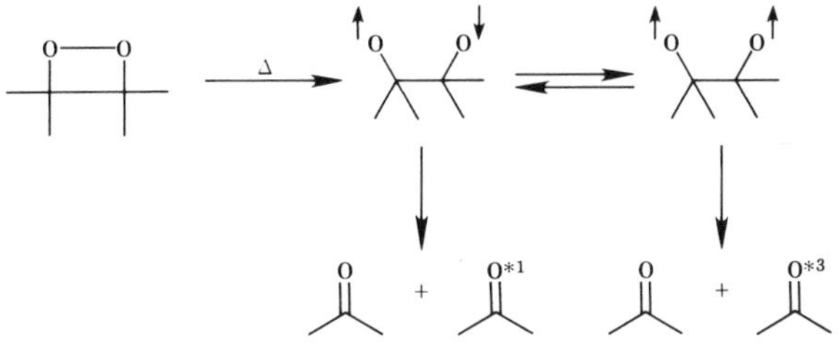

Scheme 1

rationalized according to the stepwise mechanism as follows. Soon after the cleavage of the O—O bond, the unpaired electrons on each oxygen atom are in a singlet state; however, when sufficiently separated, the bonding energy will be negligible, as will the repulsive interaction in the triplet states. Consequently, the singlet and triplet states will approach one another in energy, allow spin–orbit interactions and subsequent transitions from singlet to triplet states, and vice versa (*10*). If the C—C bond breaks, the singlet biradical will generate two carbonyl fragments, one of which may be excited. The triplet biradical will form one triplet carbonyl and one ground state singlet carbonyl. A prompt intersystem crossing from the singlet to the triplet biradical before the C—C bond breaks will increase the yield of triplet products.

On the basis of orbital symmetry arguments the retrocyclization of dioxetanes is predicted to yield excited carbonyl products. Several theoretical calculations (by *ab initio* GVB, CI, CNDO, and MINDO/3 methods) also favor the above symmetry-based arguments (*21*). A recent analysis of energy surface crossings by Turro and Devaquet (*18*) on qualitative grounds led to the expectation of a singlet–triplet surface crossing. This analysis is intermediate between the concerted and diradical mechanisms. A simple qualitative model, based on the cleavage in a more or less planar fashion, is shown in Fig. 3 for the chemiexcitation step in the thermolysis of dioxetanes. The appropriate state correlations according to the above model are shown in Fig. 4a. The center of the surface diagram corresponds to the forbidden transition state for the concerted cleavage. To the left of center the O—O bond has lengthened, and a diradical structure is expected to occur near the zero-order surface crossings of S_1 and T_1 with S_0. This "diradicaloid" structure should resemble an alkoxy radical and as such should possess substantial spin–orbit coupling, thereby causing an avoiding of the S_0 and T_1 surfaces near the diradicaloid geometry. To the right of center the C—C bond begins to break. The odd electrons originally localized on oxygen begin to delocalize into π and π^* orbitals, and the magnitude of spin–orbit coupling decreases. By the time the second

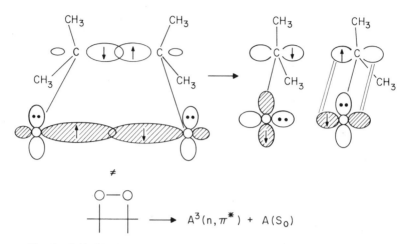

Fig. 3 Orbital basis for the cleavage of 1,2-dioxetanes to triplet fragments.

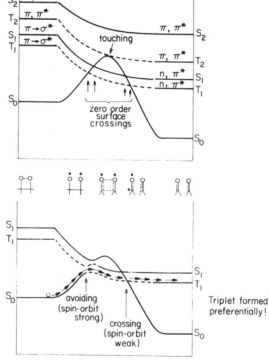

Fig. 4 (a) "Zero-order" surface correlation of the decomposition of TMD to acetone. (b) Working surface correlation for the decomposition of TMD.

surface crossing is reached, spin–orbit coupling is negligible. If we now follow a representative point along the ground state surface we see that it will climb in energy until it reaches the diradicaloid geometry. A "switch of states" corresponding to a spin flip or jump to the triplet surface occurs, and the point starts down the triplet surface. This proceeds past the crossing of the triplet and S_0 surfaces to T_1 ($n\pi^*$), i.e., produces acetone triplets. The above model is represented in Fig. 4b.

More reliable data on the yields and multiplicity of primary products as well as accurate thermochemical data are needed before a choice can be made between the diradical and concerted mechanisms.

A dioxetane decomposition that possesses the general features of Eq. (8) must be considered a molecular rearrangement. A few such reactions have been studied, and the available data are given in Table 2. The mechanistic aspects of these rearrangements are expected to bear a similarity to the fragmentation of 1,2-dioxetanes discussed above. Other systems, wherein the possibility of this type of rearrangement has been suggested, are as follows. In the photooxygenation of thujopsene (14), the formation of ketoaldehyde (16) is interpreted as proceeding via the 1,2-dioxetane 15 [Eq. (9)] (22). Similarly, the formation of 1,3-dione (19) by

TABLE 2

Activation Parameters of Some Cyclic 1,2-Dioxetanes

Dioxetane	E_a (kcal/mol)	log A	Φ^{*3}	Φ^{*1}	Ref.
	~25.5	12.9	0.17	2×10^4	a
	~23	12.7	8×10^{-3}	$<10^{-5}$	a
	~24	12.6	0.3	10^{-4}	b
	—	—	0.2	0.003	c

(a) J. E. Filby, Ph.D. Thesis, University of Alberta, Edmunton, Alberta, Canada (1973).

(b) M. E. Landis, Ph.D. Thesis, Harvard University, Cambridge, Massachusetts (1974).

(c) N. J. Turro et al., J. Am. Chem. Soc. **92**, 6553 (1970).

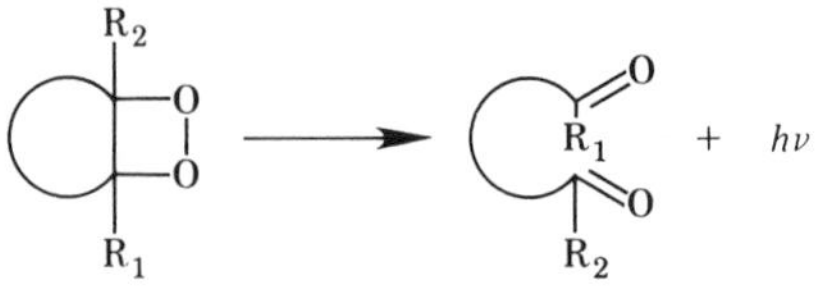

$$(8)$$

12   13

singlet oxygenation of cyclopropene (17) can be considered to involve rearrangement of the dioxetane 18 [Eq. (10)] (23). The bridged annulene 20 likewise affords the dialdehyde 22 as a minor product on singlet oxygenation, presumably via the 1,2-dioxetanone 21 [Eq. (11)] (24). Other examples can be found elsewhere (25–27).

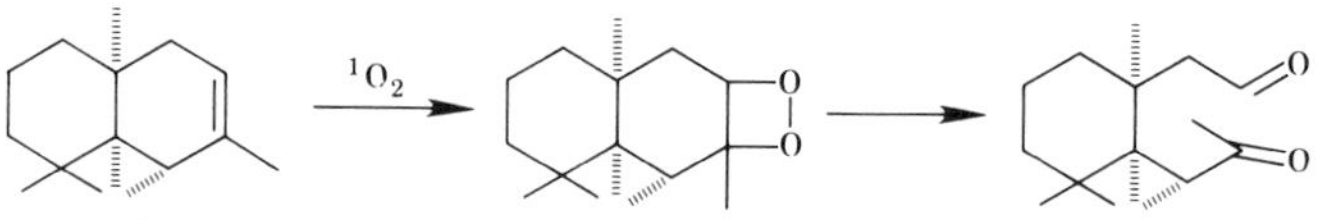

$$(9)$$

14   15   16

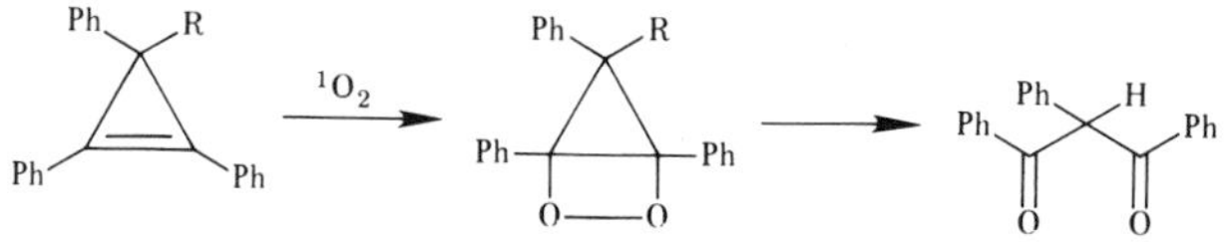

$$(10)$$

17   18   19

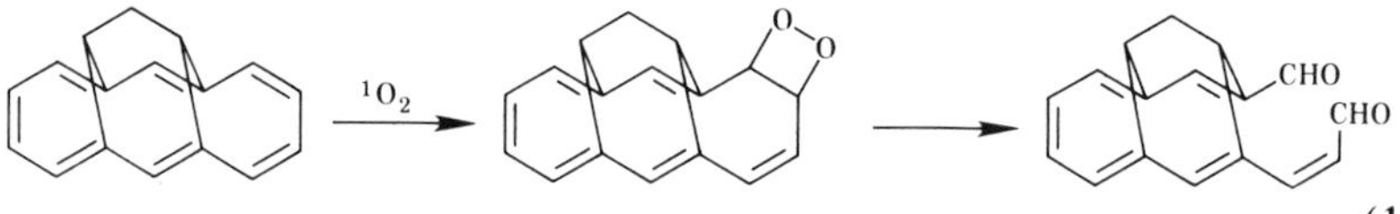

$$(11)$$

20   21   22

III. THERMOLYSIS OF PEROXIDES: CHEMICAL GENERATION OF MOLECULAR OXYGEN

The thermolysis of oxonides and peroxides often leads to fragmentation processes giving rise to electronically excited products. These reactions cannot be classified as molecular rearrangements but are discussed here for completeness and because recent reviews on chemiluminescence fail to include them.

The thermolysis of ozonides is often used as a source of molecular oxygen, as illustrated in Eqs. (12) and (13) (28). The formation of singlet molecular oxygen is established by chemical trapping and by spectroscopy. These fragmentation reactions are efficiently chemiluminescent. A clear understanding of the mechanism is lacking.

$$(PhO)_3-P \overset{O-O}{\underset{O}{\bigsqcup}} \quad \overset{\Delta}{\longrightarrow} \quad \overset{O}{\underset{(OPh)_3}{\overset{||}{P}}} \quad + \quad {}^1O_2 \qquad (12)$$

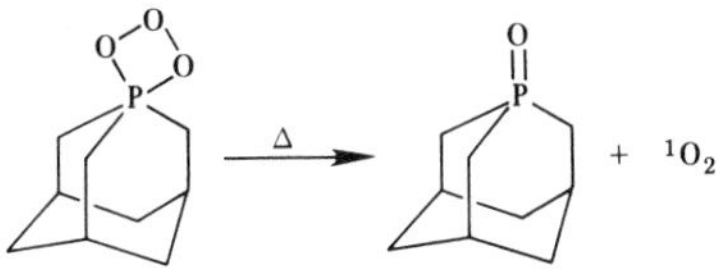

23

$$(13)$$

24

TABLE 3

Activation Parameters and Singlet Oxygen Yields from Endoperoxide

Endoperoxide	log A	E_a (kcal/mol)	$\% {}^1O_2$	Ref.
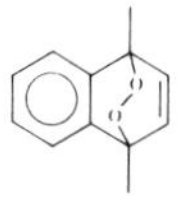	—	$t_{1/2}$ ~5 hr, 25°C	—	a
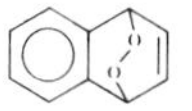	—	23.7	—	b
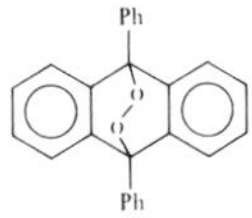	15.4	27.8 33.2	35	c,d
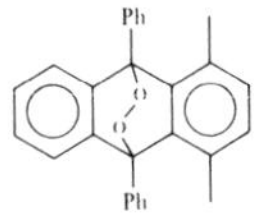	14.9	32.5	50	d
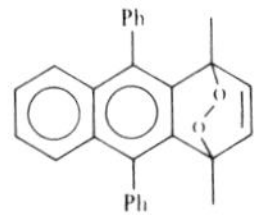	13.0	30.5	95	d
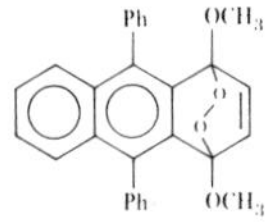	13.1	24.8	98	d

(a) H. H. Wasserman and D. L. Larsen, *Chem. Commun.* p. 253 (1972).
(b) M. Schafer-Ridder *et al.*, *Angew. Chem., Int. Ed. Engl.* **15**, 228 (1976).
(c) H. H. Wasserman *et al.*, *J. Am. Chem. Soc.* **94**, 4991 (1972).
(d) N. J. Turro *et al.*, *J. Am. Chem. Soc.* **101**, 1300 (1979).

The endoperoxides of naphthalenes and anthracenes generally undergo thermolysis to yield the parent aromatic compound and molecular oxygen [Eq. (14)] (29). In most cases chemical trapping experiments and chemiluminescence studies indicate that singlet molecular oxygen is a primary product of the thermolysis. Recently, mechanistic aspects of this fragmentation process have been studied using a number of anthracene endoperoxides (30), and the results are presented in Table 3. The results indicate a correlation between high $\Delta S\ddagger$ values (9,10-endoperoxides) and a low yield of $^1O_2$, and a nearly zero or slightly negative value of $\Delta S\ddagger$ (1,4-endoperoxides) and a quantitative yield of $^1O_2$. In the case of 9,10-DPAO$_2$ construction of a complete energy diagram (Fig. 5) for the decomposition is possible since the energy for $^3O_2 \rightarrow {}^1O_2$ excitation is known ($\sim$23 kcal/mol) (31), the activation energy of reaction of $^1O_2$ and DPA has been estimated to be $\sim$5 kcal/mol (32), and the heat of reaction for DPAO$_2$ $\rightarrow$ DPA + O$_2$ has been estimated to be $\sim$5 kcal/mol. From Fig. 5 it is clear that the inefficiency of the formation of $^1O_2$ from 9,10-

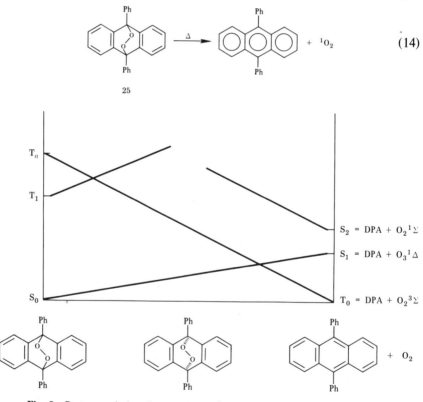

Fig. 5 State correlation diagram for the decomposition of an endoperoxide.

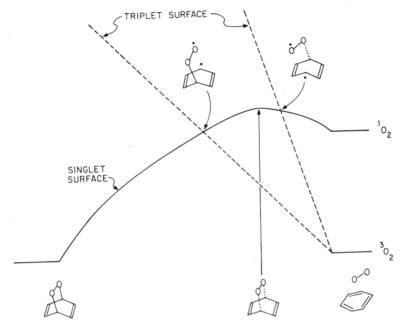

Fig. 6 Energy surface for the decomposition of an endoperoxide.

DPAO$_2$ is not simply a function of reaction energetics. It is suggested that the high efficiency of production of $^1O_2$ from 1,4-endoperoxides results from a concerted decomposition mechanism, and the low efficiency of production of $^1O_2$ from DPAO$_2$ results from a diradical mechanism. Figure 6 is a schematic representation of the pertinent energy surfaces. A singlet–triplet surface crossing is expected along the reaction coordinate for concerted thermolysis of endoperoxides (*33*). 1,4-Endoperoxides usually will have little opportunity to generate effective spin–orbit coupling anywhere along the reaction coordinate, and the system never leaves the lowest energy singlet surface. Molecular oxygen is thus produced quantitatively. In the case of DPAO$_2$, the breaking of a single C—O bond evidently occurs competitively with, or preferentially to, completely concerted bond breaking. As a result, a greater diradicaloid character develops as the system proceeds along the reaction coordinate, and more effective spin–orbit coupling is available because of developing one-electron character on an oxygen atom (*10*). In the region of the singlet–triplet crossing, the system now has a better opportunity to jump to the lower triplet surface. Thus, the above rationale explains the selective formation of triplets (excited carbonyls) when simple dioxetanes decompose thermally and the selective formation of singlets (molecular oxygen) when endoperoxides decompose thermally.

There are a few other cyclic peroxides that undergo chemiluminescent fragmentation processes [Eqs. (15) and (16)], but their mechanism is not well understood (34). Their chemiluminescence mechanism in the presence of dyes is further complicated by electron-transfer processes, as recently discovered in one system (Scheme 2) (35).

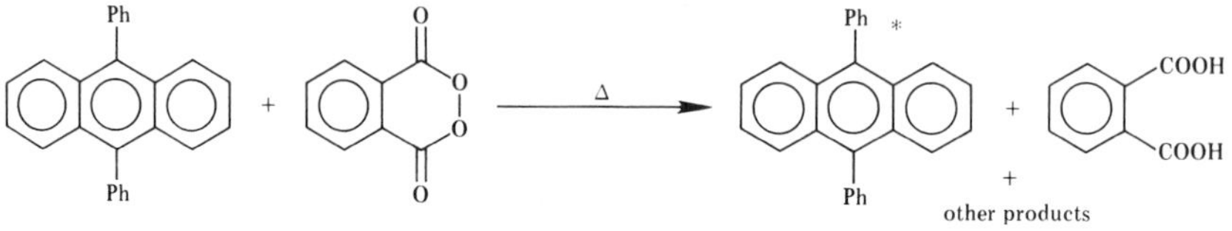

(15)

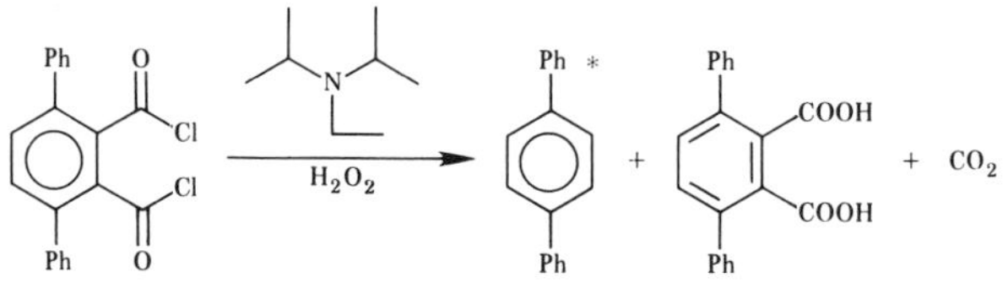

(16)

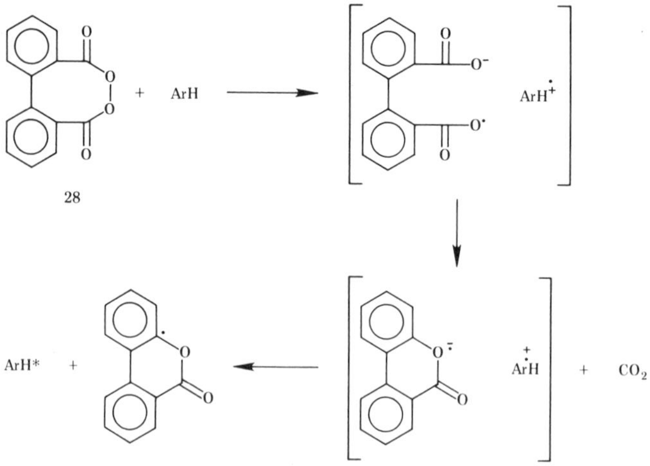

Scheme 2. ArH = 9,10-diphenylanthracene.

IV. CHEMILUMINESCENT PERICYCLIC REARRANGEMENTS

The electrocyclic conversion of benzene isomers to benzene is facile at room temperature. All these electrocyclic processes are sufficiently exothermic to generate benzene in the excited triplet state but not in the excited singlet state. Of these reactions only electrocyclic ring opening of the Dewar benzenes has been found to produce benzene triplets, and then in low yield (6). The phosphorescence of benzene in fluid solution is very weak, so that indirect methods (strongly emitting triplet energy acceptors) are required for observation. Since these ring openings are formally disrotatory four-electron processes, they correspond to orbitally forbidden

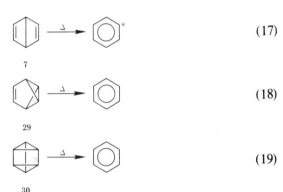

(17)

(18)

(19)

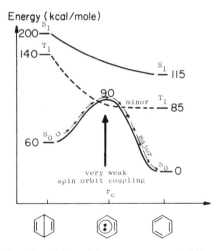

Fig. 7 Schematic surface description of the rearrangement of Dewar benzene to benzene.

TABLE 4

**Activation Parameters for the Thermal
Rearrangement of Dewar Benzene**[a]

Molecule	$\Delta H\ddagger$	ϕ^{*3}
	25.1	0.02
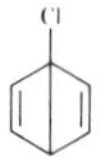	20.0	0.07
	30.2	0.10

[a] Reprinted with permission from Lechtken
et al., J. Am. Chem. Soc. **95**, 3027 (1973).
Copyright by the American Chemical Society.

reactions (*36*). This means that a touching of a triplet surface and a ground surface may occur near the geometry of the transition state for the forbidden reaction (Fig. 7). Since the atoms involved in the ring opening do not possess a strong spin–orbit coupling, it is unlikely that a spin flip will occur efficiently as the molecule passes along the reaction coordinate through the transition state geometry (*37*). The magnitude of spin–orbit coupling in the lowest states of benzenes is estimated to be 10^{-1} cm^{-1} ($\sim 3 \times 10^{-4}$ kcal/mol) (*38*). Rate constants of the order of 10^6 sec^{-1} are expected if intersystem crossing occurs by a spin–orbit coupling mechanism. Since the time that a molecule spends in structures close to that of the transition state geometry is $\sim 10^{-11}$–10^{-12} sec and since intersystem crossing must occur during this time period, the efficiency of singlet to triplet conversion should be $\sim 10^{-11}$–$10^{-12} \times 10^6$, i.e., $\sim 10^{-5}$–10^{-6}, a value consistent with the experimental findings (Table 4). Increased spin–orbit coupling should then enhance the efficiency of crossing to the triplet surface, and this is indeed found to be true. Perusal of Table 4 reveals that chlorinated Dewar benzenes show the highest chemiexcitation efficien-

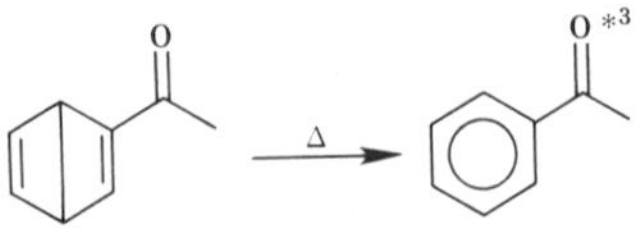

(20)

31                                  $\phi = 0.02$

cies, which suggests that a heavy-atom effect on intersystem crossing may be operating. In agreement with the above observation Dewar acetophenone also undergoes electrocyclic ring opening to give excited triplet acetophenone [Eq. (20)] (*39*).

The observation that Dewar benzene is chemiluminescent but that benzvalene and prismane are not deserves comment (*40*). A plausible explanation derives from a lack of an effective surface crossing for geometries near the transition state of reaction. If the reaction of benzvalene is concerted (as expected for a six-electron process), then a strongly avoided crossing between the ground and an excited surface is to be expected. Such a situation will have the effect of lowering the energy of the transition state without affecting the energy of the triplet state at the transition state geometry. Thus, the critical feature, crossing of the ground state and triplet state surfaces, which occurs for Dewar benzene and allows its rearrangement to benzene to be chemiluminescent, is evidently absent in the rearrangement of benzvalene. On the other hand, rearrangement of prismane to benzene is orbitally forbidden. The absence of triplet benzene formation in the above rearrangement may be taken as evidence for the conversion of prismane to benzene through benzvalene (*41*). There are many other examples of reactions that are not chemiluminescent even though sufficient reaction energy is available to populate excited singlet or triplet states of the product [Eqs. (21) and (22)] (*42*).

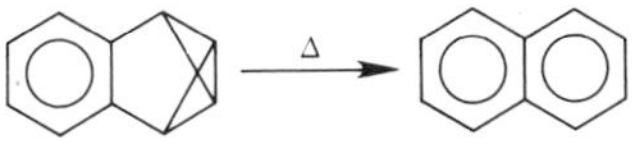

$$\qquad\qquad\qquad\qquad\qquad (21)$$

32

$$\qquad\qquad\qquad\qquad\qquad (22)$$

33

V. APPLICATIONS OF CHEMIEXCITATION TO PHOTOCHEMICAL AND MECHANISTIC PROBLEMS

By using chemical energy to generate an electronically excited state one can study photochemical processes without the need for a "photon."

Photoreactions can be initiated either by direct formation of reactive excited states via chemiexcitation or by indirect formation of excited states via energy transfer from excited molecules produced by chemiexcitation.

An interesting example of type I cleavage of dibenzyl ketone was reported in the thermolysis of 3,3-dibenzyl-1,2-dioxetane [Eq. (23)] (43). Excited hexan-2-one can undergo intramolecular γ-hydrogen abstraction

to give cyclobutanes and olefins. Interestingly, thermolysis of 3,4-dimethyl-3,4-di-*n*-butyl-1,2-dioxetane gave type II products resulting from thermally generated excited states of hexan-2-one [Eq. (24)] (44). In this connection, an important observation was made by Zimmerman *et al.*

in the thermolysis of **36**, as shown in Eq. (25) (45). The excited dienone resulting from thermolysis of **36** undergoes photorearrangement. The yields of excited (singlet or triplet) products from **36** are determined on that basis and reported to be 17.1, 14.0, and 12% for **36a**, **36b**, and **36c**, respectively. Hence, the nature of the R group seems to have little influence on the yields of excited dienone even though, in the case of **35c**, the lowest triplet ($\pi\pi^*$) of the product, β-acetonaphthone, is lower than that of the dienone.

The reaction of triplet molecular oxygen and of singlet molecular oxygen to yield strained cyclic acetylenes produces chemiluminescence identified as resulting from electronically excited 1,2-diones (46). The intermediacy of 1,2-dioxetenes has been invoked to explain these results [Eq. (26)].

Because of the high sensitivity of the devices that measure

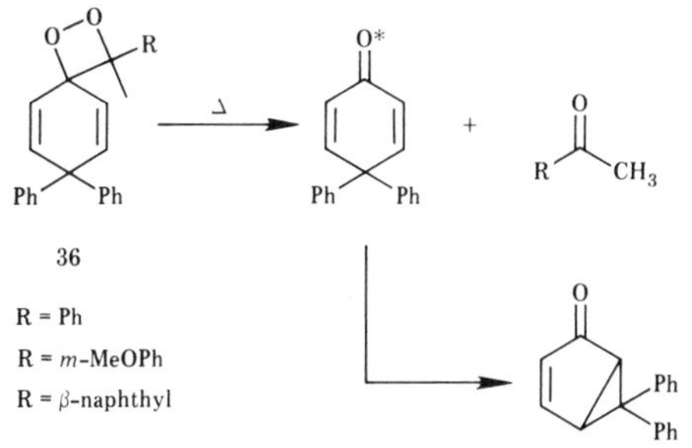

36

a: R = Ph
b: R = *m*-MeOPh
c: R = β-naphthyl

(25)

chemiluminescence, exceedingly low concentrations of chemiluminescent intermediates can be detected. For example, the rearrangement of 3,3-dimethylbis(cyclopropenyl) to xylenes has been shown to involve a Dewar

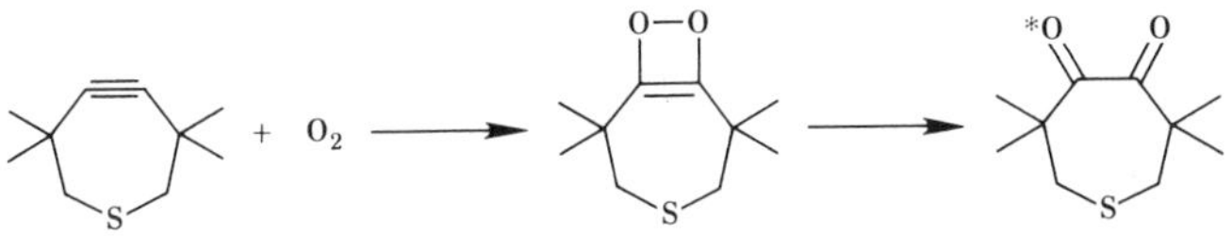

(26)

benzene by detection of the latter by means of its chemiluminescence characteristics (47). The thermal fragmentation of the polycyclic azo compound **38** also involves an initial loss of nitrogen to form Dewar ben-

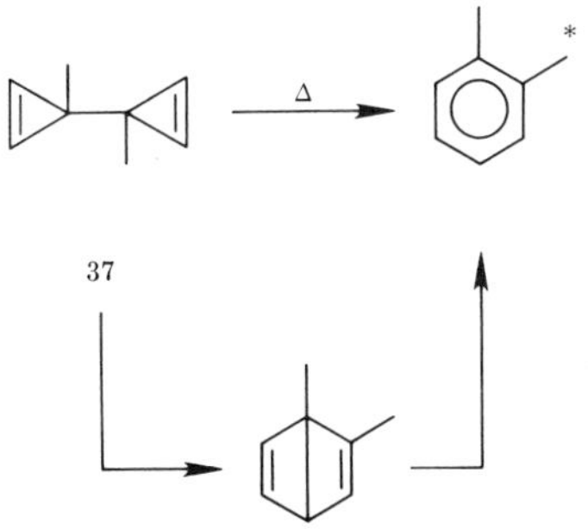

37

(27)

zene, which is unstable under the reaction conditions and undergoes chemiluminescent ring opening, as illustrated in Eq. (28) (48).

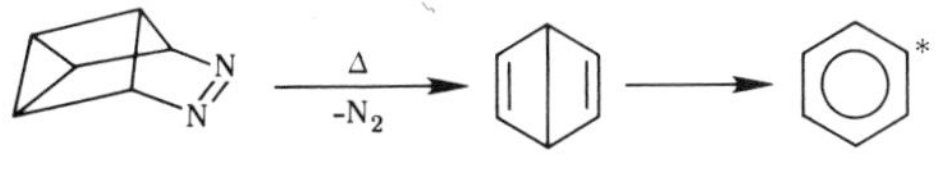

38

(28)

VI. REARRANGEMENTS TO PRODUCE CHEMILUMINESCENT INTERMEDIATES

There have been several reports of reactions that involve rearrangements to produce dioxetanes, which then undergo chemiluminescent decomposition. For example (23), reaction of **39** with $^1O_2$ leads to the formation of **42**, presumably via the sequence **39** + O_2 → **40** → **41** → **42** [Eq. (29)].

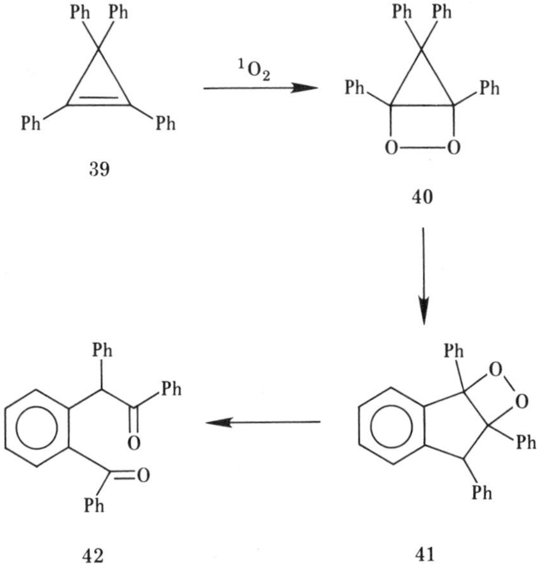

(29)

Thermolysis, (25) of the endoperoxide **43** results in a chemiluminescent reaction that yields **45**. This reaction is acid-catalyzed (26) and is proposed to proceed via the sequence **43** → **44** → **45** [Eq. (30)].

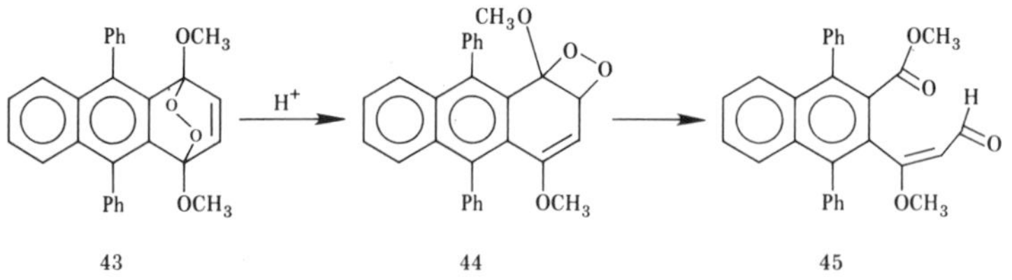

(30)

Reaction of $^1O_2$ with the anthracene **46** yields the [4 + 2] product **47**, a compound that is stable at low temperatures (27). Silica gel catalyzes the rearrangement of **47** to **48**; decomposition of the latter is chemiluminescent [Eq. (31)] and yields **49**.

$$(31)$$

The possibility exists that many dioxetane-forming processes may be preceded by a rearrangement. In particular, the initial formation of a perepoxide, in some of the addition reactions of $^1O_2$ and ethylenes, may be followed by rearrangement to a dioxetane [Eq. (32)]. To date, there is no direct spectroscopic evidence for the formation of a species such as **50**. However, indirect chemical trapping experiments are consistent with the

$$(32)$$

formation of such species. It is hoped that future research will be successful in establishing the existence, and achieving the isolation, of perepoxide structures and that their role in the formation of dioxetanes will be established.

ACKNOWLEDGMENT

The authors wish to thank the Air Force Office of Scientific Research, the National Science Foundation and the National Institute of Health for their generous support of this research.

REFERENCES

1. Review of chemiexcitation mechanisms: R. F. Vasilev, *Russ. Chem. Rev. (Engl. Transl.)* **39**, 529 (1970).
2. M. G. Evans, E. Eyring, and J. F. Kincaid, *J. Chem. Phys.* **6**, 349 (1938).
3. Review of bioluminescence: J. W. Hastings, *Annu. Rev. Biochem.* **37**, 597 (1968).
4. T. A. Hopkins *et al., J. Am. Chem. Soc.* **89**, 7148 (1967).
5. A. Weller and K. Zachariasse, *Chem. Phys. Lett.* **10**, 590 (1971).
6. P. Lechtken *et al., J. Am. Chem. Soc.* **95**, 3025 (1973).
7. Review of electron transfer chemiluminescence: A. Zweig, *Adv. Photochem.* **6**, 425 (1968); D. M. Hercules, *Phys. Methods Chem.* **2B**, 256 (1971); L. R. Faulkner and A. J. Bard, *Electroanal. Chem.* **10**, 1 (1977); L. R. Faulkner, *Phys. Chem., Ser. 2* **9**, 213 (1976).
8. Review of chemiluminescence involving dioxetanes: N. J. Turro and P. Lechtken, *Pure Appl. Chem.* **33**, 363 (1973); N. J. Turro *et al., Acc. Chem. Res.* **7**, 97 (1974); C. Mumford, *Chem. Br.* **11**, 402 (1975); N. J. Turro, in "The Exciplex" (W. Wave and M. Gordon, eds.), p. 165. Academic Press, New York, 1975; T. Wilson, *Phys. Chem., Ser. Two* **9**, 265 (1976); W. Adam, *Adv. Heterocycl. Chem.* **21**, 437 (1977).
9. Review of chemiluminescence: K. D. Gundermann, *Angew. Chem., Int. Ed. Engl.* **4**, 566 (1965); V. I. Papisova *et al., Russ. Chem. Rev. (Engl. Transl.)* **34**, 599 (1965); F. McCapra, *Q. Rev., Chem. Soc.* **20**, 485 (1966); R. F. Vasilev, *Prog. React. Kinet.* **4**, 305 (1967); E. H. White *et al., Angew. Chem., Int. Ed. Engl.* **13**, 229 (1974); F. McCapra, *Pure Appl. Chem.* **24**, 611 (1970); *Prog. Org. Chem.* **8**, 231 (1971); K. D. Gundermann, *Top. Chem.* **46**, 61 (1974); E. H. White and D. F. Roswell, *Acc. Chem. Res.* **3**, 54 (1970); M. M. Rauhut, *ibid.* **2**, 80 (1969).
10. Review of diradicals: L. Salem and C. Rowland, *Angew. Chem., Int. Ed. Engl.* **11**, 92 (1972).
11. Review of surfaces in ground and excited state reactions: J. Michl, *Mol. Photochem.* **4**, 257 and 287 (1972); *Pure Appl. Chem.* **41**, 507 (1975); *Top. Curr. Chem.* **46**, 1 (1974); L. Salem, *J. Am. Chem. Soc.* **96**, 3486 (1974); L. Salem *et al., ibid.* **97**, 479 (1975).
12. J. Lee and H. H. Seliger, *Photochem. Photobiol.* **4**, 1015 (1965); J. W. Hastings and G. Weber, *J. Opt. Soc. Am.* **53**, 1410 (1963).
13. K. R. Kopecky *et al., Can. J. Chem.* **53**, 1103 (1975); W. Adam and J. C. Liu, *J. Am. Chem. Soc.* **94**, 2894 (1972); N. J. Turro *et al., ibid.* **99**, 5836 (1977); P. D. Bartlett and A. P. Schaap, *ibid.* **92**, 3223 (1970); A. P. Schaap and P. D. Bartlett, *ibid.* p. 6056; S. Mazur and C. S. Foote, *ibid.* p. 3225.
14. J. H. Wieringa *et al., Tetrahedron Lett.* p. 169 (1972); G. B. Schuster *et al., J. Am. Chem. Soc.* **97**, 7110 (1975).
15. W. H. Richardson *et al., J. Am. Chem. Soc.* **94**, 1619 and 8665 (1972); **96**, 7525 (1974).
16. F. McCapra, *Chem. Commun.* p. 155 (1968); *Pure Appl. Chem.* **24**, 611 (1970).
17. D. R. Kearns, *Chem. Rev.* **71**, 395 (1971).
18. N. J. Turro and P. Lechtken, *J. Am. Chem. Soc.* **95**, 264 (1973); *Pure Appl. Chem.* **33**, 363 (1973); N. J. Turro and A. Devaquet, *J. Am. Chem. Soc.* **97**, 3859 (1975).
19. W. H. Richardson and H. E. O'Neal, *J. Am. Chem. Soc.* **94**, 8665 (1972); H. E. O'Neal and W. H. Richardson, *ibid.* **92**, 6553 (1970).
20. J. Y. Koo and G. Schuster, *J. Am. Chem. Soc.* **99**, 5403 (1977).
21. E. M. Evlett and G. Feller, *Chem. Phys. Lett.* **22**, 499 (1973; D. R. Roberts, *Chem. Commun.* p. 683 (1974); G. Varnett, *Can. J. Chem.* **52**, 3837 (1974); M. J. S. Dewar and S. Krishner, *J. Am. Chem. Soc.* **96**, 7578 (1974); M. J. S. Dewar, S. Kirshner, and K. W. Kollmar, *ibid.* p. 7579; T. Aoyama *et al., Chem. Phys. Lett.* **42**, 347 (1976); C. W. Eaker

and J. Hinze, *Theor. Chim. Acta* **40**, 113 (1975); L. B. Harding and W. A. Goddard, *J. Am. Chem. Soc.* **99**, 4520 (1977).

22. S. Ito *et al., Tetrahedron Lett.* p. 1181 (1971).
23. I. R. Politizer and G. W. Griffin, *Tetrahedron Lett.* p. 4775 (1974).
24. E. Vogel, A. Alscher, and K. Wilms, *Angew. Chem., Int. Ed. Engl.* **13**, 398 (1974).
25. J. Rigaudy, *Pure Appl. Chem.* **16**, 169 (1968).
26. T. Wilson, *Photochem. Photobiol.* **10**, 441 (1969).
27. A. P. Schaap, P. A. Burns, and K. A. Zaklika, *J. Am. Chem. Soc.* **99**, 1270 (1977).
28. R. W. Murray and M. L. Kaplan, *J. Am. Chem. Soc.* **90**, 537 (1968); **91**, 5358 (1969); A. P. Schaap, K. Lee, and A. L. Thayer, *J. Org. Chem.* **40**, 1185 (1975).
29. H. H. Wasserman and J. R. Scheffer, *J. Am. Chem. Soc.* **89**, 3073 (1967); H. H. Wasserman and D. Larsen, *Chem. Commun.* p. 253 (1972); H. Hart and A. Oku, *ibid.* p. 254.
30. N. J. Turro *et al., J. Am. Chem. Soc.* (submitted for publication).
31. K. Kawoka *et al., J. Chem. Phys., 46,* 1842 (1967); A. V. Khan and D. R. Kearns, *ibid.* **48**, 3272 (1968).
32. B. Stevens *et al., J. Am. Chem. Soc.* **96**, 6846 (1974).
33. D. R. Kearns, *J. Am. Chem. Soc.* **91**, 6554 (1969).
34. G. W. Lundeen and A. H. Adelman, *J. Am. Chem. Soc.* **92**, 3914 (1970); K. D. Gundermann and M. Steinfatt, *Angew. Chem., Int. Ed. Engl.* **14**, 560 (1975); G. B. Schuster, *J. Am. Chem. Soc.* **99**, 651 (1977); M. M. Rahut, *Acc. Chem. Res.* **2**, 80 (1969).
35. J. Y. Koo and G. B. Schuster, *J. Am. Chem. Soc.* **99**, 6107 (1977).
36. R. B. Woodward and R. Hoffmann, "The Conservation of Orbital Symmetry." Academic Press, New York, 1970.
37. For a discussion on spin-orbit coupling: S. K. Lowen and M. A. El-Sayed, *Chem. Rev.* **66**, 199 (1966); S. P. McGlynn, T. Azumi, and M. Kinoshita, "Molecular Spectroscopy of the Triplet State." Prentice-Hall, Englewood Cliffs, New Jersey, 1969.
38. H. F. Hameka and L. J. Oosterfoff, *Mol. Phys.* **1**, 358 (1958).
39. N. J. Turro *et al., J. Am. Chem. Soc.* **96**, 6797 (1974).
40. N. J. Turro *et al., Tetrahedron Lett.* p. 4133 (1976).
41. K. E. Wilzbach and L. Kaplan, *J. Am. Chem. Soc.* **87**, 4004 (1965); R. Criegee and R. Askani, *Angew. Chem., Int. Ed. Engl.* **5**, 519 (1966); W. Schafer *et al., ibid.* **6**, 78 (1967).
42. R. V. Corr *et al., Chem. Phys. Lett.* **39**, 57 (1976); N. J. Turro *et al., J. Am. Chem. Soc.* **95**, 2035 (1973).
43. W. H. Richardson *et al., J. Am. Chem. Soc.* **94**, 9277 (1972).
44. T. R. Darling and C. S. Foote, *J. Am. Chem. Soc.* **96**, 1625 (1974); C. S. Foote and T. R. Darling, *Pure Appl. Chem.* **41**, 495 (1975).
45. H. E. Zimmermann and G. E. Keck, *J. Am. Chem. Soc.* **97**, 3527 (1975); H. E. Zimmermann *et al., ibid.* **98**, 5574 (1976).
46. N. J. Turro, V. Ramannurthy, K. C. Liu, A. Krebs, and R. Kemper, *J. Am. Chem. Soc.* **98**, 7425 (1976).
47. N. J. Turro *et al., J. Am. Chem. Soc.* **97**, 4758 (1975).
48. C. A. Renner *et al., J. Am. Chem. Soc.* **97**, 2568 (1975).

14 | # CIS–TRANS ISOMERIZATION OF OLEFINS

J. SALTIEL and
J. L. CHARLTON

As a rearrangement, cis–trans isomerization of olefins is conceptually simple. Barring steric restraints, it involves 180° rotation about a double bond [Eq. (1)] and may be brought about thermally, catalytically, or

$$
\begin{array}{c}
\underset{B}{\overset{A}{\diagdown}} C = C \underset{E}{\overset{D}{\diagup}} \quad \rightleftharpoons \quad \underset{B}{\overset{A}{\diagdown}} C = C \underset{D}{\overset{E}{\diagup}}
\end{array}
\tag{1}
$$

photochemically. This very simplicity made possible the early application of theory, which in turn has given incentive to a multitude of experimental approaches.

I. THEORETICAL CONSIDERATIONS

Mulliken's molecular orbital calculations for ethylene served as a basis for early mechanistic discussions (1). However, recent calculations have called into question the exact ordering of excited states and their behavior as twisting about the CC bonds occurs (2,2a). These calculations place a Rydberg state, V_g, below the $\pi-\pi^*$ singlet state, V_u, at 0°, and there is an avoided crossing between these two states on twisting about the CC bond (Fig. 1B). In the twisted state, often referred to as the "p" state, the

REARRANGEMENTS IN GROUND AND EXCITED STATES, VOL. 3

The "p" state

energy of the ground state reaches a maximum since the p orbitals are orthogonal and the π-bonding interaction is at a minimum. In contrast, both the first excited singlet and triplet states are at an energetic minimum in the twisted geometry. The transition probability to the lower Rydberg state is very low, and direct excitation of ethylene will involve $\pi-\pi^*$ excitation followed by twisting and internal conversion to the Rydberg state at the point of the avoided crossing. The lowest triplet state was previously thought to be lower than the ground singlet state at a twist angle of $\pi/2$, but recent calculations have placed the triplet above or very near the ground state in this geometry (3,4). The calculations predicting the ordering of states in Fig. 1B have themselves been reexamined (3,5) and doubt has been cast (3) on the possibility that the spectroscopic observations allow for two overlapping transitions to V_g and V_u states. Accordingly, the initial picture (Fig. 1A) may still be correct.

Replacing the hydrogens in ethylene by other groups strongly affects the shapes and relative energies of the potential energy curves. In acyclic alkenes steric effects raise the energy of the cis isomer relative to the trans isomer, whereas in cyclic alkenes ring strain has the reverse effect. Conjugation generally lowers the energy of the planar relative to the twisted

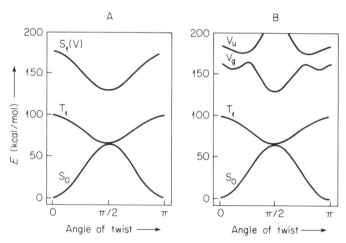

Fig. 1 Potential energy diagrams for the lowest electronic states of ethylene as a function of CC bond rotation (lowest Rydberg state at 164 kcal/mol, 0°, not shown). (A) after Mulliken (1,3); (B) after Buenker and Peyerimhoff (2,2a).

geometries, and the twisting process may become activated even in the lowest triplet state (6).

On the basis of the energetics depicted in Fig. 1, at least three mechanisms are possible for unimolecular cis–trans isomerization. From the ground state, the molecule must be activated to the top of the barrier, and an activation energy of 45 kcal/mol or greater is expected (2a). From the first excited triplet state, twisting to the "p" state will occur followed by intersystem crossing to the ground state. Isomerization via direct excitation to the $\pi–\pi^*$ state may involve internal conversion to the Rydberg state at the avoided crossing and again to the ground state at a twist angle of 90°. Alternatively, intersystem crossing to the triplet state may precede twisting in the excited singlet state.

In addition to these unimolecular mechanisms, bimolecular interactions with radicals, cations, and other reactive species may also induce isomerization by reversible formation of intermediates that have a lower barrier to rotation about the CC bond.

II. THERMAL CIS−TRANS ISOMERIZATION

The early work on both gas- and solution-phase thermal isomerization of alkenes has been reviewed (7). The earliest experiments were carried out by heating a dilute mixture of the alkene in a suitable vessel until isomerization occurred. It is now recognized that many inorganic cations and other radicals on the inside surfaces of the vessels used in these experiments were capable of catalyzing isomerization. Such adventitious catalysis led to higher than expected rates of isomerization, and, when variable-temperature studies were carried out with analysis of the rate constants by the Arrhenius equation [Eq. (2)], the activation energies E_a

$$k_r = A e^{-E_a/RT} \tag{2}$$

and A factors were abnormally small. The first three entries in Table 1 are characteristic of such results (8–12).

The early results were interpreted by Magee, Shand, and Eyring (13). They proposed that these thermal isomerizations took place by one of two mechanisms. In the first mechanism the molecule remains in S_0 throughout, whereas in the second the molecule intersystem crosses to the lowest triplet state, as illustrated by points a and b in Fig. 2. The first mechanism can be interpreted as an extension of the torsional libration about the CC double bond and is expected to lead to isomerization having an Arrhenius A factor of $10^{12}–10^{13}$ sec^{-1} and activation energy $E_a > 45$ kcal/mol. The second mechanism will have a lower activation energy,

TABLE 1

Typical Activation Parameters for Cis–Trans Isomerization

Alkene	T (K)	$\log A$	E_a (kcal/mol)	Ref.
Dimethyl maleate	270–380	6.1	26.5	8
cis-Dimethyl citraconate	280–360	5	25.0	9
cis-Dichloroethylene	295–335	2.3	16.0	10
trans-Dideuterioethylene	450–550	13	65	11
cis-2-Butene	410–476	14	62.4	12

and, since intersystem crossing is spin forbidden, the preexponential A factor should be considerably smaller. The earliest results seemed to support the latter mechanism, but later results yielded more normal A factors and activation energies, as evidenced by the last two entries in Table 1. Recent considerations also discount the possibility of triplet state involvement (14).

In order to circumvent the experimental difficulties of wall effects, measurements of thermal cis–trans isomerization have been made using shock tube methods (15). In this technique a shock wave, produced by the bursting of a diaphragm, travels through the gas sample, heating it to an intermediate temperature. As the shock wave reflects from the end of the tube, the reflected wave further heats the sample to the desired temperature. By careful "tuning" of the shock tube, further reflections of the wave can be damped, and the sample "cools" very rapidly to a low temperature. Arrhenius parameters for the isomerization of a few alkenes obtained by this method are shown in Table 2 (16,17). These measurements, which are much more precise than the previous results, also substantiate the first mechanism (S_0 throughout).

Arrhenius parameters for the isomerization of conjugated dienes have been measured using the shock tube method, and the data for cis-1,3-pentadiene are included in Table 2. Note the 13 kcal/mol drop in the

TABLE 2

Shock Tube Activation Parameters

Alkene	T (K)	$\log A$	E_a (kcal/mol)	Ref.
cis-2-Butene	993–1177	14.6 ± 0.2	66.2	16
trans-CHCl=CFCl	1057–1240	13.2 ± 0.2	55.5	16
cis-CHF=CHF	1149–1261	13.4 ± 0.2	60.7	16
cis-1,3-Pentadiene	1000–1150	13.6 ± 0.3	53 ± 2	17

activation energy for the conjugated diene as compared to the nonconjugated alkene isomerization (*cis*-2-butene). It has been suggested that this is
a reliable estimate of the allylic resonance interaction energy (*17*). Cyclobutene intermediates provide a pathway of lower energy than do allylmethylene biradical transition states for cis–trans isomerization of 1,3-
dienes that are sterically unencumbered at the 1 and 4 positions (*18*). This
allowed pathway, in the Woodward–Hoffmann sense (*19*), has been demonstrated elegantly in the parent molecule by a study of the vapor-phase
isomerization of *trans,trans*- (tt), *cis,trans*- (ct), and *cis,cis*-1,4-dideuterio-
1,3-butadiene (cc) (*18*). Conrotatory cyclization to and ring opening of the
cyclobutene interconvert the tt and cc isomers [Eq. (3)] but lead to no
isomerization of the ct isomer. These dienes were isomerized by the use of

$$ \text{D} \diagup\diagdown\diagup\diagdown \text{D} \rightleftharpoons \text{structure} \rightleftharpoons \text{structure} \tag{3} $$

vacuum flash pyrolysis, a method employing high temperature and short
contact times (910 K, 50 msec at a pressure of ~3 torr), which minimize
wall-catalyzed reactions. Measured isomerization rate constants, $k(\text{tt} \rightarrow$
$\text{cc}) \simeq k(\text{cc} \rightarrow \text{tt}) \simeq 20k(\text{ct} \rightarrow \text{tt} + \text{cc}) \simeq 12 \sec^{-1}$ at 910 K, confirm Eq. (3) as
the predominant isomerization pathway and are consistent with an ex-
pected $E_a \simeq 44.5$ kcal/mol for cyclobutene formation (*18*). The slower
isomerization rate of the ct isomer is as expected for the allylmethylene
biradical pathway, $E_a \simeq 52.5$ kcal/mol (*18*). Steric crowding in the 2 and 3
positions of the diene moiety should favor the electrocyclic pathway (*18*).
This is seen in *cis,trans*-2,3,4,5-tetraphenyl-2,4-hexadiene, which undergoes cis–trans isomerization cleanly via the cyclobutene only (*20*). It has
also been suggested for 2,3-dimethyl-1,3-pentadiene; the activation parameters for cis–trans isomerization of the latter are somewhat lower than
those required for the diradical pathway (*21*).

A new technique, called "laser-powered homogeneous pyrolysis,"
makes use of a high-powered laser to excite molecules in the gas phase
(*22*). Typically, a dilute sample of the reactive molecule in SF_6 vapor is
irradiated with a 10–20 W CO_2 laser, and the thermally excited SF_6 transfers energy to the reactive molecules. The effective temperature is found
by measuring the rate of reaction of an internal standard the rate param-
eters of which are known. Ratios of cis $\rightarrow$ trans and trans $\rightarrow$ cis isomerization rate constants at 900 K determined using this technique for 2-butene
and 1,2-dichloroethylene compare favorably with known equilibrium constants (*22*).

Besides the gas-phase measurements, many determinations of rate parameters in solution have been made (*7*). In general, solution studies have
been troubled less by wall effects, and even the earlier work yielded rate

parameters in good agreement with the recent gas-phase measurements. Provided that the activation energy is small enough to make a solvent medium practical, thermal isomerization in solution is possibly the easiest technique experimentally for the determination of isomerization rate parameters. A typical example is one in which eight thioindigo dyes of the general structure shown below were studied [Eq. (4)] (23).

$$\text{(structure)} \xrightleftharpoons[\text{benzene}]{70\,^\circ\text{C}} \text{(structure)} \qquad (4)$$

As alluded to in the above discussion, several reactive species can catalyze cis–trans isomerization by reversible conversion of the alkene to an intermediate that exhibits a low barrier to rotation about the CC bond. Reversible addition of radicals such as I· or RS· (24), complexation with metal cations (25), and complexation with noble metals (26) all fall within this class of reactions. For catalysts with nonzero spin, an attractive mechanism involves relaxation of multiplicity change forbiddeness, allowing efficient isomerization via the triplet state (Fig. 2) (27). Recent evidence shows that reversible reduction of the olefin to the radical anion or dianion also leads to isomerization (28).

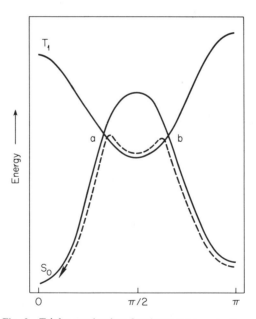

Fig. 2 Triplet mechanism for thermal isomerization.

III. PHOTOCHEMICAL CIS–TRANS ISOMERIZATION

Photochemical cis–trans isomerization of olefins has been reviewed (29,30). One review (29) is concerned with photochromic systems, i.e., those systems undergoing a color change upon cis–trans isomerization. In the following sections, the focus is on olefins for which extensive kinetic and spectroscopic measurements have defined isomerization mechanisms in detail.

A. Alkenes

Photochemical excitation of alkenes to the first excited singlet can be accomplished by direct irradiation of the alkene. Since the maximum absorbance in simple alkenes occurs at approximately 180 nm, little experimental work has been carried out on these nonconjugated systems due to the lack of readily available light sources. *trans*-Dideuterioethylene has been irradiated in the vapor phase at 147.0 and 184.0 nm, and isomerization to the cis isomer occurs, presumably via internal conversion to S_0 from the singlet "p" state (31). The large energy gap between the first excited singlet and the T_1 states precludes any intersystem crossing, and therefore the triplet state is not a likely intermediate in direct irradiation experiments. Direct irradiation of *cis*-2-butene similarly gives *trans*-2-butene and, at high concentration in solution, yields a completely stereospecific cycloaddition product [Eq. (5)] (32). This suggests that a suffi-

$$\diagdown\!\!=\!\!\diagup \quad + \quad \diagdown\!\!=\!\!\diagup \quad \xrightarrow{\ h\nu\ } \quad \square\!\!\!\!\diagup \quad + \quad \square\!\!\!\!\diagup \qquad (5)$$

ciently long-lived planar singlet state exists such that bimolecular reactions may compete with twisting and that twisting to the "p" state is followed by return to the cis and trans ground states. The "p" state cannot be an intermediate in the cycloaddition reaction because its involvement would lead to a nonstereospecific product.

The energy of the lowest triplet state of alkenes is such that triplet alkene can be prepared by triplet–triplet energy transfer from suitable donors. Such donors as benzene (E_T = 84 kcal/mol), toluene (E_T = 84 kcal/mol), cadmium ($^3P_1$) (E_T = 88 kcal/mol), and mercury ($^3P_1$) (E_T = 113 kcal/mol) sensitize simple alkenes to their lowest triplet states. Energy transfer occurs from the triplet state of the sensitizer to produce directly the triplet state of the alkene, and, although it is generally assumed that the alkene triplet is produced in a planar conformation, little experimental evidence has been obtained that bears on this point. In those cases in which the energy transfer is slightly endothermic (E_T of donor is less than E_T of alkene), it may be possible that relaxation of the alkene to the twisted state occurs within the donor–alkene complex. Such nonvertical energy-transfer processes are known in stilbene sensitization (see Section III,C,4), but there is no evidence that an analogous process occurs in simple alkenes. Regardless of the exact mechanism of energy transfer, the alkene ultimately arrives at the twisted "p" triplet state, from which it intersystem-crosses to the ground, S_0, state and then to both cis- and trans-alkene.

Certain sensitizers, notably ketones, the triplet energies of which are probably too low to promote sensitization of the alkene to its triplet state, nevertheless do photocatalyze isomerization (33). It has been proposed that even for relatively high energy ketonic sensitizers there are two mechanisms for cis–trans isomerization (34). The first is the normal triplet–triplet energy transfer, and the second involves formation of a biradical, referred to as the Schenck biradical [Eq. (6)] (35). The trans to

$$(6)$$

cis photostationary compositions, $(t/c)_s$, for sensitized equilibration of 2-pentenes are given in Table 3 (30,34). The value of t/c for benzene as sensitizer is thought to be typical of the mechanism involving pure energy transfer, whereas the value of $(t/c)_s = 5.4$ for acetophenone is near the thermodynamic equilibrium value and is more consistent with the Schenck biradical mechanism (30). Since free rotation is possible in the biradical intermediate, the cleavage to reform the olefin, following inter-

TABLE 3

Dependence of 2-Pentene Photostationary State on Sensitizer

Sensitizer	E_T (kcal/mol)	$(t/c)_s$
Benzene	84	1.0
Acetone	80	1.52
Acetophenone	74	5.4
Benzophenone	68	5.6

system crossing, can lead to an isomerized product. Alternatively, cyclization can lead to nonstereospecific oxetane formation (30). Notably only ketones with lowest $n–\pi^*$ triplet states are effective in this type of reaction, which may be due in part to the oxyradical character of the $n–\pi^*$ state. An elegant study of intramolecular and intermolecular deuterium isotope effects on the formation and partitioning of the biradical between the isomeric alkenes and oxetane in benzophenone/alkene systems provides evidence for rate-determining formation of a π complex preceding biradical formation (36,37). Studies of the dependence of ketone triplet quenching constants on alkene structure show no correlation of k_q with triplet energy and suggest that charge transfer occurs in the transition state of the rate-determining step (30,37,38). Such interaction is also nicely accommodated by the proposed exciplex intermediate. Another interesting suggestion is that triplet oxetane may be an intermediate in some cases (39). Fragmentation of triplet oxetane was proposed to account for observations suggesting a photoexchange reaction between acetone-d_6 and tetramethylethylene-d_0 giving acetone-d_0 and tetramethylethylene-d_6 (39). However, a more recent investigation of this system failed to reveal this reaction (39a).

Cycloalkenes undergo cis–trans photoisomerization provided that the ring size is sufficiently large to accommodate the trans double bond. Small-ring *trans*-cycloalkenes, C_7 and C_6, cannot generally be isolated but are proposed as intermediates in the photoaddition of alcohols and cycloaddition reactions. For example, the triplet state of 1-phenylcyclohexene, formed by triplet excitation transfer in alcoholic media, has been proposed to give the strained trans isomer, which then yields ionic adducts; 1-phenylcyclooctene in contrast, gives only *trans*-1-phenylcyclooctene [Eqs. (7) and (8)] (40). Direct spectroscopic observa-

$$(7)$$

$$(8)$$

tions made using flash-kinetic techniques have confirmed the original proposal (41) of the intermediacy of *trans*-1-phenylcyclohexene (42). Direct excitation of 1-phenylcyclohexene gives a transient absorbing in the 300–

430 nm range in methanol, the lifetime of which, ~ 9 μsec, is unaffected by oxygen but decreases as the pH of the medium is decreased, as expected for the trans isomer (42). An activation energy of 7.5 kcal/mol for un-catalyzed thermal trans $\rightarrow$ cis isomerization was inferred; this increases to 20 kcal/mol in the less strained trans-1-phenylcycloheptene (42). The di-rect excitation photoisomerizations bypass the triplet state. By employing a triplet excitation donor such as xanthone, E_T = 75 kcal/mol, the triplet precursor of trans-1-phenylcyclohexene is observed; it absorbs in the 320–345 nm region and has a lifetime of 55–60 nsec (43). Similarly, triplet–triplet absorptions are observed from 1-phenylcycloheptene, 1-phenylpropene, and styrene, τ = 40–50 nsec (43). Unusually fast quenching of cycloalkene triplets by oxygen, k_q = 6.4 $\times$ 10^9 M^{-1} sec^{-1} in benzene (43), suggests twisted geometries for these excited states (see discussion of stilbene triplets in Section III,C,4). Very low $S_1 \rightarrow$ T intersys-tem crossing yields for 1-phenylcycloalkenes with C_4 to C_8 rings have been estimated from a study of biacetyl phosphorescence sensitization (44). However, at least for the C_6 and C_7 cases, triplet lifetimes calculated from Stern–Volmer constants, assuming diffusion-controlled triplet excitation transfer to biacetyl, are several orders of magnitude longer than those measured directly (43,44). Another interesting feature of 1-phenyl-cycloalkene behavior is that fluorescence rate constants, k_f, calcu-lated from measured fluorescence quantum yields and lifetimes, are 20–30 times smaller than theoretical k_f values based on the areas of the first absorption bands (44). The failure of the theoretical expression was taken to suggest emission from considerably distorted excited state geometries (40). However, instead of the observed k_f approaching the theoretical value as ring size and, presumably, geometric distortion are decreased, the discrepancy is largest in the C_4 case. Nor are k_f discrepancies di-minished when the measurements are made in a glassy hydrocarbon me-dium at 77 K instead of 300 K (44). It would seem, therefore, that fluores-cence originates from a relatively undistorted state with weak transition probability which does not correspond to the absorption band used to calculate the observed k_f values. Such an ordering of lowest excited singlet states has been documented in all-trans-polyenes (45).

The direct and sensitized photoisomerizations of unsubstituted cyclooc-tene were studied in some detail (46). In solution at 290 K triplet excitation donors with $E_T >$ 79 kcal/mol gave invariant photostationary t/c ratios of 0.05, reflecting a strong preference for decay of the cyclooctene triplet to the less strained cis isomer (46). Somewhat higher $(t/c)_s$ ratios were ob-tained (up to 0.2 for benzene) when the sensitized experiments were car-ried out in the vapor phase (46). In contrast, direct excitation in n-pentane at 185 nm gave $([t]/[c])_s$ = 0.96, from which a t/c decay ratio of 0.9 was inferred for the excited singlet state (46). The high trans content of this stationary state was recently confirmed, but the notion of a common twisted excited singlet state that decays to cis and trans ground states with nearly identical rate constants was discounted (47). This conclusion is based on the unusual observation of identical isomerization quantum yields, approximately equal to unity, in each direction (47). The sum $\phi_{c \to t}$ + $\phi_{t \to c}$ ~ 2 suggests that, from the initially produced singlet excited state of each isomer, a completely efficient path leads to the other isomer (47). That is, the torsional momentum in the excited state carries through the internal conversion into the ground state without hesitation at a "p" geometry. The possible generality of this observation merits extensive study (47a).

B. 1,3-Dienes

Upon excitation to either the lowest singlet or triplet excited state, 1,3-dienes undergo cis–trans isomerization (30). The reaction usually occurs more cleanly and efficiently in the triplet state. Singlet excited states undergo a variety of competing reactions which, not being observed from the corresponding triplet states, demonstrate very low $S_1 \to T$ intersystem crossing efficiencies in these systems (30). An important feature of 1,3-diene photochemistry is reactivity control by ground state conformations (see Essay 15). This is introduced by facile rotation about the C-2—C-3 bond in the ground state, giving an equilibrium mixture of s-trans and s-cis conformers [Eq. (9)] (48,48a). Owing to steric crowding, the s-cis conformer

$$\diagup\!\!\diagup\!\!\diagdown\!\!\diagup \quad \rightleftarrows \quad \diagdown\!\!\diagdown\underline{}\diagup\!\!\diagup \qquad (9)$$

has a skew or gauche geometry (49,50). Substituents at C-2 and C-3 shift the equilibrium toward s-cis conformers, whereas substituents at C-1 and/or C-4 in cis-1,3-dienes shift the equilibrium toward the s-trans conformers. 1,3-Butadiene exists predominantly in the s-trans conformation, and its spectroscopic transitions are representative of s-trans-dienes. 1,3-Cyclohexadiene has been used as a model for assigning energies to s-cis-diene excited states (30). Accordingly, upper limits for the energy of the S_1 states are 124 and 100 kcal/mol for s-trans and s-cis conformers, and the energies of the lowest triplet states are 60 and 53 kcal/mol, respectively (30,51–53).

Two observations suggest that singlet excitation of s-cis conformations is important, at least with respect to cyclobutene formation. First, cyclobutene is observed only from the tt isomer of 2,4-hexadienes (54,55), and, second, the quantum yield for cyclobutene formation from trans-

1,3-pentadiene is about ten times larger than that from the cis isomer
(56,57). Clearly, cyclobutene formation is most efficient whenever s-cis
conformers represent a significant fraction, 2–4% (48,49), of ground state
diene molecules at room temperature. The different energies required for
excitation of s-trans and s-cis conformers may account for the interesting
observation that, in contrast to 254 nm light absorption, absorption at 229
nm gives no cyclobutene starting from either *trans*- or *cis*-1,3-pentadiene
(57). Involvement of s-cis singlets in cis–trans isomerization can be inferred from observations with the cyclic 1,3-diene, cyclooctadiene. Excitation of *cis,cis*- or *cis,trans*-1,3-cyclooctadiene at 248 nm leads to efficient
interconversion of these dienes, $\phi_{cc \to ct} = 0.28$, $\phi_{ct \to cc} = 0.80$ [Eq. (10)]
(58). The near unity sum of these quantum yields suggests a common

$$\text{(10)}$$

excited singlet twisted intermediate and accounts for low cyclobutene
formation efficiencies from both dienes (58). Quantum yields for the interconversion of 2,4-hexadienes in *n*-pentane upon excitation with 254 nm
radiation suggest that cis–trans isomerization is the most efficient photo-
reaction of *s-trans*-diene singlets, $\phi_{tt \to ct} \simeq \phi_{cc \to ct} \simeq 0.4$, $\phi_{ct \to tt} \simeq 0.2$,
$\phi_{ct \to cc} \simeq 0.3$, $\phi_{tt \to cc} = \phi_{cc \to tt} = 0(55)$. The latter two quantum yields show
that the lowest singlet excited states undergo torsional relaxation about
only one double bond and, as will be shown below, rule out triplet state
involvement in the isomerization process. A common 1,4 biradical excited
singlet intermediate is precluded. One-bond isomerization is nicely ac-

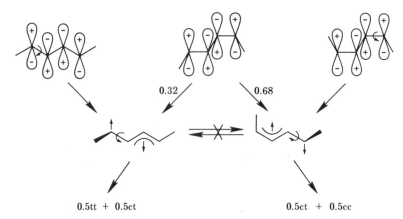

Scheme 1. The allylmethylene mechanism for direct cis–trans isomerization of 2,4-hexadienes.

counted for by noninterconverting singlet excited states having an allyl-methylene geometry (Scheme 1) *(30,55)*. An alternative mechanism involves biradicals of the cyclopropylmethylene type (**1** and **2**), which may also be precursors of bicyclobutanes, cyclopropenes, and dimeric prod-

1   2

ucts, none of which are observed under triplet excitation conditions *(30,54,55,59–61)*. To account for one-bond isomerization, stereospecific formation and ring opening of intermediates **1** and **2** would be required *(30,55)*. An attempt to study the behavior of cyclopropylmethylene biradicals generated by the decomposition of appropriate azo compounds apparently failed owing to an intervening decomposition mode *(62)*.

A pronounced inefficiency in the photoisomerization process in solution was noted for the direct excitation, at 254 nm, of 1,3-pentadienes, $\phi_{c \rightarrow t} = 0.08$, $\phi_{t \rightarrow c} = 0.10$ *(55,56,61)*. Since all competing reactions are relatively minor, an important energy-wasting step is available to 1,3-pentadiene singlets. Some theoretical and experimental results have been presented suggesting the presence of a small barrier in going from the initially formed, nearly planar S_1 molecules to the allylmethylene geometry, and it has been proposed that this process may be slow compared to radiationless decay without isomerization *(63)*. More recent MO calculations, however, show no barrier in this process *(6)*. Alternatively, it has been proposed that the S_1 and S_0 states might become nearly degenerate along the coordinate for cyclopropylmethylene biradical formation, and decay could occur without isomerization from a species in which bond formation (C-2—C-4 in 1,3-pentadiene) is incomplete *(60,61)*. A large wavelength effect on cis ⇄ trans quantum yields for 1,3-pentadienes in cyclohexane prompted the suggestion that, depending on the wavelength, different nuclear configurations are initially reached on the S_1 hypersurface. These utilize different relaxation modes, which attain different energy wells having different cis/trans decay characteristics *(57)*. In each of these mechanisms inefficiency in isomerization is attributed to inefficient formation of proposed intermediates.

In terms of the allylmethylene mechanism an alternative explanation is that low isomerization quantum yields reflect preferential decay via twisting at the C-1—C-2 diene bond, which leads to an identity reaction *(30)*. Preference for the allylmethylene biradicals as intermediates for the cis–trans isomerization process is suggested by the report that $\phi_{c \rightarrow t}$ and $\phi_{t \rightarrow c}$

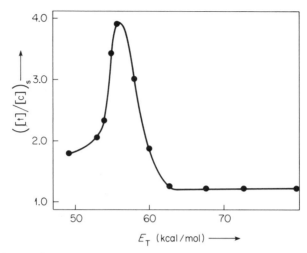

Fig. 3 1,3-Pentadiene photostationary compositions as a function of donor triplet energy (*30*).

are independent of 1,3-pentadiene concentration over the same range (up to 2.8 *M*) (*56*) which, for cyclopropene quantum yields, gives decreased values with increasing diene concentration (*30*). The changes in 1,3-pentadiene isomerization quantum yields noted at much higher concentrations (*61*) are similar to those observed in the sensitized isomerization (*64*) (see below) and cannot, as has been claimed, be taken to confirm the validity of the cyclopropylmethylene mechanism (*61*).

Triplet excitation transfer to 1,3-dienes from donors with $E_T \gtrsim 48$ kcal/mol leads to their efficient cis–trans isomerization. Photostationary t/c ratios for 1,3-pentadienes vary widely with the triplet excitation energy of the donor (Fig. 3) (*30,65,66*). Selective sensitization processes account for this variation. The spectroscopic triplet excitation energies of 1,3-pentadienes, 59.2 and 57.3 kcal/mol (*53*) for the trans and cis isomer, respectively, correspond to excitation of the predominant s-trans conformers for each diene. Sensitizers with triplet energies above 61 kcal/mol excite *cis*- and *trans*-1,3-pentadienes at identical diffusion-controlled rates, yielding identical (t/c)$_s$ values of 1.25. This ratio reflects the decay characteristics of *s-trans*-diene triplets (Scheme 2). As the energy of the sensitizer is decreased below 61 kcal/mol preferential sensitization of the cis isomer occurs, resulting in higher (t/c)$_s$ [Eq. (11), $\alpha = 0.55$], approaching a

$$(t/c)_s = (k_c/k_t)[\alpha/(1 - \alpha)] \tag{11}$$

maximum at $E_T \simeq 56$ kcal/mol. Below this donor triplet energy, (t/c)$_s$ decreases, a behavior noted with many other olefins that is generally

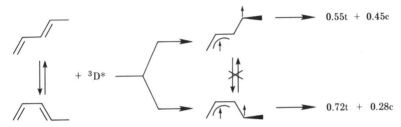

Scheme 2. Excitation and decay of *s-trans*-1,3-pentadienes.

attributed to nonvertical excitation transfer which gives twisted excited
state olefin geometries (see Section III,C,4) (65). In this instance, however,
the downward trend of $(t/c)_s$ is due, at least in part, to selective sensitization
of s-cis conformers of *trans*-1,3-pentadiene (Scheme 3) (66). Excitation of
s-cis triplets from *cis*-1,3-pentadiene is not expected owing to the very low
equilibrium concentration of s-cis conformers for that isomer.

Scheme 3. The role of s-cis conformers in diene isomerization.

In Schemes 2 and 3 1,3-pentadiene triplets are shown as having an
allylmethylene geometry. However, a 1,4 biradical geometry would result

1,4-Biradical   Allylmethylene

if distortion occurred at both ends of the diene system. Theoretical calculations suggest that the 1,4 biradical geometry represents an energy
maximum in the torsional potential energy curve of 1,3-diene triplets
and support the allylmethylene representation (6,63,67–70). The
benzophenone-sensitized photoisomerization of 2,4-hexadienes has been
utilized in an experimental approach to determining the preferred
geometry of diene triplets (71–73). The sum of the six quantum yields for
the interconversion of the three 2,4-hexadiene isomers at room temperature is 2, showing that transfer of a single quantum of excitation causes
isomerization at both double bonds via common triplet state intermediates

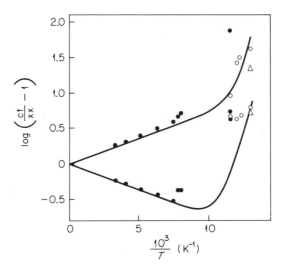

Fig. 4 Temperature dependence of isomerization quantum yield ratios starting with tt (upper) and with cc (lower): ●, MP; ○, IPMP; △, IP. [Taken from Saltiel *et al.* (*73*). Reprinted with permission of the copyright holder, the American Chemical Society.]

(*72*). Starting with the trans,trans isomer, ratios of one-bond to two-bond isomerization (tc/cc) increase as the temperature is lowered in the 300–135 K range (*73*). Starting with the cis,cis isomer there is a corresponding decrease in these ratios (tc/tt in this case) with decreasing temperature over the same temperature range. Decreasing the temperature below 135 K inhibits two-bond isomerization in both dienes (Fig. 4) (*73*). A two-bond isomerization mechanism involving facile equilibration between trans-twisted, ^{3}tp*, and cis-twisted, ^{3}cp*, allylmethylene triplets [Eq. (12)], which shifts to a one-bond isomerization mechanism at lower tempera-

$$^3\text{tp*} \underset{k_{-12}}{\overset{k_{12}}{\rightleftharpoons}} {}^3\text{cp*} \tag{12}$$

tures owing to medium and possibly thermal barriers to the equilibration in Eq. (12), provides a satisfactory explanation for these observations. Equal partitioning of the twisted bonds to trans and cis ground state bonds [Eqs. (13) and (14)] is suggested by the temperature independence of the tc

$$^3\text{tp*} \overset{k_{13}}{\to} 0.50\text{tt} + 0.50\text{ct} \tag{13}$$

$$^3\text{cp*} \overset{k_{14}}{\to} 0.50\text{ct} + 0.50\text{cc} \tag{14}$$

content of photostationary states (50% tc, 300–77 K) (73). The fit of the data to this mechanism is illustrated by the calculated curves in Fig. 4, which are obtained using $E_{12} - E_{-12} = \Delta H_{12} = 333$ cal/mol, $k_{13}/A_{12} = k_{14}/A_{-12} = 10^{-8}$, and $E_{12} = 3.5$ kcal/mol (73). Comparison between solid [3-methylpentane (MP) solvent] and open points [isopentane/3-methylpentane (IPMP), 6:1, solvent] in Fig. 4 demonstrates a large medium dependence in the barrier to the interconversion shown in Eq. (12). Two-bond isomerization in diene triplets at the higher temperatures contrasts with the direct excitation results discussed above in which only one terminal bond isomerizes per photochemical event. It probably reflects, at least in part, a large lifetime difference between triplet and singlet diene excited states.

The most recent theoretical calculations indicate that interconversion of the two allylmethylenes will proceed through a planar transition state (6). Some experimental justification for this prediction is provided by the functioning of a quantum chain mechanism for sensitized diene isomerization (74,75). At low 1,3-diene concentrations, e.g., 0.005–0.2 M for 1,3-pentadienes (76), the sum of the quantum yields for the benzophenone-sensitized cis–trans isomerization is unity, as expected for completely efficient excitation transfer from a donor with unit intersystem crossing efficiency, $\phi_{is}^D = 1.0$, $\alpha = 0.55$ [Eqs. (15) and (16)]. In fact, the

$$\phi_{c \to t} = \phi_{is}^D \alpha \tag{15}$$

$$\phi_{t \to c} = \phi_{is}^D (1 - \alpha) \tag{16}$$

benzophenone/1,3-pentadiene system has served photochemists as a convenient actinometry system (76). As the concentration of the diene is increased (up to 10 M for cis-1,3-pentadiene; up to 7.8 M for 2,4-hexadiene), isomerization quantum yields increase more than twofold. The results with 2,4-hexadienes are especially revealing since they show that this increase in the quantum yields is not accompanied by changes in quantum yield ratios, $\phi_{tt \to tc}/\phi_{tt \to cc} = 2.8 \pm 0.1$, $\phi_{cc \to tc}/\phi_{cc \to tt} = 1.7 \pm 0.1$ (75). This result, along with observations concerning the competing sensitized dimerizations of dienes, rules out the participation of adduct biradicals in the isomerization process and suggests that triplet excitation transfer from diene triplets to ground state diene molecules is the mechanism leading to enhanced isomerization quantum yields (75). Upon transferring its excitation, the diene triplet gives ground state dienes in the same ratio as does natural decay. A limiting rate constant, $k_{et} \leq 2.5 \times 10^7 M^{-1} \sec^{-1}$, has been estimated for the excitation transfer process, which is consistent with an endothermicity of ~3.3 kcal/mol if the process is vertical (75). This is similar to the activation energy for the interconversion of allylmethylene triplets and may be a measure of the stabilization achieved by the distortion of planar 1,3-diene triplets to the twisted equilibrium geometries.

A quantum chain process, in which the excitation-transfer steps give olefins in different ratios than does natural decay, may account for the concentration dependence of photostationary states and quantum yields observed in the benzophenone-sensitized photoisomerization of 1,3,5-trienes (77).

C. Stilbenes

The photoisomerization reactions of stilbene and related arylalkenes are among the most extensively studied and best understood photoreactions. For this reason this section describes in detail results on this system since it can be regarded as the prototype for both past and future work in this area.

1. Energetics

Possible potential energy curves for twisting about the central bond in the stilbene electronic states considered to play a role in the isomerization

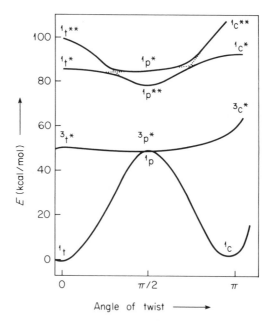

Fig. 5   Possible potential energy diagram for the lowest electronic states of stilbenes [S_0, T_1 (126); S_1, S_2 (83)].

process are given in Fig. 5. Geometries corresponding to, or nearly to, the trans and cis ground states are represented by the symbols t and c, respectively. The superscripts designate the multiplicity of the state, and asterisks denote singly (one asterisk) and doubly (two asterisks) excited states. Twisted geometries are designated by the symbol p. Energies of the t, c geometries are based on thermochemical and spectroscopic data for which most literature sources are given in Saltiel *et al.* (*30*). Room-temperature and 77 K absorption and emission spectra of *trans*-stilbene are shown in Fig. 6. Also shown in Fig. 6 is the recently measured phosphorescence of *trans*-stilbene (*78*) confirming the 49 kcal/mol value for the energy of $^3t^*$, which was previously based on weak $T_1 \leftarrow S_0$ absorption spectra. A doubly excited state for the trans isomer was observed using simultaneous, two-photon absorption spectroscopy (*79*). Because of symmetry considerations excitation by single-photon absorption directly to this state is forbidden. Nonetheless, it is included because on theoretical grounds it seems to correspond to the lowest excited singlet state having the p geometry, p** (*79–83*). Of the experimental anchor points in Fig. 5, the energies of ^1c and ^1p are the most uncertain. The energy of the former, 2.3 kcal/mol, is based on the enthalpy difference calculated from the temperature dependence of the equilibrium constant in toluene (*84*), but a higher value of 5.7 kcal/mol, based on heats of hydrogenation in acetic acid, could also have been chosen (*85*). The activation energy for

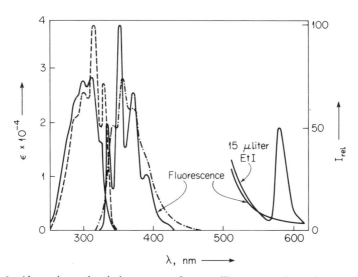

Fig. 6 Absorption and emission spectra of *trans*-stilbene: ——, absorption at room temperature and emission at 77 K; ---, absorption at 77 K; — · —, emission at room temperature (see text for references).

^{1}c → ^{1}t thermal isomerization must be added to the energy of ^{1}c in order to locate ^{1}p in the diagram. The most recent solution value of 46 ± 2 kcal/mol (86,87) was used, but it could be argued that values of 42.8 ± 2.0 (88) and 42.6 ± 1.0 kcal/mol (89) obtained in the vapor phase are preferable. As a consequence, the range of experimentally acceptable energies for ^{1}p is 45–52 kcal/mol.

It is shown below that the potential energy curves in Fig. 5 account for transient spectroscopic and photochemical observations. Theoretical calculations were used as a guide in their selection.

2. Relationship between Fluorescence and Photoisomerization

Pioneering studies of the temperature dependence of ^{1}t* fluorescence quantum yields and photoisomerization quantum yields in both directions established clearly that essentially all decay from ^{1}t* can be accounted for by either fluorescence or an activated crossing into the state from which decay to either isomer ground state takes place (90,90a). The fluorescence quantum yields have been confirmed and refined by several more recent studies (91–94). Although the activated process leading to isomerization from ^{1}t* has been associated variously with either intersystem crossing (90–92) or twisting about the central bond, ^{1}t* → ^{1}p* (93–96a), evidence supporting the latter view is now overwhelming (see below). Both ^{1}p* and ^{1}p** are used interchangeably because of the paucity of experimental evidence establishing the identity of the lowest excited twisted singlet state and because theoretical predictions of the energetics of twisting have undergone frequent revision.

The absence of fluorescence from cis-stilbene in fluid media (97) led to the rejection of the early mechanism for olefin photoisomerization (98), in which ^{1}t* and ^{1}c* were regarded as readily accessible phases of rotation in a common singlet state. A marked drop in $\phi_{c \to t}$ at 77 K was associated with increased medium ridigity, which prevented ^{1}c* → ^{1}p* rotation (91a). In very rigid media, inhibition of $\phi_{c \to t}$ is accompanied by ^{1}c* fluorescence exhibiting a large Stokes red shift (~4.5 kcal/mol) (92,99–101). When the medium imposes no constraints, $\phi_{c \to t}$ is essentially temperature independent (91,91a), indicating the absence of an internal barrier to ^{1}c* → ^{1}p*. A complication in the study of the cis isomer is competitive formation of dihydrophenanthrene (DHP) (3), the cyclization product (102,103). This

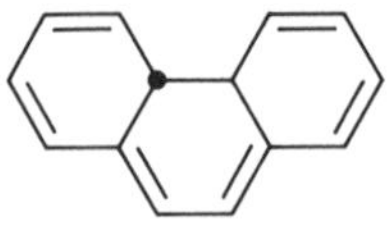

3

reversible side reaction appears to be activated modestly since it does not take place at low temperature (*101*). Analysis of $^1t^*$ fluorescence is based on Eqs. (17)–(19). If one assumes that the only activated process is ir-

$$^1t^* \xrightarrow{k_f} {}^1t + h\nu \tag{17}$$

$$^1t^* \underset{}{\overset{k_{tp}}{\rightleftharpoons}} {}^1p^* \tag{18}$$

$$^1t^* \xrightarrow{k_{is}^{1t}} {}^3t^* \tag{19}$$

reversible twisting about the central bond [Eq. (18)], then Eq. (20) de-

$$\phi_f = k_f/(k_f + k_{is}^{1t} + A_{tp}e^{-E_{tp}/RT}) = k_f\tau_f \tag{20}$$

scribes the temperature dependence of stilbene fluorescence, where A_{tp} and E_{tp} are Arrhenius parameters for k_{tp}. This expression can be rearranged to Eq. (21), where $\kappa = 1 + k_{is}^{1t}/k_f(90a)$. A corollary to this treatment

$$\ln(\phi_f^{-1} - \kappa) = \ln(A_{tp}/k_f) - E_{tp}/RT \tag{21}$$

is the prediction of very short stilbene fluorescence lifetimes [Eq. (22)] at moderate temperatures (*104*), which appear to be in conflict with the much larger fluorescence lifetimes ($\sim$1.5 nsec) reported elsewhere (*81*). These authors suggested that essentially all fluorescence from $^1t^*$ occurs after equilibration between $^1t^*$ and $^1p^*$ is achieved. Quantitative analysis of the temperature dependence of ϕ_f, including reversibility in Eq. (18), has shown that the assumption of fast equilibration is not justified and that, if the long lifetimes were due to stilbene fluorescence, they would be associated with a minor delayed component (*105*). More recent fluorescence lifetime measurements, employing instruments capable of measuring shorter lifetimes, failed to reveal a long lifetime component even at 60°C and gave single exponential decay rate constants entirely consistent with Eq. (22) (*106, 106a*). A fit of the fluorescence quantum yields and these short

$$\tau_f = (k_f + k_{is}^{1t} + A_{tp}e^{-E_{tp}/RT})^{-1} \tag{22}$$

lifetimes to kinetic expressions obtained by including reversibility in Eq. (18) suggests that the delayed fluorescence component represents at most 9% of the emission at 298 K (*107*). However, E_{pt} and A_{pt}, the Arrhenius parameters for $^1p^* \rightarrow {}^1t^*$ twisting, are very poorly defined, and the fit is almost as good if the twisting process is assumed to be irreversible. Parameters for the latter fit are given in Table 4, and a comparison between observed and calculated lifetimes and quantum yields is shown in Fig. 7 (*107*). If the higher-temperature (up to 333 K) fluorescence quantum yields (*81*) are included, the fit is somewhat improved by including reversibility in Eq. (18); however, E_{pt} and A_{pt} are still very poorly defined.

TABLE 4

Parameters for Equations (20)–(22)[a]

Parameter	Value	Standard deviation
log A_{tp}	12.6	0.1
E_{tp} (kcal/mol)	3.53	0.15
k_{is} (sec^{-1})	3.86 × 10^7	2.3 × 10^7
k_f (sec^{-1})[b]	5.89 × 10^8	0.25 × 10^8

[a] Fluorescence quantum yields from ref 92, as tabulated in Charlton and Saltiel (105); lifetimes from Sumitani et al. (106).

[b] Here, k_f is for methylcyclopentane/isohexane at 77 K; proportionality to n^2, where n is the index of refraction, was assumed (105).

It is safe to conclude that $E_{pt} \geq 7.5$ kcal/mol, so that $\Delta H_{tp} \leq -4$ kcal/mol. The small k_{is} value suggests that intersystem crossing from ^{1}t* is a minor process. Careful measurements of fluorescence quantum yields and lifetimes at higher temperatures offer the promise of defining experimentally the relative energy and the decay rate constant of ^{1}p*.

Since Eqs. (20)–(22) account for existing fluorescence data very well and k_{is} is small, the temperature dependence of $\phi_{t \to c}$ should be quantitatively accounted for by Eq. (23), where β is the fraction of ^{1}p* that decays to ^{1}t [Eq. (24)]. The data (90) shown in Fig. 7 are in excellent agreement

$$\phi_{t \to c} = (1 - \beta)\tau_f A_{tp} e^{-E_{tp}/RT} \tag{23}$$

$$^1p^* \xrightarrow{k_d^{1p}} \beta^1 t + (1 - \beta)^1 c \tag{24}$$

with the curve predicted by Eq. (23), the parameters in Table 1, and $\beta = 0.45$. The fact that $\phi_f + \phi_{t \to c}/(1 - \beta) \simeq 1$ throughout the temperature range establishes the complementarity between fluorescence and photoisomerization in ^{1}t*.

Comparative excitation-transfer studies under triplet sensitization and direct excitation conditions (see below) firmly establish that the activated process is not intersystem crossing (94–96a). Further experimental verification of this conclusion is provided by the failure to detect stilbene triplets flash spectroscopically following direct excitation of the stilbenes in fluid solution (108,108a). Theoretically, the value of A_{tp} is several orders of magnitude too high to be associated with a multiplicity-forbidden process (30,80,109). Enhancement of the A_{tp}, E_{tp} parameters as solvents of higher viscosities are employed (91–93) and ϕ_f values close to unity for electronic

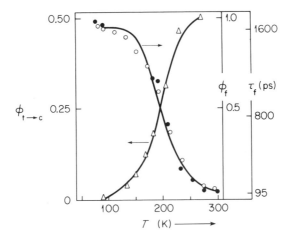

Fig. 7 Temperature dependence of ϕ_f (○), τ_f (●), and $\phi_{t\to c}$ (△) for *trans*-stilbene [curves calculated using Eqs. (20), (22), and (23)].

models of the stilbenes **4** (*110*) and **5** (*111*), which are restricted to nearly planar geometries, indicate that the process involves torsional displacement.

4   5

Results from early MO calculations of the potential energy curve for twisting in S_1, the first excited singlet state of stilbene, suggesting that the twisted geometry $^1p^*$ corresponds to an energy minimum that could readily be attained by twisting from $^1t^*$ and $^1c^*$ (*112,113*), have not been borne out by later, more sophisticated calculations (*82,83,114*). These calculations predict that twisting in S_1 is probably too endothermic to be consistent with the low experimental E_{tp} value. This contradiction is eliminated by a model involving a low-lying doubly excited state, S_2, which correlates with S_0 and is the lowest twisted excited singlet state (*80*). Two-photon absorption spectroscopy (*79*) and recent theoretical calculations (*82,83*) seem to support this model. As shown in Fig. 5, k_{tp} is now associated with $S_1 \leadsto S_2$ conversion, and E_{tp} is the energy above S_1 where the two potential energy curves cross (*80*). A large barrier for $^1t^* \to {}^1p^*$ twisting, which was inferred from the assignment of a large stretching frequency to the central bond in S_1 (*90a*), was revised downward since analysis of vibrational structure in absorption spectra of deuteriated stilbenes showed that assignment to be in error (*115*).

3. Transient Absorptions

The fluorescence measurements have been complemented by two laser kinetic investigations of the picosecond time dependence of light absorption by excited stilbene transients (*116,117*). Different approaches were employed, leading to different observations. A tentative interpretation of the data can be based on Fig. 5 and is important because it may at least give direction and stimulation to future investigations. In the first study simultaneous two-photon absorption by ^{1}t was employed to populate an excited state, which rapidly ($1/\tau = 5 \times 10^{11}e^{-1400/RT}$) decayed to a second state; absorption by the latter of a single-photon probing beam was monitored (*116*). It was suggested that initial excitation gives rise to ^{1}t*, which upon twisting gives ^{1}p** or ^{3}p*, the transient observed in absorption (*116*). If that is so, the activation parameters for ^{1}p* formation are in serious disagreement with those assigned to the same process in Table 4. Low A_{tp} and E_{tp} values could be due to compensation between these parameters and may also reflect the high stilbene concentration ($0.2\,M$) employed. At this concentration quenching of ^{1}t* by ^{1}t, leading in part to stilbene dimers, is significant (*118*) and may account for a faster overall decay rate for ^{1}t* (2–3×10^{10} sec^{-1} at 30°C in chloroform, dimethylformamide, and diethyl ether) than the rate constants obtained from fluorescence measurements (Fig. 7). Another difficulty with this study is that the transient observed in absorption has a temperature-independent rate constant, which, however, is solvent dependent ($k_d \simeq 1.5 \times 10^9$ sec^{-1} in chloroform and dimethylformamide, but $k_d \simeq 3 \times 10^7$ sec^{-1} in diethyl ether). Whereas the former could be associated with ^{1}p** decay, the latter is almost slow enough to be assigned to ^{3}p* (see below). Taking these observations at face value, one can propose an attractive alternative interpretation. Because of symmetry considerations, $S_1 \leftarrow S_0$ excitation by simultaneous two-photon absorption is forbidden, whereas $S_2 \leftarrow S_0$ absorption is allowed (*79–81*). Thus, the initial species expected is ^{1}t** and not ^{1}t*, and the rate of ^{1}p** formation should reflect ^{1}t** decay characteristics [Eqs. (25–27), where ^{1}t'** represents the stilbene geometry at the crossing between S_1 and S_2 potential

$$^1t^{**} \rightarrow {}^1t^* \tag{25}$$

$$^1t^{**} \rightarrow {}^1t'^{**} \tag{26}$$

$$^1t'^{**} \rightarrow \gamma^1t^* + (1 - \gamma)^1p^* \tag{27}$$

sents the stilbene geometry at the crossing between S_1 and S_2 potential surfaces, and γ is the decay fraction]. According to this proposal the difference between the activation parameters observed in absorption and in fluorescence measurements reflects the presence of the additional channel for ^{1}p* formation, e.g., Eqs. (26) and (27).‡

In the second laser study a short excitation pulse at 307.5 nm was employed, and absorption was monitored at 615.0 nm (117). An instantaneous rise in absorption is observed with both stilbene isomers in n-hexane, followed by partial relaxation to a lower, constant (in the picosecond time scale) absorption. Starting with ^{1}t, the initial absorption, assigned to ^{1}t*, decays with a rate constant of 1.9×10^{10} sec^{-1}, and the residual absorption, assigned to ^{1}p**, has a lifetime "on the order of nanoseconds" (117). The rate constant for ^{1}t* decay is again on the high side. Neither temperature nor concentrations are given, but values for the latter can be inferred from the optical density at 307.5 nm. The value of [t] $\simeq 3 \times 10^{-3} M$ seems too low for self-quenching to be significant in this case. Starting with ^{1}c, a very fast initial decay is observed, $\tau \simeq 7 \pm 1$ psec, which was associated with the ^{1}c* $\rightarrow$ ^{1}p** process but must also reflect the competing formation of DHP. This short lifetime of ^{1}c* is consistent with the fact that fluorescence has thus far not been reported from cis-stilbene in fluid solutions (119). Formation of a species other than, or in addition to, ^{1}p** is suggested by the observation of a larger residual absorption of unspecified lifetime starting with the cis isomer (0.55 of initial value for cis versus 0.15 of initial value for trans). An attractive candidate for the additional absorption is electronically excited dihydrophenanthrene [^{1}DHP′*, Eqs. (28)–(30) (94,120).]‡

$$^1c \rightarrow {}^1p* \tag{28}$$

$$^1c* \rightarrow {}^1DHP'* \tag{29}$$

$$^1DHP'* \rightarrow \delta^1DHP + (1 - \delta)^1c \tag{30}$$

4. The Triplet State

The geometry, lifetime, and reactivity of stilbene triplets have to a large measure been inferred from experiments in which the stilbenes function as acceptors or donors of triplet excitation (30,121). Useful, but less informative, have been experiments employing internal or external heavy-atom effects to enhance $S_1 \rightarrow T$ intersystem crossing and experiments involving direct excitation into the triplet manifold, $T_1 \leftarrow S_0$, in the presence or absence of high O_2 pressures or methyl iodide. Transient measurements have allowed direct observation of stilbene triplets at low temperatures and, employing triplet energy donors, at room temperature.

Under triplet (sensitized) excitation conditions stilbene photoisomeriza-

‡ See Note Added in Proof on p. 82.

tion has been proposed to occur via common twisted triplet intermediates, $^3p^*$, which lie lower in energy than cisoid triplets but are nearly isoenergetic with transoid triplets $(30,65,121–123)$ [Eqs. (31)–(35), where D is the

$$^3D^* + {}^1t \underset{k^t_{-et}}{\overset{k^t_{et}}{\rightleftharpoons}} {}^1D + {}^3t^* \tag{31}$$

$$^3D^* + {}^1c \overset{k^c_{et}}{\rightarrow} {}^1D + {}^3c^* \tag{32}$$

$$^3t^* \overset{k_{tp}}{\rightleftharpoons} {}^3p^* \tag{33}$$

$$^3c^* \overset{k_{cp}}{\rightarrow} {}^3p^* \tag{34}$$

$$^3p^* \overset{k_d}{\longrightarrow} \epsilon^1t + (1 - \epsilon)^1c \tag{35}$$

donor and ϵ is the fraction of twisted triplets that decay to ^1t. Photostationary cis/trans compositions achieved in the presence of different donors depend primarily on the triplet energy, E_T, of the donor (Fig. 8). Reference to the potential energy curve for twisting in the triplet state (Fig. 5) readily accounts for this behavior. Vertical excitation of ^1t and ^1c [Eqs. (31) and (32)] requires donors with E_T of >49 and >57 kcal/mol, respectively. Experimentally measured k^t_{et} and k^c_{et} values in benzene at room temperature are near the diffusion-controlled limit for E_T values slightly exceeding these values (124). Excitation-transfer rate constants decrease from this limit as donor E_T drops below 62 and 53 kcal/mol for ^1c and ^1t, respectively, the decrease being substantially steeper for ^1t. Photostationary c/t ratios are nicely accounted for by observed rate constants through Eq. (36), as predicted by the mechanism in Eqs. (31)–(35), where $\epsilon \simeq 0.4$

$$([c]/[t])_s = (k^t_{et}/k^c_{et})(1 - \epsilon)/\epsilon \tag{36}$$

$(30,65,124)$. Since the drop of k^t_{et} with ΔE_T, the spectroscopic energy difference between donor and acceptor, nearly obeys Eq. (37), it was reasoned that ^1t is vertically excited to $^3t^*$, even when the transfer is endothermic, the energy deficiency being supplied as an activation energy (124). In contrast, the observation of k^c_{et} values much larger than predicted by Eq. (37) suggests that nonvertical excitation of ^1c [Eq. (38)] becomes

$$\Delta \ln k_{et} = -\Delta E_T/RT \tag{37}$$

$$^3D^* + {}^1c \overset{k'_{et}}{\rightarrow} {}^1D + {}^3p^* \tag{38}$$

the dominant activation mechanism for this isomer with donors in the E_T range of 42–58 kcal/mol $(30,124,125)$. This accounts for the decrease in $([c]/[t])_s$ for donors with $E_T < 50$ kcal/mol. Interestingly, similarly low

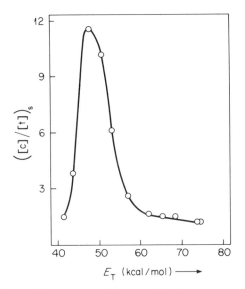

Fig. 8 Stilbene photostationary compositions as a function of donor triplet energy (30).

Arrhenius A factors for excitation transfer from anthracene triplets, $E_T =$ 42.7 kcal/mol, to stilbenes suggest that endothermic excitation transfer to ^1t may also be nonvertical [Eq. (39)]. The activation enthalpies give 48.1

$$^3D* + {}^1t \xrightarrow{k_{et}^{-1}} {}^1D + {}^3p* \tag{39}$$

and 49.1 kcal/mol as the energies of the stilbene triplets attained from ^1t and ^1c, respectively (126).

Another line of evidence suggests similar energies for $^3t*$ and $^3p*$. Reversibility of triplet excitation between donors and $^3t*$ is reflected by a strong linear dependence of $([t]/[c])_s$ on donor concentration, provided that donor E_T is less than 49 kcal/mol (65). No concentration effect is observed when donor energy dips below 57 kcal/mol, the vertical excitation energy of ^1c, precluding reversibility of Eq. (32) and suggesting either rapid $^3c* \rightarrow$ $^3p*$ torsion or direct $^1c \rightarrow {}^3p*$ excitation. Compounds the triplet energies of which are too low to allow measurable transfer of excitation to stilbenes, e.g., azulene (65,121,123) or carotene (127), deactivate stilbene triplets to ^1t exclusively, e.g., Eq. (40). Di-t-butyl nitroxide (128) and oxygen

$$^3t* + {}^1A \xrightarrow{k_q} {}^1t + {}^3A* \tag{40}$$

(127,129), on the other hand, belong to a different quencher class which appears to interact efficiently with $^3p*$, causing a decrease in the stilbene triplet lifetime without changing significantly its decay distribution. Equation (41) shows this interaction for oxygen ($\epsilon/\epsilon' = 1.0$; $\epsilon/\epsilon' = 1.11$ for the

$$^3p^* + {}^3O_2 \xrightarrow{k_{ox}} \epsilon't + (1 - \epsilon')c + {}^3O_2 \qquad (41)$$

nitroxide). A comparative study of the quenching interactions of oxygen and β-carotene with triplets strongly suggests that electronic excitation is not transferred to oxygen (127). β-Carotene was employed in this comparison because the electronic energy required to excite it to the lowest triplet state is approximately equal to the energy required to excite oxygen to its lowest singlet state (130–132). Results from experiments demonstrating the very different behavior of oxygen and β-carotene as quenchers of stilbene triplets are plotted in Fig. 9. Figure 9 shows the effect of azulene on ([t]/[c])$_s$ compositions for the benzophenone-sensitized isomerization of stilbene in the presence or absence of oxygen or β-carotene. Oxygen strongly attenuates the slope of the azulene effect without affecting the intercept, whereas β-carotene does not affect the slope but changes the intercept. As in the case of azulene, quenching interactions with β-carotene lead to ¹t exclusively, suggesting that a transoid geometry is readily attained by the stilbene triplet [Eq. (40)]. This geometry could also be attained in an encounter complex following initial interaction of β-carotene or azulene with ³p* [Eq. (42)]. In the case of oxygen and

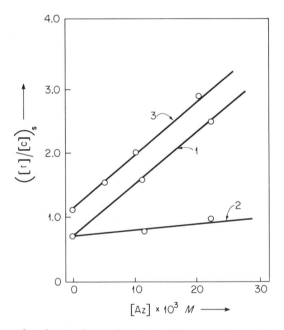

Fig. 9 Effect of azulene on benzophenone-sensitized photoisomerization of stilbene in benzene: line 1, degassed; line 2, oxygen bubbled through solution; line 3, degassed with 2.90 × 10⁻³ M β-carotene. [Taken from Saltiel and Thomas (127).]

$$^3p^* + {}^1A \rightarrow (^3p^{*1}A) \rightleftarrows (^3t^{*1}A) \rightarrow {}^1t + {}^3A^* \qquad (42)$$

di-t-butyl nitroxide a spin exchange mechanism becomes effective because of the energetic proximity of the lowest singlet and triplet states of stilbene in the twisted geometry ($127,128$). Such radiationless steps are related to those proposed to account for enhancement of thermal cis–trans isomerization of olefins by catalysts with nonzero spin (27). Since oxygen should also be an efficient quencher of $^3t^*$ the results suggest that $^3p^*$ is the thermodynamically favored triplet in solution at room temperature. Analysis of the attenuation of the azulene effect by oxygen using $k_{ox} = 7.0 \times 10^9 \ M^{-1} \ sec^{-1}$, the known value of the rate constant of nitrostilbene quenching by oxygen (108), gives $\tau \simeq 125 \pm 10 \ nsec$ for $^3p^*$, confirming the value of $110 \pm 10 \ nsec$ assigned earlier to a weak transient absorption at 360 nm observed in benzene solutions of trans-stilbene following pulse radiolytic excitation (133). More recently, transient absorptions observed in the 345–390 nm region following 2-acetonaphthone-sensitized excitation of the stilbenes have been assigned to an equilibrating mixture of $^3t^*$ and $^3p^*$ (134). In nonviscous media (n-heptane, benzene, ethanol) the same transient absorption is observed starting with either stilbene isomer, in contrast to t-butyl alcohol, with which different absorptions are observed. It is suggested that the equilibration in Eq. (33) is achieved rapidly in the former solvents ($[^3t^*]/[^3p^*] = 0.12$, $\tau = 110 \pm 10 \ nsec$ in heptane) but is not complete after 50 nsec in t-butyl alcohol ($[^3t^*]/[^3p^*] = 1.4$ and 0.06 starting from ^1t and ^1c, respectively) (134). Unfortunately, this interesting study is not reported in sufficient detail, and some of its conclusions are questionable. For example, the rate constants of 10^8 and $10^7 \ sec^{-1}$, assigned to k_{tp} and k_{pt}, respectively, in heptane, are so low that different transients should have readily been observed from the two isomers even in this solvent. (At 0.1 M stilbene excitation transfer from the donor should have been complete within the duration of the excitation flash, ~7 nsec.) Nonetheless, this result seems to invalidate the analysis of the temperature dependence of c → t and t → c isomerization efficiencies obtained by laser excitation at 488 nm (58.4 kcal/mol) (135). Direct excitation to $^3t^*$ and $^3c^*$ was assumed, and decay from each was proposed to be slow compared to their interconversion since isomerization efficiency decreased with temperature in both directions, giving low Arrhenius A factors, ~10^7 sec^{-1}, for this process in isohexane. Aside from predicting different transient absorptions in the hydrocarbon solvent starting from ^1c and ^1t, the interpretation of these observations is inconsistent with the temperature independence of benzophenone-sensitized photoisomerization quantum yields (136)(see also Section III,C,5). A further puzzle is the assignment of a shorter lifetimes to $^3t^*$ (80 nsec, $\lambda_{max} \simeq 376$ nm) than to $^3p^*$ (120 nsec, $\lambda_{max} \simeq$ 360 nm, t-butyl alcohol) without indicating the wavelength at which each absorption was monitored (134). Direct decay of ^{3}t* in fluid solution to the ground state is precluded by high isomerization quantum yields in that solvent (see below).

At low temperatures, 77–195 K, and in glassy media the lifetime of stilbene triplets is sufficiently long to be measured by conventional flash-kinetic spectroscopy (123,137–140). A large deuterium isotope effect on triplet decay rates is found. This effect is largest in 3-methylpentane and EPA (k_{d_0} = 56 and 45.5 sec^{-1}; $k_{d_{12}}$ = 11 and 10.9 sec^{-1}, respectively) and decreases as either the temperature is increased or the medium viscosity is decreased. In the most rigid media, torsional displacements into non-planar configurations [Eq. (33)] are expected to be inhibited severely and decay is due mainly to intersystem crossing from ^{3}t* [Eq. (43)] (123,137–

$$^3t^* \xrightarrow{k'_d} {}^1t \tag{43}$$

140). As the medium viscosity is decreased rate-determining twisting to ^{3}p* competes with Eq. (43), and the deuterium isotope effect is accordingly diluted. Lifetimes of specifically deuteriated trans-stilbenes in the olefinic and aromatic positions show that olefinic C—H vibrations are much more effective in promoting Eq. (43) than are aromatic C—H vibrations, this positional dependence being most pronounced in the most viscous medium (17-fold and 7-fold per H atom in EPA and isopentane/3-methylpentane, 6 : 1, respectively). Apparently, the relative importance of aromatic C—H vibrations in step 43 increases as the viscosity of the medium is decreased (123).

A comparative study of stilbene-d_0, stilbene-d_{12}, vinyl-substituted stilbene-d_2, and aromatic-substituted stilbene-d_{10} was carried out in benzene at 298 K. No deuterium effect on the t/c decay distribution of the triplet state was observed, supporting the view that Eq. (43) does not contribute to triplet decay in fluid solution and that ϵ in Eq. (35) is not affected by deuteriation (95,123). The benzophenone-sensitized ([t]/[c])$_s$ ratios of stilbene-d_{12} and stilbene-d_2 are 30% more sensitive to changes in azulene concentration than are the corresponding ratios of stilbene-d_0 and stilbene-d_{10}, suggesting that deuterium substitution of the olefinic positions increases the lifetime of ^{3}p* by 30%. The total absence of a deuterium isotope effect on the lifetime for deuteriation of aromatic positions further distinguishes ^{3}p* from ^{3}t* decay. It is in accord with a theoretical prediction that very little, if any, electronic excitation will be concentrated in C—H stretching vibrations upon ^{3}p* deactivation. Rather, it was predicted that the torsional mode of the central double bond should serve as a primary acceptor of electronic energy, leading to a notable absence of a deuterium isotope effect in Eq. (35) (141). The differential deuterium isotope effect that is observed may reflect the ability of olefinic C—H vibrations in $^3p^*$ to induce intersystem crossing (123).

In attempts to produce stilbene triplets directly methyl iodide (142) and high oxygen pressures (143) have been employed to enhance light absorption probabilities in the region of the $T_1 \leftarrow S_0$ transitions. The results are qualitatively consistent with observations in the presence of sensitizers. In the case of methyl iodide large uncertainties in extinction coefficients of the two isomers at the exciting wavelength, 436 nm, introduce uncertainties in isomerization quantum yields. Also, despite extreme precautions to scavenge photochemical formation of iodine atoms, their possible involvement as efficient catalysts of thermal c → t isomerization (84,144) may account in part for the very large quantum yield reported in that direction. In contrast, in the case of oxygen relatively small isomerization quantum yields are reported for excitation at $\lambda = 405$ nm ($\phi_{t \to c} = 0.42 \pm 0.03$; $\phi_{c \to t} = 0.22 \pm 0.04$) (143). However, the ratio of these quantum yields agrees with that predicted from sensitization experiments (145,146), indicating that no significant quenching of $^3t^*$ by oxygen occurs even at 120–140 atm O_2.

5. Comparison of Singlet and Triplet Behavior

Observations following steady-state irradiation conditions allow inferences to be made concerning the behavior of excited state intermediates produced by direct excitation into the singlet manifold or by triplet excitation transfer. Properties evaluated are the decay characteristics of the excited states and their interaction with electronic energy acceptors or spin exchange quenchers. Isomerization quantum yields and photostationary ratios in the absence of quenchers reflect decay fractions, whereas the sensitivities of these quantities to quencher concentration reflect efficiencies of quenching interactions. In principle, a crossing of the isomerization pathways under singlet (direct) and triplet (sensitized) excitation conditions could occur by intersystem crossing from the potential energy surface of S_1 to the triplet manifold, the probability of the process being higher at geometries that are near a crossing point with a triplet state surface or that have longer residence times because they represent free-energy minima, e.g., Eqs. (19) and (44). This crossing of reaction path-

$$^1p^* \xrightarrow{k_{p}^{i}} {}^3p^* \qquad (44)$$

ways in common triplet states, first postulated by Förster (147), does not account for observations with the parent stilbenes. An earlier mechanism (97), in which internal conversion from $^1t^*$ and $^1c^*$ gives vibrationally hot ground states the vibrational relaxation of which is slow compared to the intramolecular concentration of excess energy to the appropriate rotational mode, has been rejected on theoretical grounds (148) and because it is inconsistent with the absence of deuterium isotope effects on photoisomerization (95) and fluorescence quantum yields (91).

Accordingly, in the absence of quenchers, quantum yields for direct and sensitized photoisomerization of the stilbenes are given by Eqs. (45) and (46) and Eqs. (47) and (48), respectively. Neglecting intersystem crossing,

Direct:

$$\phi_{t \to c} = (1 - \phi_f)(1 - \beta) \tag{45}$$

$$\phi_{c \to t} = (1 - \phi_{DHP})\beta \tag{46}$$

Sensitized:

$$\phi_{t \to c} = 1 - \epsilon \tag{47}$$

$$\phi_{c \to t} = \epsilon \tag{48}$$

$(1 - \phi_f)$ and $(1 - \phi_{DHP})$ give the efficiencies of $^1p^*$ formation from $^1t^*$ and $^1c^*$, respectively. In Eqs. (47) and (48) unit intersystem crossing efficiency in the donor and complete excitation transfer to the stilbenes without energy-wasting interactions are assumed [see Valentine and Hammond (146), and Gajewski and Caldwell (149) for small deviations from the latter condition]. Photostationary states are related to isomerization quantum yields, as shown in Eqs. (49) and (50) for direct and sensitized excitation, respectively, where ϵ_c, ϵ_t are extinction coefficients at the excitation wavelength and k_{et}^c, k_{et}^t are triplet excitation rate constants. Experimental observations are consistent with nearly identical decay characteristics from excited states produced by either excitation mode, suggesting that the similar geometries of $^1p^*$ and $^3p^*$ give rise to similar decay fractions $\beta \simeq \epsilon \simeq 0.4$ (95). Equation (49) is adequately obeyed for both 254 and 313 nm excitation (94), and experimentally measured triplet excitation-transfer rate constants predict stationary compositions when Eq. (50) and β are employed (124).

$$([t]/[c])_s = (\epsilon_c/\epsilon_t)(\phi_{c \to t}/\phi_{t \to c}) \tag{49}$$

$$([t]/[c])_s = (k_{et}^c/k_{et}^t)(\phi_{c \to t}/\phi_{t \to c}) \tag{50}$$

In the presence of triplet excitation acceptors, such as azulene, $t \to c$ quantum yields and photostationary states for the benzophenone-sensitized reaction obey Eqs. (51) and (52), respectively (94,121), where K_t is the Stern–Volmer constant for stilbene triplet quenching, and $k_{et}^c = k_{et}^t$ is assumed in Eq. (52). The same K_t values are obtained from either Eq. (51) or (52) in a variety of solvents and over a wide temperature range (121), suggesting that equilibration between $^3t^*$ and $^3p^*$ is maintained throughout the azulene concentration range. Limited $c \to t$ quantum yield data for the benzophenone-sensitized isomerization in benzene show azulene enhancement of the isomerization in that direction, as predicted by Eq. (53), which can be derived from Eqs. (50)–(52) (96a).

$$(\phi^\circ_{t\to c}/\phi_{t\to c}) = 1 + K_t[Az] \tag{51}$$

$$([t]/[c])_s = (\epsilon + K_t[Az])/(1 - \epsilon) \tag{52}$$

$$(\phi^\circ_{c\to t}/\phi_{c\to t}) = \epsilon(1 + K_t[Az])/(\epsilon + K_t[Az]) \tag{53}$$

In aprotic solvents K_t values at 30°C are to a good approximation invesely proportional to solvent viscosity (Fig. 10), as would be expected if the excitation-transfer step were diffusion-controlled (121). Deviations of K_t values in alcoholic media from the line may be due in part to a slower equilibration between stilbene triplet conformations in these solvents, as suggested by the spectroscopic observations (134). A tentative analysis of the temperature dependence of K_t was based on Eq. (52) assuming k_d in Eq. (35) to be medium and temperature independent (121). It was further based on the assumption that experimental rate constants for excitation transfer from indeno[2,1-a]indene (4) triplets to azulene could be used as empirical values for a diffusion-controlled process (121). Since direct measurements of the decay dynamics of stilbene triplets are now possible (134,135) a less speculative analysis of the variation of K_t should be possi-

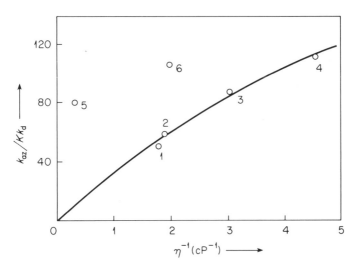

Fig. 10 Variation of k_{az}/Kk_d (K_t) with η^{-1} at 30°C. Solvents: 1, benzene; 2, toluene; 3, acetonitrile; 4, n-pentane; 5, t-butyl alcohol; 6, methanol. [Taken from Saltiel et al. (121).]

ble in the near future, revealing a more accurate description of the excitation-transfer process.

Under direct excitation conditions, acceptors, such as azulene, can intercept singlet and, if formed, triplet stilbene excited states. The expected dependence of t → c quantum yields on azulene concentration for the two limiting cases of no triplet participation, $\phi_{is}^{1t*} \simeq \phi_{is}^{1p*} \simeq 0$, and of complete triplet participation, $\phi_{is}^{1p*} = 1.0$, is given by Eqs. (54) and (55),

$$\phi_f^0/\phi_f = \phi_{t\to c}^0/\phi_{t\to c} = 1 + K_s[Az] \tag{54}$$

$$\phi_{t\to c}^0/\phi_{t\to c} = (1 + K_s[Az])(1 + K_t[Az]) \tag{55}$$

respectively, where K_s is the Stern–Volmer constant for $^1t^*$ quenching by azulene and, as indicated in Eq. (54), is accessible experimentally from fluorescence measurements (150,151). Observed responses of $\phi_{t\to c}^0/\phi_{t\to c}$ to azulene, shown in Fig. 11, obey Eq. (54) closely, especially when irradiations are carried out in the presence of visible light to minimize DHP formation (94). As expected, in view of the short lifetime of $^1c^*$ (117), azulene does not influence c → t quantum yields (94). These results clearly require that no triplets participate in the isomerization process following direct excitation of the stilbenes. The same conclusion had been reached earlier because of the relatively small sensitivity of $([t]/[c])_s$ values to [Az]

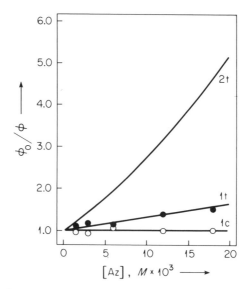

Fig. 11 Effect of azulene on $\phi_{t\to c}$ and $\phi_{c\to t}$ for the direct photoisomerization of stilbenes. Lines 1t, 2t, and 1c calculated with Eqs. (54), (55), and (58) ($\phi_{is}^p = 0$), respectively; points are experimental (94).

(*30,96,96a,150*), consistent with the failure of laser flash spectroscopy to reveal triplet formation following direct excitation of ^{1}t in solution at room temperature (*108,108a,152*).

6. Substituted Stilbenes

A broad study of substituent effects on the cis–trans photoisomerization of stilbenes has been carried out (*153*). Other studies have focused on specific substituent types, such as halogens (*90,90a,94,154,155*) and nitro groups (*108,108a,155–159*). Representative photoisomerization quantum yields for direct excitation and, for the trans isomers, fluorescence quantum yields are given in Table 5. Only data in hydrocarbon solvents were selected, and, when available, results at a low temperature, above the glass-setting temperature of the medium, are also given. Aside from a considerable discrepancy between results from different laboratories, $\phi_{c \to t}$ values of all the stilbenes are remarkably insensitive to temperature changes, provided that rigid media are avoided (e.g., see entries p-bromostilbene at 90 K in MCH/IH and MCH/IP). Small changes in $\phi_{c \to DHP}$ may also play a significant role. The absence of fluorescence from the cis isomers in nonviscous media suggests that ${}^1c^* \to {}^1p^*$ and/or ${}^1c^* \to {}^1DHP^*$ remain fast in all cases. Substituent behavior is separated roughly into three major groups based, when possible, on the responses of $\phi_{t \to c}$ and ϕ_f^t to the change in temperature. In group 1 are substituents that do not influence $S_1 \to T$ intersystem crossing significantly and do not cause deviations from planarity due to steric effects. Stilbenes in group 1 are expected to follow the isomerization mechanism described above for the parent hydrocarbon. Unfortunately, generally the data are too meager to allow this conclusion to be made, since only in the case of p-methoxystilbene do the $\phi_{t \to c}$ and ϕ_f values appear to be coupled throughout the temperature range. In group 2 are substituents that are expected to cause substantial population of triplet states due either to a heavy-atom effect, as in the case of the halogens, or to the introduction of low-lying $n-\pi^*$ states, as in the carbonyl or nitro substituents. In these stilbenes low ϕ_f values are observed throughout the temperature region, and uncoupling between $\phi_{t \to c}$ and ϕ_f variations is expected due to ${}^1t^* \to {}^3t^*$ intersystem crossing and subsequent isomerization from the triplet state. For example, in p-bromostilbene ϕ_f increases modestly as the temperature is lowered, whereas $\phi_{t \to c}$ remains unaffected. Group 3 includes stilbenes with relatively large substituents at the ortho and α positions. Steric hindrance is relieved mainly by twisting about the 1-α bonds, as evidenced by hypsochromic and hypochromic shifts of the long-wavelength transition (*47,153,160,161*). Significant torsional displacements about these bonds also contribute to the diffuse nature of the $S_1 \leftarrow S_0$ absorption spectrum of

TABLE 5

Representative Isomerization and Fluorescence (^{1}t*) Quantum Yields of Substituted Stilbenes

X	T (K)^a	λ (nm)	Solvent^b	$\phi_{t\to c}$	$\phi_{c\to t}$	ϕ_f	Reference
			Group 1				
H	298	313	MCH/IH	0.50	0.35	0.044	90, 92, 105^c, 153
	298	313	P	0.52	0.35	0.040	94^d
	RT	313	CH^e	0.40	0.22		155
	133	313	MCH/IH	0.04	0.35	0.89	90, 92, 153
p-CH$_3$O	298	313	MCH/IP	0.46	0.25	0.03	153
	RT	313	CH^e	0.40	0.29		155
	153	313	MCH/IP	0.10	0.34	0.79	153
m-CH$_3$O	RT	313	CH^e	0.31	0.19		155
p-F	RT	313	CH^e	0.42	0.40		55
	290	313	MP's			0.05	90a^f
	110	313	MP's			0.43	90a^f
m-F	RT	313	CH^e	0.39	0.34		155
α,α'-diF	298	313	MCH/IP	0.35	0.45	<0.001	153
	90	313	MCH/IP	0.20	0.40		153
	90	313	MCH/IH			0.35	153
p-(CH$_3$)$_2$N	298	366	MCH/IP	0.52	0.22	0.05	153
	RT	313	CH^e	0.52	0.22		155
	153	366	MCH/IP	0.006	0.33	0.22	153
p-CN	RT	313	CH^e	0.46	0.41		155
m-CN	RT	313	CH^e	0.39	0.44		155
p-CN, p'-CH$_3$O	298	366	T			0.013	159
	198	366	T			0.16	159
			Group 2				
p-Cl	298	313	MCH/IH	0.60	0.42	0.08	90, 153
	RT	313	CH^e	0.41	0.21		155
	133	313	MCH/IH	0.13	0.50	0.52	90, 153
m-Cl	RT	313	CH^e	0.40	0.23		155
α,α'-diCl	298	313	MCH/IP	0.41	0.14	<0.001	153
	98	313	MCH/IP	0.08	0.15	0.002	153
p-Br	298	313	MCH/IH	0.35	0.16	0.065	153
	298	313	P	0.53	0.44	0.046	94^d
	RT	313	CH^e	0.39	0.35		155
	118	313	MCH/IH	0.35	0.19	0.12	153
	90	313	MCH/IH	0.003	0.05	0.17	90, 153
	90	313	MCH/IP	0.35	0.16		153
m-Br	298	313	P	0.56	0.36	0.015	94^d
	298	313	H	0.46	0.18		
	RT	313	CH	0.38	0.40		155
	77	294	P			0.08^g	94^d

TABLE 5 (*Continued*)

X	T (K)[a]	λ (nm)	Sol-vent[b]	$\phi_{t\to c}$	$\phi_{c\to t}$	ϕ_f	Reference
m,m'-diBr	298	313	P	0.56	0.24	0.020	94[d]
	298	313	H	0.53	<0.05		154
	77	296	P			0.053[g]	94
p-NO$_2$	298	366	MCH/IH	0.15	0.20	Low	153
	RT	313	CH[e]	0.45	0.36		155
	123	365	MCH/IH	0.15	0.20	Low	153
m-NO$_2$	RT	313	CH[e]	0.45	0.21		155
p-CH$_3$CO	298	313	MCH/IH	0.5	0.3		153
	123	313	MCH/IH	0.5	0.3		153
p-⬡-CO	298	313	MCH/IH	0.54	0.27		153
	123	313	MCH/IH	0.57	0.27		153
p-⬡-COCH$_2$	298	313	MCH/IH	0.5	0.3		153
	123	313	MCH/IH	0.5	0.3		153
p-NO$_2$, p'-CH$_3$O	298	313	MCH/D	0.60	0.38		153
	RT	366	CH	0.55	0.34		158
	298	366	T			0.007	159
	193	366	T			0.43	159
	173	313	MCH/D	0.55	0.37		153
	117	313	MCH/D	0.03	0.37		153
p-NO$_2$, p'-(CH$_3$)$_2$N	298	436	MCH/D	0.37	0.35		153
	223	436	MCH/D	0.015	0.42		153
Group 3							
α-CH$_3$	298	313	IH	0.48	0.58	0.003	153
	98	313	MCH/IP	0.32	0.46		153
	86	313	MCH/IH			0.21	153
o,p,o'-triCH$_3$	298	313	MCH/IH	0.47	0.39	0.003[h]	153
	93	313	MCH/IH	0.13	0.40	0.35[h]	153
o,o',p,p',o,o'-hexaCH$_3$	298	313	MCH/IH	0.48	0.40	<0.001[h]	153
	93	313	MCH/IH	0.52		0.13[h]	153
	93	254	MCH/IH	0.51	0.42		153

[a] RT, room temperature.

[b] Solvents: methylcyclohexane (MCH)/isohexane (IH), 2:1 by volume; MCH/isopentane (IP), 1:4 by volume; MCH/decalin (D), 1:1 by volume; cyclohexane (CH); *n*-pentane (P); mixture of 2-methyl- and 3-methylpentanes (MP's); *n*-hexane (H); benzene (B); toluene (T).

[c] See Charlton and Saltiel (*105*) for ϕ_f.

[d] Fluorescence excitation wavelengths are 280, 280, 294, and 296 nm for stilbene, *p*-bromo-, *m*-bromo-, and *m,m'*-dibromostilbenes, respectively.

[e] In the presence of air.

[f] Estimated from Fig. 15 (*90a*).

[g] Extrapolated value.

[h] Excited at 315 nm.

stilbene itself at room temperature (*93,162,163*). The room-temperature absorption spectrum of the rigid analogue *trans*-1,1'-biindanylidene (**6**) shows well-resolved vibrational components (*93*), which are present in

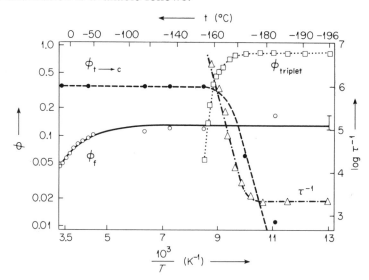

6

stilbene only at low temperature in glassy media (*90,162*). Nonplanarity in the methyl-substituted stilbenes causes them to behave somewhat like the generally nonplanar *cis*-stilbenes; i.e., $\phi_{t\to c}$ values for these compounds are much less temperature dependent than for those in group 1. Fluorescence quantum yields are accordingly smaller for group 3 stilbenes, provided that rigid media are avoided.

In addition to the temperature dependence of fluorescence and isomerization quantum yields, comparative singlet and triplet quenching studies and spectroscopic observation of transient intermediates are crucial in determining mechanistic details for each specific case. A discussion of the photoisomerization mechanisms of bromo- and nitrostilbenes for which such information is available follows.

Fig. 12 Variation of $\phi_{t\to c}$, ϕ_f, $\phi_{triplet}$, and τ^{-1} [in (seconds)$^{-1}$] with temperature for *trans*-p-bromostilbene. [Taken from Görner and Schulte-Frohlinde (*165*). Reprinted with permission of the copyright holder, the American Chemical Society.]

The temperature dependence of ϕ_f^l and $\phi_{t\rightarrow c}$ for p-bromostilbene in MCH/IH (Fig. 12) ($90a$) demonstrates that, in contrast to stilbene, the two processes are not complementary. Even when owing to medium rigidity ($91a$) the isomerization process is almost completely inhibited, the fluorescence quantum yield is much smaller than unity. Small limiting fluorescence quantum yields are also found in MP's ($90a$) and P for p-bromostilbene and in P for m-bromo- and m,m'-dibromostilbenes (94). It has been reasoned that heavy-atom-enhanced intersystem crossing brings Eq. (19) into play as an unactivated initial step for an additional channel for isomerization ($30,94$). Triplet state parameters obtained by application of Eq. (52) to the benzophenone-sensitized isomerization of the bromostilbenes, with and without added azulene, are given in Table 6, along with K_s values obtained from a careful study of fluorescence quenching by azulene [Eq. (54)] (151). Similar triplet decay fractions, ϵ, and values of $\phi_{c\rightarrow t} = 0.45 \pm 0.04$ and $\phi_{t\rightarrow c} = 0.48 \pm 0.03$ for the benzophenone-sensitized isomerization of p-bromostilbene in n-pentane suggest efficient formation of $^3p^*$ from both $^3t^*$ and $^3c^*$ (94). The suggestion that enhanced spin–orbital coupling induces very rapid $^1c^* \rightarrow {}^3c^* \rightarrow {}^1c$ decay ($154,164$), accounting for a decrease in $\phi_{c\rightarrow t}$ for the direct excitation photoisomerization, can therefore be discounted.

Application of Eq. (21) to fluorescence quantum yields in n-pentane gives A_{tp}/k_f, E_{tp}, and κ parameters, from which the ϕ_{is}^{1t} values at 30°C, shown in Table 6, were calculated using Eq. (56) (94). The A_{tp} and E_{tp}

$$\phi_{is}^{1t} = (\kappa - 1)/[\kappa + (A_{tp}/k_f)e^{-E_{tp}/RT}] \tag{56}$$

parameters are in the ranges 0.3–3×10^{13} sec^{-1} and 3–4 kcal/mol, respectively, consistent with values assigned to the twisting process in stilbene (Table 4) (94). Intersystem crossing rate constants from $^1t^*$ can be calculated using Eq. (57) and k_f values calculated with the Birks–Dyson rela-

$$k_{is}^{1t} = (\phi_{is}^{1t}/\phi_f)k_f \tag{57}$$

TABLE 6

Decay and Azulene Quenching Parameters of Bromostilbenes[a]

	ϵ	K_t	K_s	ϕ_{is}^{1t}	ϕ_{is}^{1p}
H	0.36 (0.40)	118 (50)	29.7	0.002	0
p-Br	0.40 (0.43)	22 (14)	24.8	0.33	1.0
m-Br	0.45 (0.53)	63 (44)	8.3	0.17	0.9
m,m'-DiBr	0.39 (0.52)	153 (67)	16.4	0.34	0.7

[a] Pentane, 30°C; values in parentheses are for benzene, 30°C.

tionship (94,152). Values of 5.0×10^9, 7.1×10^9, and 10.4×10^9 sec^{-1} for
p-bromo-, m-bromo-, and m,m'-dibromostilbenes are obtained, indicating
a somewhat larger enhancement of intersystem crossing for meta than for
para substitution. Bromine's influence in spin–orbital coupling *is not diminished* when it is substituted at a near node of the highest occupied and
lowest unoccupied π MO's of stilbene ($c_m = 0.0791$ and $c_p = 0.3138$ in the
Hückel approximation) (94).

The ϕ_{is}^{1p} values in Table 6 are obtained from the response of $\phi_{t \to c}$ for the
direct photoisomerization to azulene concentration. The simplest case is
that of p-bromostilbene, for which all excited singlets intersystem-cross
either from $^1t^*$ or from $^1p^*$. As expected for this condition, observed
$\phi_{t \to c}^\circ / \phi_{t \to c}$ ratios are predicted closely by Eq. (55) (Fig. 13) (94). When
intersystem crossing from $^1p^*$ is not complete, a rather complex relation-
ship between $\phi_{t \to c}^\circ / \phi_{t \to c}$ and [Az] is predicted (94). The ϕ_{is}^{1p} values in Table
6 were those giving the best adherence of quantum yield ratios to this
relationship, with the further simplifying assumption of $\beta = \epsilon$ (94).

The mechanism of lowest triplet population proposed above for the
isomerization of bromostilbenes is not entirely consistent with direct measurements of triplet–triplet absorption spectra, triplet lifetimes, and rela-

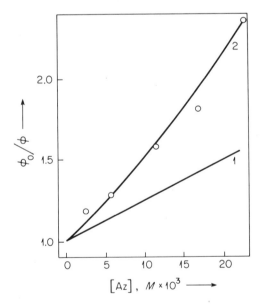

Fig. 13 Effect of azulene on $\phi_{t \to c}$ for direct photoisomerization of *trans-p*-bromostilbene.
Lines 1 and 2 calculated with Eqs. (54) and (55), respectively; points are experimental.
[Taken from Saltiel *et al.* (94). Reprinted with permission of the copyright holder, the Ameri-
can Chemical Society.]

tive triplet yields obtained for *trans-p*-bromostilbene as a function of temperature (-159 to $-196°C$ in methylcyclohexane/isohexane, $1:1$) *(165)*. Since, owing to medium rigidity, $\phi_{t \to c}$ approaches zero at low temperatures, the triplet absorption spectrum, which is independent of temperature, has been assigned to $^3t^*$ throughout the temperature range *(165)*. Lifetimes of $^3t^*$ and relative O.D.'s for triplet–triplet absorption (expressed as $\phi_{triplet}$) are shown in Fig. 12. The decrease in triplet lifetime, observed over the same temperature range wherein $\phi_{t \to c}$ decreases, is attributed to inhibition of $^3t^* \to {}^3p^*$ twisting. The surprising observation is that, along with the decrease in lifetime, there is a sharp decrease in the signal for $^3t^*$ absorption. It follows that the unactivated radiationless process, labeled ϕ_{is}^{1t} in Table 6, which competes with fluorescence, cannot be identified with $^3t^*$ formation [Eq. (19)]. A higher triplet pathway for $^3p^*$ formation has been suggested ($^1t^* \to {}^3t_h^* \to {}^3p_h^* \to {}^3p^*$, where the subscript designates higher energy) which bypasses $^3t^*$ *(165)*. At the lower temperatures, $^3t_h^* \to {}^3p_h^*$ twisting is probably also inhibited, which allows for $^3t_h^* \to {}^3t^*$ internal conversion and the observation of $^3t^*$ absorption. A corollary to this interpretation is that, because of either low transition probabilities or short lifetime, no triplet–triplet absorption corresponding to $^3p^*$ is observed. In view of these results the temperature-independent step competing with fluorescence in the bromostilbenes is probably $^1t^* \to {}^3t_h^*$, and quenching of triplets by azulene involves $^3p^*$, as shown in Eq. (42).

Owing to its very short lifetime *(117)* no significant quenching of $^1c^*$ by azulene is expected. Since $^1c^* \to {}^1p^*$ twisting probably accounts for a large fraction of $^1c^*$ decay, ϕ_{cp}, intersystem crossing from $^1p^*$ should be reflected in an increase in $\phi_{c \to t}$ with increased azulene concentration [Eq. (58)]. In the case of *cis*-stilbene, $\phi_{c \to t}$ is independent of azulene concentra-

$$\phi_{c \to t} = \phi_{cp}\left[(1 - \phi_{is}^{1p})\beta + \frac{\epsilon + K_t[Az]}{1 + K_t[Az]}\ \phi_{is}^{1p} \right] \tag{58}$$

tion, as expected for $\phi_{is}^{1p} \simeq 0$ *(94)*. For bromostilbenes the large values of ϕ_{is}^{1p} lead to the prediction of substantial decreases in $\phi_{c \to t}^{\circ}/\phi_{c \to t}$ with [Az]. The opposite trend is generally observed *(94)*. It follows that if the $^1c^* \to {}^1p^*$ pathway is important for bromostilbenes, there must be at least one additional cis–trans isomerization pathway which, being quenched rather than enhanced by azulene, gives rise to the observed net quenching effects. An attractive possibility involves bromine-enhanced intersystem crossing in $^1DHP^*$, giving dihydrophenanthrene triplets, $^3DHP^*$, which, in the absence of quencher, ring-open to give $^3p^*$ *(94)*. Excitation transfer from $^3DHP^*$ to azulene diverts molecules from this isomerization pathway to ^1DHP and eventually to ^1c. This mechanism is supported by the observation of ^1DHP formation enhancement by azulene starting with *cis-*

m,m'-dibromostilbene (22). The quenching of cis–trans isomerization by azulene is also reflected in relatively low sensitivity of $([t]/[c])_s$ to [Az] (94). This behavior had initially been interpreted as suggesting low intersystem crossing efficiency in bromostilbenes, a conclusion that was not borne out by the quantum yield observations (121,166).

The temperature dependencies of $^1t^*$ fluorescence (90,90a) and photoisomerization quantum yields (90a) for p-chlorostilbene show intermediate behavior between that of stilbene and bromostilbenes, suggesting that chlorine, too, opens a significant intersystem crossing channel for photoisomerization. Apparently, the two chlorines in α,α'-dichlorostilbene exert a large enhancement in spin–orbital coupling, which accounts for the low fluorescence quantum yields (153). However, since a positional dependence of the heavy-atom effect, correlating with the size of the coefficient of the highest occupied and lowest unoccupied π MO's, was not found in bromostilbenes, alternative explanations for the low fluorescence efficiency, possibly involving steric interactions because of the size of the chlorine atoms, must also be considered (153). Comparative singlet and triplet studies have not been carried out in these systems.

Spectroscopic observation of triplet intermediates following direct laser excitation of several nitrostilbenes has greatly improved our understanding of the mechanism of cis–trans photoisomerization in these systems (108,108d,158,167,167a). For several p-nitrostilbenes the optical density for triplet–triplet absorption is independent of temperature and medium viscosity, suggesting efficient intersystem crossing under all conditions studied (167). This contrasts with the behavior of m-nitrostilbene, for which a marked increase in triplet yield is observed as the temperature is decreased (167). Triplet–triplet absorption spectra of p-nitrostilbenes having an electron-donating substituent at the p' position, i.e., methoxy or N,N-dimethylamino, show pronounced red shifts as the polarity of the solvent is increased, whereas the spectra of the remaining nitrostilbenes are relatively independent of solvent polarity (167). When the same solvent is employed (EPA, glyceryl triacetate, or ethanol/methanol), the triplet absorption spectra of p-nitrostilbenes are temperature independent. This is illustrated in Fig. 14 for p-nitro-p'-methoxystilbene (NMS) in glycerol triacetate at room temperature and $-82°C$ (167). The spectrum at $-82°C$ has been assigned to $^3t^*$ since $\phi_{t\rightarrow c}$ drops two orders of magnitude relative to its room temperature value whereas ϕ_{is} is not affected. The important implication is that the transient observed in fluid solutions at higher temperatures starting from either trans- or cis-NMS is also transoid in geometry (158,167,167a). A rapid $^3t^* \rightleftarrows {^3p^*}$ equilibration is proposed to occur in fluid media which is inhibited at low temperatures (167,167a). Population of $^3p^*$ from $^1c^*$ is much less sensitive to temperature or medium viscosity, however, since $\phi_{c \to t}$ is independent of temperature in EPA in the range 20° to -175°C and decreases slightly in glycerol triacetate below -70°C (*167,167a*). Intersystem crossing enhancement is entirely associated with the participation of n–π^* states of the nitro group in the decay process. The charge-transfer character of the excited states of NMS does not seem to influence intersystem crossing, as indicated by observations with p-cyano-p'-methoxystilbene (CMS), which, lacking a nitro group, shows much weaker triplet–triplet absorption at low temperatures ($-40°$ to -75°C) in glyceryl triacetate (*167*). A study of the sensitized photoisomerizations of three nitrostilbenes and CMS (*168*) gave results paralleling those for stilbenes and bromostilbenes. A modified triplet decay fraction, ϵ', was defined [Eq. (59)] which includes decay from $^3t^*$

$$\epsilon' = \frac{\epsilon + k_d^t / K_{tp} k_d^p}{1 + k_d^t / K_{tp} k_d^p} \tag{59}$$

[Eq. (43)]. Values of ϵ' were obtained from photostationary states for high triplet energy donors and from quenching measurements for the direct and the naphthalene-sensitized photoisomerization employing ferrocene as the quencher (*168*). For p-nitro- and p,p'-dinitrostilbenes, ϵ' values in the range 0.39–0.46 were obtained, which show only a slight increase with medium polarity (benzene versus methanol), suggesting that decay is ex-

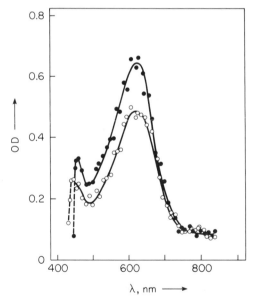

Fig. 14 Triplet–triplet absorption spectra for NMS in glyceryl triacetate: $\bigcirc$, room temperature; $\bullet$, -82°C. [Taken from Görner and Schulte-Frohlinde (*167*).]

clusively from $^3p^*$, i.e., $\epsilon = \epsilon'$, as in stilbene. A moderate increase in ϵ' is observed with NMS ($\epsilon' = 0.38$ in cyclohexane versus $\epsilon' \geq 0.56$ in dimethylformamide), and a much more pronounced increase in ϵ' is observed with p-nitro-p'-dimethylaminostilbene ($\epsilon' = 0.50$ in cyclohexane versus $\epsilon' \geq 0.95$ in methanol). In the latter two cases substantial decay from $^3t^*$ is indicated in polar solvents (168). However, the shift in ϵ' is not sufficiently large to account for a pronounced decrease in $\phi_{t\to c}$ for the direct photoisomerization of NMS as the solvent polarity is increased ($\phi_{t\to c} = 0.67$ in petroleum ether versus 0.035 in dimethylformamide) (157,158), suggesting that $^1t^*$ intersystem crossing efficiency drops significantly from unity in polar solvents (168). On the other hand, the moderate increase in $\phi_{c\to t}$ for the direct photoisomerization of NMS (157,158) as solvent polarity is increased seems entirely consistent with the change in ϵ'.

Temperature and solvent dependencies of ϕ_f^i have been determined for NMS and CMS (159). Except for NMS in dimethylformamide, an activated process competing with fluorescence is found in all cases. Arrhenius A factors are generally larger for NMS than for CMS, reaching a high of 3.1×10^{16} sec^{-1} in toluene. In CMS, where spectroscopic and quenching observations reveal little triplet formation, the activated process has been assigned to $^1t^* \to {}^1p^*$ twisting (159). In NMS, where spectroscopic observations indicate intersystem crossing to be very efficient, the activated process has been assigned to $^1t^* \to {}^3t^*$ intersystem crossing (159). The reintroduction of this mechanism (90,90a) specifically for NMS is based on the observation of much larger ferrocene quenching in the trans $\to$ cis direction than enhancement in the cis $\to$ trans direction upon direct excitation (Fig. 15) (158). If twisting to $^1p^*$ were the only decay channel from $^1c^*$, then the low ferrocene enhancement of $\phi_{c\to t}$ would suggest inefficient triplet formations from $^1p^*$ ($\phi_{ls}^p = 0.3$) due to competing decay directly to ground state isomers (158). If, in addition, triplets were formed with unit efficiency from $^1t^*$, then the activated decay process from $^1t^*$ could not be twisting to $^1p^*$. Three considerations suggest that some of the above conclusions and underlying assumptions may not be secure. First, the A factors for $^1t^*$-activated decay seem too high to be associated with a multiplicity-forbidden process (see also below). Second, the assumption of completely efficient triplet formation from $^1t^*$ is based in part on an incomplete analysis of the dependence of $\phi_{t\to c}^o/\phi_{t\to c}$ in ferrocene concentration (158). Singlet quenching of $^1t^*$ was neglected, although $K_s = 12 M^{-1}$ is known from fluorescence measurements (158). Using Eq. (55), $K_s = 12$ M^{-1}, and $K_t = 360 M^{-1}$, measured flash-kinetically (158), the expected quenching effect for $^1t^*$ decay entirely via triplets is larger than observed (Fig. 15), allowing for some inefficiency of triplet formation from $^1t^*$,

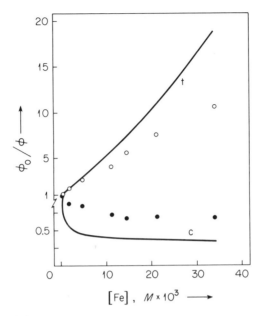

Fig. 15 Effect of ferrocene on $\phi_{t\to c}$ and $\phi_{c\to t}$ for the direct photoisomerization of *p*-nitro-*p'*-methoxystilbenes. Lines calculated with Eqs. (55) and (58) with $\phi_{is} = 1$; points are experimental (*158*).

possibly due to branching at $^1p^*$. Finally, a more severe divergence of quenching effects was described above for bromostilbenes: Instead of the expected enhancement, quenching to no effect is observed for $\phi_{c\to t}$, precluding exclusively common intermediates, $^1p^*$ and $^3p^*$, for the isomerization in the two directions. Involvement of DHP in the isomerization of NMS has been discounted owing to the low quantum yields of DHP formation from *cis-m-* and *p*-nitrostilbenes ($\phi < 0.001$) (*169*). However, since the nitro group enhances intersystem crossing, such low quantum yields could be due to efficient intersystem crossing in the nitro-^{1}DHP*'s followed by ring opening in the triplet state.

Likely involvement of n–π^* states associated with the nitro group in NMS probably introduces features in the decay of its excited states that, being absent in the bromostilbenes, make analogy between these systems less than perfect. A striking difference between bromo- and nitrostilbenes is that bromine enhances intersystem crossing when substituted at either the meta or para position (*94*), whereas the nitro group does so only at the para position (*167*). A similar positional dependence on radiationless decay involving n–π^* states has been proposed for stilbazoles and 1,2-bispyridylethylenes (BPE) (*170,171*). As in stilbene, differential quenching behavior under singlet and triplet photoisomerization conditions suggests that very few, if any, triplets are involved in the reaction following direct excitation of the stilbene analogue having a nitrogen in place of an aromatic CH in one or both rings *(170,171)*. However, in *trans-p*-stilbazole and *trans-p,p'*-BPE, ϕ_f is much lower than that of stilbene and remains low in EPA glass at 77 K under conditions which restrict rotation *(171)*. In contrast to this behavior, ϕ_f for *trans-m,m'*-BPE is similar to that of stilbene and approaches unity at low temperature *(171)*. The uncoupling of fluorescence and isomerization in *p*-azastilbenes has been attributed to a ^{1}t* → ^{1}t decay channel involving an intermediate n–π* singlet that does not operate when the nitrogen is substituted at a near node of the highest bonding and lowest antibonding π MO's as in *m*-azastilbenes *(170)*. For *p*-stilbazole and *p,p'*-BPE the effect of azulene on trans → cis quantum yields for the direct photoisomerization in *t*-butyl alcohol is substantially larger than would be expected if only the very weakly fluorescent π–π* singlets were quenched. To account for this observation and for competing addition and reduction photoreactions not observed under sensitization conditions, quenching of a longer-lived nonfluorescent n–π* lowest excited singlet state by azulene was postulated *(170,171)*. However, the possibility that the larger azulene effect is due in part to some triplet state formation was not rigorously ruled out.

In the presence of oxygen the quenching effects of ferrocene and azulene on nitrostilbene photoisomerization are attenuated as previously discussed for unsubstituted stilbene *(158)*. The intercepts of the quenching plots are unaffected by oxygen *(108,108a,158)*, suggesting that a spin exchange quenching process enhances decay from ^{3}p* without changing the trans/cis decay ratio. Since the equilibrium geometry of nitrostilbene triplets appears to be ^{3}t*, the large oxygen quenching rate constants (7.0×10^9 M^{-1} sec^{-1} and 5.3×10^9 M^{-1} sec^{-1} for nitrostilbene and NMS, respectively) *(108,108a)* indicate that the initial encounter must be sufficiently sticky to allow ^{3}t* → ^{3}p* twisting to occur before diffusive separation [Eq. (60)]. Preference for the transoid geometry in the nitrostilbene triplets gives

$$^3\text{t*} + {}^3\text{O}_2 \rightarrow ({}^3\text{t*}{}^3\text{O}_2) \rightarrow ({}^3\text{p*}{}^3\text{O}_2) \rightarrow \epsilon^1\text{t} + (1 - \epsilon)^1\text{c} + {}^3\text{O}_2 \qquad (60)$$

rise to much larger triplet excitation-transfer rate constants than in stilbene itself. For example, the rate constant for azulene quenching of NMS triplets in benzene, 6.0×10^9 M^{-1} sec^{-1}, *(108,108a)*, can be compared with the value of 4.0×10^8 M^{-1} sec^{-1} *(129)* for the corresponding process in stilbene. The preference for the ^{3}p* geometry in the latter is clearly reflected in a marked decrease in the quenching constant. A group 3 compound, α-methylstilbene, provides an extreme example of the relationship between triplet geometry and excitation-transfer efficiency. In this case azulene does not influence stationary-state compositions for the sensitized isomerization because steric hindrance in the transoid geometry shifts the $^3t^* \rightleftarrows {}^3p^*$ equilibrium further toward $^3p^*$ (30). This change in the potential energy surface of the triplet state also accounts for strong deviations from Eq. (37) of endothermic excitation-transfer rate constants to α-methylstilbenes, indicating that nonvertical excitation to $^3p^*$ is energetically favored starting from either isomer (124). Steric hindrance similarly accounts for the direct excitation observations in Table 5 for all group 3 compounds. Alkyl substitution in the ortho or α position generally raises the energy of the transoid and cisoid geometries of the lowest excited singlet state, thereby lowering the activation energy for twisting to $^1p^*$ or $^3p^*$.

No fluorescence data have been reported for the carbonyl-substituted stilbenes in group 2. However, the insensitivity of the isomerization quantum yields in both directions to a 175 K drop in temperature suggests that the lowest stilbene triplet states are efficiently reached by intramolecular excitation transfer from the carbonyl n–π^* triplet states (153). It also suggests that the decay of the stilbene triplets is independent of temperature changes in fluid media, which casts further doubt on the validity of the analysis of the apparent temperature dependence of stilbene isomerization quantum yields obtained using laser excitation at 488 nm (135).

7. Medium Effects

Low fluorescence quantum yields are a general phenomenon in flexible molecules in which double bonds link strongly interacting chromophore moieties (see, e.g., 172,173). For group 1 stilbenes the high isomerization quantum yields that accompany low ϕ_f values in fluid media are associated with facile rotation about the central bond in the excited singlet state. Rigid analogues, e.g., 4 and 5, in which torsional modes of that bond are "frozen" are strongly fluorescent. As indicated in previous sections, viscous media can inhibit torsional displacements in flexible molecules, rendering even nonfluorescent molecules fluorescent. Increased medium viscosities are achieved by lowering the temperature in a single solvent (91–93) and by varying the solvent (93) or increasing the pressure at constant temperature (174).

The simple model depicted in Fig. 16 explains medium effects on fluorescence data (93). In solvents of low viscosity there is an inherent barrier, E_t, to twisting about the central bond [Eq. (18)], with which a temperature-dependent rate constant, k_t, is associated. In stilbene the value of E_{tp} given in Table 4 for a low molecular weight hydrocarbon medium can be taken as a reasonable estimate of the intrinsic barrier E_t. In high-viscosity regions the solvent imposes an additional barrier, which

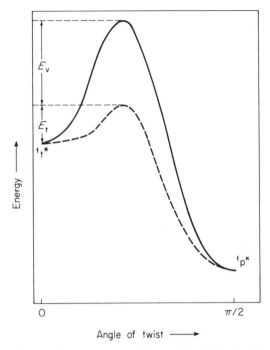

Fig. 16 Proposed potential energy curves for $^1t^* \rightarrow {}^1p^*$ twisting for stilbene in solvents of low (---) and high (——) viscosity. The depth of the energy minimum at $^1p^*$ is arbitrary. [Taken from Saltiel and D'Agostino (93). Reprinted with permission of the copyright holder, the American Chemical Society.]

must be overcome before twisting may take place. This medium-dependent barrier, E_v, has associated with it a medium-dependent rate constant, k_v, and is presumed to arise from restriction of changes in solute geometry by the slower rate at which the solvent cage is capable of rearranging.

Since the thermal and medium-dependent steps are assumed to be one and the same, the overall rate constant for twisting, k_{obs}, is expressed as the product of thermal- and medium-dependent rate constants. Enhanced Arrhenius parameters, from the treatment of the temperature dependence of fluorescence quantum yields in viscous media using Eq. (21), are accordingly expected since $A_{obs} = A_t A_v$ and $E_{obs} = E_t + E_v$. For example, E_{obs} values of 9.7 and 12.3 kcal/mol and log A_{obs} values of 16.3 and 18.5 obtained for *trans*-stilbene and *trans*-1,1'-biindanylidene (**6**), respectively, in glycerol (93) can be compared with the corresponding parameters in Table 4.

The temperature dependence of viscosity is given approximately by the

Andrade equation [Eq. (61)], where η is the viscosity coefficient in poise,

$$\ln \eta = \ln A_\eta + E_\eta/RT \tag{61}$$

E_η is the activation energy for viscous flow, and A_η is a constant for a given solvent system. Solution for $1/T$ in Eq. (61) and substitution into the Arrhenius equation gives Eq. (62), which expresses the medium-

$$\ln k_v = \ln A_v + (E_v/E_\eta)\ln A_\eta - (E_v/E_\eta)\ln \eta$$

dependent rate constant in terms of viscosity (93). Equation (62) can be applied to systems in which viscosity is varied at constant temperature and allows for the obtention of E_v. The ratio E_v/E_η may be thought to be a measure of the extent of the solute–medium interaction. The greater the physical interaction of a given solute with the solvent cage, the more nearly the E_v/E_η ratio is expected to approach unity. The application of Eq. (62) to ϕ_f values of trans-stilbene and 6, measured at 20°C in glycerol–water mixtures, gives E_v values of 6.2 and 9.9 kcal/mol, respectively. The large volume required for twisting in 6 is reflected in a larger E_v/E_η ratio, 0.66 versus 0.41, for trans-stilbene (93). This model for treating medium effects has been applied to fluorescence data for several other systems. The results suggest the existence of an isokinetic relationship for A_v and E_v (93). A good linear fit is obtained when E_v is plotted versus $\log (A_t A_v)$, the plot having a slope of 0.71 and an intercept of 11.7 [adjusted upward due to the use of a better k_f value (105,106)] (93). Inherent in the good fit of this plot is the requirement that $\log A_t$ values for these rate processes be very similar. Values for A_t of $\sim 10^{12}$ sec^{-1} are consistent with spin-allowed relaxation processes such as $^1t^* \rightarrow {}^1p^*$. On the other hand, in the case of anthracene, where the activated process competing with fluorescence is intersystem crossing (175–178), a lower A_t value is expected, reflecting the multiplicity forbiddenness of this process, and it is not surprising that the point for anthracene falls well below the isokinetic plot (93). The very existence of an isokinetic relationships is strong evidence supporting a constant mechanism for medium interference with radiationless decay (179). It is probably more than coincidental that for a large number of molecules Arrhenius parameters for radiationless processes competing with fluorescence cluster in the vicinity of the straight line: $\log A_{obs}/k_f = 0.8E_{obs}$ (180). It is likely that the medium effects discussed here underlie this relationship, with deviations reflecting differences in A_t and k_f values.

With respect to the mechanism of the medium effect it is noteworthy that, for all the systems that define the $\log A_v$, E_v isokinetic relationship, the rate constant for the activated process at the onset of the medium dependence falls within an order of magnitude of the rate constant for solvent relaxation (93). It appears that the solvent does not interfere with the rate of the process if the mobility of solvent molecules is fast relative to the rate of the solute relaxation process. If, on the other hand, the rate of solvent relaxation is similar to, or somewhat slower than, that of solute torsional relaxation, the activated process requires cooperative solvent rearrangement in order to occur. This physical interaction between the solute and its solvent cage gives rise to the increased activation energy associated with a viscosity effect. A theoretical quantum mechanical model accounting for modification of the potential energy surface of the solute by the medium, as proposed in Fig. 16, has been developed (181). Other models for treating medium effects have also been proposed (91a, 92,182).

In light of the above, assignment of the activated process competing with fluorescence in NMS to ^{1}t* $\rightarrow$ ^{3}t* (159) represents something of an anomaly. An isokinetic plot of activation parameters obtained for NMS and CMS in different solvents is fairly linear, having an unexceptional slope of ~0.8 and revealing no mechanistic differences between the activated radiationless process in NMS and that in other stilbenes. Since A_{obs} values as high as 3.1×10^{16} sec^{-1} (NMS, toluene) are not likely to be associated with a unimolecular process in an isolated solute molecule, it appears that this radiationless process in NMS also involves a geometric change allowing for appreciable solvent–solute (assuming no solute–solute interactions in the dilute solutions employed) interaction. Solvent interference with the ^{1}t* $\rightarrow$ ^{1}p* process would explain enhanced activation parameters as illustrated above. Alternatively, if the activated decay process is correctly assigned to ^{1}t* $\rightarrow$ ^{3}t* in NMS (159), then this process, too, must be associated with a geometry change that is fast compared to solvent relaxation times, and the corresponding A_{obs} values must not reflect inefficiency generally associated with multiplicity changes. Neither of these requirements may be insurmountable since each may be associated with a specific mechanism of intersystem crossing involving intermediate nitro group n–π* states.

Torsional motions of molecules in their first excited triplet state are also medium dependent, although due to generally longer lifetimes medium influences on reaction yields may become evident at lower temperatures and higher viscosities than for corresponding reactions in singlet excited states. A good example concerns the interconversion of trans-twisted and cis-twisted allylmethylene 2,4-hexadiene excited states [Eq. (12)]. In the first excited singlet state this interconversion does not occur even in fluid solution at room temperature (Scheme 1), but in the lowest triplet state it is inhibited by the medium only at very low temperatures and high viscosities (Fig. 5) (6,55,73,183). In the discussion of deuterium isotope effects on stilbene triplet lifetimes it was noted that medium rigidity decreases the rate of $^3t^* \rightarrow {}^3p^*$ twisting in stilbene and deuteriated derivatives (123,138). Similar effects have been demonstrated in p-bromostilbenes (165) and p-nitro-p'-methoxystilbenes (167b). The sharp increase in the triplet lifetime of the former in MCH/IH as the temperature is lowered (Fig. 12) is due entirely to medium inhibition of $^3t^* \rightarrow {}^3p^*$ (91a,165). A more complete study is available in the case of NMS (167a). Arrhenius plots of $^3t^*$ decay rate constants are linear when media of low viscosity are used, but they show different linear regions in the case of viscous media. For the latter, below a temperature T_v characteristic of the medium, the slope of the Arrhenius plot assumes a much larger value, signaling inhibition of $^3t^* \rightleftarrows {}^3p^*$ equilibration as $^3t^* \rightarrow {}^3p^*$ twisting becomes the rate-limiting step in $^3t^*$ decay. In accord with this interpretation, $\phi_{t \rightarrow c}$ remains unaffected as the temperature is decreased another 20°–40°C below T_v and begins to decrease only when the slow rate of twisting allows $^3t^* \rightarrow {}^1t$ to become a significant decay channel (167a). For example, in glyceryl triacetate T_v is 250 K (E and A parameters change from 2.5 kcal/mol and $2.3 \times 10^8 \text{ sec}^{-1}$ to 24 kcal/mol and $1 \times 10^{27} \text{ sec}^{-1}$ at T_v!), but $\phi_{t \rightarrow c}$ remains temperature independent down to 212 K (167a).

An early example of medium effects on triplet decay processes was described for 1,3,1',3'-tetramethyldianthrone triplets (184).

8. Ground State Conformations

The role of ground state conformations in controlling product distributions in photochemical reactions was first recognized by Havinga in connection with vitamin D photochemistry (185) and later applied generally to 1,3,5-trienes (186). That and related work are reviewed elsewhere in this book (187). In this essay, the topic was encountered in the discussion of the role of s-trans and s-cis ground state conformations in 1,3-diene photochemistry (30,188). The principle can be generalized as follows (186). In the ground state, polyenes exist as a readily interconverting mixture of conformations derived by rotation about the essentially single bonds of the conjugated moiety. Upon excitation, an alternation of double- and single-bond character occurs, causing a freezing of rotation about formerly single bonds and allowing more facile rotation about bonds that were formerly double, e.g., Scheme 3. In this manner conformations that were in equilibrium in the ground state become distinct noninterconverting excited molecules having different lifetimes and favoring different reaction paths.

Rotation about 1-α bonds in ortho- and/or meta-substituted arylethylenes also gives mixtures of interconverting ground state conformations. However, due to different degrees of steric hindrance in ortho derivatives, nearly equal populations of planar conformations are expected only for meta derivatives. Spectroscopic evidence suggests the presence of more than one singlet excited state in several *trans*-1-(2-naphthyl)-2-arylethylenes (*189,189a*). For example, fluorescence spectra of *trans*-1-(2-naphthyl)-2-phenylethylene at room temperature and at 88 K can be analyzed as the superposition of two sets of emission peaks, the relative contributions of which vary widely with excitation wavelength. The fluorescence decay at room temperature could be expressed only as the sum of two exponentials, and, although the contribution of each varies with excitation and with monitoring wavelengths, only two lifetimes could be defined within rather narrow limits, $\tau = 3.4$–3.7 nsec, $\tau_2 = 19$–24 nsec (*189,189a*). Different absorption spectra for the two interconverting, nearly isoenergetic conformers in Eq. (63) leading to different lowest ex-

$$\text{(63)}$$

cited singlet states having characteristic emission spectra and lifetimes provides an attractive interpretation for these observations. Since the shorter lifetime probably corresponds to a species that undergoes trans–cis isomerization more readily [presumably via a triplet state (*190,191*)], this conformational equilibrium may account for the observed variation of trans → cis quantum yields with excitation wavelength (*192,194*). In contrast to these observations only one set of emission peaks and a single lifetime can be discerned in the fluorescence of *trans*-1-(1-naphthyl)-2-phenylethylene, for which due to steric hindrance only one major ground state conformation is expected (*189,189a*).

Equilibration between distorted s-trans and s-cis ground state conformations has been proposed to play a significant role in accounting for the temperature dependence of the absorption spectrum and the photochemical properties of 11-*cis*-retinal (*195*).

9. Summary

Following direct light absorption *trans*-stilbene attains a transoid excited singlet state, ${}^1\text{t}^*$, which reaches a twisted singlet excited state of "p" geometry upon passing over a small thermal barrier of ~ 4.0 kcal/mol. According to the latest theoretical calculations, this barrier is due to an avoided crossing between the lowest singly excited singlet state and a doubly excited singlet state. Decay from the twisted state, ${}^1\text{p}^*$ if singly, or ${}^1\text{p}^{**}$ if doubly excited, then gives *cis*- and *trans*-stilbene in nearly equal amounts. The excited singlet state of cis-stilbene, $^1c^*$, gives the twisted state in competition with ring closure to DHP, but there is no evidence for a thermal barrier to twisting in this case. The barrier to twisting is introduced in $^1c^*$ and enhanced in $^1t^*$ by viscous media. The major result of this medium effect is the appearance of fluorescence in the cis isomer and an increase in ϕ_f in the trans isomer, intersystem crossing being inefficient in both. Intersystem crossing is introduced by heavy-atom substituents or by substituents having low-lying $n–\pi^*$ excited states. Decay from the lowest triplet state to the two ground state isomers occurs naturally from $^3p^*$ or by interaction with spin exchange quenchers. Alternatively, interaction with suitable triplet excitation acceptors leads to trans-stilbene exclusively. Substituents influence the energetics for twisting in the triplet state. For bromostilbenes, as in stilbene itself, $^3p^*$ appears to be favored thermodynamically, whereas for nitrostilbenes $^3t^*$ is the thermodynamically favored geometry. Nonetheless, both transoid and twisted geometries are accessible during quenching interactions. Alkyl substitution in the α or ortho position causes steric crowding and raises the energy of the planar geometries. Accordingly, faster twisting in such stilbenes decreases their fluorescence quantum yields. In the triplet manifold the $^3t^*$ geometry is no longer accessible, e.g., α-methylstilbene triplets are not quenched by low triplet energy acceptors.

D. Other Olefins

Constraints on length prevent consideration of much work that would ordinarily be delegated to this section. Thus, the cis-trans photoisomerization of enones, dienones, polyenes, retinals, and corresponding Schiff bases related to the process of vision are not discussed. The discussion is limited to aryl substituted olefins and to indigoid dyes.

A relatively well studied example of olefins having different 1,2-aryl substitution is trans-1-(2-naphthyl)-2-phenyl-ethylene, t-2-NPE, which was discussed in Section III,C,8 dealing with selective excitation of different ground state conformations. Hammond et al. (192) have argued that, in contrast to symmetrical olefins like stilbene, unsymmetrical olefins are likely to have lowest excited states with less ethylene-like character and more localization of electronic excitation in one of the aryl groups. For example, in the lowest excited states of the 2-NPE, excitation should tend to become localized in the naphthalene moiety (192). The high fluorescence quantum yield of the trans isomer at room temperature, $\phi_f = 0.7$, and the long fluorescence lifetimes, $\tau_f = 4$ to 20 nsec, depending on conformation (189,189a), relative to the corresponding values for trans-stilbene (Fig. 7) are consistent with this view. The strong influence of the styryl substituent is evident, however, when one considers that for 2-methylnaphthalene $\phi_f = 0.32$ and $\tau_f = 59$ nsec (196). Furthermore, as the temperature is raised to 90°C a pronounced decrease in fluorescence quantum yield is accompanied by a corresponding increase in $\phi_{t \to c}$ (193). Thus, fluorescence and isomerization appear to be coupled processes, as in stilbene. Similarly, ϕ_f on the one hand and $\phi_{c \to t}$ and $\phi_{c \to DHP}$ on the other appear to be complementary for c-2-NPE, except that fluorescence is observed only at low temperatures (below $-80°C$) and high viscosities (193).

In view of the similarity in behavior with stilbene, general agreement that photoisomerization of the 2-NPE involves intersystem crossing as a key step seems surprising ($190,191,193$). Two lines of evidence suggest that, once formed, the triplet states undergo efficient cis $\to$ trans isomerization. First, benzophenone photosensitizes the isomerization in both directions, $\phi_{t \to c} = 0.64$, $\phi_{c \to t} = 0.12$ (192), and second, molecular oxygen quenches the fluorescence of t-2-NPE and increases $\phi_{t \to c}$ for the direct photoisomerization ($191,197,198$). It is well known that oxygen quenching of aromatic hydrocarbon singlet states generally leads to enhanced intersystem crossing (199). The oxygen effect on olefin photoisomerization is especially pronounced when the fluorescence yield is high and the unperturbed isomerization yield is low (198). For example, for $trans$-4,4'-diphenylstilbene where $\tau_f = 1.2$ nsec, ϕ_f is nearly unity ($198,200$) and $\phi_{t \to c} = 0.0025$ at 25°C (198), the presence of $\sim 10^{-2}$ M oxygen in methylcyclohexane quenches the fluorescence somewhat and increases $\phi_{t \to c}$ $\sim$20-fold (198). On the other hand, in stilbene oxygen has no effect at room temperature when $\phi_{t \to c}$ is high, but enhances the photoisomerization at lower temperatures, e.g., $-120°C$, when $\phi_{t \to c}$ is low and τ_f is sufficiently long to allow for competitive interaction with oxygen (198). It is important to note here that the behavior of diphenylstilbene, in which the double bond is symmetrically substituted, is profoundly different from that of the parent aryl compound biphenyl where in the absence of oxygen $\tau_f = 16$ nsec, $\phi_f = 0.12$–0.23, and $\phi_{is} = 0.51$–0.81 (201).

While sensitization and oxygen quenching experiments demonstrate that 2-NPE triplets can serve as intermediates in cis-trans photoisomerization, they fall short of proving their intermediacy following direct excitation of 2-NPE to singlet states. A long-lived transient absorption ($\tau \gg \mu s$) observed following laser excitation of t-2-NPE at 77 K in EPA was probably correctly assigned to the triplet state of t-2-NPE ($190,190a$). However, the assignment of a short-lived transient absorption $\tau \simeq 20$ nsec, observed in n-heptane at 300 K to the same triplet state ($190,190a$) is almost certainly incorrect. This lifetime corresponds closely to one of the fluorescence lifetimes observed for t-2-NPE (189) and is most probably due to $S_n \leftarrow S_1$

absorption. A shorter-lived transient absorption, $\tau \simeq 12$ nsec, was assigned to S_1 of t-2-NPE (190,190a), and in view of the fact that the excitation pulse width was 7 nsec, it could be due to absorption by the S_1 state of the conformer having the shorter fluorescence lifetime, $\tau_f \simeq 3.4$–3.7 nsec (189). The absence of a longer-lived transient at 300 K in n-heptane casts serious doubt on the notion that intersystem crossing is a key step in the direct photoisomerization of 2-NPE. No comparative quenching observations for direct and sensitized photoisomerization of 2-NPE have been made and the origin of the quenching of t-2-NPE photoisomerization and fluorescence by $trans$-stilbene is not clear (190).

While indigo itself does not undergo trans–cis photoisomerization, probably owing to a competing reversible tautomerization [Eq. (64)] (202,203) photochromism in many of a large family of indigoid dyes is

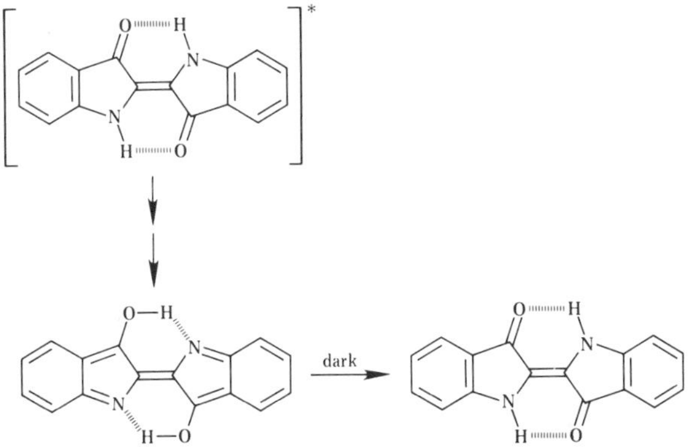

(64)

accounted for by reversible cis-trans photoisomerization (29). Dyes having the general chromophore 7, where X = NR, O, S or Se, and a variety of substituents in the aromatic positions, have been studied most

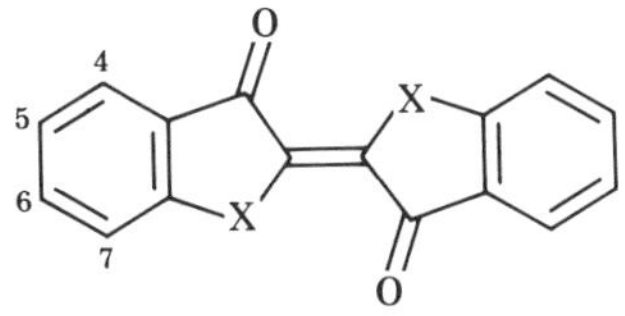

7

thoroughly. Of these, the photoisomerization of thioindigos has been the subject of several recent studies and appears to be understood best. Comparative oxygen quenching studies of the direct and sensitized photoisomerization of several thioindigos (Table VII, 7–7k) reveal that the degree of triplet state involvement in each direction is substituent dependent

TABLE 7

Decay and Oxygen Quenching Parameters of Thioindigos[a]

Compound 7, X = S	K_{sv}	$(s/i)_d$	$(s/i)_s$	ϵ^b
7 Thioindigo	950 (890)	1020 (1255)	1038	0.53
7a 4,4′,7,7′-tetramethyl	930	910	1590	0.50
7b 5,5′-di*tert*-butyl	930	1000	1010	0.59
7c 5,5′-di*tert*-amyl				
7d 5,5′-di*neo*pentyl				
7e 6,6′-diethoxy	420 (420)	440 (456)	419	0.56
7f 6,6′-dichloro-4,4′-dimethyl	620	1010	1100	0.69
7g 6,6′-dichloro-7,7′-dimethyl	620	975	991	0.67
7h 4,4′-dichloro	1810	2545	2425	0.68
7i 5,5′-dichloro-7,7′-dimethyl	1195	1785	1785	0.70
7k 7,7′-dichloro	440	875	893	0.70
7l X = *N*-acetyl				

[a] From Kirsch and Wyman (*204*) except for values in parentheses which are from Grellmann and Hentzschel (*205*).

[b] Based on the photostationary composition for sensitized isomerization.

(*204*). The oxygen effects are attributed entirely to interaction with triplet state intermediates since the presence of oxygen has been shown not to diminish the fluorescence quantum yields of *trans*-thioindigos (*204–206*). In view of the rather long lifetimes of some of the *trans*-thioindigo singlets, ~13 nsec, the apparent inability of oxygen to deactivate them is surprising and as yet unexplained. Normally, when air-saturated solutions are employed, ϕ_f of singlets having $\tau \simeq 13$ nsec is diminished by a factor of 1.6 (*206,207*). No fluorescence is observed from the cis isomers suggesting that the nonplanarity inherent in the cis chromophore causes very rapid $^1c^* \rightarrow {}^1p^*$ relaxation (*204,206*). The alternative explanation, that decay from $^1c^*$ occurs initially to a cis singlet state which owing to symmetry considerations is associated with a small transition dipole moment, has also been proposed (*205*). This state could correspond to the doubly excited state which was discussed above for the stilbenes. Because evidence for the involvement of this state has not been advanced $^1c^* \rightarrow {}^1p^*$ deactivation is assumed in the following.

Oxygen decreases $\phi_{t \rightarrow c}$ for the direct photoisomerization and increases $(t/c)_s$ for both the direct and the sensitized photoisomerizations. Deactivation of thioindigo triplets by oxygen exclusively to trans isomers with concomitant formation of singlet oxygen suggests triplet excitation transfer from $^3t^*$ rather than spin-exchange quenching of $^3p^*$ (*204*). Stern–Volmer constants, K_{sv}, are obtained from the effect of oxygen on $\phi_{t \rightarrow c}$ [Eq.

(51) with $[O_2]$ instead of $[Az]$], and linear plots of $(t/c)_s$ versus $[O_2]$ (up to 8×10^{-3} M) give characteristic slope–intercept ratios for the direct and sensitized isomerizations, $(s/i)_d$ and $(s/i)_s$, respectively. The relationship of K_{sv}, $(s/i)_d$, $(s/i)_s$ and ϵ [see Eq. (35) for the definition of ϵ] is a useful mechanistic criterion (204). It allows assignment of the thioindigos for which these quantities have been determined, Table VII, to one of three limiting mechanisms (204):

1. *The quenched triplet $^3t^*$ forms only by intersystem crossing from $^1t^*$ or by triplet excitation transfer to ^1t.* For this mechanism $K_{sv}/(s/i)_d$, $= K_{sv}/(s/i)_s$ $= 1.0$, a condition which is approximately fulfilled for **7** and **7e**. This mechanism also assumes that the $^3t^*$ to $^3p^*$ conversion is irreversible so that no $^3p^*$, formed by intersystem crossing from $^1p^*$ or by excitation transfer to ^1c, leads to triplets which are quenched by oxygen to ^1t.

2. *Triplets form efficiently from $^1t^*$ and not at all from $^1c^*$ ($\phi_{is} = 0$) and triplet excitation transfer gives freely equilibrating $^3t^*$ and $^3p^*$ triplets.* For this mechanism $K_{sv}/(s/i)_d = 1.0$, but $K_{sv}/(s/i)_s = \epsilon$, conditions fulfilled approximately only for **7a**. Efficient triplet quenching by oxygen only to ^1t indicates that $^3t^*$ predominates at equilibrium.

3. *Triplets form efficiently from $^1t^*$ and $^1c^*$ with twisting to $^1p^*$ being a possible intermediate step. The triplets behave as in mechanism 2.* For this mechanism $K_{sv}/(s/i)_d = K_{sv}/(s/i)_s = \epsilon$ as appears to be the case for **7f**, **7g**, **7h**, **7i**, and **7k**.

Direct observations of triplet transients using laser flash photolysis have confirmed triplet participation in the photoisomerization of **7**, **7c**, **7d**, **7e**, and **7l**. Thus, for **7** and **7e** in benzene triplets have been observed having lifetimes of 279 and 143 nsec, respectively, whose dependences on oxygen concentration give K_{sv} values in good agreement with those obtained from $\phi_{t \to c}$ (Table VII) (205). However, since the same transients are observed starting either with trans- or cis-rich solutions it was suggested that excitation of ^1c-**7** or ^1c-**7e** also gives triplets (205). This conclusion contradicts the analysis of the data in Table VII by placing **7** and **7e** in mechanism 3 instead of 1. A significant increase in $\phi_{c \to t}$ with $[O_2]$ reported for **7** (205), in conflict with other results (204), also suggests that mechanism 3 is followed at least in part for this compound. Deviation of $K_{sv}/(s/i)$ values from unity, especially employing the spectroscopically determined K_{sv} value, allows for a mixed mechanism in this case. For **7e**, on the other hand, the increase in $\phi_{c \to t}$ with $[O_2]$ is modest (205), and there is little if any deviation of $K_{sv}/(s/i)$ ratios from unity suggesting that mechanism 1 is dominant for this molecule.

Extention of the oxygen quenching experiments to higher oxygen concentrations (up to 0.2 M) has been carried out for $\phi_{t \to c}$ of thioindigo, **7** (206). Initially $\phi^0_{t \to c}/\phi_{t \to c}$ increases steeply to a value of ~7 for $[O_2] \simeq 0.01$

M. However, beyond this concentration a sharp break in the Stern–Volmer plot is observed with $\phi^\circ_{t\to c}/\phi_{t\to c}$ slowly increasing to a value of ~ 10 for $[O_2] \simeq 0.22\,M$ (206). Such behavior suggests strongly that a significant if minor ($\sim 15\%$), singlet pathway which is weakly quenched by high oxygen concentrations, contributes to the isomerization process of **7**. It lends credence to the assignment of the temperature dependence of ϕ_f of thioindigos to an activated $^1t^* \to {}^1p^*$ process, as in the stilbenes (206). However, the possibility that the $^1t^* \to {}^3t^*$ process is also activated in some thioindigos cannot be excluded, especially in view of the small A factors (4.5×10^9–$4.8 \times 10^{10}\,\mathrm{sec}^{-1}$) associated with the process competing with fluorescence (206). Bearing on this point are laser flash kinetic observations of the temperature and medium dependence of the optical density and lifetime of triplets from the trans isomers of **7**, **7c**, **7d**, and **7l** (208). The observations are generally analogous to those for the 4-nitrostilbenes. This evidence provides strong support for a transoid thioindigo triplet equilibrium geometry at all temperatures (208). It is pleasing to note that this conclusion was reached above for **7a** which most closely resembles **7b** and **7c**, on the basis of the oxygen quenching experiments in fluid solution at room temperature (204). The strong temperature and medium dependence of triplet lifetimes is consistent with twisting to $^3p^*$ as the initial step of an activated decay channel from $^3t^*$ (208).

Hydrogen bonding solvents suppress intersystem crossing by quenching $^1t^*$ (205,206). In EPA the optical density of triplet absorption of all indigos examined increases as the temperature is decreased (208). Interestingly, this behavior is also observed with **7l** in glyceryl triacetate, a non-hydrogen-bonding solvent, showing that a significant decay channel for $^1t^*$ does not involve intersystem crossing in N,N-diacetylindigo (208). While it appears that $\phi_{c\to t}$ is relatively insensitive to temperature and medium changes, much remains to be learned from a study of the temperature dependence of triplet yields and spectra of triplets obtained by exciting pure cis isomers. The oxygen quenching experiments suggest that these properties should strongly depend on substituents.

ACKNOWLEDGMENT

Work on this essay at Florida State University was supported by National Science Foundation Grant No. CHE 77-23582.

NOTE ADDED IN PROOF

Since the completion of this essay, laser kinetic investigations of the spectral characteristics and picosecond time dependence of light absorption and emission by excited stilbene transients have appeared which conflict, in part, with the earlier work. A transient spectrum (λ_{max} = 585 nm, τ = 90 ± 5 psec) is generated immediately following excitation by a 265-nm pulse for *trans*- but not *cis*-stilbene solutions ($10^{-3}M$, *n*-hexane) (*209*). The lifetime is consistent with assignment of this absorption to $^1t^*$. The narrowing of this spectrum over the first 25 psec suggests that relaxation of excess vibrational energy is also observable (*209*). No transients with longer lifetimes or any evidence of twisted forms could be identified in the spectra. It was suggested that higher stilbene concentrations employed before (*116,209a*) may have been a source of discrepancies with earlier measurements. The possibility that simultaneous two photon excitation utilized in one of the earlier studies (*116*) may be essential for $^1p^{**}$ population was not considered. Aside from the sharpening of the $^1t^*$ spectrum, which was not investigated, an independent transient absorption study (first pulse at 266 nm) reached similar conclusions (*210*). The lifetime of $^1t^*$ in 3-methylpentane was 110 ± 10 psec at 297 K. No transient absorption was observed starting with *cis*-stilbene, except at 77 K when the rigid medium inhibits $^1c^*$ relaxation (λ_{max} ≈ 650 nm, τ = 4.7 nsec). A search for transients in the nsec time scale at room temperature failed to reveal absorptions described earlier (*116,117*). Surprisingly, no evidence for ^{1}DHP or ^{1}DHP* formation from *cis*-stilbene was found in either study (*209,210*). Finally, an investigation in which the first laser pulse (266 nm) excites ^1c ($10^{-4}M$, *n*-hexane) and the second pulse (266 nm) excites the product ^1t to $^1t^*$ whose fluorescence is monitored, indicates that, following the initial excitation of ^1c, the sequence $^1c^* \to {}^1p^* \to \alpha^1t + (1 - \alpha)^1c$ is complete within a few picoseconds (<10–15 psec) (*211*).

REFERENCES

1. R. S. Mulliken and C. C. J. Roothaan, *Chem. Rev.* **41**, 219 (1947); A. J. Meyer and R. S. Mulliken, *ibid.* **63**, 639 (1969).
2. S. D. Peyerimhoff and R. J. Buenker, *Theor. Chim. Acta* **27**, 243 (1972).
2a. R. J. Buenker and S. D. Peyerimhoff, *Chem. Phys.* **9**, 75 (1976).
3. R. S. Mulliken, *J. Chem. Phys.* **66**, 2448 (1977).
4. V. Staemmler, *Theor. Chim. Acta* **45**, 89 (1977); H. Kollmar and V. Staemmler, *ibid.* **48**, 223 (1978).
5. L. E. McMurchie and E. R. Davidson, *J. Chem. Phys.* **66**, 2959 (1977).
6. V. Bonačić-Koutecký and Shengo-Ishimaru, *J. Am. Chem. Soc.* **99**, 8134 (1977), and references cited.
7. R. B. Cundall, *Prog. React. Kinet.* **2**, 167 (1964).
8. M. Nelles and G. B. Kistiakowsky, *J. Am. Chem. Soc.* **54**, 2208 (1932).
9. G. B. Kistiakowsky and W. R. Smith, *J. Am. Chem. Soc.* **56**, 638 (1934).
10. B. Tamamushi, H. Akiyama, and T. Ishi, *Z. Elektrochem.* **47**, 340 (1941); B. Tamamushi, *Bull. Chem. Soc. Jpn.* **19**, 147 (1958).
11. J. E. Douglas, B. S. Rabinovitch, and F. S. Looney, *J. Chem. Phys.* **23**, 315 (1955).
12. R. B. Cundall and T. F. Palmer, *Trans. Faraday Soc.* **80**, 2384 (1958).
13. J. L. Magee, W. Shand, Jr., and H. Eyring, *J. Am. Chem. Soc.* **63**, 677 (1941).
14. M. C. Lin and K. J. Laidler, *Can. J. Chem.* **46**, 973 (1967).
15. A. Lifshitz and S. H. Bauer, *J. Chem. Phys.* **38**, 2056 (1963).
16. P. M. Jeffers, *J. Phys. Chem.* **78**, 1469 (1974).
17. W. M. Marley and P. M. Jeffers, *J. Phys. Chem.* **79**, 2085 (1975).
18. L. M. Stephenson and J. I. Brauman, *Acc. Chem. Res.* **7**, 65 (1974), and references cited.
19. R. B. Woodward and R. Hoffmann, "The Conservation of Orbital Symmetry." Academic Press, New York, 1970.
20. G. A. Doorakian and H. H. Freedman, *J. Am. Chem. Soc.* **90**, 5310 and 5896 (1968).

21. H. M. Frey, A. M. Lamont, and R. Walsh, *J. Chem. Soc. D* p. 1583 (1975).
22. W. M. Shaub and S. H. Bauer, *Int. J. Chem.* **79**, 2085 (1975).
23. M. Erler, G. Haucke, and R. Paetzold, *Z. Phys. Chem. (Leipzig)* **258**, 315 (1977).
24. D. C. Nonhebel and J. C. Walton, "Free Radical Chemistry," p. 274. Cambridge Univ. Press, London and New York, 1974.
25. E. A. Lombardo and J. Velez, *Adv. Chem. Soc.* **121**, 553 (1973).
26. J. L. Bilhou, J. M. Basset, R. Mutin, and W. F. Graydon, *J. Chem. Soc., Chem. Commun.* p. 970 (1976).
27. H. M. McConnell, *J. Chem. Phys.* **20**, 1043 (1952); **23**, 2440 (1955).
28. F. Jachimowicz, G. Levin, and M. Szwarc, *J. Am. Chem. Soc.* **100**, 5426 (1978); S. Sorensen, G. Levin, and M. Szwarc, *ibid.* **97**, 2341 (1975).
29. D. L. Ross and J. Blanc, *in* "Photochromism" (G. H. Brown, ed.), p. 471. Wiley, New York, 1971.
30. J. Saltiel, J. D'Agostino, E. D. Megarity, L. Mett·, K. R. Neuberger, M. Wrighton, and O. C. Zafiriou, *Org. Photochem.* **3**, 1 (1973).
31. D. R. Arnold and V. Y. Abraitys, *Mol. Photochem.* **2**, 27 (1970).
32. H. Yamazaki and R. J. Cvetanović, *J. Am. Chem. Soc.* **91**, 520 (1969); H. Yamazaki, R. J. Cvetanović, and R. S. Irwin, *ibid.*, **98**, 2198 (1976).
33. N. C. Yang, J. I. Cohen, and A. Shani, *J. Am. Chem. Soc.* **90**, 3264 (1968).
34. J. Saltiel, K. R. Neuberger, and M. Wrighton, *J. Am. Chem. Soc.* **91**, 3658 (1969).
35. G. O. Schenck and R. Steinmetz, *Bull. Soc. Chim. Belg.* **71**, 781 (1962).
36. R. A. Caldwell and S. P. Jones, *J. Am. Chem. Soc.* **91**, 5184 (1969).
37. R. A. Caldwell, *J. Am. Chem. Soc.* **92**, 1439 (1970).
38. I. H. Kochevar and P. J. Wagner, *J. Am. Chem. Soc.* **92**, 5742 (1970).
39. S. M. Japar, M. Pomerantz, and E. W. Abrahamson, *Chem. Phys. Lett.* **2**, 137 (1968); S. M. Japar, J. A. Davidson, and E. W. Abrahamson, *J. Phys. Chem.* **76**, 478 (1972).
39a. Cf., however, H. A. J. Carless, *J. Chem. Soc., Perkin Trans. 2* p. 834 (1974).
40. N. J. Turro, "Modern Molecular Photochemistry," p. 399. Benjamin/Cummings, Menlo Park, California, 1978.
41. P. J. Kropp, *J. Am. Chem. Soc.* **91**, 5783 (1969); P. J. Kropp, E. J. Reardon, Jr., Z. L. F. Gaibel, K. F. Willard, and E. J. Hattaway, *ibid.* **95**, 7058 (1973).
42. R. Bonneau, J. Joussot-Dubien, L. Salem, and A. J. Yarwood, *J. Am. Chem. Soc.* **98**, 4329 (1976); R. Bonneau, J. Joussot-Dubien, J. Yarwood, and J. Pereyne, *Tetrahedron Lett.* p. 235 (1977).
43. R. Bonneau, submitted for publication. We are indebted to Dr. Bonneau for a preprint of this paper.
44. H. E. Zimmerman, K. S. Kamm, and D. P. Werthemann, *J. Am. Chem. Soc.* **96**, 7821 (1974); **97**, 3718 (1975).
45. B. S. Hudson and B. E. Kohler, *J. Chem. Phys.* **59**, 4984 (1973), and references cited; K. Schulten and M. Karplus, *Chem. Phys. Lett.* **14**, 305 (1972).
46. Y. Inoue, S. Takamuku, and H. Sakurai, *J. Phys. Chem.* **81**, 7 (1977).
47. R. Srinivasan and K. H. Brown, *J. Am. Chem. Soc.* **100**, 2589 (1978).
47a. R. M. Weiss and A. Warshel, *J. Am. Chem. Soc.* **101**, 6131 (1979).
48. J. G. Aston, G. Szasz, H. W. Wooley, and F. G. Brickwedde, *J. Chem. Phys.* **14**, 67 (1946).
48a. M. E. Squillacote, R. S. Sheridan, O. L. Chapman, and F. A. L. Anet, *J. Am., Chem. Soc.* **101**, 3657 (1979).
49. R. L. Lipnick and E. W. Garbish, Jr., *J. Am. Chem. Soc.* **95**, 6370 (1973).
50. A. J. P. Devaquet, R. E. Townshend, and W. J. Hehre, *J. Am. Chem. Soc.* **98**, 4068 (1976).

51. R. Srinivasan, *Adv. Photochem.* **4**, 113 (1966), and references cited.
52. D. F. Evans, *J. Chem. Soc.* p. 1735 (1960).
53. R. E. Kellogg and W. T. Simpson, *J. Am. Chem. Soc.* **87**, 4230 (1965).
54. R. Srinivasan, *J. Am. Chem. Soc.* **90**, 4498 (1968).
55. J. Saltiel, L. Metts, and M. Wrighton, *J. Am. Chem. Soc.* **92**, 3227 (1970).
56. S. Boué and R. Srinivasan, *J. Am. Chem. Soc.* **92**, 3226 (1970).
57. P. Vanderlinden and S. Boué, *J. Chem. Soc., Chem. Commun.* p. 972 (1975).
58. W. J. Nebe and G. J. Fonken, *J. Am. Chem. Soc.* **91**, 1249 (1969).
59. S. Boué and R. Srinivasan, *Mol. Photochem.* **4**, 93 (1972).
60. R. Srinivasan and S. Boué, *Angew. Chem., Int. Ed. Engl.* **11**, 320 (1972).
61. M. Bigwood and S. Boué, *Tetrahedron Lett.* p. 4311 (1973).
62. D. F. Eaton, R. G. Bergman, and G. S. Hammond, *J. Am. Chem. Soc.* **95**, 135 (1972).
63. K. Inuzuka and R. S. Becker, *Bull. Chem. Soc. Jpn.* **44**, 3323 (1971).
64. J. Saltiel, D. Townsend, and A. Sykes, *J. Am. Chem. Soc.* **95**, 5968 (1973).
65. G. S. Hammond, J. Saltiel, A. A. Lamola, N. J. Turro, J. S. Bradshaw, D. O. Cowan, R. C. Counsell, V. Vogt, and C. Dalton, *J. Am. Chem. Soc.* **86**, 3197 (1964), and references cited.
66. J. Saltiel, L. Metts, A. Sykes, and M. Wrighton, *J. Am. Chem. Soc.* **93**, 5302 (1971).
67. R. Hoffmann, *Tetrahedron* **22**, 521 (1966).
68. E. M. Evleth, *Chem. Phys. Lett.* **3**, 122 (1969).
69. N. C. Baird, *Mol. Photochem.* **2**, 53 (1970).
70. N. C. Baird and R. M. West, *J. Am. Chem. Soc.* **93**, 4427 (1971).
71. H. L. Hyndman, B. M. Monroe, and G. S. Hammond, *J. Am. Chem. Soc.* **91**, 2852 (1969).
72. J. Saltiel, L. Metts, and M. Wrighton, *J. Am. Chem. Soc.* **91**, 5684 (1969).
73. J. Saltiel, A. D. Rousseau, and A. Sykes, *J. Am. Chem. Soc.* **94**, 5903 (1972).
74. R. Hurley and A. C. Testa, *J. Am. Chem. Soc.* **92**, 211 (1970).
75. J. Saltiel, D. E. Townsend, and A. Sykes, *J. Am. Chem. Soc.* **95**, 5968 (1973), and references cited.
76. A. A. Lamola and G. S. Hammond, *J. Chem. Phys.* **43**, 2129 (1965).
77. R. S. H. Liu, *Pure Appl. Chem., Suppl.* (*23rd Congr.*) **1**, 335 (1971); R. S. H. Liu and Y. Butt, privated communication.
78. J. Saltiel, G.-E. Khalil, and K. Schanze, *Chem. Phys. Lett.* **70**, 233 (1980).
79. R. J. M. Anderson, G. R. Holton, and W. M. McClain, *J. Chem. Phys.* **66**, 3832 (1977); T. M. Stachelek, T. A. Pazoha, W. M. McClain, and R. P. Drucker, *ibid.* p. 4540.
80. G. Orlandi and W. Siebrand, *Chem. Phys. Lett.* **30**, 352 (1975).
81. D. J. S. Birch and J. B. Birks, *Chem. Phys. Lett.* **38**, 432 (1976).
81a. J. B. Birks, *Chem. Phys. Lett.* **38**, 437 (1976); **54**, 430 (1978).
82. P. Torvan and K. Schulten, *Chem. Phys. Lett.* **56**, 200 (1978).
83. G. Orlandi, P. Palmieri, and G. Poggi, *J. Am. Chem. Soc.* **101**, 3492 (1979).
84. G. Fischer, K. A. Muszkat, and E. Fischer, *J. Chem. Soc. B* p. 156 (1968).
85. R. B. Williams, *J. Am. Chem. Soc.* **64**, 1395 (1942).
86. A. V. Santoro, E. J. Barrett, and H. H. Hoyer, *J. Am. Chem. Soc.* **89**, 4545 (1967).
87. Cf., however, F. W. J. Taylor and A. R. Murray, *J. Am. Chem. Soc.* **60**, 2078 (1938).
88. G. B. Kistiakowsky and W. R. Smith, *J. Am. Chem. Soc.* **56**, 638 (1934).
89. W. W. Schmiegel, F. A. Litt, and D. O. Cowan, *J. Org. Chem.* **33**, 3334 (1968).
90. S. Malkin and E. Fischer, *J. Phys. Chem.* **68**, 1153 (1964), and earlier papers in this series.
90a. R. H. Dyck and D. S. McClure, *J. Chem. Phys.* **36**, 2336 (1962).
91. K. A. Muszkat, D. Gegiou, and E. Fischer, *J. Am. Chem. Soc.* **89**, 4814 (1967).

91a. D. Gegiou, K. A. Muszkat, and E. Fischer, *J. Am. Chem. Soc.* **90**, 12 (1968).
92. S. Sharafi and K. A. Muszkat, *J. Am. Chem. Soc.* **93**, 4119 (1971).
93. J. Saltiel and J. T. D'Agostino, *J. Am. Chem. Soc.* **94**, 6445 (1972).
94. J. Saltiel, A. Marimari, D. W. L. Chang, J. C. Mitchener, and E. D. Megarity, *J. Am. Chem. Soc.* **101**, 2982 (1979).
95. J. Saltiel, *J. Am. Chem. Soc.* **89**, 1036 (1967); **90**, 6394 (1968).
96. J. Saltiel and E. D. Megarity, *J. Am. Chem. Soc.* **91**, 1265 (1969).
96a. J. Saltiel and E. D. Megarity, *J. Am. Chem. Soc.* **94**, 2742 (1972).
97. G. N. Lewis, T. T. Magel, and D. Lipkin, *J. Am. Chem. Soc.* **62**, 2973 (1940).
98. A. R. Olson, *Trans. Faraday Soc.* **27**, 69 (1931); A. R. Olson and F. L. Hudson, *J. Am. Chem. Soc.* **55**, 1410 (1932); **56** 1320 (1930).
99. H. Stegemeyer and H. H. Perkampus, *Z. Phys. Chem. (Frankfurt am Main)* [N.S.] **39**, 125 (1953).
100. F. Aurich, M. Hauser, E. Lippert, and H. Stegemeyer, *Z. Phys. Chem. (Frankfurt am Main)* [N.S.] **42**, 123 (1964); E. Lippert, *ibid.* p. 125.
101. A. A. Lamola, G. S. Hammond, and F. B. Mallory, *Photochem. Photobiol.* **4**, 259 (1965).
102. F. B. Mallory, C. S. Wood, and J. T. Gordon, *J. Am. Chem. Soc.* **86**, 3094 (1964).
103. K. A. Muszkat and E. Fischer, *J. Chem. Soc. B* p. 662, (1967).
104. J. Saltiel, J. T. D'Agostino, O. L. Chapman, and R. D. Lura, *J. Am. Chem. Soc.* **93**, 2804 (1971).
105. J. L. Charlton and J. Saltiel, *J. Phys. Chem.* **81**, 1940 (1977).
106. M. Sumitani, N. Nakashima, K. Yoshihara, and S. Nagakura, *Chem. Phys. Lett.* **51**, 183 (1977).
106a. Cf, however, J. R. Taylor, M. C. Adams, and W. Sibbett, *Appl. Phys. Lett.* **35**, 590 (1979).
107. J. L. Charlton and J. Saltiel, unpublished results.
108. D. V. Bent and D. Schulte-Frohlinde, *J. Phys. Chem.* **78**, 446 (1974).
108a. D. V. Bent and D. Schulte-Frohlinde, *J. Phys. Chem.* **78**, 451 (1974).
109. F. Momicchioli, G. R. Corrandini, M. C. Bruni, and I. Baraldi, *J. Chem. Soc., Faraday Trans. 2* **71**, 215 (1975); W. M. Gelbart and S. A. Rice, *J. Chem. Phys.* **50**, 4775 (1969).
110. J. Saltiel, O. C. Zafiriou, E. D. Megarity, and A. A. Lamola, *J. Am. Chem. Soc.* **90**, 4759 (1968).
111. C. D. DeBoer and R. H. Schlessinger, *J. Am. Chem. Soc.* **90**, 803 (1968).
112. P. Borrell and H. H. Greenwood, *Proc. Soc. London, Ser. A* **298**, 453 (1967).
113. C.-H. Ting and D. S. McClure, *J. Chin. Chem. Soc. (Taipei)* **18**, 95 (1971).
114. F. Momicchioli, M. C. Bruni, I. Baraldi, and G. R. Corradini, *J. Chem. Soc., Faraday Trans. 2* **70**, 1325 (1974).
115. C.-H. Ting, Ph.D. Thesis, University of Chicago, Chicago, Illinois (1965).
116. E. Heumann, W. Triebel, R. Uhlmann, and B. Wilhelmi, *Chem. Phys. Lett.* **45**, 425 (1977).
117. O. Teschke, E. P. Ippen, and G. R. Holton, *Chem. Phys. Lett.* **52**, 233 (1977).
118. H. Stegemeyer, *Z. Naturforsch. Teil A* **16**, 643 (1961); *Chimia* **19**, 535 (1965).
119. G. Fischer, G. Seger, K. A. Muszkat, and E. Fischer, *J. Chem. Soc., Perkin Trans. 2* p. 1569 (1975).
120. Cf, for example, F. B. Mallory and C. W. Mallory, *J. Am. Chem. Soc.* **94**, 6041 (1972).
121. J. Saltiel, D. W. L. Chang, E. D. Megarity, A. D. Rousseau, P. T. Shannon, D. Thomas, and A. K. Uriarte, *Pure Appl. Chem.* **41**, 559 (1975).
122. J. Saltiel, *J. Am. Chem. Soc.* **89**, 1036 (1967); **90**, 6394 (1968).
123. J. Saltiel, J. T. D'Agostino, W. G. Herkstroeter, G. Saint-Ruf, and N. P. Buu-Hoï, *J. Am. Chem. Soc.* **95**, 2593 (1973).

124. W. G. Herkstroeter and G. S. Hammond, *J. Am. Chem. Soc.* **88**, 4769 (1966).
125. G. S. Hammond and J. Saltiel, *J. Am. Chem. Soc.* **85**, 2516 (1963).
126. J. Saltiel, J. L. Charlton, and W. B. Mueller, *J. Am. Chem. Soc.* **101**, 1347 (1979).
127. J. Saltiel and B. Thomas, *Chem. Phys. Lett.* **37**, 147 (1976).
128. R. A. Caldwell and R. E. Schwerzel, *J. Am. Chem. Soc.* **94**, 1035 (1972); **95**, 1382 (1973).
129. J. Saltiel and B. Thomas, *J. Am. Chem. Soc.* **96**, 5660 (1974).
130. A. Farmilo and F. Wilkinson, *Photochem. Photobiol.* **18**, 447 (1973).
131. P. B. Merckel and D. R. Kearns, *J. Am. Chem. Soc.* **94**, 7244 (1972).
132. W. G. Herkstroeter, *J. Am. Chem. Soc.* **97**, 4161 (1975).
133. F. S. Dainton, E. A. Robinson, and G. A. Salmon, *J. Phys. Chem.* **76**, 3897 (1972).
134. M. Sumitani, K. Yoshihara, and S. Nagakura, *Bull. Chem. Soc. Jpn.* **51**, 2503 (1978).
135. R. Benson and D. F. Williams, *J. Phys. Chem.* **81**, 215 (1977).
136. J. Saltiel and B. Thomas, unpublished results.
137. G. Heinrich, H. Blume, and D. Schulte-Frohlinde, *Tetrahedron Lett.* p. 4693 (1967).
138. W. G. Herkstroeter and D. S. McClure, *J. Am. Chem. Soc.* **90**, 4522 (1968).
139. G. Heinrich, G. Holzer, H. Blume, and D. Schulte-Frohlinde, *Z. Naturforsch., Teil B* **25**, 496 (1970).
140. G. Heinrich, H. Gusten, F. Mark, G. Olbrich, and D. Schulte-Frohlinde, *Ber. Bunsenges. Phys. Chem.* **77**, 103 (1973).
141. W. M. Gelbart, K. F. Freed, and S. A. Rice, *J. Chem. Phys.* **52**, 2460 (1970).
142. G. Fischer, K. A. Muszkat, and E. Fischer, *Isr. J. Chem.* **6**, 965 (1968).
143. A. Bylina and Z. R. Grabowski, *Trans. Faraday Soc.* **65**, 458 (1969).
144. S. Yamashita, *Bull. Chem. Soc. Jpn.* **34**, 972 (1962).
145. H. A. Hammond, D. E. DeMeyer, and J. R. Williams, *J. Am. Chem. Soc.* **91**, 5180 (1969).
146. D. Valentine, Jr. and G. S. Hammond, *J. Am. Chem. Soc.* **94**, 3449 (1972).
147. T. Förster, *Z. Elektrochem.* **56**, 716 (1952).
148. G. Zimmerman, L. Chow, and V. Paik, *J. Am. Chem. Soc.* **80**, 3528 (1958).
149. R. P. Gajewski and R. A. Caldwell, *J. Am. Chem. Soc.* **93**, 532 (1971).
150. J. Saltiel, E. D. Megarity, and K. G. Kneipp, *J. Am. Chem. Soc.* **88**, 2336 (1966).
151. A. Marinari and J. Saltiel, *Mol. Photochem.* **7**, 225 (1976).
152. R. Bonneau, private communication.
153. D. Gegiou, K. A. Muszkat, and E. Fischer, *J. Am. Chem. Soc.* **90**, 3907 (1968).
154. K. Krüger and E. Lippert, *Z. Phys. Chem.* (*Frankfurt am Main*) [N.S.] **66**, 293 (1969).
155. H. Güsten and L. Klansinc, *Tetrahedron Lett.* p. 3097 (1968).
156. D. Schulte-Frohlinde, *Justus Liebigs Ann. Chem.* **615**, 114 (1958).
157. D. Schulte-Frohlinde, H. Blume, and H. Gusten, *J. Phys. Chem.* **66**, 2486 (1962).
158. H. Görner and D. Schulte-Frohlinde, *Ber. Bunsenges. Phys. Chem.* **81**, 713 (1977).
159. M. N. Pisanias and D. Schulte-Frohlinde, *Ber. Bunsenges. Phys. Chem.* **79**, 662 (1975).
160. H. H. Jaffe and M. Orchin, "Theory and Applications of Ultraviolet Spectroscopy," Chapter 15. Wiley. New York, 1962; *J. Chem. Soc.* p. 1078 (1960).
161. H. Suzuki, *Bull. Chem. Soc. Jpn.* **33**, 396 and 406 (1960).
162. R. N. Beal and E. M. F. Roe, *J. Chem. Soc.* p. 2775 (1953).
163. A. Wolf, H.-H. Schmidtke, and J. V. Knop, *Theor. Chim. Acta* **48**, 37 (1978), and references cited.
164. E. Lippert, *Z. Phys. Chem.* (*Frankfurt am Main*) [N.S.] **42**, 125 (1964); *Acc. Chem. Res.* **3**, 74 (1970).
165. H. Görner and D. Schulte-Frohlinde, *J. Am. Chem. Soc.* **101**, 4388 (1979). We are indebted to Professor Schulte-Frohlinde for a preprint of this paper.
166. J. Saltiel, D. W.-L. Chang, and E. D. Megarity, *J. Am. Chem. Soc.* **96**, 6521 (1974).

167. H. Görner and D. Schulte-Frohlinde, *Ber. Bunsenges. Phys. Chem.* **82,** 1102 (1978).
167a. H. Görner and D. Schulte-Frohlinde, *J. Phys. Chem.* **82,** 2653 (1978).
168. H. Görner and D. Schulte-Frohlinde, *J. Photochem.* **8,** 91 (1978).
169. H. Jungmann, H. Gusten, and D. Schulte-Frohlinde, *Chem. Ber.* **101,** 2690 (1968).
170. Y. J. Lee, D. G. Whitten, and L. Pedersen, *J. Am. Chem. Soc.* **93,** 6330 (1971).
171. D. G. Whitten and Y. J. Lee, *J. Am. Chem. Soc.* **94,** 9142 (1972).
172. A. Reiser, L. J. Leyshon, D. Saunders, M. V. Mijovic, A. Bright, and J. Bogie, *J. Am. Chem. Soc.* **94,** 2414 (1972).
173. J. Kordas and M. A. El-Bayoumi, *J. Am. Chem. Soc.* **96,** 3043 (1974).
174. L. A. Brey, G. B. Schuster, and H. G. Drickamer, *J. Am. Chem. Soc.* **101,** 129 (1979).
175. R. G. Bennett and P. J. McCartin, *J. Chem. Phys.* **44,** 1969 (1966).
176. E. C. Lim, J. D. Laposa, and J. M. H. Yu, *J. Mol. Spectrosc.* **19,** 412 (1966).
177. R. E. Kellogg, *J. Chem. Phys.* **44,** 411 (1966).
178. R. S. H. Liu and R. E. Kellogg, *J. Am. Chem. Soc.* **91,** 250 (1969).
179. J. E. Leffler, *J. Org. Chem.* **20,** 1202 (1955); J. E. Leffler and E. Grunwald, "Rates and Equilibria of Organic Reactions," pp. 315–402. Wiley, New York, 1963; L. P. Hammett, "Physical Organic Chemistry," 2nd ed., pp. 249–251 and 397–408. McGraw-Hill New York, 1970.
180. V. P. Kazakov, *Opt. Spectrosc. (USSR)* **18,** 27 (1965).
181. B. Dellinger and M. Kasha, *Chem. Phys. Lett.* **36,** 410 (1975); **38,** 9 (1976).
182. T. Förster and G. Hoffman, *Z. Phys. Chem. (Frankfurt am Main)* [N.S.] **75,** 63 (1971).
183. J. Baraldi, M. C. Bruni, M. Momicchioli, J. Langlet, and J. P. Malrieu, *Chem. Phys. Lett.* **51,** 493 (1977).
184. T. Bercovici, R. Korenstein, K. A. Muszkat, and E. Fischer, *J. Pure Appl. Chem.* **24,** 531 (1970).
185. E. Havinga and J. L. M. A. Schlatmann, *Tetrahedron* **16,** 146 (1977); E. Havinga, *Chimia* **16,** 145 (1962).
186. P. J. Vroegop, J. Lugtenburg, and E. Havinga, *Tetrahedron* **29,** 1393 (1973).
187. W. G. Dauben, E. L. McInnis, and D. M. Michno, Essay 15 of this book.
188. For other examples, see F. D. Lewis, R. W. Johnson, and D. E. Johnson, *J. Am. Chem. Soc.* **96,** 6090 and 6100 (1974), and references cited.
189. E. Hass, G. Fischer, and E. Fischer, *J. Phys. Chem.* **82,** 1638 (1978).
189a. G. Fischer and E. Fischer, *Mol. Photochem.* **6,** 463 (1974); C. Goedicke, H. Stegemeyer, G. Fischer, and E. Fischer, *Z. Phys. Chem. (Frankfurt am Main)* [N.S.] **101,** 181 (1976).
190. M. Sumitani, S. Nagakura, and K. Yoshihara, *Chem. Phys. Lett.* **29,** 410 (1974).
191. G. G. Aloisi, U. Mazzucato, J. B. Birks, and L. Minuti, *J. Am. Chem. Soc.* **99,** 6340 (1977).
192. G. S. Hammond, S. C. Shin, and S. P. Van, *Mol. Photochem.* **1,** 89 (1969).
193. M. Kaganowitch, G. Fischer, E. Fischer, C. Goedicke, and H. Stegemeyer, *Z. Phys. Chem. (Frankfurt am Main)* [N.S.] **76,** 79 (1971); T. Wismonski-Knittel, G. Fischer, and E. Fischer, *J. Chem. Soc., Perkin Trans. 2* p. 1930 (1974).
194. N. P. Kovalenko, Yu, B. Scheck, L. Ya. Malkes, and M. V. Alfimov, *Bull. Acad. Sci. USSR Ser. Chem.* p. 298 (1975).
195. B. Honig and M. Karplus, *Nature (London)* **229,** 558 (1971).
196. I. B. Berlman, "Handbook of Fluorescence Spectra of Aromatic Molecules," 2nd ed., p. 333. Academic Press, New York, 1971.
197. P. Bortolus and G. Galiazzo, *J. Photochem.* **2,** 361 (1974).
198. G. Fischer and E. Fischer, *Mol. Photochem.* **6,** 463 (1974).
199. B. Stevens and B. E. Algar, *J. Phys. Chem.* **72,** 3468 (1968).

200. I. B. Berlman, "Handbook of Fluorescence Spectra of Aromatic Molecules," 2nd ed., p. 320. Academic Press, New York, 1971.
201. P. S. Engel and B. M. Monroe, *Adv. Photochem.* **8**, 245 (1971).
202. G. M. Wyman, *Chem. Commun.* p. 1332 (1971).
203. G. M. Wyman and B. M. Zarnegar, *J. Phys. Chem.* **77**, 1204 (1973).
204. A. D. Kirsch and G. M. Wyman, *J. Phys. Chem.* **81**, 413 (1977); **79**, 543 (1975).
205. K. H. Grellmann and P. Hentzschel, *Chem. Phys. Lett.* **53**, 545 (1978); *Abstr. Symp. Intern. Rotation Excited Org. Molecules,* Cambridge, England, August 10, 1978.
206. G. Haucke and R. Paetzold, *Nova Acta Leopold. Suppl.* **11** (1978).
207. I. B. Berlman, "Handbook of Fluorescence Spectra of Aromatic Molecules," 2nd ed., p. 58. Academic Press, New York, 1971.
208. H. Görner and D. Schulte-Frohlinde, *Chem. Phys. Lett.* **66**, 363 (1979).
209. B. I. Greene, R. M. Hochstrasser, and R. B. Weisman, *Chem. Phys. Lett.* **62**, 427 (1979).
209a. B. I. Greene, R. M. Hochstrasser, and R. B. Weisman, *J. Chem. Phys.* **70**, 1247 (1979).
210. K. Yoshihara, A. Namiki, M. Sumitani, and N. Nakashima, *J. Chem. Phys.* **71**, 2892 (1979).
211. M. Sumitani, N. Nakashima, and K. Yoshihara, *Chem. Phys. Lett.* **68**, 255 (1979).

ESSAY 15 | **PHOTOCHEMICAL REARRANGEMENTS IN TRIENES**

W. G. DAUBEN, E. L. McINNIS,
and D. M. MICHNO

I. INTRODUCTION

The photochemical transformations of the conjugated 1,3,5-hexatriene moiety have constituted a major area of interest in modern photochemical research. Although this chromophore represents one of the simplest polyenes investigated thus far, a fully systematic interpretation of the photochemical behavior of trienes is still lacking. In this essay the photochemical reactions of the triene chromophore in a variety of structural environments are examined. These results are then discussed in terms of general principles that govern the photochemical transformations of the moiety.

II. PHOTOCHEMICAL REACTIONS

A. Acyclic Trienes

Investigations of the photochemistry of simple acyclic trienes have shown that a wide variety of transformations occur. With short irradiation

91

REARRANGEMENTS IN GROUND AND EXCITED STATES, VOL. 3

times, a photoequilibrium is rapidly established between 1,3,5-hexatriene (1) and 1,3-cyclohexadiene (2). Extended irradiation of an ethereal solution of 1,3,5-hexatriene (1) through a Vycor filter ($\lambda > 220$ nm) led to the production of 12% of 3-vinylcyclobutene (3) (*1*) and 12% of bicyclo-[3.1.0]hex-2-ene (4). In addition, the formation of vinylallene (5) was observed when 1,3,5-hextriene was irradiated in the gas phase (*2*).

A tetrasubstituted derivative of this parent triene, the terpene alloocimene 6, similarly produces a bicyclo[3.1.0]hex-2-ene isomer (7), a 1,3-cyclohexadiene isomer (8), and an allene (9) upon ultraviolet irradiation (*3*).

A variety of other substituted trienes have also been studied, and some typical examples are presented in Fig. 1 (*4–7*).

In all the aforementioned photochemical isomerizations, the central double bond has possessed a Z configuration. Photoisomerization of this central double bond to an E configuration also competes with the described photorearrangements. However, it has been found that the E isomers fail to yield the cyclobutenes, bicyclo[3.1.0]hex-2-enes, or allenes upon ultraviolet irradiation, and, thus, it is apparent that a Z configuration

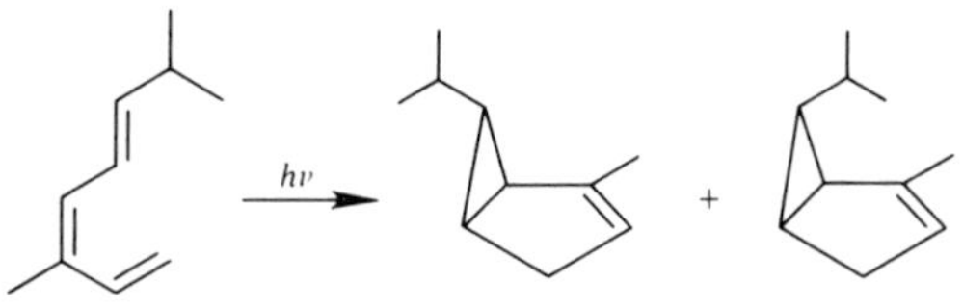

10 11 12 (4)

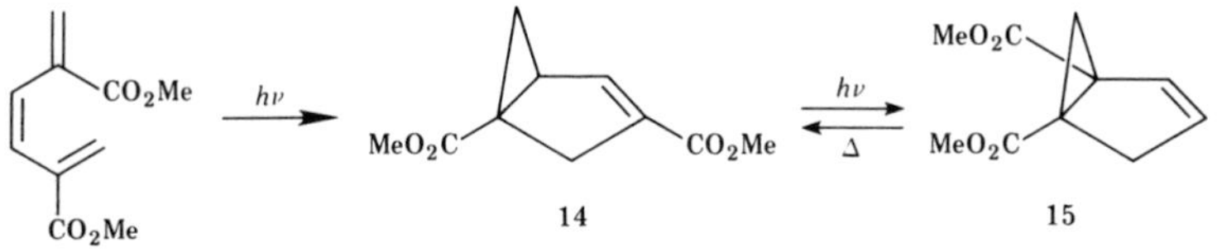

13 14 15 (5)

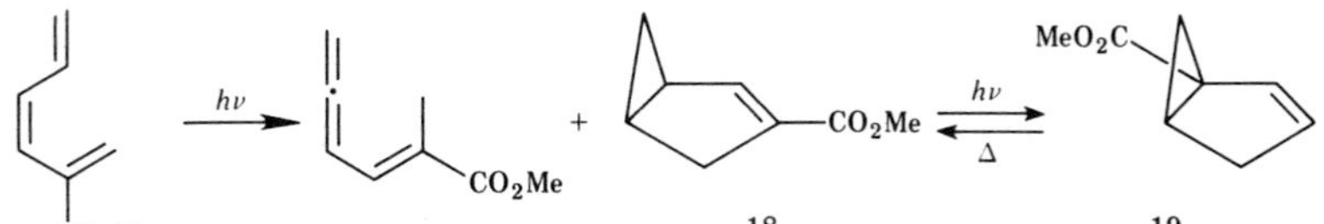

16 17 18 19 (6)

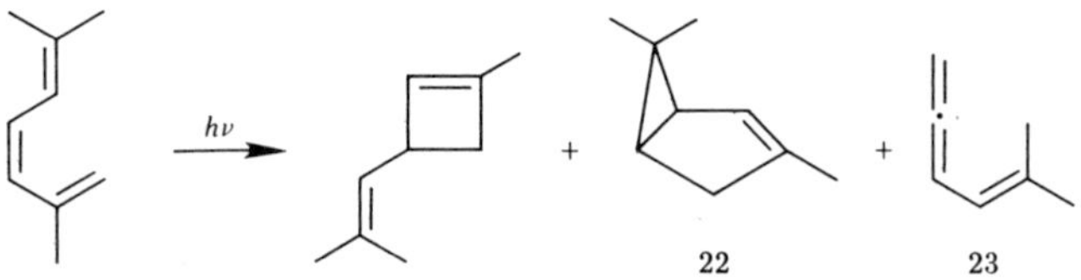

20 21 22 23 (7)

Fig. 1 Examples of typical photochemical transformations of substituted 1,3,5-hexatrienes.

of the central double bond is necessary for these types of isomerizations (*8*).

A more subtle effect is the role the ground state conformation of the triene plays in the distribution of photoproducts found. The concept of ground state conformational control of the photochemistry of trienes (*9*) implies that the products formed from a given compound are geometrically related to, and easily derived from, its major conformations existing in solution. For example, in the case of 1,3,5-hexatriene it would be expected that nonbonding steric interactions would be minimized if the molecule adopted an s-trans,s-trans conformation (t*Z*t) rather than an s-trans,s-cis (c*Z*t) or an s-cis,s-cis (c*Z*c) conformation. When this simple hexatriene (**1**) is irradiated, the major photochemical process is isomerization of the central double bond to give the *E* isomer ($\phi_{Z \to E} = 0.016$; $\phi_{E \to Z} =$

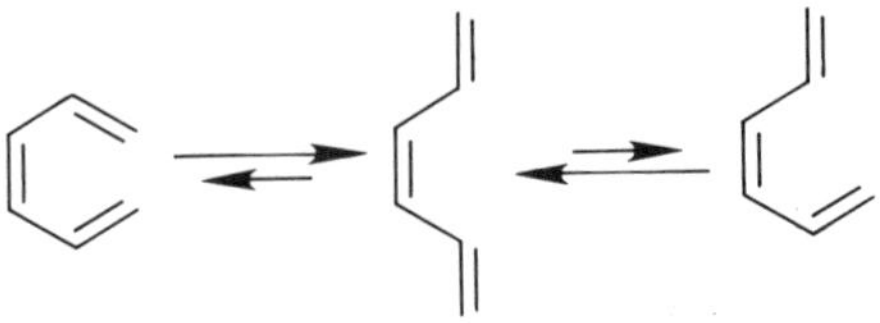

cZc   tZt   cZt

1

0.034) (8). The valence-isomerized products 3 and 4 are formed only upon extended irradiation. The quantum efficiencies for the transformations are low, but these materials predominate upon prolonged irradiation since they are stable to the photochemical reaction conditions.

When the hexatriene is substituted at the 2 position, as in 2-methyl-1,3,5-hexatrienes, a minimization of nonbonding interactions should result in the molecule preferentially assuming an s-cis,s-trans conformation (cZt) in solution. When a solution of 24 is irradiated, the forma-

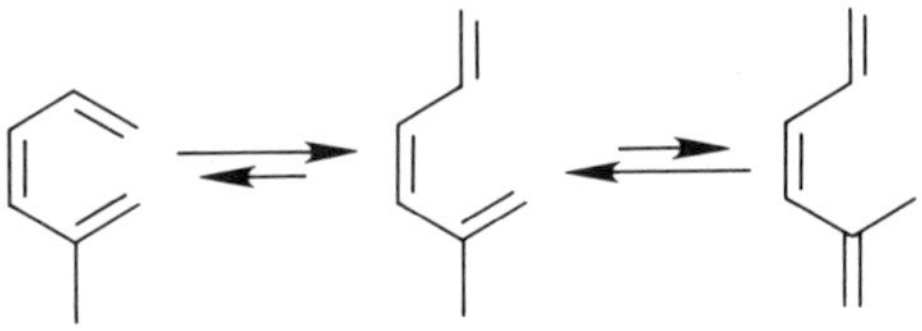

cZc   cZt   tZt

24

tion of cyclobutene 25, allene 26, and bicyclo[3.1.0]hex-2-ene 27 competes more efficiently with isomerization to the E isomer 28 than in the previous case (8). Finally, substitution at both the 2 and 5 positions should result in the s-cis,s-cis conformer (cZc) predominating in solution, and in this sys-

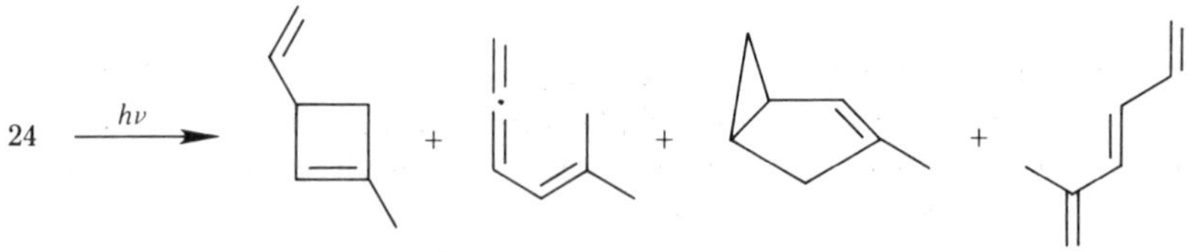

24   $\xrightarrow{h\nu}$

25   26   27   28

tem a considerable amount of the 1,3-cyclohexadiene derivative 30, in addition to the cyclobutene 31, is formed upon irradiation (8). Therefore, it appears that the tZt conformer dissipates its excitation energy by isomerization about the central double bond, whereas the cZt conformer is transformed to cyclobutenes, bicyclo[3.1.0]hex-2-enes, and allenes, and

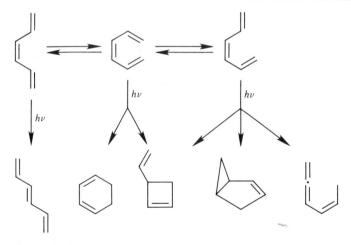

tZt   cZc   cZt

29

29    $\xrightarrow{h\nu}$ +

30   31

the cZc conformer gives predominantly 1,3-cyclohexadienes and cyclobutenes. These generalizations based on ground state conformational
control of the photochemistry of the 1,3,5-hexatriene chromophore are
summarized in Fig. 2.

Although the generality of the principle of ground state conformational
control is clearly illustrated by the simple acyclic triene examples, the
original concept was developed by the study of more complicated
3-alkyl-6,6,9,9-tetramethyl-$\Delta^{3,5(10)}$-hexalins (32), for which there was more
detailed knowledge of the conformational equilibrium (10). The course of
the photoreactions of the various 3-substituted derivatives was the same

Fig. 2   Conformations of 1,3,5-hexatrienes and their photoproducts.

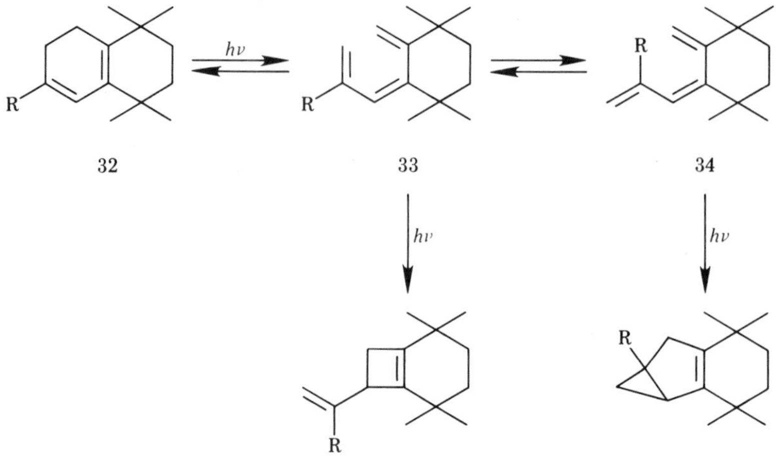

R = H, Me, *i*-Pr, *t*-Bu   35   36

in all cases, but the rates of disappearance of the starting material and the ratio of the photoproducts **35** and **36** changed with the size of the 3-substituent. The results are summarized in Table 1.

The results in Table 1 show that, as the steric bulk of the 3-substituent increases, the rate of disappearance of the starting diene decreases and the ratio of the products **35 : 36** increases. These results are most conveniently discussed in terms of the conformational equilibrium between the first-formed triene in its s-cis conformer **33** and s-trans conformer **34**. An increase in steric bulk of the R group results in a concomitant increase in the concentration of the *cZc* conformer **33** in solution, a conformation that is efficiently ring-closed to starting diene **32** and thus reduces the rate of disappearance of the diene. Although either rotamer of the initially formed triene (**33** or **34**) can yield the cyclobutene **35**, the results clearly indicate that a decrease in the steric bulk of the R group results in a decrease in the

TABLE 1

**Relative Rates and Product
Composition of Photochemical
Transformation of 32.**

R	$t_{1/2}$ (hr)	Ratio 35/36
H	0.4	1 : 2.3
Me	2.1	1 : 1
i-Pr	8.5	1 : 0.3
t-Bu	43.5	1 : 0.2

amount of cyclobutene formed in comparison to the competitive formation of the bicyclo[3.1.0]hex-2-ene **36**. These data strongly suggest that
tZc conformer **34** yields **36**, whereas the cZc conformer **33** yields **35**.

It is well established that the conformation of a triene has a profound
effect both on the position and the magnitude of the ultraviolet absorption
maximum of the molecule (8,11). This knowledge in combination with the
concept of ground state conformational control of photochemical transformations of trienes has been utilized to explain the wavelength dependence of the photoisomerization of 2,6-dimethylhepta-1,3,5-triene (**20**) (7).
At the longer wavelength, the cZt conformer, which yields photoproducts
21–23 and **37**, is the major absorbing species, and, thus, these products

cZt-**20**   tZt-**20**

hv | $\lambda > 300$ nm hv | $\lambda = 254$ nm

21   **22**   **23**   **37**   **37**

predominate. When light of shorter wavelength is employed, the tZt conformer is the major absorbing species and isomerization about the central
double bond to form **37** is the only photochemical process observed.

A final controlling factor that must be considered in the evaluation of
the course of a photochemical reaction is the role of orbital symmetry
concepts. This topic is discussed in greater detail later in this essay (see
Section III,C), but a cursory examination of the concept is worthy of presentation now. Orbital symmetry concepts call attention to the controlling
role of the highest occupied molecular orbital (12). In the photochemical
reaction of a triene, it is the fourth molecular orbital (**38**) that must be examined in order to make definite stereochemical predictions for the various photoprocesses.

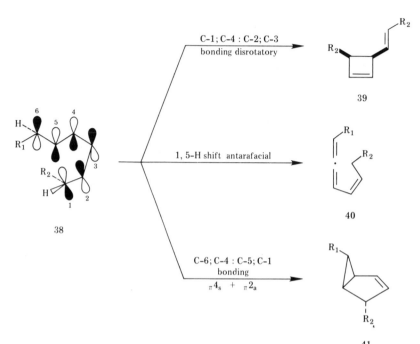

For the first two cases, the formation of the cyclobutene **39** and the allene **40**, the experimental results agree with the stereochemical prediction (under arrow). In the third case, the formation of the bicyclo[3.1.0]hex-2-enes, an interesting dichotomy is found. The triene **42**

42

43 ($_\pi 4_s + {}_\pi 2_a$)

44

45 ($_\pi 4_a + {}_\pi 2_a$)

gave **43** (*13*), the stereochemistry of which was that predicted above. The related triene **44**, having a methyl group in place of a phenyl group, gave **45** (*14*), the stereochemistry of which is not that predicted but rather that of a so-called forbidden pathway. This dilemma pertaining to the role of orbital symmetry in photochemical reactions is discussed later in this review (see Section III,D).

B. Cyclooctatriene and Divinylbenzenes

The photochemistry of the triene chromophore, when incorporated into a medium-sized ring or when a benzene ring is part of the triene, follows reaction pathways similar to that of the acyclic systems. Ultraviolet irradiation of 1,3,5-cyclooctatriene (**46**) (*15*) in ether solution yielded 20% of the reduction product, 1,5-cyclooctadiene (**47**), 16% of the vinyl cyclobutene **48**, and 6% of the bicyclo[3.1.0]hex-2-ene **49**. Similar photo-

chemical transformations have been found with 1,3,5,7-cyclooctatetraene (**50**) (*16*), with substituted 7,8-dimethylene-1,3,5-cyclooctatriene (**51**) (*17*), and with cycloheptatriene (**52**) (*18*).

The investigation of specifically deuteriated *O*-divinylbenzenes (**53**) provided insight into the mechanism of bicyclo[3.1.0]hex-2-ene formation in the system (*19*). The structure of the final product (**55**) can best be explained by an initial photochemical ring closure to **54**, which undergoes

a 1,3 shift to yield the aromatic derivative **55**. In addition to this major reaction pathway other pathways leading to the formation of trace amounts of deuteriated naphthalene and its dihydro- and tetrahydro derivatives were found (*20*).

In contrast to the behavior of the acyclic 1,3,5-hexatrienes discussed earlier, terminal alkyl substituents in the 1,2-divinylbenzene series do not greatly influence the regioselectivity of the bicyclization reaction. When o-(2-methylpropenyl)styrene (56) is irradiated, two benzobicyclo-[3.1.0]hex-2-enes (57 and 58) are found (21); both products undergo further photochemical transformation. Similar photochemical transformations have been reported for o-di(methylpropenyl)benzene (59).

Upon ultraviolet irradiation, 1,2-dihydronaphthalene is transformed to a benzobicyclo[3.1.0]hex-2-ene isomer (22–25). Study of the deuterated derivatives 60 and 61 indicated the involvement of vinyl-xylylidenes 62 and

63, the deuterium distribution in 64 and 65 being that expected from their photochemical closure (23). Further evidence was obtained by irradiation of 1,2-dihydronaphthalene simultaneously with 280 and 400 nm light. The yield of the bicyclohexene is dependent on the intensity of the 400 nm light (24). Also in agreement with this mechanistic postulate is the formation of 68 upon irradiation of trans-1,2-dimethyl-1,2-dihydronaphthalene (66).

Conrotatory opening of 66 would yield vinyl-xylylidene (67), which upon ring closure via the $[_\pi 4_a + _\pi 2_a]$ pathway, discussed earlier, would yield the exo–exo isomer 68 (26).

C. Cyclic Trienes

The incorporation of the 1,3,5-hexatriene into a carbocycle allows one to investigate the more subtle geometric effects on the photochemical transformations. However, since many cyclic trienes are generated by the photochemically induced opening of a bicyclic cyclohexadiene, brief mention must be made of the factors governing such openings. This photochemical $[_\pi 4 + _\sigma 2]$ pericyclic reaction is predicted to proceed in a conrotatory fashion. The role of ground state conformational control has been investigated for the case of α-phellandrene (69) (27). When 69 is irradiated at various temperatures, a correlation is noted between the temperature-dependent ORD spectrum and the ratio of terminal cis and trans olefins 70

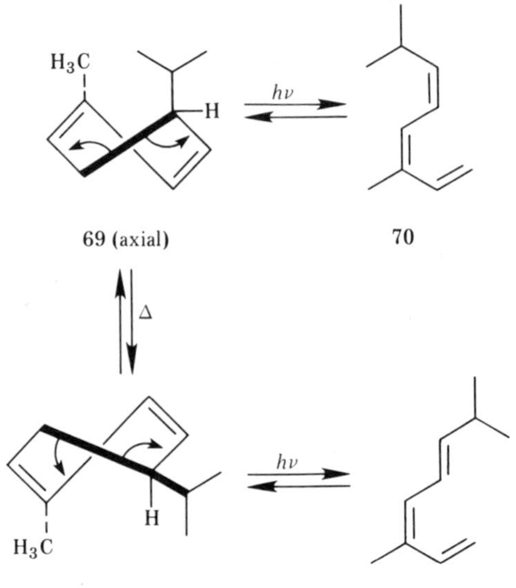

69 (axial)　　　　　　　　　　70

Temp (°C)	71/70
−196	29
−160	9.7
−110	5.2
0	3.7
30	3.0
100	2.7

69 (equatorial)　　　　　　　71

and 71. It has been demonstrated that the ORD spectra of homoannular conjugated hexadienes are dependent on the helicity of the chromophore (28). The results imply that the conformer containing a pseudoaxial isopropyl group yields the terminal cis isomer, and the conformer containing a pseudoequatorial isopropyl group yields the trans isomer. In order for this to be true the diene must open in the conrotatory fashion indicated. Such an opening is termed "accordant" (27) since it is in accord with the chirality of the diene, and it should be noted that this mode requires the

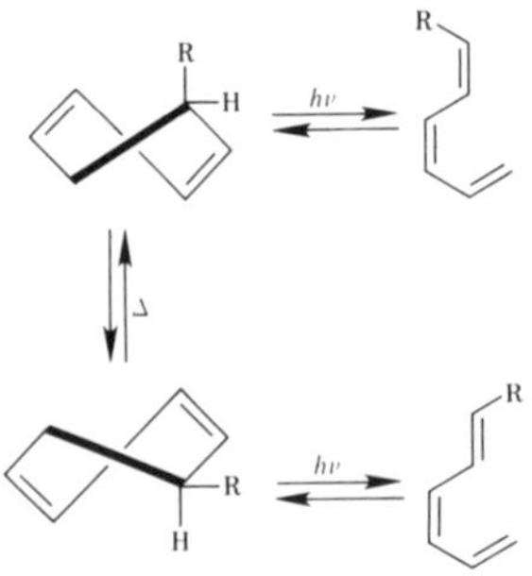

Substituent	trans/cis
CH$_3$	1.5
i-Pr	5.0
t-Bu	15.0

least motion for the developing sp² centers to overlap with the existing π system. The alternative allowed conrotatory opening is "discordant" with the helicity and requires the developing p orbital to pass through the nodal plane of the π system. Further support for this argument is found in the results of the irradiation of 5-substituted cyclohexadienes (29).

Similar results have been found for annulated cyclohexadienes. Thus, when cis-bicyclo[4.3.0]nona-2,4-diene (72) is irradiated, the accordant product cis,cis,trans-1,3,5-cyclononatriene (73) is obtained (30). It is interesting that, although cis,cis,trans-1,3,5-cyclodecatriene (76) could not be detected in the irradiation of diene 75, its presence can be inferred by the formation of vinylcyclobutene 77, vinylallene 78, and two bicyclo-

[3.1.0]hex-2-ene isomers (79 and 80) (31). Similarly, diene 81 yields the accordant triene product cis,cis,trans-cycloundecatriene (82) upon electronic excitation. Further irradiation of the triene results in the formation of 83, 84, and isomeric trienes (32).

The substituted cis-9,10-dimethyl-Δ¹·³-hexalin (85) opens photochemically to give the cis,cis,trans-triene 86 (33). Continued irradiation of 86 affords 89 and the isomeric triene 87, which under the conditions em-

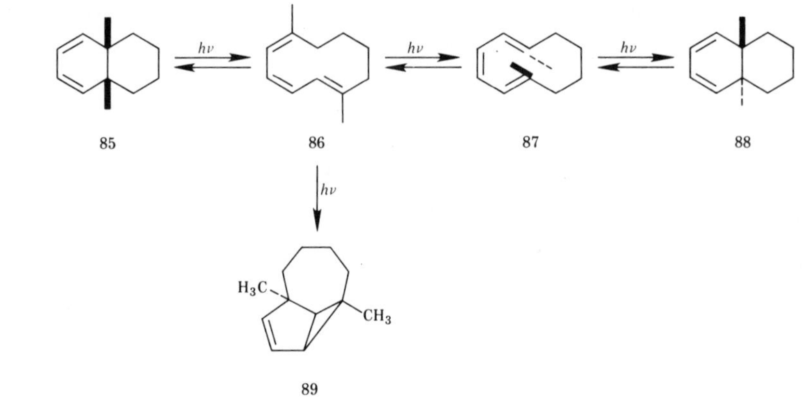
hν
hν
hν
85
86
87
88
hν
H_3C
CH_3
89

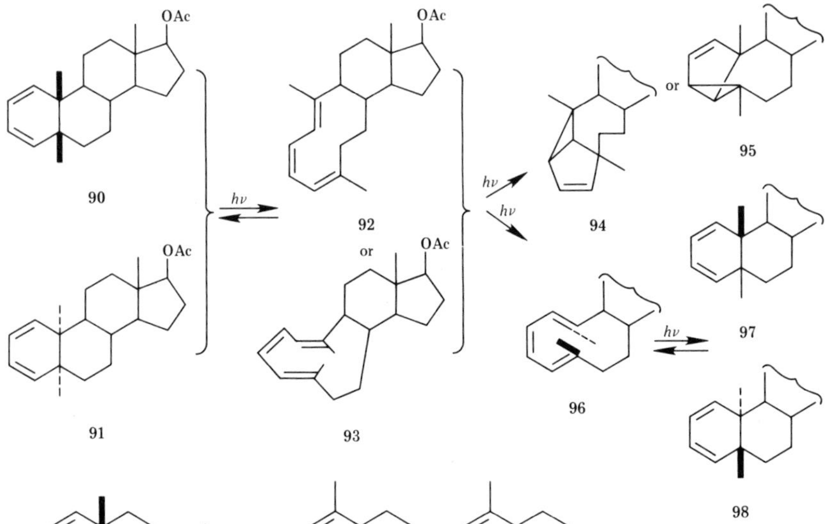
OAc
OAc
or
90
hν
92
or
OAc
hν
hν
94
95
OAc
97
91
93
96
hν
98

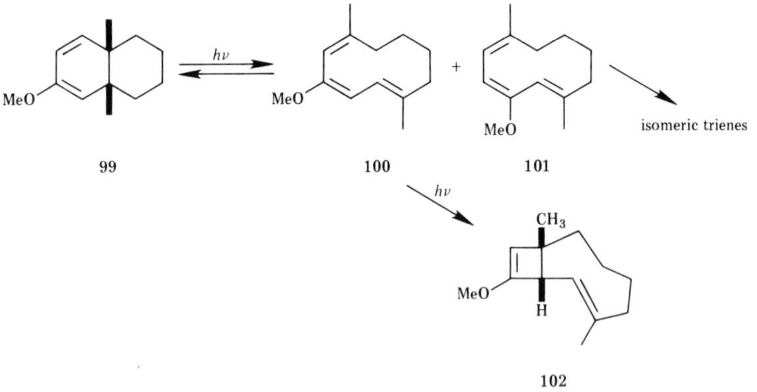
hν
+
MeO
MeO
MeO
isomeric trienes
99
100
101
hν
CH_3
MeO
H
102

ployed, cyclizes to the trans-fused hexalin **88**. The photochemistry of a mixture of the steroidal dienes **90** and **91** follows a course very similar to that of **85** (*33*). A bicyclo[3.1.0]hex-2-ene isomer is produced, and, although it is not possible to choose between the two possible isomers (**94** and **95**), this product is best explained on the basis of a *cis,cis,trans*-triene precursor (**92** or **93**). In addition, the *trans,cis,trans*-triene **96** and the product of its photochemical ring closure (**97** and **98**) are isolated.

The dienol ether **99** opens upon electronic excitation to the trienes **100** and **101**. The former yields a vinylcyclobutene upon extended irradiation, whereas the latter isomerizes to an unidentified isomeric triene, possibly by means of a [1,7]sigmatropic shift (*34*).

The photochemistry of trans-fused bicyclic homoannular dienes follows a much different course (*35*). A discordant opening of *trans*-bicyclo[4.3.0]nona-2,4-diene (**103**), presumably due to the ring strain generated in an accordant opening, yields the *cis,cis,cis*-triene **104**, which reacts further to give the isomeric triene **105** and a bicyclo[3.1.0]hex-2-ene (**106**). *trans*-Bicyclo[4.4.0]deca-2,4-diene (**107**), however, opens in an accordant fashion to yield the thermally unstable *trans,cis,trans*-triene **108**, the presence of which was inferred by means of matrix isolation techniques and low-temperature hydrogenation. This triene cyclizes to diene **75** at a finite rate, even at −70°C, presumably due to the geometric ar-

| 103 | 104 | 105 | 106 |

| 107 | 108 | 75 |

| 109 | 110 | 81 |

rangement of orbitals in the triene which facilitates such a motion. Similar arguments apply to diene **109**. Irradiation of this diene results in the production of the cis-fused **81**. The intermediacy of triene **110** was inferred by hydrogenation of a low-temperature irradiation mixture, which yielded bicyclo-[5.4.0]undecane and cycloundecane. The facile thermal rearrangement of this triene strongly suggests that it possess the expected accordant trans,cis,trans geometry.

trans-9,10-Dimethyl-$\Delta^{1,3}$-hexalin (**111**) yields the triene **87**, which efficiently recyclizes to **111** upon electronic excitation and thermally closes to **85** only with heating (*33*). Likewise, the steroidal diene **97** yields the cyclic

triene **96**, which recyclizes to **97** and **98** (*33*). The dienol ether **112** also gives a *trans,cis,trans*-triene upon photochemically induced opening (*34*). It is interesting that irradiation of diene **114** leads to the production of cis-fused diene **116**. This is presumably a result of the thermal ring closure of the *trans,cis,trans*-triene **115** (*33*). That such a closure is facile is further demonstrated by the case of *trans*-Δ^{1,3}-hexalin vinyl ether (117), which gave the corresponding cis isomer upon irradiation (36), and by the case of diene 120, in which again the thermal lability of the triene 121 was demonstrated (37).

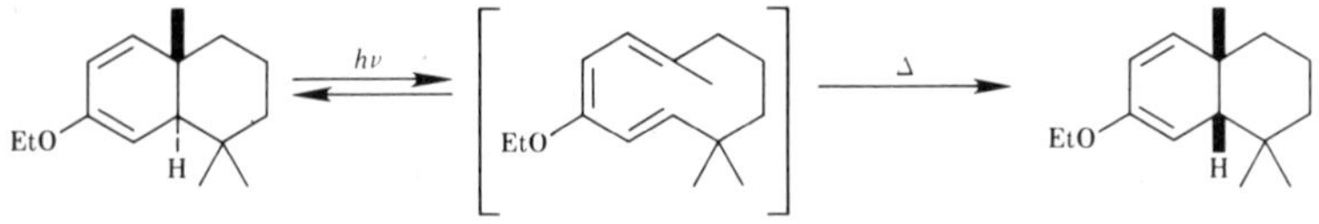

117   118   119

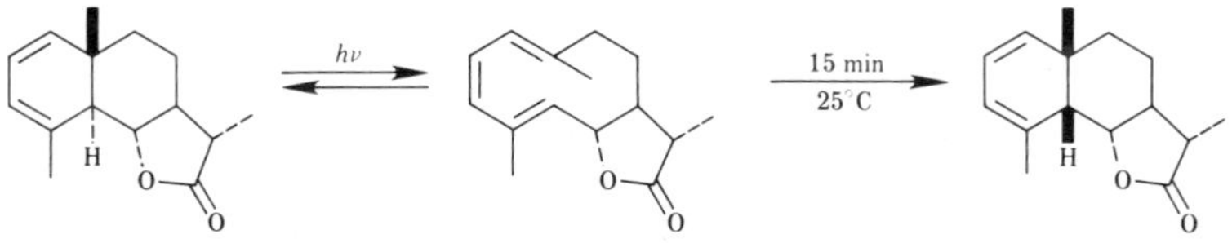

120   121   122

The above discussion represents a review of the photochemistry of cyclic *trans,cis,cis*- and *trans,cis,trans*-1,3,5-trienes. Investigation has shown that *cis,cis,cis*-1,3,5-cyclodecatriene (123) at 300 nm undergoes both a hydrogen migration to the nonconjugated triene 124 and a [1,5] sigmatropic shift to the thermally labile *trans,cis,cis*-1,3,6-cyclodecatriene 125 (38). At shorter wavelength (254 nm), the photochemistry of 123 displays an interesting temperature dependency. Thus, at room temperature vinylcyclobutene 127 is formed at the expense of 125. This result is conveniently explained in terms of the triene having a helical and a tublike conformation available to it, the latter than giving rise to 127 and the

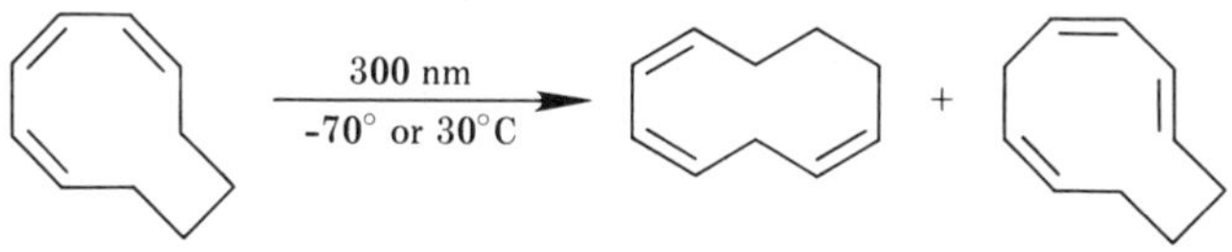

123   124   125

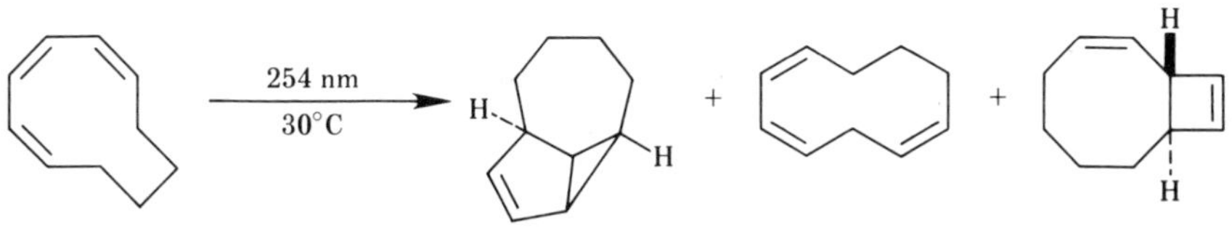

123   126(30%)   124(26%)   127(17%)

former being the progenitor of **125.** Furthermore, *cis,cis,cis*-1,3,5-cycloundecatriene (**128**) appears to assume both the tub and helical conformations at −70°C, yielding the bicyclo[3.1.0]hex-2-ene **129** and the diene **130**, respectively. Because of the increased ring size of **128**, a cyclohexadiene product is formed, whereas in the case of **123** torsional strain precludes the formation of such a product.

The cyclic *cis,trans,cis*-1,3,5-trienes (*38*) also show a wavelength dependency. Thus, compounds **131, 132, 134,** and **136** all undergo a simple bond

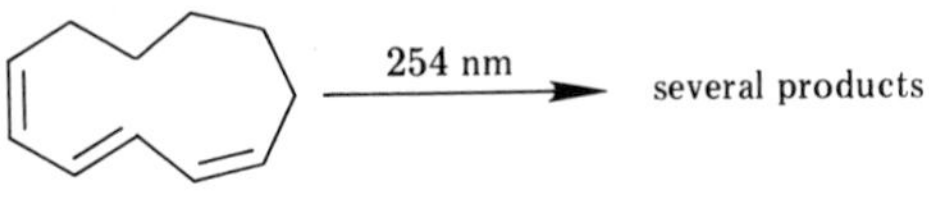

136

isomerization to give the corresponding all-cis isomers when the irradiation is performed with 254 nm light. In contrast, the use of 300 nm light leads to a different product mixture composed of sigmatropic shift prod-

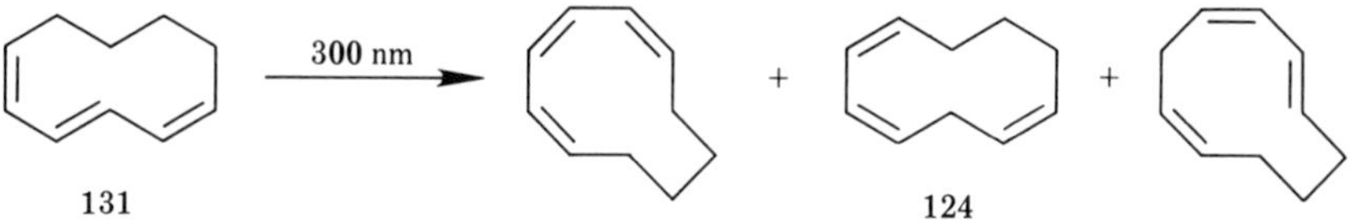

131   123   124   125

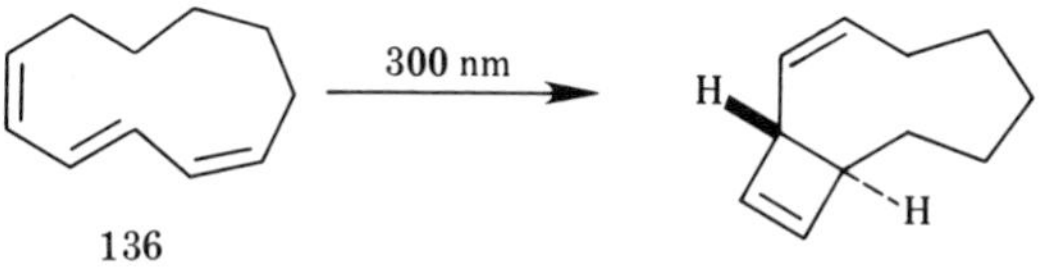

136   137

ucts and a vinylcyclobutene. It is proposed that a planar geometry of the triene is the major absorbing species at longer wavelength, whereas at shorter wavelength a twisted conformer is the major absorbing species and loses electronic excitation energy by means of a strain-releasing bond isomerization.

D. Vitamin D

The sequence of events leading to the production of vitamin D (**140**) is well established (Fig. 3) (*39,40*). Ultraviolet irradiation of provitamin D (**138**), a 7-dehydrocholesterol, gives rise to previtamin D (**139**) via a conrotatory opening of the cyclohexadiene chromophoric unit. In a remarkably facile thermal reaction at 37°C (*41*), previtamin D is transformed to vitamin D by an antarafacial [1,7]sigmatropic hydrogen shift. Although an s-cis,s-cis conformation is required for such a concerted process, the vitamin once formed adopts an s-cis,s-trans conformation (*42*).

Since vitamin D possesses a chromophore that absorbs ultraviolet light in the same range as does provitamin D and previtamin D, the vitamin undergoes photochemical transformations under the same conditions in which it is formed. The three important overirradiation routes followed lead to the valence isomeric suprasterols **141,** which possess a

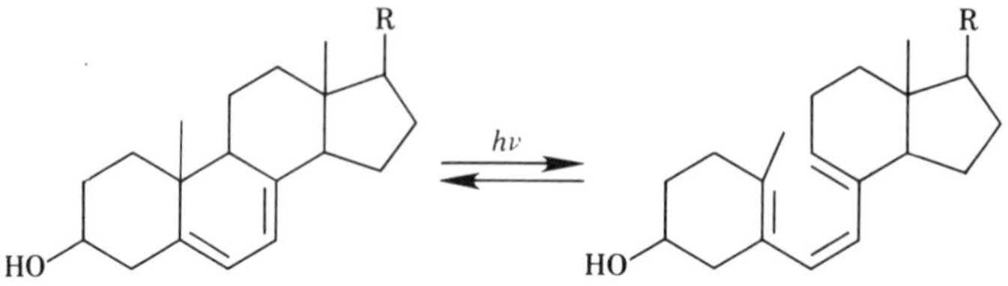

Provitamin D (138)   Previtamin D (139)

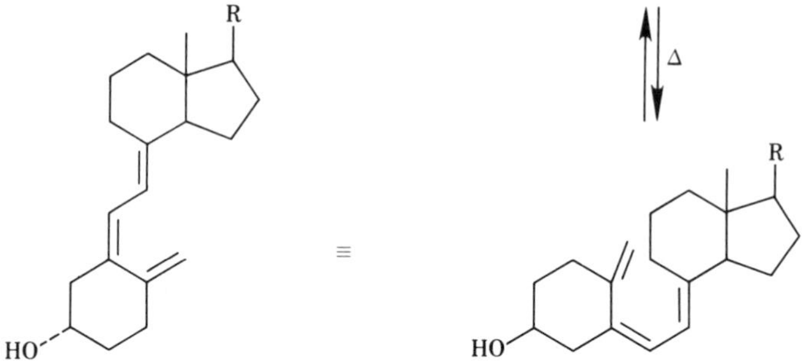

Vitamin D (140)

Fig. 3   Reaction sequence for vitamin D formation (vitamin D_2, R = C_9H_{17}; vitamin D_3, R = C_8H_{17}).

bicyclo[3.1.0]hex-1-ene moiety (*43*), to the cyclobutenes **142**, and to the 1,5-hydrogen sigmatropic-rearranged allenes **143** (*44,45*) (Fig. 4). The overall reaction sequence for the transformation of a steroidal 1,3-cyclo-hexadiene to an acyclic triene and, in turn, to new cyclic olefinic products was found to be a general photochemical reaction sequence, as discussed earlier.

The entire sequence of transformations in the vitamin D series from provitamin D to suprasterol involves a single thermal (nonphotochemical) reaction, i.e., the reversible, facile 1,7-hydrogen sigmatropic rearrange-ment relating previtamin D to vitamin D. Thus, under appropriate condi-tions the reactions of previtamin D can be studied. The stereospecific thermal transformation of previtamin D intrigued investigators long before the orbital symmetry rules of Woodward and Hoffmann provided a theo-retical rationale for the results. Upon heating to 180°C, both previtamin D_2 and vitamin D_2 cyclize to yield pyrocalciferol (**144**) and isopyrocalciferol (**145**) (*46,47*), molecules with 9,10-syn stereochemistry. The stereochemi-cal outcome results from the orbital symmetry-preferred disrotatory clo-sure of a 1,3,5-hexatriene (Fig. 5).

In this 9,10-*syn*-cyclohexadiene series, the orbital symmetry-preferred,

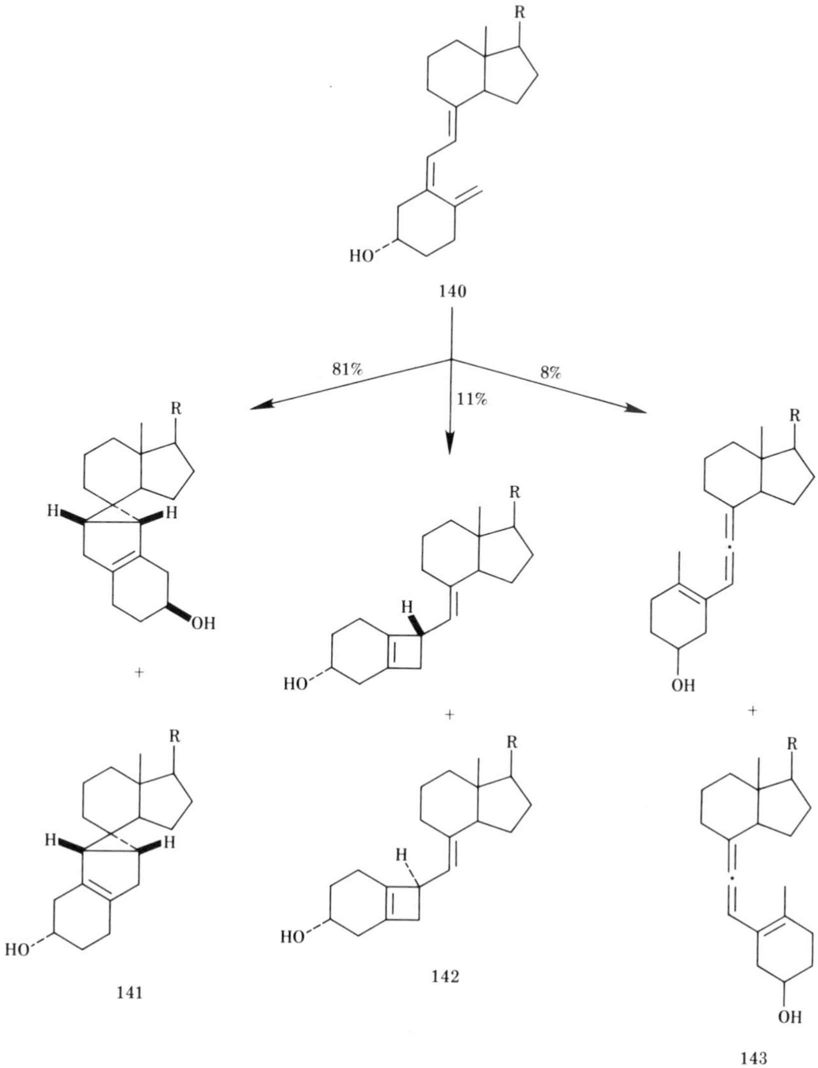

Fig. 4 Overirradiation products of vitamin D.

light-induced conrotatory ring opening is strongly inhibited since such a reaction course would result in the formation of a highly stained *trans*-cyclohexene. It was found (47) that these steroidal dienes upon ultraviolet irradiation undergo a stereospecific disrotatory ring closure to the less strained cyclobutene valence isomers photoisopyrocalciferol (**146**) and photopyrocalciferol (**147**), respectively. As is common with such valence

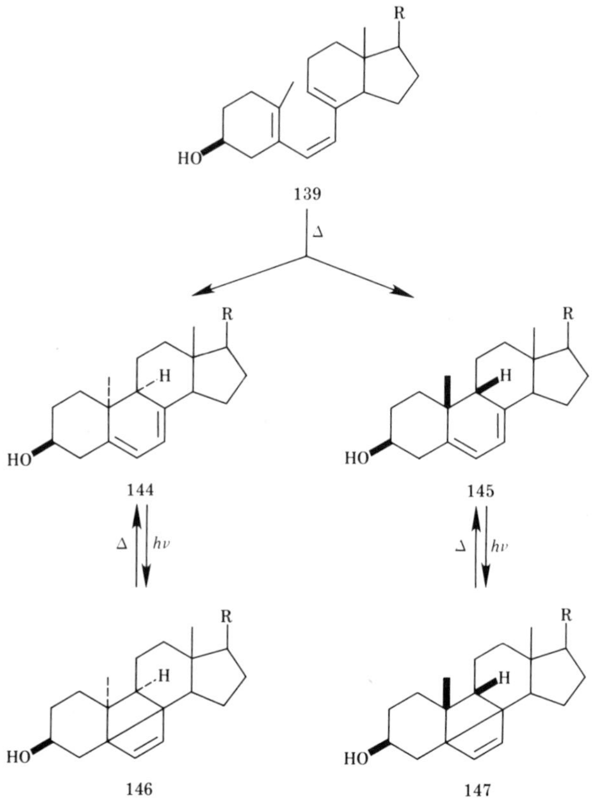

Fig. 5 Thermal and photochemical transformations of vitamin D and related products.

isomeric cyclobutenes, these compounds upon heating to 180°C revert, stereospecifically, to their related steroidal dienes (47).

The photochemical transformation of previtamin D is solvent dependent. The irradiation (254 nm) of the previtamin D_3 in ether at 5°C (a condition that prevents formation of vitamin D) yields a quasi-photostationary state (Fig. 6), the composition of which strongly favors tachysterol$_3$ (**148,** 75%) and previtamin D_3 (**139,** 20%). Only small amounts of the starting diene **138** and its 9,10-anti isomer, lumisterol$_3$ (**149**), are present (48). The quantum yields for this series of reversible reactions are also listed in Fig. 6, the cis–trans isomerization of the central double bond being the most efficient process (48).

Upon prolonged irradiation at 5°C, the above initially formed compounds, all possessing intense absorption bands between 250 and 300 nm, gradually disappear and a large number of overirradiation products are

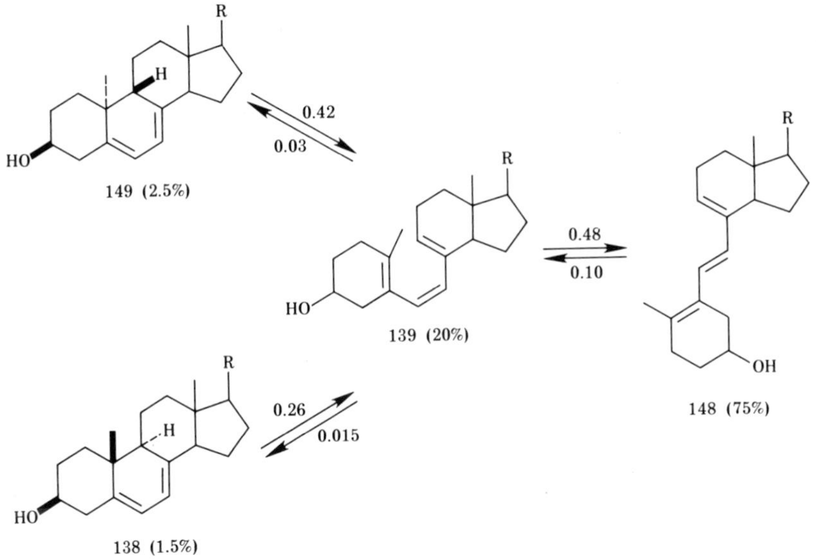

Fig. 6 Quantum yields and photostationary state composition at 254 nm for photo-isomerization of previtamin D_3.

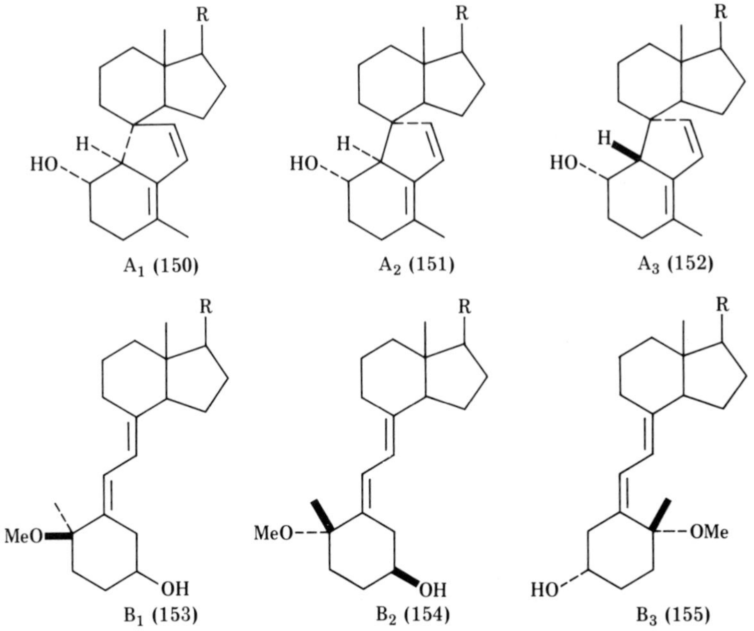

Fig. 7 Toxisterols from extended irradiation of provitamin D_3 in ether and/or methanol at 5°C.

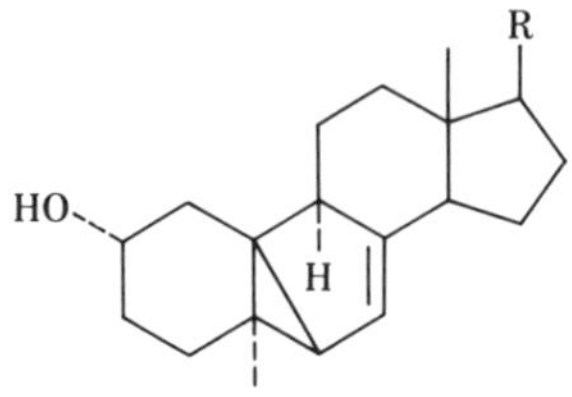

C₁ (156)   C₂ (157)

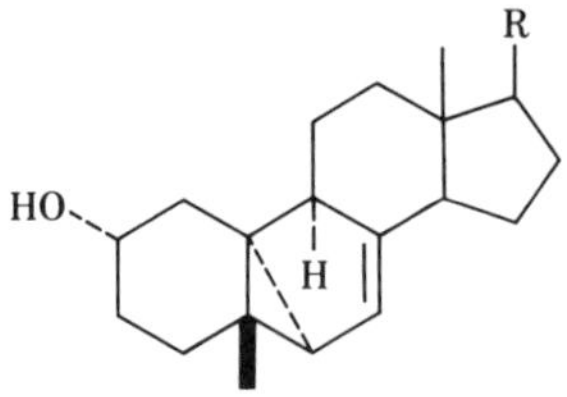

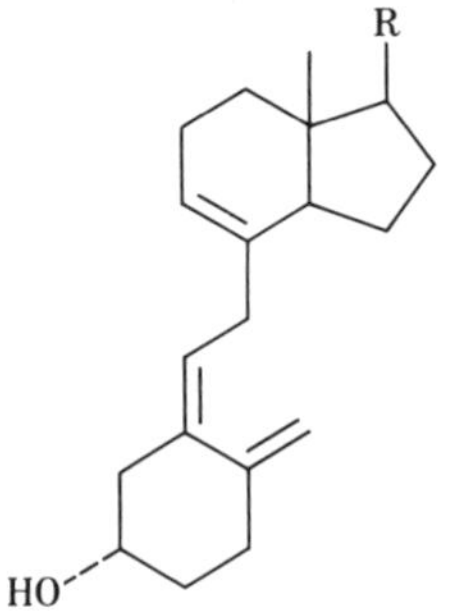

D₁ (158)   D₂ (159)   D₃ (160)

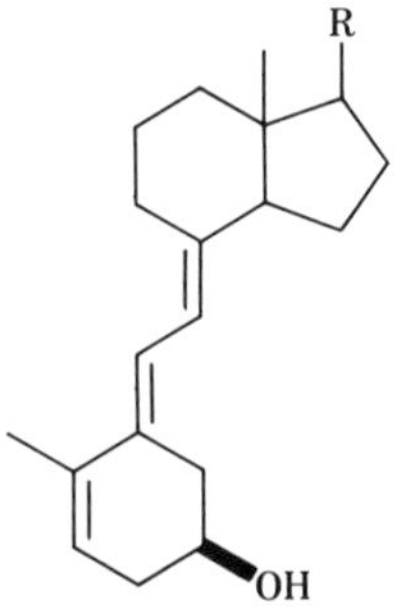

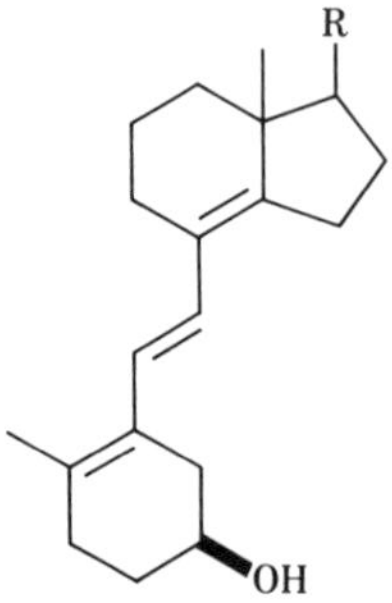

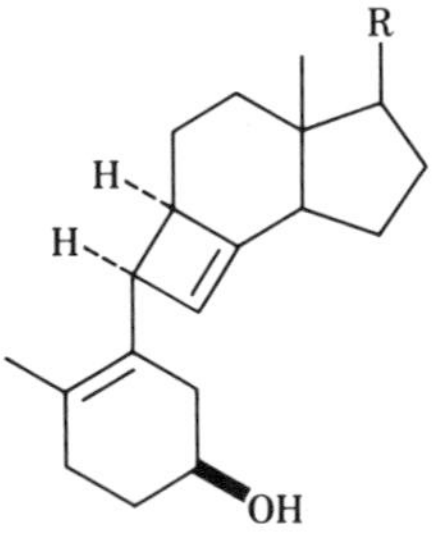

E₁ (161)   R₁ (162)

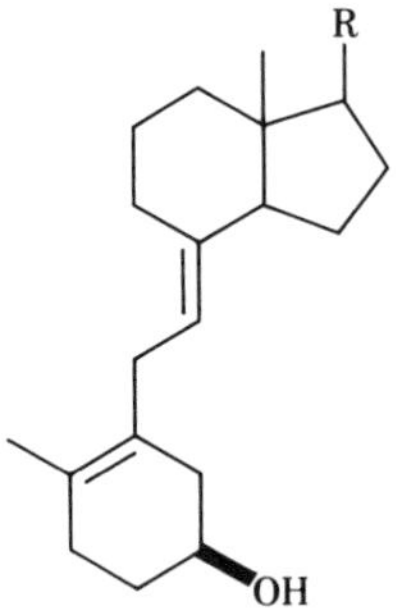

Fig. 7 (Continued).

formed. These materials are called toxisterols since the compounds are allegedly toxic. The materials that are formed depend on the solvent, and the structures of all the compounds presently known are given in Fig. 7 (45,49). The toxisterols of the A, C, D, and E groups are formed in ether solution and result from a combination of sigmatropic hydrogen rearrangements and electrocyclic reactions. In methanol solvent, the B family of toxisterols is also formed and appears to be the result of a 1,6 addition of methanol to the conjugated triene system. In addition, toxisterol R_1 is formed by a photoreduction reaction, and toxisterols D_2 and D_3 by loss of methanol from toxisterol B. The formation of materials in the B and D series is enhanced by the presence of acid during the irradiation (49). Under this reaction condition cyclic ethers 163 and 164 are also formed, as are small amounts of the C_{19} and C_{20} hydrocarbon fragments 165 and 166, derived by loss of ring A, and related vinyl ethers (49).

The photochemical reactivity displayed in the vitamin D series complicates any study of the system and makes the efficient preparation of any particular photoproduct difficult. The industrial preparation of vitamin D takes advantage of the fact that at 0°C the previtamin is the major photoproduct when the irradiation is discontinued after 25–50% of the provitamin conversion. At this point, the unreacted starting material is removed and the remaining previtamin D is converted thermally to vitamin D.

Much work has been done to determine the biological role of the vitamin, and the reader is referred to the appropriate reviews (50). Recently, several vitamin D analogues have been synthesized in order to study the hormonal mode of action (51). Also, detailed spectral studies have been performed to determine the populations of the two ring A chair comformations available to the vitamin (52), and this partitioning has been used to explain the formation of the two isomeric suprasterols, cyclobutenes, and vinylallenes upon the irradiation of vitamin D (44).

III. DISCUSSION OF RESULTS

A. Role of Hypersurfaces in Photochemical Reactions

The preceding summary of results has demonstrated the wide range of transformations that trienes undergo upon electronic excitation. Thus, cis–trans isomerization, [1,5]sigmatropic shifts, and electrocyclic reactions are commonly observed reactions in conjugated triene photochemistry (Fig. 2).

In recent years numerous theoretical justifications for these transformations have been postulated (*12,53*), and it is easy to rationalize the products obtained from a given triene using these treatments. However, it is still not possible to predict with certainty which of the many allowed processes will prove to be most efficient. There are several reasons for this apparent nonsystematic nature of photochemistry. Chief among these is the limited understanding of the relationship between the excited states of starting materials and the excited or ground states of the variety of possible products and the factors that influence these relationships.

Through the agency of state correlation diagrams (*54*) and the evaluation of potential energy surfaces of different electronic states (*55*), three general classes of relationships can be envisioned (*56*). Assuming a reaction coordinate in which the ground state G and the excited state E of the starting material are linked in some fashion with the states I and J of the first-formed intermediate or products (Fig. 8), there are three general cases that represent the relationship between the ground and excited state surfaces.

In the first, there exists a matching relationship in which the excited states of the reactant and product are linked to form an energy surface that is well separated from the energy surface generated by the ground states. Since the surfaces are well separated throughout the reaction coordinate, there is no "link" or crossing that would lead to an easy transition from the excited state surface to the ground state surface (Fig. 9). Mechanistically, this process requires that the excited state of starting material go directly in an isothermal reaction to excited state of product. In reality, such a situation is rarely encountered experimentally for energetic reasons.

A much more common situation is one in which the excited state species is linked in some fashion with the ground state of product, and the

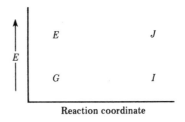

Reaction coordinate

Fig. 8 Relative energies of the ground and the excited states of reactant and product.

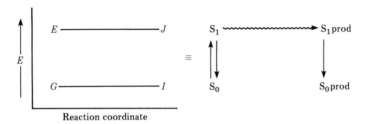

Fig. 9   Qualitative potential energy diagram of ground and excited states.

molecule follows a continuous exothermic pathway, which passes through some higher vibrational state of ground state product and ends in a lower

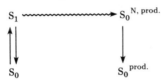

vibrational state. Such a process is consistent with two possible excited state–ground state relationships (Fig. 10).

In the allowed crossing relationship, the state symmetries are such that the symmetry of the ground state of the starting material G correlates with the higher-energy primary photoproduct, state J, and is of a different state symmetry than the excited state of starting material E, which correlates with the lower-energy primary product state I. With such a spacial symmetry relationship, the crossing of the hypersurfaces is allowed. The two surfaces can be described as orthogonal wave functions that are completely independent of one another.

In avoided crossings, the state symmetries are such that the symmetry of the ground state of the starting material G, which correlates with a higher-energy primary photoproduct, state J, is the same as that of an excited state of the starting material E, which correlates with the lower-

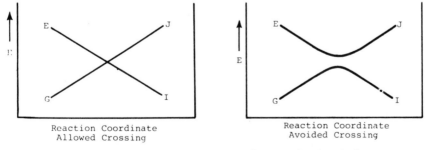

Fig. 10   Qualitative potential energy curves for ground and excited states.

energy primary product state I. In distinction to the situation above, the two surfaces G and E have the same spacial symmetry and spin multiplicities and are no longer independent of each other. Under such conditions, if exact wave functions are used, the intersection is avoided [i.e., the noncrossing rule (26)]. However, the two surfaces are dynamically linked by virtue of their intended crossing, a feature that is discussed in detail later (see Section III,C).

It now becomes necessary to evaluate the importance of each of these three relationships in photochemical transformations. It would appear that the matching relationship must represent an unlikely extreme. Since the excited and ground state surfaces are never in close proximity, the probability of a molecule undergoing a surface crossing is small. The efficiency of crossing is related to the degree of vibronic coupling between the two surfaces. With surfaces of greatly different energy, this coupling is small and represents an inefficient mode of demotion when compared to the more favorable relationships discussed below. It should be remembered that for polyatomic molecules the system is multidimensional, and there is competition between the various modes of demotion.

The allowed crossing relationship represents yet another extreme. Every excited state species correlates with a potential ground state product, and such a process would be expected to be efficient since no surface crossing is required. The scarcity of highly efficient photochemical processes, especially in the singlet manifold of hexatrienes, indicates that the rigorously allowed crossing is a relatively rare relationship.

B. Landau–Zener Relationship

It appears, therefore, that most photochemical transformations are more accurately represented by an avoided crossing in which the two surfaces are dynamically linked by virtue of their intended crossing (57). However, it may be easier for the nuclei to follow the dashed line along the intersecting diabatic surfaces because of the extensive electronic rearrangement necessary to remain on the avoided adiabatic surfaces (Fig. 11). The probability of such a surface crossing has been related to three factors by Landau (58) and Zener (58a). These factors are the energy gap between the surfaces (ΔE), the slope of the surfaces in the region of the avoided crossing (δS), and the "velocity" (V) with which a molecule travels along a given surface:

$$P = \exp[(-\pi^2/h)(\Delta E^2/4V\ \delta S)]$$

Thus, as the energy difference between the two surfaces becomes smaller, the probability of decay from one adiabatic surface to another becomes

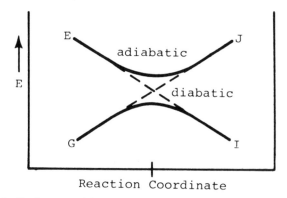

Fig. 11 Qualitative potential energy curves for adiabatic and diabatic processes.

large (Fig. 12). Similarly, a large change in the slope of an energy surface in the region of an avoided crossing results in a greater probability of decay. It is intuitively obvious that as a molecule enters the region of an avoided crossing a large δS requires the molecule to make drastic changes in geometry and energy rapidly in order to remain on the same adiabatic surface (Fig. 13). The excited surface is therefore linked in a dynamic sense to the ground state surface by virtue of the avoided crossing (the diabatic surface), and, due to the momentum of the molecule, there is a high probability of decay to the ground state surface. The third factor, the velocity with which the system crosses the avoided region is a result of the dynamics of such a process and would appear to be related to the absolute value of the slope of the surface as the avoided region is approached. The

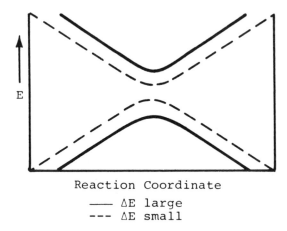

Fig. 12 Key: ——, ΔE large; ---, ΔE small. Qualitative potential energy curves for ground and excited states.

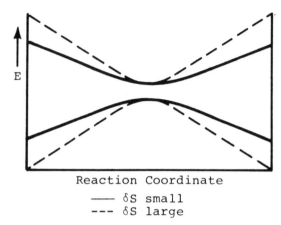

Reaction Coordinate

——— δS small

--- δS large

Fig. 13 Key: ———, δS small; ---, δS large. Qualitative potential energy curves for ground and excited states.

greater this velocity, the greater the probability of the jump, since for large kinetic energies the system is carried on through as though it were ignoring the avoided nature of the crossing.

C. The Photochemical Process

Having discussed the relationship between potential energy surfaces, we will find it instructional to follow the course of a hypothetical chemical reaction in some detail. The Franck–Condon principle (59) states that the promotion of a molecule to an excited electronic surface takes place more rapidly ($\sim 10^{-15}$ sec) than the period of vibration of the nuclei ($\sim 10^{-13}$ sec). Therefore, the positions and velocities of the nuclei are almost unchanged during an electronic transition. The molecule possesses $3N - 6$ vibrational degrees of freedom, and associated with each of these is a potential energy surface. Thus, a polyatomic molecule upon excitation is promoted to the excited state surface and rapidly reaches a lower vibrational level of S_1 (Fig. 14). If a minimum exists in the immediate region of the spectroscopic excited state, the molecule may return to S_0 from this minimum by a radiative or radiationless process, and the starting material in its ground state is produced unless a hot ground state reaction occurs. In some cases the excited molecule will acquire kinetic energy at the expense of the original electronic energy and move to one of the several lower minima in the region of the excited state. If the latter represents a region of an avoided crossing, the molecule will pass onto the ground state surface, coming to rest in a minimum that corresponds to products. Due to the dynamic linkage of the surfaces, different ground state minima can be

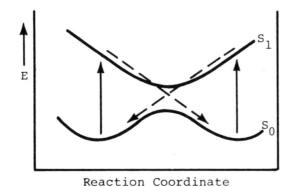

Reaction Coordinate

Fig. 14 Qualitative potential energy surfaces with dynamic linkage.

reached via the same intended crossing zone, depending on the direction from which the zone is approached (*60*). As a result of this dynamic linkage, the molecule is directed toward a specific product. This crossing area has also been termed a "funnel" (*60*) since the molecule clearly has no chance to reach thermal equilibrium in S_1. It is this linkage that often gives high specificity to photochemical reactions even though the ground state product is formed with an excess of vibrational energy.

The presence of thermal barriers on the excited surface may prevent a molecule from gaining access to a region in which the probability of crossing is high, and many such minima may be inaccessible due to the extensive nuclear reorientation necessary during the relatively short lifetime of the excited species or the number of intervening minima. It should also be pointed out that many minima in the excited state will not represent efficient crossover points since they will not correspond to a maximum on the ground state surface and therefore present an inefficient mode of decay.

It is of some interest that in many reactions it is the shape of the ground state surface that makes a photochemical reaction possible. An example is the photochemical closure of butadiene to cyclobutene (*61*) (Fig. 15). Calculations reveal that there is no great bias toward closure in the disrotatory sense on the excited state surface but that such a motion on the ground state surface must pass through a high thermal barrier. Such barriers in the ground state potential energy surfaces are due to avoided crossing between states of similar symmetries—in the case of butadiene–cyclobutene, the S_2 state. Thus, these ground state barriers occur because of the memory of an intended crossing, and these same high-energy barriers that bring the ground state energy surface near the excited state energy surface are what make the photochemical reaction efficient.

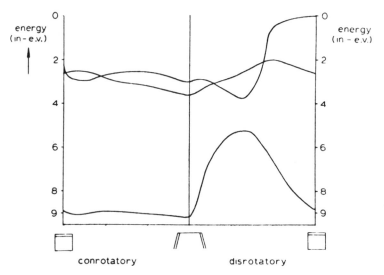

Fig. 15   The energies of the ground state and two excited states during the reaction.

D. *Mechanistic Interpretations of the Photochemistry of Conjugated Hexatrienes*

The Woodward–Hoffman rules (*12*), based on the conservation of orbital symmetry, accurately predict that butadiene should close, photochemically, in a disrotatory fashion. The above discussion reveals that such a reaction course is not due to consideration of the lowest unoccupied orbital (i.e., ψ_4) as stated in the rules but, indeed, is due to the higher-energy peak in the ground state surface, which arose from an avoided crossing brought about by similar state symmetries of the second electronic excited state and the ground state. More simply stated, it is to be expected that any reaction course that has a high energy barrier in the ground state due to orbital symmetry correlations will follow this stereochemical reaction pathway in the photochemical reaction since this high energy surface in the ground state will make the energy gap between excited and ground state surfaces smaller and thus increase the efficiency of the reaction course (*61*). With these concepts in mind, let us turn our attention to the photochemistry of conjugated 1,3,5-hexatrienes and attempt to relate the results of the previous sections with the above remarks.

Since the π^* level of hexatriene is more antibonding than the π level is bonding (*62*), the total π-electron energy for a $\pi\pi^*$ electronic configuration is net antibonding. This situation can be alleviated by a twisting of the

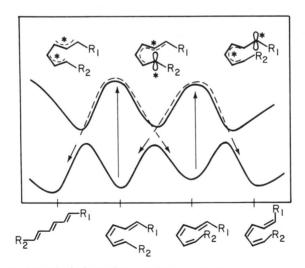

chromophore to relieve one of the antibonding combinations in ψ_4 of the triene, producing either an orthogonal pentadienyl–methylene or a bisallyl species (63), these species representing local minima on the excited state surface. If these wells are efficiently coupled with the ground state surface, the molecule may pass onto the lower surface, and simple bond isomerization occurs (Fig. 16). From this it can be seen that there is a directionality involved with the surface crossing; the product obtained

Fig. 16 Hypothetical reaction coordinate profile for triene isomerization.

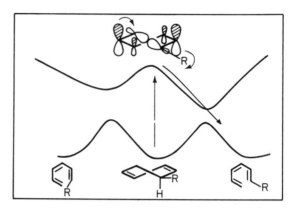

Fig. 17   Hypothetical reaction coordinate profile for 1,3 cyclohexadiene reaction

depends on the direction from which the well is approached. This scheme also helps to explain why only one bond is isomerized upon absorption of a photon by a conjugated triene (63). Due to the depth of the wells and the brief lifetime of the species, complete thermal equilibration of the several minima is not possible. Two-bond isomerizations do occur in the triplet manifold (63), presumably as a result of the increased lifetime of the excited species.

The principles of accordancy (27), least motion (64), and continuous overlap are invaluable aids in the understanding of many photochemical phenomena. It is instructive to consider the role of these factors in the photochemical ring opening of cyclohexadienes to conjugated hexatrienes (Fig. 17). As described previously, although two allowed conrotatory openings of the hexadiene are possible from a given conformer, the mode that is in accord with the helicity of the existing π system predominates (27,29). Thus, in the accordant conrotatory opening, the developing p orbitals begin to overlap with the existing π system very early in the reaction, whereas in the discordant conrotatory opening the developing p orbitals must pass through the nodal plane of the π framework. According to the principle of least motion, those elementary reactions will be favored that involve the least change in atomic position and electronic configuration (65). Thus, least-motion considerations also predict the accordant mode to be favored since less nuclear movement is necessary to attain conjugative overlap. In terms of hypersurfaces, the rapid reduction of the energy of the system by means of continual overlap creates a steeper surface and perhaps predisposes the excited molecule to move in the accordant direction. These factors are felt most greatly during the early stages of the reaction. This is clear from the case of compound **103**, in which the ring strain resulting from an accordant opening becomes quite severe during the initial stage of the reaction (35). Other openings that give highly strained products still proceed in accordance with the π system since this strain does not become an important factor until much later in the reaction.

In view of the multidimensionality of the excited state, it is evident that other photochemical processes are initiated by a twisting motion that brings two orbitals into a potentially bonding orientation. It is difficult to determine at which point along the hypersurfaces the new bonds are made in such transformations as vinylcyclobutene, cyclohexadiene, vinylallene, and bicyclo[3.1.0]hex-2-ene from the conjugated triene.

In the case of bicyclo[3.1.0]hex-2-ene formation, however, considerable attention has been given to the role of twisting in the reaction. For s-cis, s-trans-trienes it is clear that only twisting of the central double bond will lead to products, and the cyclopropane formation must begin in the s-trans portion of the bis triad. The alternative, cyclopropane formation from the s-cis portion, yields a species in which the final cyclopentene formation is prohibited since the remaining allyl portion is too remote to

permit facile bonding. In those systems in which an s-cis,s-trans conformation is not attainable but an s-cis,s-cis conformation is possible, the
initial cyclopropane can occur in either allyl portion. Furthermore, in
many cyclic systems twisting about the central double bond is prohibited

due to strain generated by this motion. For these cases, formation of a
pentadienyl–methylene species may result in closure of the five-
membered ring followed by cyclopropane formation.

    Recent calculations have indicated that the photochemically generated
bisallyl species is highly polarizable (66). In those cases in which the
termini of the triene were labeled, the initial cyclopropane formation appears to be the result of a conrotatory closure. These data are consistent
with the intermediacy of the zwitterionic species in which the s-trans
portion bears a partial negative charge and closes stereospecifically (32).

Due to the orthogonality of the two triads, the final closure to bicyclo-
[3.1.0]hex-2-ene is not under the constraints of orbital symmetry. This

may explain the large number of cases in which the stereochemistry of the bicyclo[3.1.0]hexenes is at odds with orbital symmetry predictions.

The intermediacy of zwitterionic species of opposite polarity has been used as a rationale for the production of the C and A toxisterols from previtamin D (68). Calculations reveal that for the terminal methyl s-cis, s-trans-diallyl skeleton the two zwitterionic forms are of similar energy, indicating that both oppositely polarized forms are possible if zwitterionic intermediates are involved (67).

REFERENCES

1. J. Meinwald and P. H. Mazzochi, *J. Am. Chem. Soc.* **88**, 2850 (1966).
2. R. Srinivasan, *J. Am. Chem. Soc.* **83**, 2807 (1961); *J. Chem. Phys.* **38**, 1039 (1963).
3. K. J. Crowley, *Proc. Chem. Soc., London* p. 17 (1964); G. J. Fonken, *Tetrahedron Lett.* p. 549 (1962); K. J. Crowley, *ibid.* p. 2863 (1965).
4. K. J. Crowley, *J. Am. Chem. Soc.* **86**, 5692 (1964); J. Meinwald, A. Eckell, and K. L. Erickson, *ibid.* **87**, 3532 (1965).
5. H. Prinzbach, H. Haglmann, J. H. Hartenstein, and R. Kitzing, *Chem. Ber.* **98**, 2201 (1965).
6. H. Prinzbach and E. Druckery, *Tetrahedron Lett.* p. 2959 (1965).
7. P. Courtot and R. Rumin, *Tetrahedron* **32**, 441 (1976).
8. P. J. Vroegop, J. Lugtenburg, and E. Havinga, *Tetrahedron* **29**, 1393 (1973).
9. W. G. Dauben, M. S. Kellogg, J. I. Seeman, N. D. Vietmeyer, and P. H. Wendschuh, "Steric Aspects of the Photochemistry of Conjugated Dienes and Trienes," IUPAC, Photochemistry IV. Butterworth, London, 1972.
10. W. G. Dauben, J. Rabinowitz, N. D. Vietmeyer, and P. H. Wendschuh, *J. Am. Chem. Soc.* **94**, 4285 (1972).
11. H. E. Simmons, *Prog. Phys. Org. Chem.* **7**, 1 (1970); N. L. Allinger and M. A. Miller, *J. Am. Chem. Soc.* **86**, 2811 (1964); N. L. Allinger and J. C. Tai, *ibid.* **87**, 2081 (1965).
12. R. B. Woodward and R. Hoffmann, *Angew. Chem., Int. Ed. Engl.* **8**, 814 (1969).
13. A. Padwa and S. Clough, *J. Am. Chem. Soc.* **92**, 5803 (1970); A. Padwa, L. Brodsky, and S. Clough, *ibid.* **94**, 6767 (1972); *J. Chem. Soc., Chem. Commun.* p. 417 (1971).
14. P. Courtot, J.-Y. Salun, and R. Rumin, *Tetrahedron Lett.* p. 2061 (1976); P. Courtot, R. Rumin, and J.-Y. Salun, *Pure Appl. Chem.* **49**, 317 (1977).
15. O. L. Chapman, G. W. Borden, R. W. King, and B. Winkler, *J. Am. Chem. Soc.* **86**, 2660 (1964); W. R. Roth and B. Peltzer, *Angew. Chem.* **76**, 378 (1964).
16. H. E. Zimmerman and H. Iwamura, *J. Am. Chem. Soc.* **92**, 2015 (1970).
17. J. A. Elix, M. V. Sargent, and F. Sondheimer, *J. Am. Chem. Soc.* **92**, 969 (1970).
18. W. G. Dauben and R. L. Cargill, *Tetrahedron* **12**, 186 (1961).
19. M. Pomerantz, *J. Am. Chem. Soc.* **89**, 694 (1967); J. Meinwald and P. H. Mazzocchi, *ibid.* p. 696.
20. M. Pomerantz and G. W. Gruber, *J. Am. Chem. Soc.* **93**, 6615 (1971).
21. J. Meinwald and D. A. Seeley, *Tetrahedron Lett.* p. 3739 (1970).
22. J. Meinwald and D. A. Seeley, *Tetrahedron Lett.* p. 3743 (1970); L. Ulrich, H.-J. Hansen, and H. Schmid, *Helv. Chim. Acta* **53**, 1323 (1970).
23. R. C. Cookson, S. M. de B. Costa, and J. Hudec, *J. Chem. Soc., Chem. Commun.* p. 1272 (1969).

24. D. A. Seeley, *J. Am. Chem. Soc.* **94**, 4378 (1972).
25. K. Salisbury, *Tetrahedron Lett.* p. 737 (1971).
26. R. B. Woodward and R. Hoffmann, "The Conservation of Orbital Symmetry." Academic Press, New York, 1970.
27. J. E. Baldwin and S. M. Krueger, *J. Am. Chem. Soc.* **91**, 6444 (1969).
28. A. W. Burgstahler, J. Gawronski, T. F. Niemann, and B. A. Feinberger, *J. Chem. Soc., Chem. Commun.* p. 16 (1972); A. Moscowitz, E. Charney, U. Weiss, and H. Ziffer, *J. Am. Chem. Soc.* **83**, 4661 (1961).
29. C. W. Spangler and R. P. Hennis, *J. Chem. Soc., Chem. Commun.* p. 24 (1972).
30. W. G. Dauben and M. S. Kellogg, *J. Am. Chem. Soc.* **93**, 3805 (1971).
31. M. S. Kellogg, Ph.D. Thesis, University of California, Berkeley (1972).
32. W. G. Dauben and M. S. Kellogg, *J. Am. Chem. Soc.* **94**, 8951 (1972).
33. W. G. Dauben, R. G. Williams, and R. D. McKelvey, *J. Am. Chem. Soc.* **95**, 3932 (1973).
34. W. G. Dauben and J. Francis, unpublished results.
35. E. G. Olsen, Ph.D. Thesis, University of California, Berkeley (1975).
36. M. Miyashita, H. Uda, and A. Yoshikoshi, *J. Chem. Soc., Chem. Commun.* p. 1396 (1969).
37. E. J. Corey and A. G. Hortman, *J. Am. Chem. Soc.* **85**, 4033 (1963); **87**, 5736 (1965).
38. D. M. Michno, Ph.D. Thesis, University of California, Berkeley (1977).
39. E. Havinga, A. Verloop, and A. L. Koevoet, *Recl. Trav. Chim. Pays-Bas* **75**, 371 (1956); E. Havinga, A. L. Koevoet, and A. Verloop, *ibid.* **74**, 1230 (1955); E. Havinga and J. L. M. A. Schlatmann, *Tetrahedron* **16**, 146 (1961); E. Havinga, R. J. DeKock, and M. R. Rappoldt, *ibid.* **11**, 276 (1956); G. M. Sanders, J. Pot, and E. Havinga, *Fortschr. Chem. Org. Naturst.* **27**, 131 (1969).
40. L. Velluz and G. Amiard, *C.R. Hebd. Seances Acad. Sci.* **253**, 603 (1961); L. Velluz, G. Amiard, and B. Goffiner, *Bull. Soc. Chim. Fr.* p. 1341 (1955); L. Velluz, G. Amiard, and A. Petit, *ibid.* p. 501 (1949).
41. J. L. M. A. Schlatmann, J. Pot, and E. Havinga, *Recl. Trav. Chim. Pays-Bas* **83**, 1173 (1964).
42. V. P. Delaroff, P. Rathle, and M. Legrand, *Bull. Soc. Chim. Fr.* p. 1739 (1963); for the anomolous case of 6-methyl vitamin D see M. Sheves and Y. Mazur, *J. Chem. Soc., Chem. Commun.* p. 21 (1977).
43. W. G. Dauben and P. Baumann, *Tetrahedron Lett.* p. 565 (1961).
44. S. A. Bakker, J. Lugtenberg, and E. Havinga, *Recl. Trav. Chim. Pays-Bas,* **91**, 1459 (1972).
45. F. Boomsa, H. J. C. Jacobs, E. Havinga, and A. van Der Gen, *Recl. Trav. Chim. Pays-Bas* **96**, 104 and 113 (1977).
46. J. Casteus, E. R. H. Jones, G. D. Meakins, and R. W. J. Williams, *J. Chem. Soc.* p. 1159 (1959); P. Busse, *Hoppe-Seyler's Z. Physiol. Chem.* **214**, 211 (1933).
47. W. G. Dauben and G. H. Fonken, *J. Am. Chem. Soc.* **81**, 4060 (1959); for x-ray structure determination, see G. L. Hardgrove, R. W. Duerst, and L. D. Kispert, *J. Org. Chem.* **33**, 4393 (1968).
48. E. Havinga, *Experientia* **29**, 1181 (1973).
49. A. G. M. Barrett, D. H. R. Barton, R. A. Russell, and D. A. Widdowson, *J. Chem. Soc., Perkin Trans. 1* p. 631 (1977).
50. A. W. Norman and H. Henry, *Recent Prog. Horm. Res.* **30**, 431 (1974); J. L. Omdahl, H. F. Deluca, and H. K. Schnoes, *Annu. Rev. Biochem.* **45**, 929 (1976); P. E. Georghiou, *Chem. Soc. Rev.* **6**, 83 (1977).
51. M. Sheves, E. Berman, D. Freeman, and Y. Mazur, *J. Chem. Soc., Chem. Commun.* p.

643 (1975); B. L. Onisko, H. K. Schnoes, and H. F. Deluca, *Tetrahedron Lett.* p. 4317 (1975); W. H. Okamura, M. L. Hammond, P. Condron, Jr., and A. Mourino, *Vitam. D: Biochem., Chem. Clin. Aspects Relat. Calcium Metab., Proc. Workshop Vitam. D, 3rd, 1977* p. 33 (1977).

52. G. N. LaMar and D. L. Budd, *J. Am. Chem. Soc.* **96,** 7317 (1974); R. M. Wing, W. H. Okamura, M. R. Pirio, S. M. Sine, and A. W. Norman, *Science* **186,** 939 (1974); R. M. Wing, W. H. Okamura, A. Rego, M. R. Pirio, and A. W. Norman, *J. Am. Chem. Soc.* **97,** 4980 (1975).

53. H. E. Zimmerman, *Acc. Chem. Res.* **4,** 57 (1971); M. J. S. Dewar, *Angew. Chem., Int. Ed. Engl.* **10,** 761 (1971); K. Fukui, *Acc. Chem. Res.* **4,** 57 (1971); H. Katz, *J. Chem. Educ.* **48,** 84 (1971).

54. H. C. Lonquet-Higgins and E. W. Abrahamson, *J. Am. Chem. Soc.* **87,** 2045 (1965).

55. L. Salem, *J. Am. Chem. Soc.* **96,** 3486 (1974).

56. W. G. Dauben, L. Salem, and N. J. Turro, *Acc. Chem. Res.* **8,** 41 (1975).

57. A. Devaquet, *Pure Appl. Chem.* **41,** 455 (1975); D. Grumbert, G. Segal, and A. Devaquet, *J. Am. Chem. Soc.* **97,** 6629 (1975); L. Salem, C. Leforestier, G. Segal, and R. Wetmore, *ibid.* p. 479.

58. L. Landau, *Phys. Z. Sowetunion* **2,** 46 (1932).

58a. C. Zener, *Proc. R. Soc., London, Ser. A* **137,** 696 (1932).

59. N. J. Turro, "Molecular Photochemistry." Benjamin, New York, 1967.

60. J. Michl, *Mol. Photochem.* **4,** 243, 257, and 287 (1972); *Top. Curr. Chem.* **46,** 1 (1975).

61. W. T. A. M. Van der Lugt and L. J. Oosterhoff, *J. Am. Chem. Soc.* **91,** 6042 (1969).

62. N. C. Baird, *J. Chem. Soc., Chem. Commun.* p. 199 (1970).

63. R. S. H. Liu and Y. Butt, *J. Am. Chem. Soc.* **93,** 1532 (1971).

64. J. Hine, *J. Am. Chem. Soc.* 5525 (1966); O. S. Tee and K. Yates, *ibid.* **94,** 3074 (1972).

65. J. Hine, *J. Org. Chem.* **31,** 1326 (1966).

66. V. Bonacic-Koutecky, P. Bruckmann, P. Hiberty, J. Koutecky, C. Leforestier, and L. Salem, *Angew. Chem., Int. Ed. Engl.* **14,** 575 (1975).

67. V. Bonacic-Koutecky, *J. Am. Chem. Soc.* **100,** 396 (1978).

68. C. M. Meerman-van Benthem, H. J. C. Jacobs, and J. J. C. Mulder, *Nouveau J. Chim,* **2,** 123 (1978).

THE DI-π-METHANE (ZIMMERMAN) REARRANGEMENT*

HOWARD E. ZIMMERMAN

I. GENERAL FORMULATION OF THE REACTION: AN INTRODUCTION

The search for really general photochemical reactions is an important feature of the progress in organic photochemistry. With a very large number of examples of a given reaction, one can determine the intimate details of the process and add to our understanding of the theoretical basis of photochemistry.

The di-π-methane rearrangement is one such reaction. The reaction generality and mechanism were first recognized (1) when it was noted that the reaction is common to molecules in which two π moieties are substituted on an sp^3-hybridized (i.e., methane) carbon. The rearrangement leads to a π-substituted cyclopropane. Formally, it involves migration of one π moiety originally bonded to the methane carbon (i.e., C-3) to

---

* The designation of the transformations described in this essay as the "Zimmerman rearrangement" was first made by Professor L. Salem. It has the support of the present Editor. Few reactions of such importance and generality have been dragged out of obscurity, studied in meticulous detail, and transformed in chemical sense, all essentially by one man and his collaborators. The work stands as a model for the systematic approach; more is needed. The interpolation in the title is the editor's.

131

REARRANGEMENTS IN GROUND AND EXCITED STATES, VOL. 3

C-4 of the other π moiety with concomitant bonding between C-3 and C-5 and three-membered ring formation, as shown in Eq. (1).

$$(1)$$

In this essay we review selected examples of the di-π-methane rearrangement with a view toward considering the various mechanistic features controlling the rearrangement. We consider the reaction multiplicity, the reaction regioselectivity and stereochemistry, the role of the second π bond, the effect of substituents and structure on excited state reactivity, and the reaction mechanism and generality.

II. THE GROSS REACTION MECHANISM

It was noted (1b,1c) that one basic mechanism describes the skeletal change in the di-π-methane rearrangement. Equation (2a) depicts this mechanism in simple resonance terms for the simplest case, in which two vinyl groups are present. In Eq. (2b) the sequence is repeated, but with one π moiety being a phenyl group.

It is necessary to note that the structures drawn are approximations of species along the reaction coordinate and are not necessarily intermediates (i.e., energy minima). These may simply be points on the energy hypersurface leading from excited state of reactant to product ground state, and each case must be considered separately. The utility of these resonance structures lies in their ability to describe and predict a rather large number of examples of the di-π-methane rearrangement, just as they

$$(2a)$$

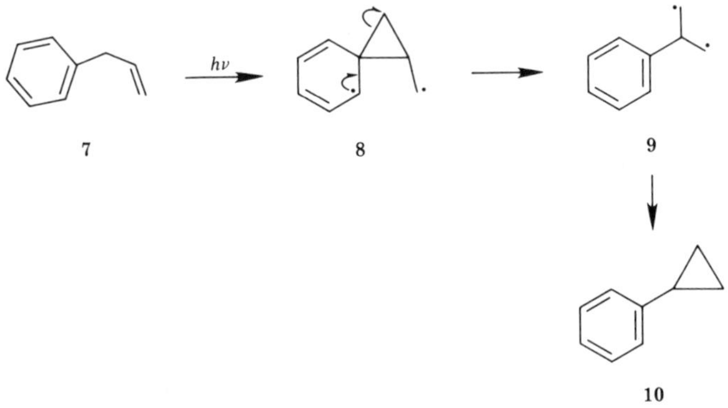

(2b)

have proved useful in describing photochemical mechanisms in general (2).

In 1966–1967 there were scattered in the literature a number of examples of rearrangements fitting the description of Eqs. (2a) and (2b). However, the rearrangement of barrelene (11) to semibullvalene (12) (1a), and consideration of its mechanism, prompted the realization that the mechanism in Eqs. (2a) and (2b) accounted not only for this specific transformation, but also for a larger number of transformations described in literature.

In the barrelene (11) to semibullvalene (12) example the mechanism can be written as in Eq. (3). Evidence for this mechanism was derived from the study of the hexadeuteriobarrelene, in which the bridgehead hydrogen atoms were used as labels. The hydrogen distribution in the product was that shown, in accord with the mechanism of Eq. (3).

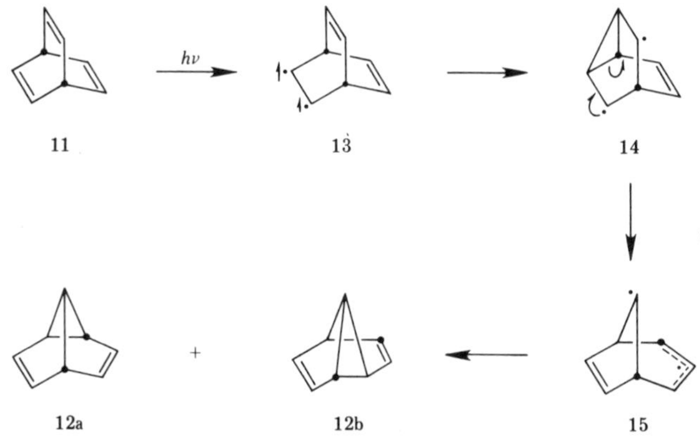

(3)
(Refs. 1a, b)

(● represents H label, deuterium elsewhere)

Actually, one might be tempted to consider the rearrangements of 4,4-disubstituted 2,5-cyclohexadienones (3) [e.g., **16**, Eq. (4)] and of 4-aryl-substituted cyclohexenones (4a,4b) [e.g., **18**, Eq. (5)] to be examples of the di-π-methane process. However, the evidence (5) is that these proceed via n–π* excited states, albeit by somewhat parallel mechanisms. Hence, these processes are not normally construed as being di-π-methane rearrangements and are not discussed here.

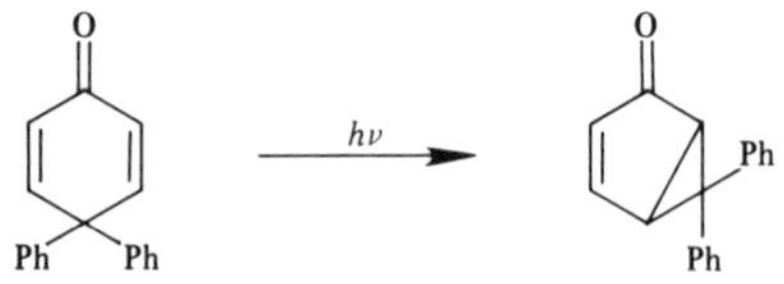

(4)
(Refs. 2a, 2b)

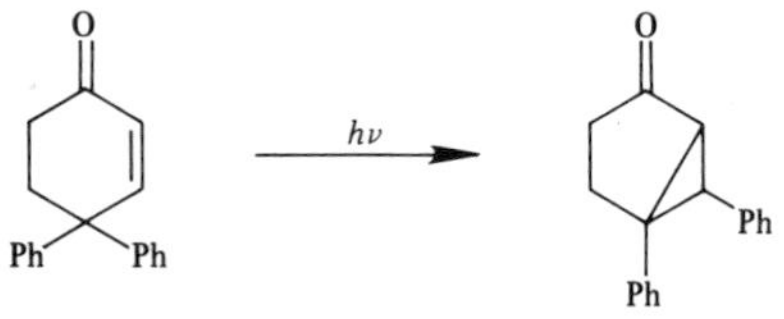

16   17

(5)
(Ref. 4)

18   19

Another noteworthy example of the di-π-methane rearrangement is the rearrangement of 1,1,5,5-tetraphenyl-3,3-dimethyl-1,4-pentadiene (**20**) (*1c*). This diene rearranged on direct irradiation with a quantum yield of 0.082 to give vinylcyclopropane (**21**). In contrast, sensitized irradiation using benzophenone or acetophenone gave no product at all, although it was demonstrated that triplet energy transfer to the diene was occurring. As before, the mechanism in Eqs. (2a) and (2b) leads reactant to product.

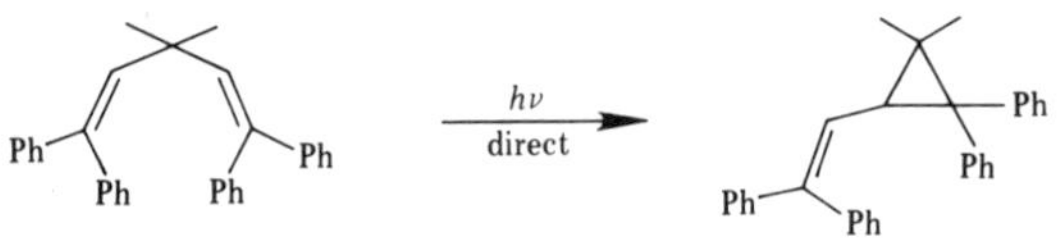

(6)
(Ref. 1c)

20   21

III. REACTION MULTIPLICITY

The di-π-methane rearrangement of barrelene to semibullvalene, which occurred only on sensitization, together with the finding that tetraphenyl-diene (**20**) rearranged only from its singlet, led to the generalization that acyclic di-π-methane reactants rearrange effectively from their singlet excited states, whereas bicyclic di-π-methane systems prefer to rearrange via their triplet excited states (*1c*). This generalization has turned out to be reasonably accurate despite some exceptions. The basis for the effect is considered below.

One example, in particular, provided especially clear evidence concerning the fate of the excitation energy in the case of acyclic triplets. Thus, the rearrangement of *cis*- and *trans*-1,1-diphenyl-3,3-dimethyl-1,4-hexadiene (**22**) was investigated (*6*). The stereochemical aspects observed in the direct irradiation are dealt with later. For the present it suffices to note that the reaction of the singlet was a normal di-π-methane rearrangement. However, sensitized irradiation, in which the reactant excited state was the triplet, led to no di-π-methane rearrangement, but rather to cis–trans isomerization of reactant [Eq. (7)]. Thus, triplet excitation

$$\text{(7)}$$
$$\text{(Ref. 6)}$$

22   23 But no di-π-methane
                                    rearrangement

energy was found to be diverted into a rotation about one of the acyclic π bonds.

This confirmed the earlier generalization and led to the suggestion that triplet energy dissipation derived from the presence of a "free rotor," here the —CH=CH—Me group, which, by rotation, can lead the excited triplet to the ground state.

Indeed, there is independent evidence that the rate of radiationless decay of both singlets and triplets is increased as the possibilities for such free rotation are increased (*7*). These studies on excited state energy dissipation revealed (*7*) that both singlet and triplet excited states decay more rapidly as molecular flexibility allows enhanced π-bond twisting. In fact, singlets with free rotors tend to decay several orders of magnitude more rapidly than the corresponding triplets.

Hence, the free-rotor effect must be operative but ineffective in the case of singlets, probably because of the still more rapid rates of unimolecular rearrangements observed for excited singlets relative to their rates of free-rotor decay. In the case of triplets, free-rotor decay is most often more rapid than rearrangement.

In the above it has still not been considered why bicyclic singlet excited states tend not to undergo the di-π-methane rearrangement. It seems that for many bicyclic singlets there are alternative electrocyclic rearrangements (e.g., fragmentation, $2\pi + 2\pi$) which are exceedingly rapid and overshadow the di-π-methane rearrangement.

The generalization that bicyclic di-π-methane systems without a free rotor invariably rearrange only by way of their triplet excited states and that acyclic di-π-methane systems rearrange only by way of their singlets does have exceptions. This should not be surprising, since in order for an exception to the generalization to exist the rate of triplet energy dissipation by a free-rotor mechanism must simply be slower than the rate of rearrangement, or the rate of singlet free-rotor energy dissipation must be faster than the di-π-methane rearrangement. In the case of bicyclic singlets, there would be an exception if there were no facile alternative electrocyclic rearrangement to overshadow the di-π-methane process. Occasionally, not recognizing the basis of the multiplicity correlation, workers have naively considered some exceptions as invalidating the free-rotor effect. They do not.

Some examples of the multiplicity generalization are given in Eqs. (8)–

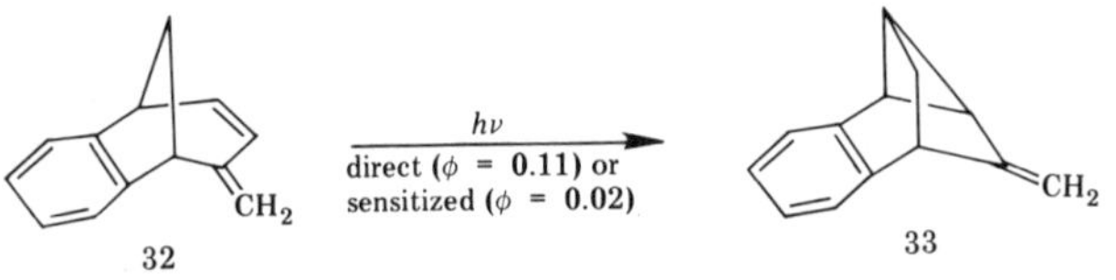

hν
direct (ϕ = 0.11) or
sensitized (ϕ = 0.02)
CH2
CH2
32
33

(11)
(Ref. 11)

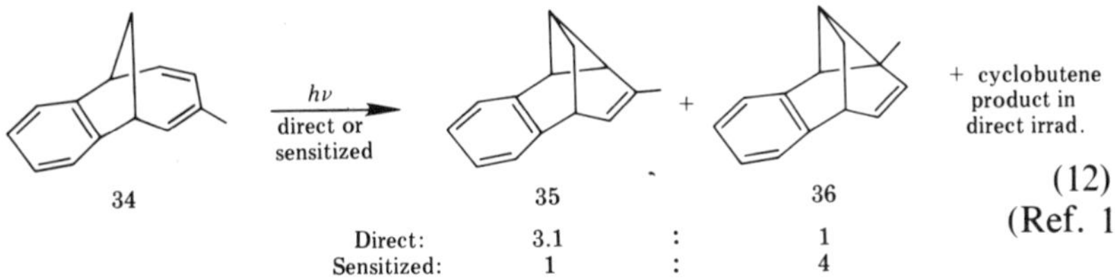

hν
direct or
sensitized
+
34
35
36
Direct: 3.1 : 1
Sensitized: 1 : 4
+ cyclobutene
product in
direct irrad.

(12)
(Ref. 12)

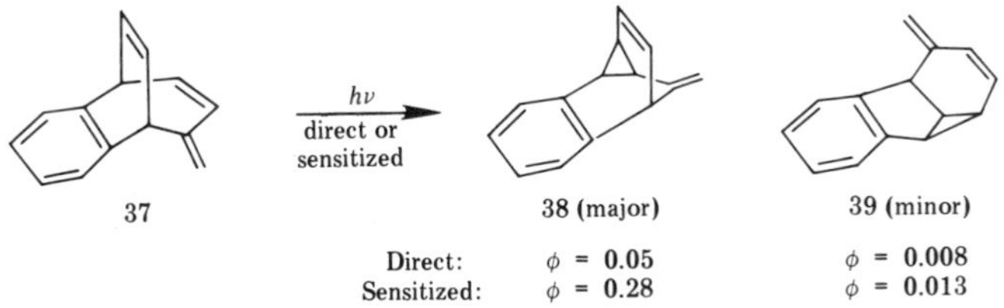

hν
direct or
sensitized
37
38 (major)
39 (minor)
Direct: ϕ = 0.05 ϕ = 0.008
Sensitized: ϕ = 0.28 ϕ = 0.013

(13)
(Ref. 13)

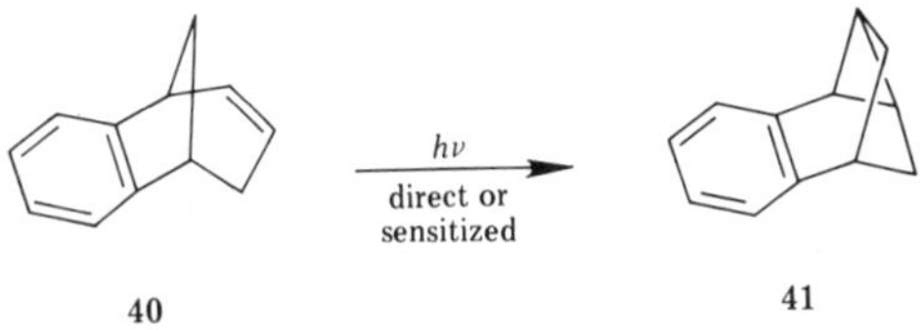

hν
direct or
sensitized
40
41

(14)
(Ref. 14)

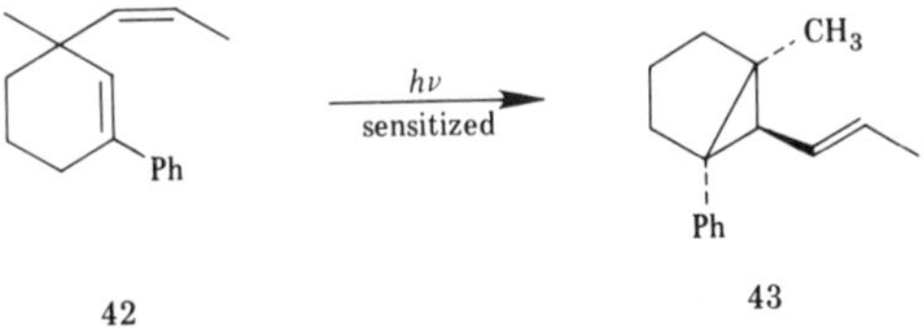

hν
sensitized
Ph
CH3
Ph
42
43

(15)
(Ref. 15)

(10), and some examples that do not fit the generalization are given in Eqs. (11)–(15).

In the case of the *exo*-methylene reactant **24,** direct irradiation leads to a di-π-methane rearrangement resulting from initial vinyl–phenyl bridging of the kind shown in Eq. (2b). The triplet is unreactive, and this lack of reactivity can be ascribed to free rotation of the *exo*-methylene moiety leading the triplet to its destruction via a rapid radiationless decay with which the triplet di-π-methane process does not successfully compete.

Benzobarrelene rearranges as shown in Eqs. (9a) and (9b), in which the bridgehead is labeled by hydrogen whereas all other sites bear deuterium.

Only the sensitized photolysis involving the triplet excited state gives di-π-methane rearrangement. Direct irradiation leads to benzocyclooctatetraene (27) by a $2\pi + 2\pi$ cycloaddition (between one vinyl moiety and the benzo ring) followed by a retro $2\pi + 2\pi$ fission. Thus, the generalization, again, is followed in that the triplet gives di-π-methane rearrangement, as would be expected in the absence of a free rotor. Also, the singlet does not give the di-π-methane rearrangement; such is often the case in bicyclic systems in which a more facile electrocyclic process is available to the singlet.

The endocyclic diene 29 is of interest because of its structural similarity to the exocyclic diene 24. However, in 29 the exo-methylene group is absent. In this case the triplet undergoes a di-π-methane rearrangement; there is no free rotor present, and therefore a facile radiationless decay mode is absent. Thus, the contrast with the triplet behavior of exocyclic methylene derivative 24 is not surprising. Similarly, in the case of the endocyclic diene 29, the singlet undergoes a facile electrocyclic opening, which turns out to be more rapid than the di-π-methane rearrangement.

Looking now at Eqs. (11)–(15), we find some representative examples of exceptions. The benzodiene 32 does rearrange on sensitization despite the presence of an exo-methylene group; this merely means that the rate of rearrangement is rapid enough to compete with free-rotor decay. The same is true of benzotriene 37 and phenyldiene 42. Thus, whenever the rates of triplet rearrangement are exceptionally rapid or the free-rotor decay is slow, the possibility exists that the free-rotor generalization will not hold. Still, the free-rotor effect remains a mode of energy dissipation even when hidden by faster processes.

This point is illustrated dramatically in the case of dienes 44 and 46, in which the exo-methylene group of diene 24 is now incorporated in five- and six-membered rings (16). It is seen that the more flexible six-membered ring of diene 46 still permits free-rotor energy dissipation, although the ring constraint is enough to allow observation of some di-π-methane rearrangement (i.e., $\phi = 0.003$); in the case of the unconstrained diene 24 no triplet reaction was observed at all. Turning to the

$$\xrightarrow[\text{sensitized}]{\substack{h\nu \\ \text{direct or}}}$$

(16)
(Ref. 16)

44   45 (major stereoisomer)

Direct: $\phi = 0.11$
Sensitized: $\phi = 0.36$

(17)
(Ref. 16)

46

47 (major stereoisomer)

Direct: $\phi = 0.12$
Sensitized: $\phi = 0.003$

more constrained diene **44,** where the potential free rotor is now part of a five-membered ring, the triplet quantum yield has risen to $\phi = 0.36$. We note that the direct irradiations give rearrangements with comparable reaction efficiencies, independently of ring size or even the presence of the ring; hence, free-rotor energy dissipation is operating only in the triplet reactions.

Finally, in Eq. (12) we have an example of a bicyclic di-π-methane system that rearranges by way of the singlet excited state as well as by the triplet. For the singlet, electrocyclic cyclobutene formation competes with di-π-methane rearrangement. In Eq. (14) no electrocyclic process competes, and di-π-methane rearrangement occurs exclusively. Thus, the part of the generalization dealing with the propensity of bicyclic di-π-methane systems to rearrange by their triplets and not their singlets does not arise from a fundamental inability of the singlet to undergo a di-π-methane rearrangement but rather from the frequent incursion of a more facile singlet process.

IV. REACTION REGIOSELECTIVITY

An especially interesting situation arises when there are two vinyl groups with different substitution, since in this case regioselectivity becomes important. It was noted (6) that there was a marked preference for migration of one of the two π moieties bonded to the methane carbon. Thus, direct irradiation of the isobutenyldiphenylvinylmethane **48** leads to only one of the two *a priori* possible products; that is, it gives vinylcyclopropane (**51**) and none of **53**. The preference for mechanism A can be understood as arising from utilization of the electron density at the diradical center that has the least delocalization; here this is the isopropyl rather than the benzhydryl center. Thus, for path B to be followed a benzhydryl-stabilized diradical center would be required to lose this delocalization in forming diradical **52**. In the formation of diradical **50,** as in mechanism A, benzhydryl delocalization is retained.

For hydrocarbon systems such reasoning seems to rationalize a rather

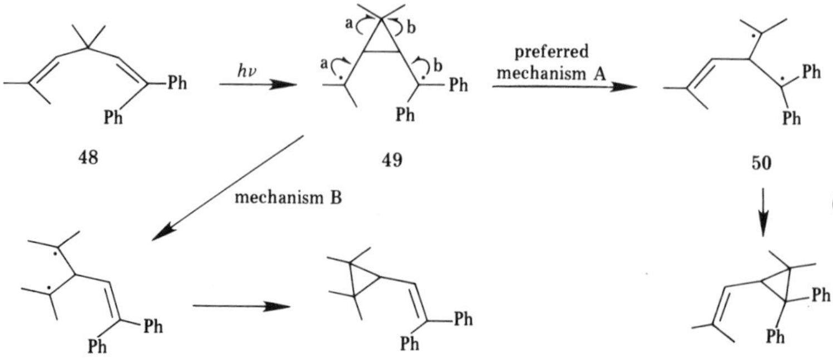

48 49 50 52 53 51

(18) (Ref. 6)

large number of cases of regioselectivity in the di-π-methane rearrangement. Two additional examples are given in Eqs. (19)–(20). One can sum-

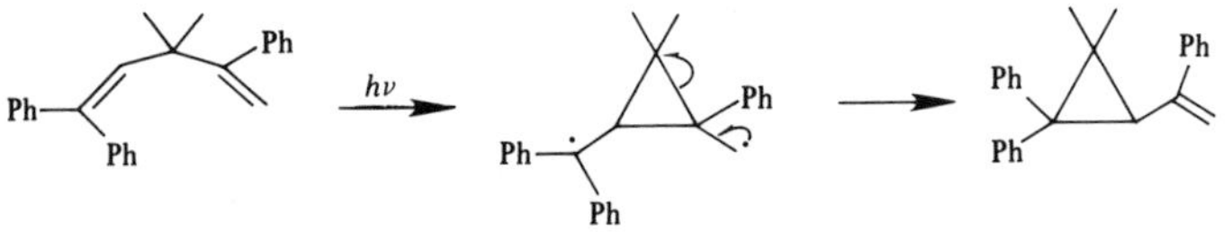

54 55 56

(19) (Ref. 17)

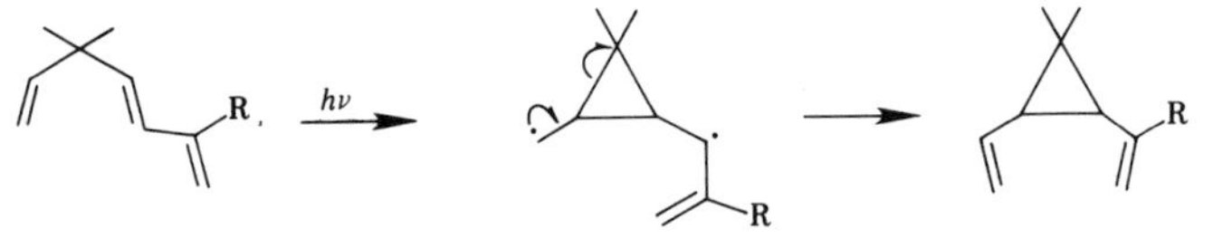

57a R = H
57b R = CH_3
58a
58b
59a (Ref. 18)
59b (Ref. 19)

(20)

marize the overall process as a preferential migration of the less terminally substituted vinyl group to the more substituted one.

In the case of phenylvinylmethane systems, regioselectivity operates in such a way as to regenerate the aromatic system in the three-membered ring opening process. An example is given in Eq. (21) [see also Eqs. (8)–(14)].

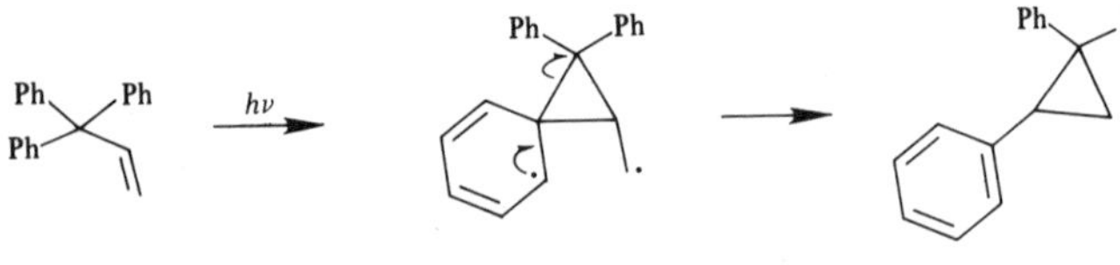

60 61 62

(21) (Ref. 20)

When heteroatom-bearing substituents are involved, regioselectivity is more complicated. Equations (22)–(26) detail some representative examples of interest. In the case of Eq. (22) the related dicyano relative having

the $=C(CN)_2$ moiety has been shown (22) to behave similarly. Inspection of these cases reveals that electron-donating groups tend to appear on the vinyl group of vinylcyclopropane product whereas electron-withdrawing groups tend to appear on the three-membered ring of vinylcyclopropane product. This suggests that the carbinyl carbons in the cyclopropyl-dicarbinyl diradicals (e.g., **64, 67, 70, 73, 76**) are electron rich, and as the diradical opens its three-membered ring this negative charge is dissipated

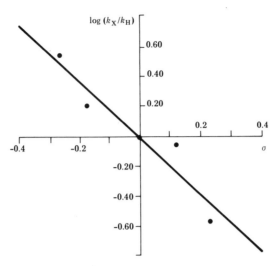

Fig. 1 Plot of log (k_X/k_H) versus Hammett σ. Correlation coefficient, 0.96 (25); k_X corresponds to formation of $(p\text{-}X\text{—Ar})_2C=$ isomer.

TABLE 1

Regioselectivity and the Hammett σ Constant (25)

Reactant	$k_X/k_H{}^a$	$\log(k_X/k_H)$	$\sigma_X{}^b$
Di-p-methoxydiene (**63**)^c	3.41	0.532	−0.27
Di-p-methyldiene^d	1.52	0.182	−0.18
Tetraphenyldiene (**20**)^e	1.00	0.000	0.00
Di-m-methoxydiene^f	0.84	−0.076	0.12
Di-p-chlorodiene^g	0.25	−0.595	0.23

^{a} Ratio obtained from ratio of photoproduct quantum yields.

^{b} S. L. Murov, "Handbook of Photochemistry." Dekker, New York, 1973.

^{c} Zimmerman and Gruenbaum (24).

^{d} 1,1-Bis(p-methylphenyl)-3,3-dimethyl-5,5-diphenyl-1,4-pentadiene dimethyl-5,5-diphenyl-1,4-pentadiene (26).

^{e} Zimmerman and Mariano (1c).

^{f} 1,1-Bis(m-methoxyphenyl)-3,3-dimethyl-5,5-diphenyl-1,4-pentadiene.

^{g} 1,1-Bis(p-chlorophenyl)-3,3-dimethyl-5,5-diphenyl-1,4-pentadiene.

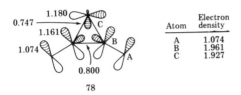

Atom	Electron density
A	1.074
B	1.961
C	1.927

78

Fig. 2 Electron densities for orbitals and atoms of the unsubstituted cyclopropyl-dicarbinyl diradical in the S_1 state. Note that a density of 2.0 at a two-orbital site (B and C) or a density of 1.0 at a one-orbital site (A) corresponds to neutrality. Also note that the electron density at each atom is the sum of contributions from orbitals centered at each atom.

on the carbon developing π-bond character. Thus, with an electron-donating group present there is driving force for the carbinyl carbon bearing this donor to be that involved in ring opening and in becoming the π-bonded carbon. Conversely, for electron-withdrawing substituents there is an energetic advantage in this carbon retaining its electron-rich character and not being the one generating the π bond. This point is considered more quantitatively below.

One way of seeing this substituent effect is to plot the log of the ratio of two regioisomeric products derived from a series of unsymmetrically substituted 1,1,5,5-tetraaryl-3,3-dimethyl-1,4-pentadienes against the Hammett σ constant for the substituents in the para or meta positions. This is shown in Fig. 1, with the corresponding data in Table 1. Note that the plot has a negative slope (i.e., a negative ρ), which confirms that the carbinyl carbon is becoming more positive, or less negative, as the π bond is engendered at the site of substitution.

Not included in the Hammett plot are the p-cyano- and p-dimethylamino-bearing compounds **69** and **75**. The regioselectivity observed experimentally in these cases was too great to obtain a product ratio. Use of the plot in Fig. 1, together with $+0.66$ and -0.83 σ values leads us to predictions of 17:1 regioselectivity favoring formation of the observed p-cyano photoproduct **71** and a 40:1 regioselectivity favoring the dimethylamino photoproduct **77**.

The regioselectivity observed is also supported by SCF–CI calculations (*21b,25*). Thus, calculations including the Walsh orbitals of the three-membered ring of the cyclopropyldicarbinyl diradical reveal that the carbinyl carbons are electron rich in the S_1 state (see Fig. 2). The calculations also lead to the conclusion that weakening of the three-membered ring bond adjacent to the electron donor requires less energy than weakening adjacent to an electron acceptor.

V. ROLE OF THE SECOND π BOND

A question that is often asked is whether the reaction is truly a di-π-methane rearrangement or, instead, $\sigma + \pi$ process. One can formally arrive at the product, on paper, by writing a mechanism utilizing only the electrons in one σ bond and those in the other π bond, as in Eq. (27).

$$(27)$$

Such a mechanism makes no use of the second π bond, and this is not in accord with the evidence. Thus, it has been shown (27) that irradiation of the dihydro relative (i.e., **81**) of the classic 1,1,5,5-tetraphenyl-3,3-dimethyl-1,4-pentadiene (**20**) does not give a di-π-methane type of reaction. First of all, the molecule is exceptionally unreactive as compared with its divinylmethane relative **20**. Beyond this, we note in Eq. (28) that the observed photochemistry is not that of a di-π-methane type of rearrangement. On the basis of limits of detection, the reaction efficiency of the formation of any cyclopropane product arising from a $\sigma + \pi$ process can be estimated to be less than 0.00008.

$$(28)$$
(Ref. 27)

This is not to say that $\sigma + \pi$ reactions are not possible when competing reactions are not available. t-Butylstyrene does rearrange to give tri-methylphenylcyclopropane (28,29) [Eq. (29)], and the reaction is quite general (29). However, as Hixson has shown (30), the reaction is a relatively inefficient one. Similar $\sigma + \pi$ rearrangements utilizing the C—H σ bond are known (20,30–33) again, these are inefficient.

The discussion above reveals that only with two π moieties does the rearrangement proceed efficiently, and it is clear that there is a necessity

$$PhCH=CH-\overset{\overset{\displaystyle CH_3}{|}}{\underset{\underset{\displaystyle CH_3}{|}}{C}}-CH_3 \quad \xrightarrow{h\nu} \quad \text{(structure)} \qquad (29)$$

85   86 (ϕ = 0.0010)   (Refs. 28, 29)

for the second π bond whose role then is to allow formation of a cyclopropyldicarbinyl radical.

VI. REACTION STEREOCHEMISTRY

Reaction stereochemistry exists at carbons 1, 3, and 5 in the di-π-methane rearrangement of a 1,4-diene. In our present discussion we shall consider the behavior at each of these three centers separately and in order.

Concerning C-1 stereochemistry, in the rearrangement of methyl-labeled diene 22 [see also Eq. (7)] it was (6) determined that the reaction is stereospecific. Thus, on direct irradiation the cis isomer of reactant 22a affords the cis isomer of product (i.e., 87a), whereas the trans isomer of di-π-methane reactant leads to trans product 87b [Eq. (30)]. At first

$$\text{(structure 22a)} \quad \xrightarrow[h\nu]{\text{direct}} \quad \text{(structure 87a)} \qquad \begin{array}{c}(30a)\\(\text{Ref. }6)\end{array}$$

22a   87a

$$\text{(structure 22b)} \quad \xrightarrow[\text{direct}]{h\nu} \quad \text{(structure 87b)} \qquad \begin{array}{c}(30b)\\(\text{Ref. }6)\end{array}$$

22b   87b

glance, this might appear to be an obvious, if not mandatory, stereochemical result. However, consideration of the mechanism in Eq. (31) indicates that the results bear on the nature of the cyclopropyldicarbinyl diradical species involved. Thus, these species (i.e., 88a and 88b) must not interconvert conformationally. This might be because of a low rate of rotation compared to the rate of further reaction, or, instead, it could arise because these biradicals are not true intermediates, but merely species on the excited state hypersurface. Such species, however, are not permitted, according to the experimental observations, to interconvert conformationally.

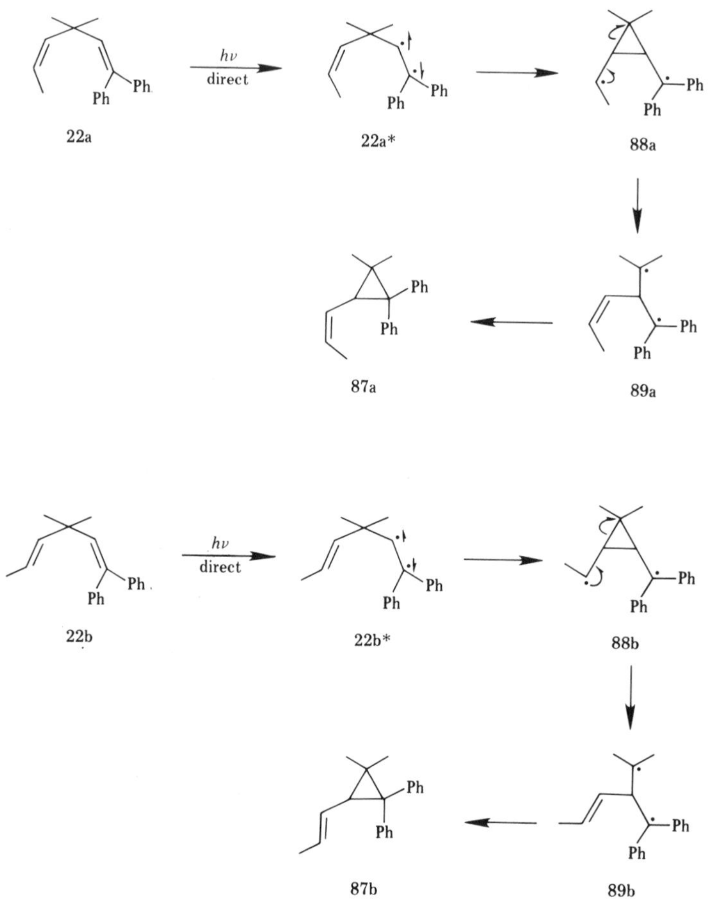

(31)

Another perspective is derived from consideration of the orbital array involved in the rearrangement. One needs a minimum of six basis orbitals to describe the reaction. This set is depicted in Eq. (32). Here, we have included only those orbitals that are involved in primary bonding changes in the reaction. We have excluded those orbitals that are merely changing hybridization or are uninvolved.

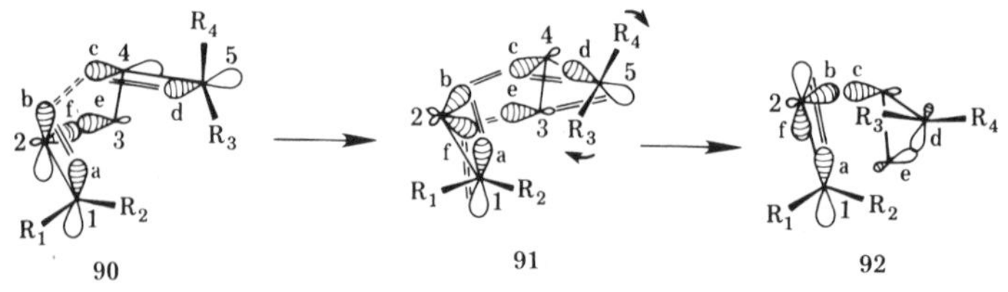

(32)

This truncated model (*1c*) accommodates the stereochemical course of the di-π-methane rearrangement at all three centers of interest. The six orbitals are labeled a–f, and, at part reaction, there is a cyclic array in which orbital a overlaps with b, which overlaps with c, etc., so that the sequence is a–b–c–d–e–f–a. However, the overlap between all pairs of adjacent orbitals cannot be plus–plus (or minus–minus) with this stereochemistry. With the arbitrary choice of sign orientations in species **91** there is plus–minus overlap between orbitals f and a. With a different choice of orientations, the number of plus–minus overlaps will remain odd, and this, by definition, is a Möbius system (*34*). The delocalized system has six electrons and thus would correspond to a forbidden species in the ground state. However, photochemically this is allowed (*34*).

With regard to the stereochemistry at C-1, an intriguing point is that the π bond of the product is not the π bond of the reactant, as might be thought from simply writing the divinylmethane reactant and the vinylcyclopropane product. Thus, the vinyl group of reactant results from overlap between orbitals a and b, whereas that of product derives from overlap between orbitals a and f. Hence, the C-1 stereochemistry is not as obvious as one might think.

The stereochemistry at the methane carbon (i.e., C-3 of the divinylmethane systems) also has been investigated. The reaction stereochemistry has been studied [Eqs. (33) and (34)] for two different systems with a central asymmetric carbon bearing methyl and ethyl groups (*35,36*).

$$\tag{33}$$
(Ref. 35)

$$\tag{34}$$
(Ref. 36)

These investigations involved the resolution of di-π-methane reactants and products and then correlation of the configurations of reactants with products. In each case two diastereomers were obtained (i.e., phenyl or vinyl cis and trans to ethyl), but the methane carbon was shown to be inverted in all cases (*35,36*). Reference to Eq. (32) shows that the postulated array does, indeed, invert the methane carbon (i.e., C-3) in the case of the divinylmethane variation of the reaction [Eq. (33)], and a similar array can be written for the arylvinyl situation.

Another example of inversion of configuration is found in the work of Mariano and Ko (15), as delineated in Eq. (35). Here, the "methane

$$\text{(35)}\quad\text{(Ref. 15)}$$

carbon" is labeled with an m. The inversion of configuration can be envisaged if one recognizes that the new, "banana-like" three-membered ring bond (3–5 or m–5) projects below the plane of the five-membered ring and arises from bonding on the side of the molecule opposite to the migrating vinyl group. In addition, this example provides another case in which the configuration at C-1 is retained. The rearrangements (8,10) in Eqs. (8) and (10b) parallel this example, except that a phenyl migrates instead of vinyl, and methane carbon inversion again results in the major stereoisomer.

The last center of stereochemical interest is carbon 5. Pertinent information was derived from a study of the di-π-methane rearrangement shown in Eq. (36) (37). Rearrangement of the cis and trans isomers of the

$$\text{(36a)}\quad\text{(Ref. 37)}$$

$$\text{(36b)}\quad\text{(Ref. 37)}$$

diene gave the cis-cyclopropane from cis reactant and trans-cyclopropane from trans reactant (37). This outcome is less predictable than the stereochemistry at, e.g., C-1. Least-motion arguments are not helpful in this case, since an equal twist at C-5 in the two possible directions leads to the two possible products. Reference to Eq. (32) shows that the clockwise twist that uses the "rear" or "anti" lobe of the p orbital at C-5 leads to the observed product. It is also utilization of this lobe that affords a Möbius system and thus allowed electronics.

An interesting point is that the three-membered ring closure involving orbitals e, c, and d in Eq. (32) is disrotatory. The acyclic examples have used the rear (anti) lobe of orbitals e and d (i.e., at atoms 3 and 5). However, a Möbius system also would result from a disrotatory twist using the front (or syn) lobes of orbitals e and d. This is a real possibility, as has been elegantly shown by Mariano (38) in the case of spirodiene **101** [Eq. (37)]. Because of the constraints of the spiro system, which allows only a cis fusion between the three- and seven-membered rings, a disrotatory twist utilizing the front lobes is enforced.

Still another case of front lobe disrotatory closure, this enforced by conformation, is given in Eq. (38) (39).

Thus, the stereochemistry at carbon 1 seems generally to be that of retention of the original configuration. That at carbons 3 and 5 is disrotatory, with inversion at C-3 being preferred in the absence of restricting geometric factors.

VII. STRUCTURAL EFFECTS: CENTRAL SUBSTITUTION AND CONFORMATION

Many of the examples of the di-π-methane rearrangement given thus far have central geminal dimethyl substitution, and the question was posed early whether such substitution is necessary. The photochemistry of diene **106**, which lacks central substitution, was then investigated (*33*). In order to obtain definitive results it was necessary to label the reactant with deuterium, as shown in Eq. (39). It is clear that the geminal dihydrogen

$$\text{(39)}$$
$$\text{(Ref. 33)}$$

$$\text{106-}d \qquad\qquad 107\text{-}d \qquad\qquad 108\text{-}d$$

substitution of the methane carbon does not remain intact, and the reaction is not a simple di-π-methane rearrangement, although without the deuterium substitution the vinylcyclopropane product **107** would be easily confused as arising from such normal rearrangement. The reaction mechanism involves, in fact, a 1,2-hydrogen rearrangement, as depicted in Eq. (40) (*33*). It can be seen that the most likely source of the suppression of the di-π-methane rearrangement in this case is an inhibition of the ring-opening process A, with reversion of the cyclopropyldicarbinyl diradical **112** to reactant **106** by pathway B. The reaction quantum yield for this

$$\text{(40)}$$
$$\text{(Ref. 33)}$$

diene (i.e., **106**) is, indeed, quite low ($\phi = 0.0024$) as compared to that of diene **20**, which has central methyl substitution ($\phi = 0.080$). Also, the excited singlet rate for product formation is 62 times slower for the diene lacking the central methyl substitution (i.e., **106** versus **20**).

A difference in the requirement for central substitution is found in the arylvinylmethane variation of the di-π-methane rearrangement. Thus, the rearrangement of phenylvinylmethanes to phenylcyclopropanes is a known reaction (*28a*); see, for example, Eq. (41) (*28a,41*). However, as has

$$(41)$$
$$(\text{Refs. 28, 41})$$

been noted (*32*), this rearrangement can arise by a phenyl migration or hydrogen migration. Only the former is a di-π-methane process. Hixson, in an elegant study (*32*), investigated the photochemistry of the monodeuteriated system (i.e., **113–d**). This was shown to give a product with the central hydrogens geminally substituted on the original methane carbon and thus one in which hydrogen had not migrated. Hence, the rearrangement had proceeded by a traditional di-π-methane rearrangement despite the lack of central substitution. The reaction is shown in Eq. (42). Hixson additionally concluded that phenyl migration occurs in preference to that of hydrogen.

$$(42)$$
$$(\text{Ref. 32})$$

Considering our suggestions above that with no central substitution the second portion of the di-π-methane rearrangement is inhibited, as de-

$$(43)$$

picted in Eq. (40), we note that, for phenyl migration, recovery of aromatic delocalization energy provides additional driving force for completion of the di-π-methane process in the arylvinyl systems [Eq. (43)].

In the divinylmethane version of the di-π-methane rearrangement, not only methyl but also phenyl substitution allows the reaction to proceed. Two examples are given in Eqs. (44) and (45).

We turn now to conformational effects and the question of whether there is some requirement for utilization of only the *cis-* or only the *trans-*cyclopropyldicarbinyl diradical (e.g., 123 and 124). A test of this facet of the problem was found (*44*) in a study of dienes 125 and 128 [Eqs. (46) and (47)]. Actually, both rearrangements were observed to occur. The regioselectivities were in accord with theory developed earlier, namely, the less delocalized radical center participates in the three-membered ring opening (i.e., pathway A in each case). The bicyclic transoid diene 128 exhibited a singlet rate ten times higher than that of the monocyclic cisoid diene **125**; however, this difference seems ascribable to minor structural effects. In any case there is no strict requirement for cisoid or transoid diradical formation (*44*).

Another interesting conformational effect was encountered in the irradiation of dienes **131** and **132** (*44*). These were totally unreactive, a

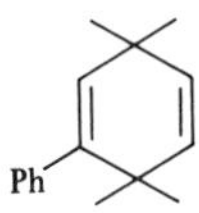

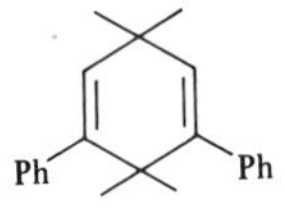

result that is understandable when one realizes, from the three-dimensional representation of diradical **133**, that severe methyl–methyl van der Waals repulsions are generated in bridging.

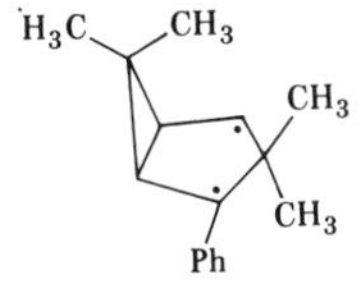

VIII. SUBSTITUENT EFFECTS

Before we begin our discussion it is necessary to point out that substituent effects may operate in controlling the overall excited state rate or, instead, in controlling the reaction regioselectivity. Scheme 1 suggests that the rate-limiting step is bridging and that the second step (opening of the three-membered ring) controls regioselectivity (i.e., path a versus path b). The evidence supporting bridging as rate limiting is considered

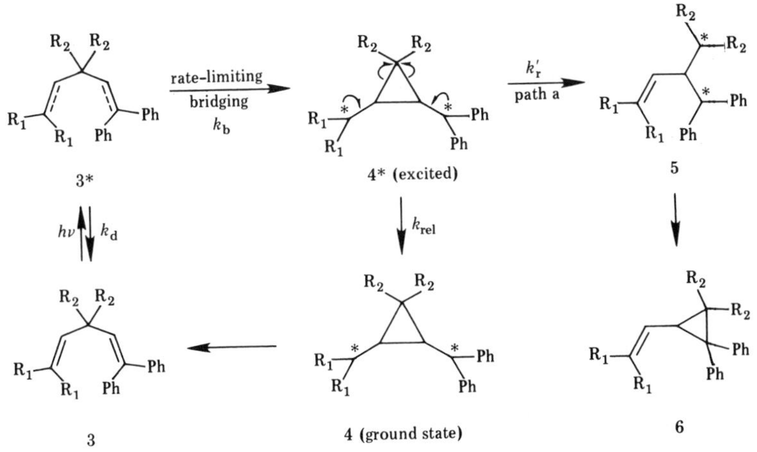

Scheme 1. Overall reaction mechanism of the di-π-methane rearrangement.

below. However, we must first tabulate the rates at which the excited singlet states (the S_1 states) proceed to product for a typical assortment of divinylmethane systems (see Scheme 2).

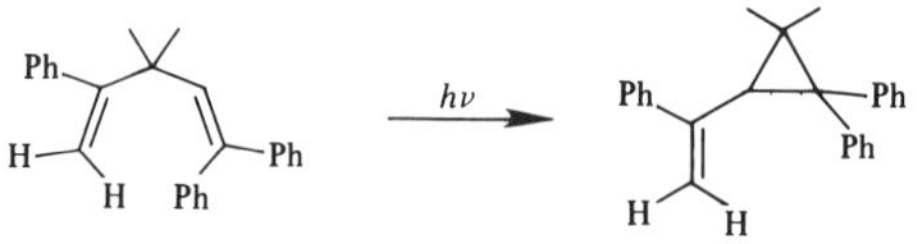

134 → 135

$k_r = 5.8 \times 10^{8}\ \mathrm{sec}^{-1}$
$k_{dt} = 7.2 \times 10^{10}\ \mathrm{sec}^{-1}$
$\tau_{RT} = 14$ psec
$\phi_r = 0.008$ (Ref. *17*)
$M = 210$ (48)

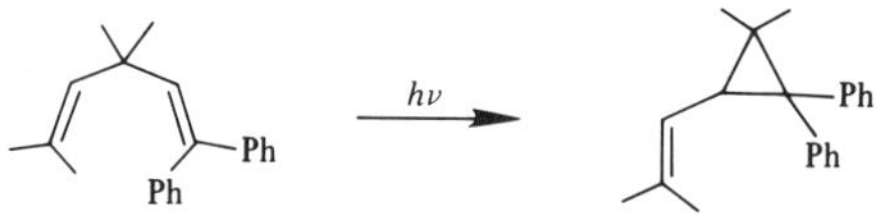

48 → 51

$k_r = 6.9 \times 10^{9}\ \mathrm{sec}^{-1}$
$k_{dt} = 7.1 \times 10^{10}\ \mathrm{sec}^{-1}$
$\tau_{RT} = 14$ psec
$\phi_r = 0.097$ (Ref. *6*)
$M = 222$ (49)

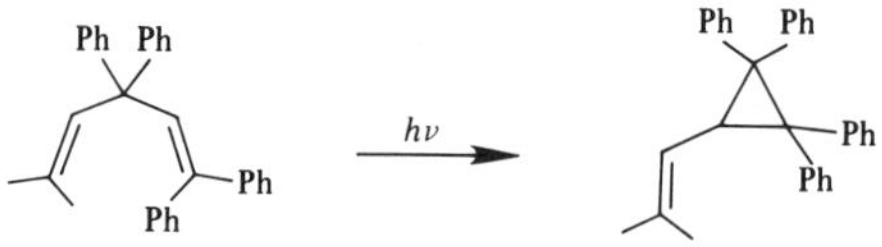

117 → 118

$k_r = 8.5 \times 10^{9}\ \mathrm{sec}^{-1}$
$k_{dt} = 1.13 \times 10^{11}\ \mathrm{sec}^{-1}$
$\tau_{RT} = 9$ psec
$\phi_r = 0.076$ (Ref. *43*)
$M = 216$ (50)

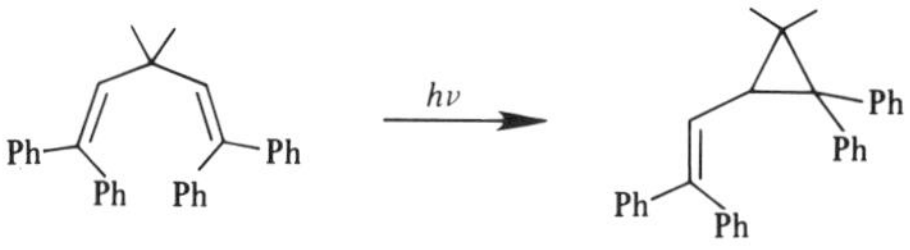

20 → 21

$k_r = 1.4 \times 10^{11}\ \mathrm{sec}^{-1}$
$k_{dt} = 1.8 \times 10^{12}\ \mathrm{sec}^{-1}$
$\tau_{RT} = 0.55$ psec
$\phi_r = 0.080$ (Ref. *1c*)
$M = 225$ (51)

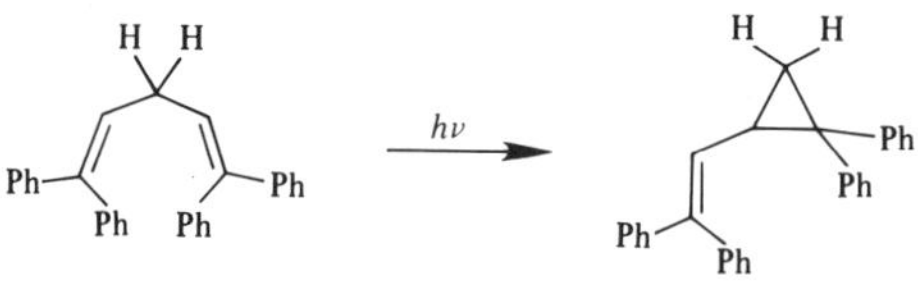

106 → 107

$k_r = 2.6 \times 10^{9}\ \mathrm{sec}^{-1}$
$k_{dt} = 1.1 \times 10^{12}\ \mathrm{sec}^{-1}$
$\tau_{RT} = 0.9$ psec
$\phi_r = 0.0024$ (Ref. *33*)
$M = 800$ (52)

Scheme 2. Some rearrangement rates obtained by single-photon counting (*45*).

Inspection of the S_1 rates of the dienes in Scheme 2 reveals that terminal substitution by electron-delocalizing groups accelerates the rearrangement of the vertical excited state, whereas substitution on the methane carbon has little effect as long as there is at least methyl substitution. Thus, the 1,1,5,5-tetraphenyldiene **20** has an excited state that rearranges at the rate of 1.4×10^{11} sec^{-1}, whereas the 1,1-diphenyl-5,5-dimethyl analogue **48** has an S_1 rearranging only at 6.9×10^9 sec^{-1}. With only terminal phenyls but no terminal methyls the excited state of diene **134** is still slower ($k_r = 5.8 \times 10^8$ sec^{-1}). Thus, there is indeed a trend in which the S_1 rate of reaction increases as terminal substitution increases. Only in the extreme case of diene **106**, which has central hydrogen substitution, is the rate diminished; this seems to be a situation in which the second step has become so unfavorable that it finally inhibits the reaction.

We turn now to substitution on the aromatic rings themselves. The

A.

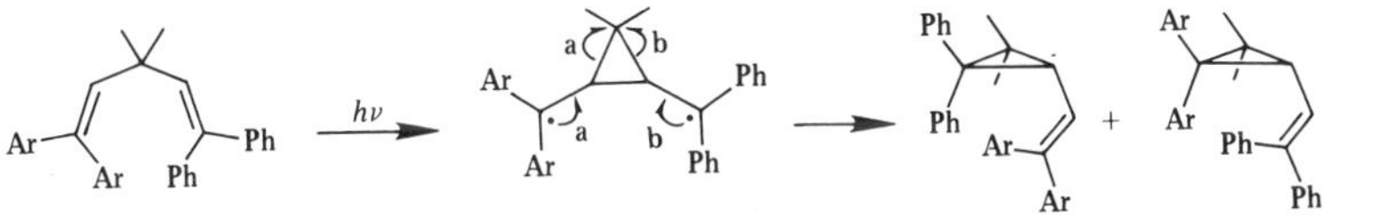

Ar	^1k_r (sec^{-1})	ϕ (path a)	ϕ (path b)
Ph	1.4×10^{11}	0.082	
p-MeOPh	3.4×10^9	0.075	0.022
p-Me$_2$NPh	5.4×10^7	0.0027	Not observed
p-NCPh	2.2×10^{11}	Not observed	0.094
m-MeOPh	8.8×10^9	0.072	0.086

B.

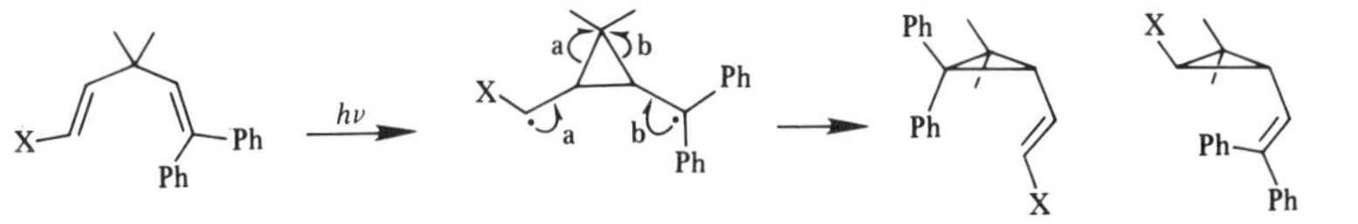

X	^1k_r (sec^{-1})	ϕ (path a)	ϕ (path b)
H	4.7×10^8	0.011	Not observed
OMe	1.9×10^9	0.051	Not observed
CN	1.5×10^{10}	Not observed	0.35

C.

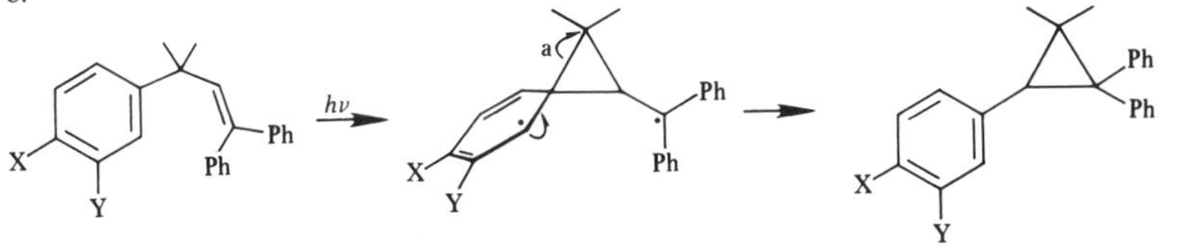

X	Y	^1k_r (sec^{-1})	ϕ
H	H	1.8×10^9	0.036
OMe	H	9.5×10^9	0.058
H	OMe	1.3×10^9	0.024
CN	H	2.1×10^9	0.044

Scheme 3. Substitution effects in the di-π-methane rearrangement. [From Zimmerman *et al.* (*21,23–25,45–47*).]

situation is summarized in Scheme 3. In a series of studies (*21,23–25,46,47*) Zimmerman and his co-workers investigated the effect of methoxy, dimethylamino, and cyano substitution on aromatic rings of divinylmethanes and phenylvinylmethanes and also of substitution directly on the π bond of divinylmethanes (*21b,47*). In each case the regioselectivity followed is that described above.

In the various examples, cyclopropyldicarbinyl diradical ring opening by path b retaining cyano or cyanophenyl stabilization of a diradical center is preferred over retention of a diphenyl-stabilized center (path a). Also, retention of a diphenyl-stabilized center (path a) is favored over retention of a methoxy- or *p*-methoxyphenyl-stabilized center.

For each di-π-methane reactant in Scheme 3, the quantum yield and the rate of excited singlet rearrangement are given. In the case of the arylvinylmethanes (group C of Scheme 3) *p*-methoxy substitution leads to a rate acceleration. *p*-Cyano substitution very slightly accelerates the rate. These results on the arylvinylmethane system (i.e., C) parallel results obtained by an alternative experimental approach used by Hixson (*48*).

The entire spread of rates for all of the compounds in Scheme 3 is large, ranging from 10^7 to 10^{11} sec^{-1}, indicating that structural effects play a very large role in controlling the di-π-methane rearrangement.

Interestingly, again in series B, where the substituent is directly attached to one vinyl group, both cyano and methoxy accelerate the reaction.

However, in contrast to series B and C, the excited state reaction rates are inhibited in the tetraaryl dienes of series A by substitution of electron donors as *p*-methoxy and *p*-dimethylamino. Calculations (*25*) of the SCF–CI variety reveal that the source of the rate inhibition by the electron donors is excessive stabilization of the reacting vertical excited state, stabilization that exceeds stabilization of the cyclopropyldicarbinyl diradicals formed in the rate-limiting step. Indeed, calculations showed that both cyano- and methoxy-type groups stabilized the diradical despite the electron-rich nature of these carbinyl centers.

$$\text{136} \xrightarrow[\overline{k_r = 3.8 \times 10^8 \text{ sec}^{-1}}]{h\nu} \text{137} \qquad (53)$$
$$\text{(Ref. 46)}$$

$$\text{138} \xrightarrow[\overline{k_r = 4.1 \times 10^8 \text{ sec}^{-1}}]{h\nu} \text{139} \qquad (54)$$
$$\text{(Ref. 46)}$$

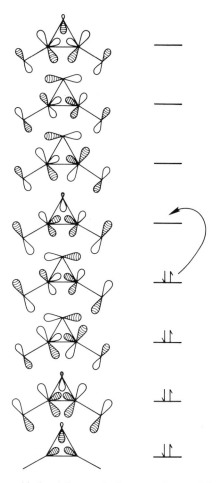

Fig. 3 SCF molecular orbitals of the unsubstituted cyclopropyldicarbinyl diradical.

Two other examples of interest, along with the observed S_1 rates, are given in Eqs. (53) and (54). In the case of the phenylvinylmethane **136** the absence of central methyl substitution does slow the rate about fivefold compared with the related centrally dimethyl-substituted phenyl-vinylmethane (i.e., the first entry of series C in Scheme 3). The same inhibition is encountered with removal of one phenyl group on the vinyl as a phenylstrylmethane (**138**).

One comment is needed. The rate constants we have been discussing are the effective rates of S_1 proceeding successfully to di-π-methane product. This is given algebraically by the product of the reaction quantum yield (ϕ_r) and the total rate of excited state disappearance ($^1k_{dt}$); that is, $k_r = \phi_r(^1k_{dt})$. This operational rate constant is interpreted mechanistically as the rate of bridging to give cyclopropyldicarbinyl diradical multiplied by the probability of this diradical proceeding to product. To the extent that the probability of proceeding to product is inhibited, as in the case of **136**, where three-membered ring opening has diminished driving force, the operational rate constant, k_r, will decrease. SCF–CI calculations (25) for the tetraaryldienes reveal a linear correlation between calculated energies of vinyl–vinyl bridging and the log of the S_1 rate constant.

Finally, Fig. 3 depicts the MO's of the cyclopropyldicarbinyl diradical. Although substitution changes the situation quantitatively, the basic electronic situation remains unchanged for the molecules discussed here. One interesting point is that 1,4 biradicals are known to undergo Grob fragmentation with fission of bond 2–3. In Scheme 1 this corresponds to the reversion of species **4** to diene reactant **3**. The mechanisms above implicitly assume that the excited cyclopropyldicarbinyl diradical (e.g., **4***) does not undergo such extensive fragmentation that the di-π-methane opening of the three-membered ring is excluded. Inspection of Fig. 3 shows that excitation involves promotion of an electron to MO 5, which is bonding between the two vinyl groups, whereas MO 4 from which the electron is promoted, is antibonding between these groups. Thus, excitation is expected to lead to approach and bonding of the vinyl groups as well as a diminished tendency to Grob fragmentation and reversion to diene. Also, we find that, when considered quantitatively, excitation weakens the bond that must open for di-π-methane rearrangement; this derives from the fact that sp^2–sp^2 overlap is energetically more important than p–p and from the increase in antibonding between these orbitals in the excitation process (Fig. 3).

IX. BARRELENE-RELATED EXAMPLES

Although the photolysis of barrelene was one of the first examples recognized as a di-π-methane process, we still have not dealt with the rather large body of literature on this type of molecule. A variety of barrelene derivatives have been photolyzed, and, in general, these rearrange on sensitization. Some of these examples are listed in Eqs. (55)–(65). In these equations the solid dot represents a labeled carbon. In all cases except Eq. (61), the label is hydrogen, with deuterium at all other positions; in Eq. (61) the label is deuterium, with hydrogen elsewhere.

It is interesting to compare the rearrangement of 1,2-naphthobarrelene with 2,3-naphthobarrelene [Eqs. (55) and (56)]. If one transforms the reac-

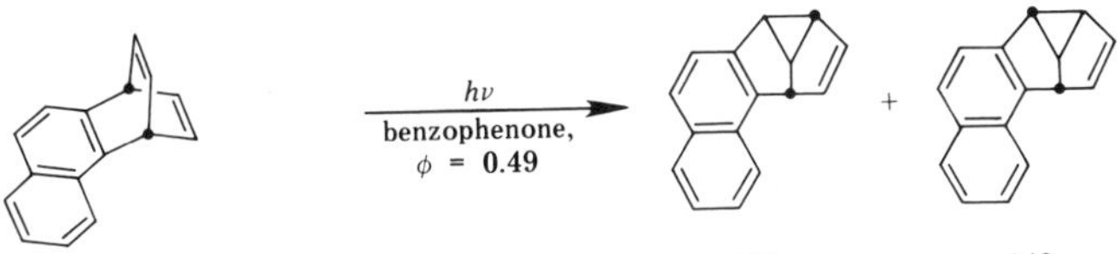

(55)
(Ref. 49)

140   141   142

(56)
(Ref. 49)

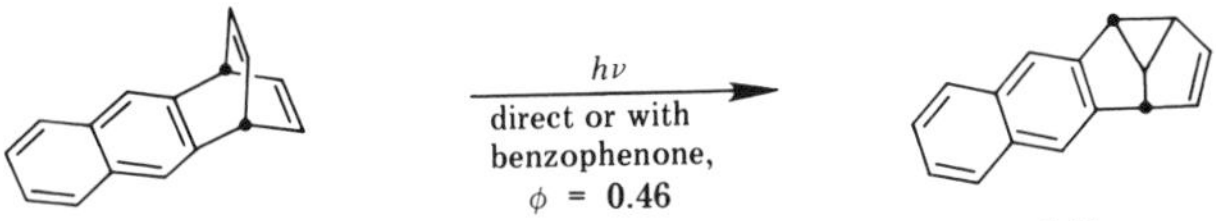

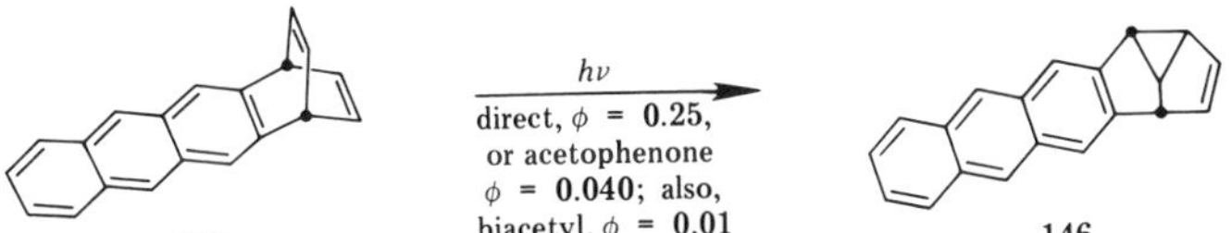

143   144

(57)
(Ref. 50)

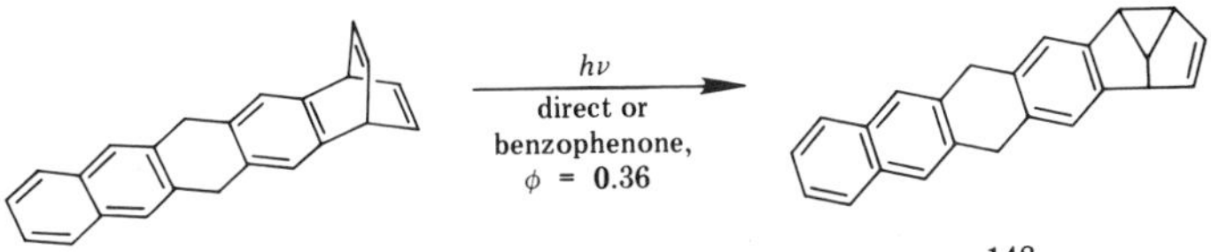

145   146

(58)
(Ref. 51)

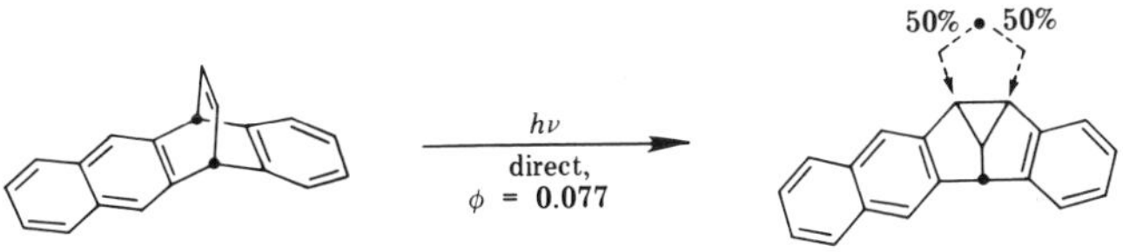

147   148

(59)
(Ref. 52)

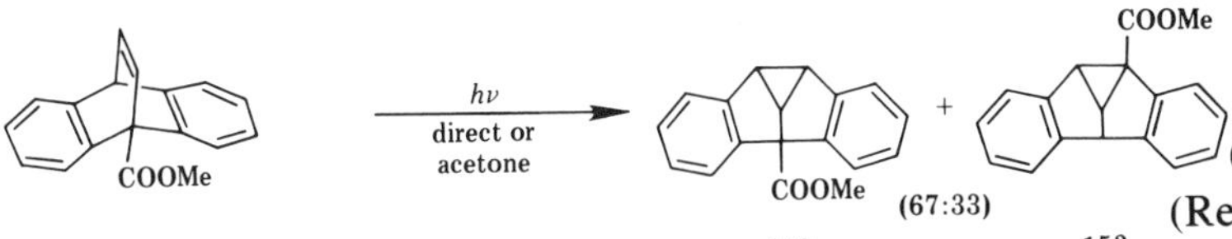

149   150

(60)
(Ref. 53)

151   152   153

tant according to the mechanism in Eq. (3), one finds that 1,2-naphtho-barrelene rearranges by initial α-naphtho–vinyl bridging, whereas 2,3-naphthobarrelene reacts by initial vinyl–vinyl bonding. That one obtains the same quantum yield directly or by sensitization from 2,3-naphtho-barrelene merely means that the intersystem crossing efficiency of polysubstituted naphthalenes is high and that no alternative process of low energy is available to the singlet.

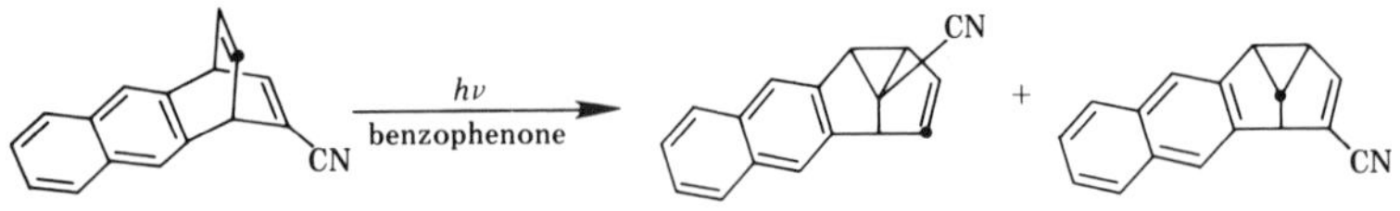

(61)
(Ref. 54)

154   155   (8.3:1)   156

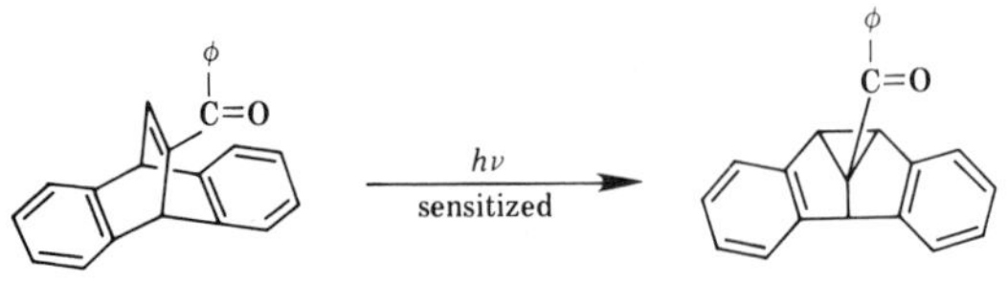

(62)
(Ref. 55)

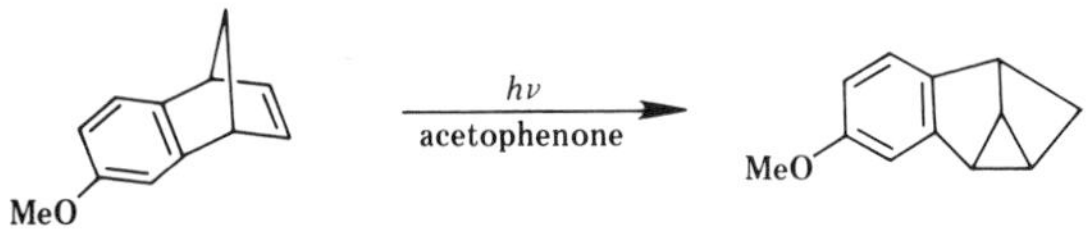

157   158

(63)
(Ref. 56)

159   160 (major product)

(64)
(Ref. 56)

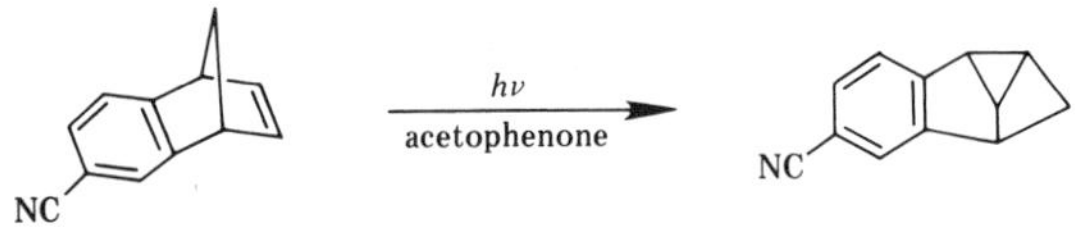

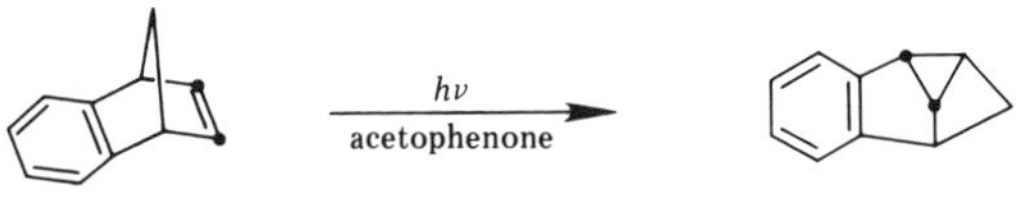

161   162

(65)
(Ref. 57)

163   164

Anthracenobarrelene [Eq. (57)] is an interesting case since sensitization with acetophenone (74 kcal/mol) should be enough to generate T_1 (43 kcal/mol). Biacetyl ($E_T = 55$ kcal/mol) should also have sufficient energy and yet little reaction is observed. In this study (50) it was demonstrated that energy transfer was indeed occurring from the triplet of biacetyl since biacetyl phosphorescence was quenched. The singlet energy of anthrabarrelene is 76 kcal/mol. This is sufficient to allow for formation of T_2, the energy of which should be similar to that of T_2 of anthracene; the latter has been estimated (58) to be 74 kcal/mol. Thus, T_2 must be the reacting species, whereas T_1 must be unreactive. Another point of interest in this rearrangement is the preference for vinyl–vinyl bridging indicated by the labeling pattern of the anthrasemibullvalene product **146**.

The dihydronaphthacenobarrelene example in Eq. (58) is unusual in that sensitization or direct irradiation should lead to excitation of the low-energy naphthalene chromophore which is only transannularly conjugated to the benzobarrelene moiety. Nevertheless, the reaction efficiency is high ($\phi = 0.36$). The fluorescence and phosphorescence emission spectra were characteristically naphthalene-like, indicating that energy is indeed available, initially, in the naphthalene moiety. The energy must thus be proceeding upwards, eventually giving an excited benzobarrelene triplet that rearranges either after or during the excitation process. It is possible that the excess energy is provided thermally from the solvent. Alternatively, the excess energy from the intersystem crossing process may allow leakage into the benzobarrelene moiety, or possibly a nonvertical energy transfer occurs to the reacting benzobarrelene system.

The benzonaphthobarrelene **149** is of interest in view of the fact that the position of the label in the product demonstrates that benzo–vinyl bridging of the triplet is about equally as facile as β-naphthyl–vinyl bridging. Also, the quantum yield is low ($\phi = 0.077$) compared to vinyl–vinyl bridging examples.

The example in Eq. (60) is of interest because of the unusual regioselectivity involving a carbomethoxyl group. Actually, this parallels the effect in acyclic examples in which di-π-methanes with central cyano substitution rearrange with low S_1 rates. This correlates with the electron deficiency that develops on the methane carbon in the bridging process (see Fig. 2). Thus, the preferred product (**152**) is the one in which the carbomethoxyl group avoids the methane carbon during reaction.

The examples in Eqs. (61) and (62) illustrate the preference for that bridging which will leave a cyano or benzoyl group at the carbinyl carbon; this has parallel in the acyclic singlet reactivity discussed above, in which electron-withdrawing groups accelerate the bridging when at the potential carbinyl carbons. Equations (63) and (64) illustrate the effect of ring substitution with m-methoxyl and p-cyano favoring bridging. The last example [Eq. (65)] was originally presented without mechanism in 1966. This reveals how very strained systems may be engendered in the di-π-methane rearrangement.

X. INDEPENDENT GENERATION OF CYCLOPROPYLDICARBINYL DIRADICALS

One approach to the understanding of the behavior of cyclopropyldicarbinyl diradicals was derived from the study of the three azo compounds **165, 166,** and **167** (59). Each provided an independent source of the previously proposed corresponding cyclopropyldicarbinyl diradical

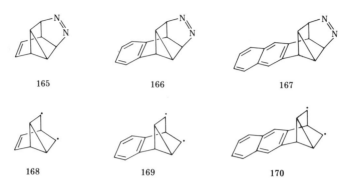

165   **166**   **167**

168   **169**   **170**

Scheme 4. Azo precursors and derived diradicals.

(*i.e.*, **168**, **169** and **170**, respectively) (Scheme 4). It was observed that the ground state diradical species, generated by thermolysis of the azo compounds, led to Grob fragmentation and cycloreversion to the corresponding barrelenes. The triplets, instead, led preferentially to the semibullvalenes. The excited singlets showed mixed reactivity.

In this study it was noted that the models employed may not afford free diradicals with the nitrogen removed to infinity. This is especially true in the thermolysis in which the reaction seems to be an allowed $_\sigma 2_s + {}_\sigma 2_s + {}_\sigma 2_s$ retro Diels–Alder cycloreversion; here, the model is the corresponding transition state, and the nitrogen is only partially removed. The transition state is the diradical plus a nitrogen molecule brought into juxtaposition. That this limitation is not too severe is shown by correlation diagrams for the conversions: azo precursor → diradical → barrelene, and azo precursor → barrelene (i.e., concerted, not through the diradical). The two correlation diagrams differ in the timing of nitrogen removal to infin-

165
a thermolysis
b *hν*, direct
c *hν*, sensitized
+ **11** + **12** + **171**   (66)   (Ref. 59)

	11	**12**	**171**
a:	100%	0%	0%
b:	24%	73%	3%
c:	0%	100%	0%

166
a thermolysis
b *hν*, direct
c *hν*, sensitized
26 + **28**   (67)

	26	**28**
a:	100%	0%
b:	$\phi = 0.70$	$\phi = 0.21$
c:	$\phi = 0.08$	$\phi = 0.58$

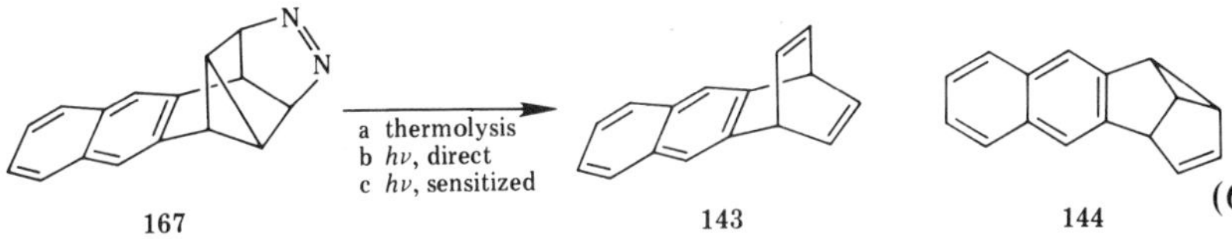

$$a: 100\% \qquad\qquad 0\%$$
$$b: \phi = 0.78 \qquad \phi = 0.20$$
$$c: \phi = 0.1 \qquad\quad \phi = 0.63$$

(68)

ity, but differ only in degree and not in character. Thus, all mechanisms differing in concertedness have similar energetics and are on the same hypersurface. This means that the azo model must reasonably approximate the photochemically derived diradical.

XI. ADDITIONAL EXAMPLES

One interesting variation of the di-π-methane rearrangement involves replacement of one of the two vinyl groups by a three-membered ring (60). The course of the reaction is outlined in Scheme 5. The mechanisms

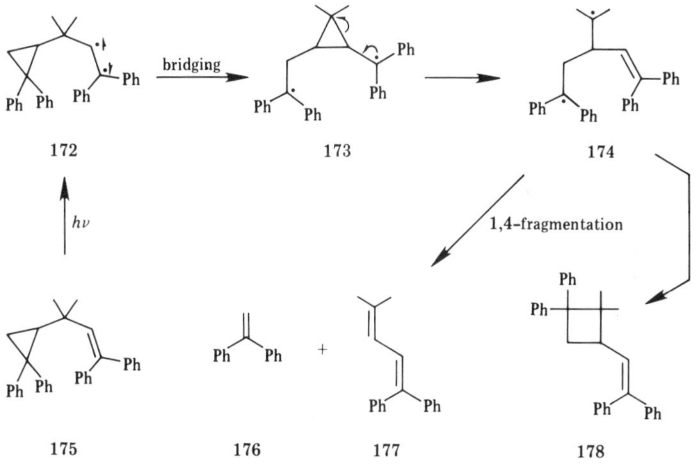

Scheme 5. Cyclopropyl analogue of the di-π-methane rearrangement.

involved are parallel to those of the ordinary di-π-methane rearrangement, and, as with acyclic dienes, the rearrangement proceeds via the singlet. Interestingly, the quantum yield for four-membered ring product formation is only $\phi = 0.0045$ and the S_1 rate is only $k_r = 1.7 \times 10^8 \ \text{sec}^{-1}$, indicating that cyclopropyl–vinyl bridging is relatively slow.

Still another example of interest is the semidegenerate rearrangement of 3-arylcyclopropenes, as in Eq. (69). This represents an incipient di-π-

methane rearrangement followed by a reversal to give a product analogous to the original reactant (*61*).

$$(69)$$

REFERENCES

1a. H. E. Zimmerman and G. L. Grunewald, *J. Am. Chem. Soc.* **88**, 183 (1966).
1b. H. E. Zimmerman, R. W. Binkley, R. S. Givens, and M. A. Sherwin, *J. Am. Chem. Soc.* **89**, 3932 (1967).
1c. H. E. Zimmerman and P. S. Mariano, *J. Am. Chem. Soc.* **91**, 1718 (1969).
2a. H. E. Zimmerman, *17th Natl. Org. Symp., 1961* Abstracts, p. 31 (1961).
2b. H. E. Zimmerman and D. I. Schuster, *J. Am. Chem. Soc.* **83**, 4486 (1961).
2c. H. E. Zimmerman and D. I. Schuster, *J. Am. Chem. Soc.* **84**, 4527 (1962); H. E. Zimmerman, *Adv. Photochem.* **1**, 183 (1963).
3. See Zimmerman and Schuster (*2b,2c*); H. E. Zimmerman and J. S. Swenton, *J. Am. Chem. Soc.* **89**, 906 (1967).
4a. H. E. Zimmerman and J. W. Wilson, *J. Am. Chem. Soc.* **86**, 4036 (1964); H. E. Zimmerman and K. G. Hancock, *ibid.* **90**, 3749 (1968).
4b. H. E. Zimmerman, R. D. Rieke, and J. R. Scheffer, *J. Am. Chem. Soc.* **89**, 2033 (1967).
5. H. E. Zimmerman, G. E. Keck, and J. L. Pflederer, *J. Am. Chem. Soc.* **98**, 5574 (1976); see Zimmerman *et al.* (*4b*); H. E. Zimmerman, R. W. Binkley, J. J. McCullough, and G. A. Zimmerman, *J. Am. Chem. Soc.* **89**, 6589 (1967).
6. H. E. Zimmerman and A. C. Pratt, *J. Am. Chem. Soc.* **92**, 1409, 6259, and 6267 (1970).
7. H. E. Zimmerman, K. S. Kamm, and D. W. Werthemann, *J. Am. Chem. Soc.* **96**, 439 (1974).
8. H. E. Zimmerman and G. E. Samuelson, *J. Am. Chem. Soc.* **91**, 5307 (1969); **89**, 5971 (1967).
9. H. E. Zimmerman, R. W. Binkley, R. S. Givens, and M. A. Sherwin, *J. Am. Chem. Soc.* **89**, 3932 (1967).
10. H. E. Zimmerman and G. A. Epling, *J. Am. Chem. Soc.* **92**, 1411 (1970); J. S. Swenton, A. L. Crumrine, and T. S. Walker, *ibid.* p. 1406.
11. Z. Goldschmidt and U. Gutman, *Tetrahedron* **30**, 3327 (1974).
12. R. C. Hahn and R. P. Johnson, *J. Am. Chem. Soc.* **97**, 212 (1975).
13. Z. Goldschmidt and A. S. Kende, *Tetrahedron Lett.* p. 4625 (1971).
14. R. C. Hahn and L. J. Rothman, *J. Am. Chem. Soc.* **91**, 2409 (1969).
15. P. S. Mariano and J. K. Ko, *J. Am. Chem. Soc.* **94**, 1766 (1972); **95**, 8670 (1973).
16. H. E. Zimmerman, F. X. Albrecht, and M. J. Haire, *J. Am. Chem. Soc.* **97**, 3726 (1975).
17. H. E. Zimmerman and A. A. Baum, *J. Am. Chem. Soc.* **93**, 3646 (1971).
18. W. R. Roth and B. Peltzer, *Justus Liebigs Ann. Chem.* **685**, 56 (1965).
19. T. Sasaki, S. Equchi, M. Ohno, and T. Umemura, *Tetrahedron Lett.* p. 3895 (1978).
20. G. W. Griffin, A. F. Marcantonio, and H. Kristinsson, *Tetrahedron Lett.* p. 2951 (1965).
21a. H. E. Zimmerman and R. T. Klun, *Tetrahedron* **34**, 1775 (1978).
21b. H. E. Zimmerman, W. T. Gruenbaum, R. T. Klun, M. G. Steinmetz, and T. R. Welter, *J. Chem. Soc., Chem. Commun.* p. 228 (1978).

22. P. W. Alexander, A. C. Pratt, O. H. Rowky, and A. E. Tipping, *J. Chem. Soc., Chem. Commun.* p. 161 (1978).
23. H. E. Zimmerman and B. R. Cotter, *J. Am. Chem. Soc.* **96**, 7445 (1974).
24. H. E. Zimmerman and W. T. Gruenbaum, *J. Org. Chem.* **43**, 1997 (1978).
25. H. E. Zimmerman and T. R. Welter, *J. Am. Chem. Soc.* **100**, 4131 (1978).
26. H. E. Zimmerman and T. R. Welter, unpublished results.
27. H. E. Zimmerman and R. D. Little, *J. Am. Chem. Soc.* **94**, 8256 (1972); **96**, 5143 (1974).
28a. G. W. Griffin, J. Covell, R. C. Peterson, R. M. Dodson, and G. Klose, *J. Am. Chem. Soc.* **87**, 1410 (1965).
28b. H. Kristinson and G. W. Griffin, *J. Am. Chem. Soc.* **88**, 378 (1966).
29. S. S. Hixson and T. P. Cutler, *J. Am. Chem. Soc.* **95**, 3032 (1978).
30. S. S. Hixson, *J. Am. Chem. Soc.* **98**, 1271 (1976).
31. The mechanism of such sigma migrations remains to be investigated in a detailed fashion and will not be discussed in this review.
32. S. S. Hixson, *Tetrahedron Lett.* p. 1155 (1972).
33. H. E. Zimmerman and J. A. Pincock, *J. Am. Chem. Soc.* **95**, 2957 (1973).
34. H. E. Zimmerman, *J. Am. Chem. Soc.* **88**, 1564 (1966); *Acc Chem. Res.* **5**, 393 (1972).
35. H. E. Zimmerman, J. D. Robbins, R. D. McKelvey, C. J. Samuel, and L. R. Sousa, *J. Am. Chem. Soc.* **96**, 1974 and 4630 (1974).
36. H. E. Zimmerman, T. P. Gannett, and G. E. Keck, *J. Am. Chem. Soc.* **100**, 323 (1978).
37. H. E. Zimmerman, P. Baeckstrom, and D. W. Kurtz, *J. Am. Chem. Soc.* **96**, 1459 (1974); **94**, 5502 (1972).
38. P. S. Mariano, R. B. Steitle, D. G. Watson, M. J. Peters, and E. Bay, *J. Am. Chem. Soc.* **98**, 5899 (1976).
39. P. S. Mariano, D. G. Watson, and E. Bay, *Tetrahedron* **33**, 11 (1977).
40. The mechanism of formation of housane **108** is not shown explicitly but involves 1,3-biradical addition across the remaining π-bond.
41. E. Valyocsik and P. Sigal, *J. Org. Chem.* **36**, 66 (1971).
42. H. E. Zimmerman, R. B. Boettcher, and W. Braig, *J. Am. Chem. Soc.* **95**, 2155 (1973).
43. Unpublished results of H. E. Zimmerman and G. T. Lisowski; G. T. Lisowski, Ph.D. Thesis, University of Wisconsin, Madison (1975).
44. H. E. Zimmerman and L. M. Tolbert, *J. Am. Chem. Soc.* **97**, 5497 (1975).
45a. H. E. Zimmeman, D. P. Werthemann, and K. S. Kamm, *J. Am. Chem. Soc.,* **96**, 439 (1974).
45b. For a simplified discussion of single photon counting see H. E. Zimmerman, *Pure Appl. Chem.* **49**, 389 (1977).
46. H. E. Zimmerman, M. G. Steinmetz, and C. L. Kreil, *J. Am. Chem. Soc.* **100**, 4146 (1978).
47. H. E. Zimmerman and R. T. Klun, *Tetrahedron* **34**, 1775 (1978).
48. S. S. Hixson, *J. Am. Chem. Soc.* **94**, 2507 (1972).
49. H. E. Zimmerman and C. O. Bender, *J. Am. Chem. Soc.* **92**, 4366 (1970); **91**, 7516 (1969).
50. H. E. Zimmerman and D. R. Amick, *J. Am. Chem. Soc.* **95**, 3977 (1973).
51. H. E. Zimmerman, D. R. Amick, and H. Hemetsberger, *J. Am. Chem. Soc.* **95**, 4606 (1973).
52. H. E. Zimmerman and M. L. Viriot-Villaiume, *J. Am. Chem. Soc.* **95**, 1274 (1973).
53. E. Ciganek, *J. Am. Chem. Soc.* **88**, 2882 (1966).
54. C. O. Bender and H. D. Burgess, *Can. J. Chem.* **51**, 3486 (1973).
55. N. K. Saxena, M. Maya, and P. S. Venkataramani, *Indian J. Chem.* **13**, 1075 (1975); *Chem. Abstr.* **84**, 17016 (1976).

56. L. A. Paquette, D. M. Cottrell, and R. A. Snow, *J. Am. Chem. Soc.* **99**, 3723 (1977); for similar examples note also R. C. Hahn and R. P. Johnson, *ibid.* p. 1508.
57. J. R. Edman [*J. Am. Chem. Soc.* **91**, 7103 (1969)], used deuterium labeling and advanced a di-π-methane mechanism (*1*) involving benzo-vinyl bridging; an earlier paper [**88**, 3454 (1966)] described the rearrangement without mechanism.
58. R. E. Kellogg, *J. Chem. Phys.* **44**, 411 (1966).
59. H. E. Zimmerman, R. J. Boettcher, N. E. Buchler, G. E. Keck, and M. G. Steinmetz, *J. Am. Chem. Soc.* **98**, 7680 (1976).
60. H. E. Zimmerman and C. J. Samuel, *J. Am. Chem. Soc.* **97**, 4025 (1975).
61. H. E. Zimmerman and S. M. Aasen, *J. Org. Chem.* **43**, 1493 (1978); H. E. Zimmerman and M. C. Hovey, *J. Org. Chem.* **44**, 2331 (1979).

ESSAY 17 | # PHOTOCHEMICAL REARRANGEMENTS OF ENONES

DAVID I. SCHUSTER

I. GENERAL INTRODUCTION

Investigations of photochemical rearrangements of cyclic unsaturated ketones (enones) were initiated soon after the molecular pattern followed

REARRANGEMENTS IN GROUND AND EXCITED STATES, VOL. 3

in photochemical rearrangements of cross-conjugated cyclohexadienones had been clarified and mechanisms had been proposed to account for these complex molecular reorganizations (see Essay 18 for an account of this subject). Attention naturally focused initially on simple cyclo-hexenones and steroid enones and later expanded to include many other types of α,β-enones in acyclic, bicyclic, and polycyclic molecular frame-works. Reviews of progress in this field have appeared periodically (1–4), so that attention in this essay is directed mainly at recent developments of mechanistic interest.

Since spectroscopists had been aware for some time of the extensive interaction between the alkene and carbonyl chromophores of β,γ-enones (5–9), it was natural for photochemists to be curious about the chemical consequences of this interaction. The types of rearrangements observed with β,γ-enones were found to be quite different from those of the α,β-enones and led to an enormous spurt of activity, which was exhaustively reviewed by Houk in 1976 (10). Discussion here centers on reports in the last few years that appear to resolve a number of the anomalies discussed by Houk (10).

Competitive photoreactions of these systems not involving molecular rearrangements are briefly discussed only insofar as these bear directly on the mechanisms of the photorearrangements, and particularly on the as-signments of configurations to the reactive excited states.

II. PHOTOREARRANGEMENTS OF CYCLOHEX-2-EN-1-ONES

A. Rearrangements to Lumiketones and Ring Contraction to Cyclopentenones

1. Structural Considerations and Scope of Reaction

The molecular rearrangements seen on ultraviolet excitation of cyclohex-2-en-1-ones are typified by the first examples reported, namely that of Gardner et al. (11) on cholest-4-en-3-one (1) and that of Chapman et al. (12) on 4,4-dimethylcyclohex-2-en-1-one (2) and testosterone acetate (3), as shown below. In the latter systems, one observes both rearrange-ment to a bicyclo[3.1.0]hexan-2-one (lumiketone) and ring contraction to a 3-substituted cyclopent-2-en-1-one when the enones are irradiated in t-butyl alcohol (t-BuOH). Irradiation of 2 in acetic acid gives mainly the ketoacetate 4 as well as rearrangement and elimination products.

These rearrangements are competitive with a number of other photo-transformations of variable importance from one system to another (Sec-

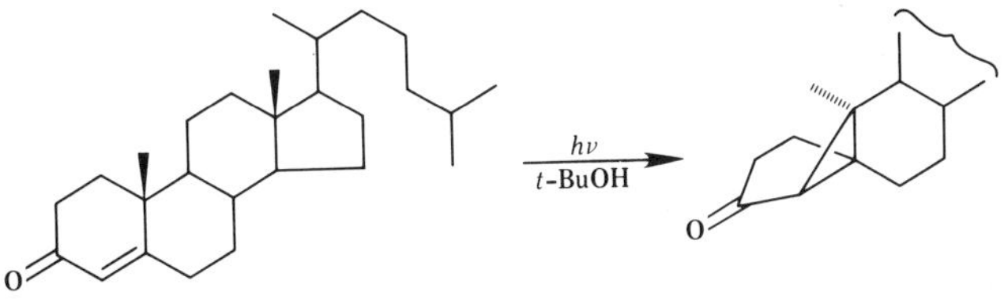

1

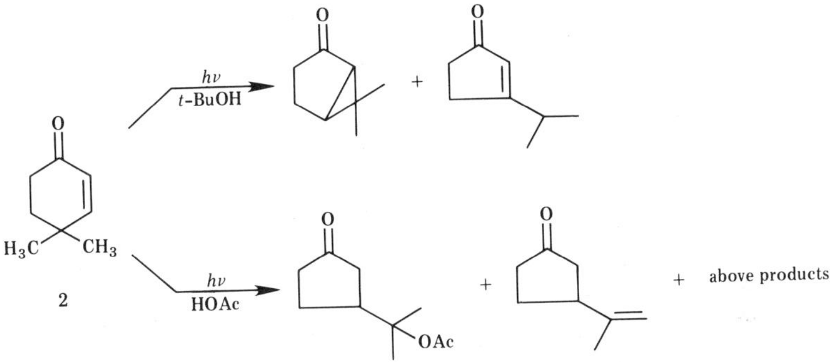

2

4

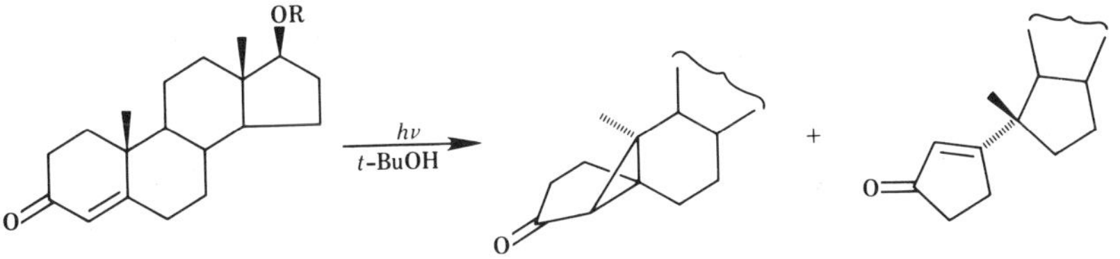

3a R = OAc
3b R = H

tion II,C,2). Dimerization to cyclobutanes is a common reaction of monocyclic enones and is, in fact, the exclusive reaction of 2-cyclohexenone itself (13–15). Cyclobutane dimers are formed, albeit in low yield, even in steroid systems such as testosterone acetate (3a) (16). Hydrogen abstraction from the solvent, or from a second molecule of substrate, can also occur to give reduced products (cyclohexanones, pinacols, solvent adducts) (Section II,C,1) and deconjugated products in which the double bond has shifted from the α,β to the β,γ position (Section II,B,2). Octalone 5, studied by Schaffner and co-workers (17), exhibits the full spectrum of reaction possibilities depending on the choice of solvent medium, as shown below, with the apparent exception of dimerization. Similar behavior was also noted for testosterone acetate (3a) (17).

The photochemical behavior of a large number of conjugated cyclohexenones with alkyl substituents at various positions and some bicyclic enones were studied in *t*-BuOH and other solvents (*18*). Qualitatively, it was found that the lumiketone rearrangement was limited to those cyclohexenones possessing two alkyl substituents at C-4. This is a necessary, but not sufficient, condition for occurrence of the lumiketone rearrangement since compounds **6, 7,** and **8** do not afford lumiketones.* It had previously been observed (*19*) that 10-α-testosterone (**9**) does not undergo the rearrangements characteristic of **3a** and **3b,** but rather undergoes only

deconjugation to **10.** The most commonly observed photoreaction in *t*-BuOH of the enones lacking dialkyl substitution at C-4 was dimerization. As expected, photoreduction was relatively unimportant in *t*-BuOH. In the absence of quantitative reactivity data (quantum efficiencies and excited state lifetimes; see below), one cannot draw any firm conclusions

---

* See Note Added in Proof, p. 269.

from this study (*18*) as to the precise effect of alkyl substitution in enhancing or retarding one or another reaction mode of the reactive excited state(s). Qualitatively, however, it is clear that the lumiketone and cyclopentenone rearrangements are reactions of quite limited scope.

The yield of lumiketone in those systems that show the reaction depends sensitively on the solvent medium. Yields are usually optimal in *t*-BuOH, in which the predominant side reactions (dimerization, reduction, and deconjugation) seem to be minimized. This was most clearly demonstrated (*17*) in a study of **3a** and **5**; the percent yields of lumiketone (based on unreacted starting material) reached 77% and 80% in *t*-BuOH but were substantially lower in 2-propanol, toluene, pyridine, benzonitrile, benzene, and α,α,α-trifluorotoluene. Reduction is observed to some extent in all solvents, although several lack readily abstractable hydrogens, but it occurs least in *t*-BuOH for reasons that are still obscure. A mechanistic alternative to H abstraction from benzene, a solvent that is notoriously poor as a H donor toward the most reactive free radicals (*20*), has been discussed (*21*). This involves initial addition of the ketone triplet to the aromatic system (*22*), but experimental evidence to distinguish between the two alternative mechanisms is lacking.

2. Stereochemistry of the Lumiketone Photorearrangement

In examining the reaction mixture from irradiation of testosterone (**3b**), Jeger and co-workers (*23*) ruled out the formation of traces of the other possible rearrangement products **11** and **12** shown below. These are diastereomers of the actual photoproducts. Later, it was shown (*17*) that the photorearrangement of 1α-deuteriotestosterone acetate (**13**) was completely stereospecific, affording only the lumiketone stereoisomer **14**, which indicates that in this system the reaction proceeded with complete retention of configuration at C-1 and inversion at C-10 (steroid numbering). Chapman and co-workers (*24*) showed that photorearrangement of optically active phenanthrenone **15** to lumiketone **16** occurred with 95% retention of optical purity. By relating the absolute configurations of the phenanthrenone and lumiketone, they showed that this reaction also occurred with inversion of configuration at the chiral center (C-10).

These results clearly rule out the intermediacy of planar achiral intermediates (in the enone portion of the molecule) in the lumiketone rear-

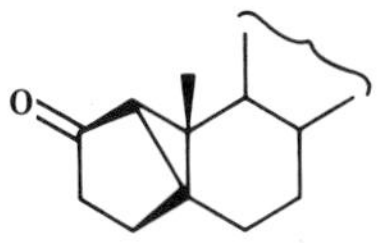

11 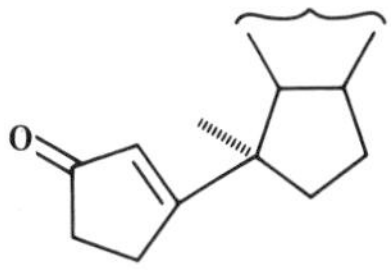   12

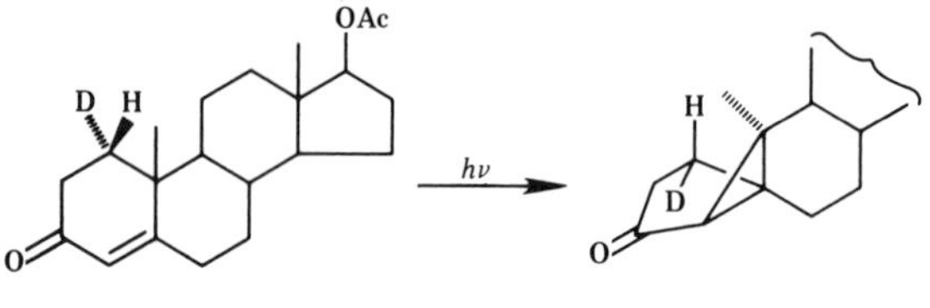

13   14

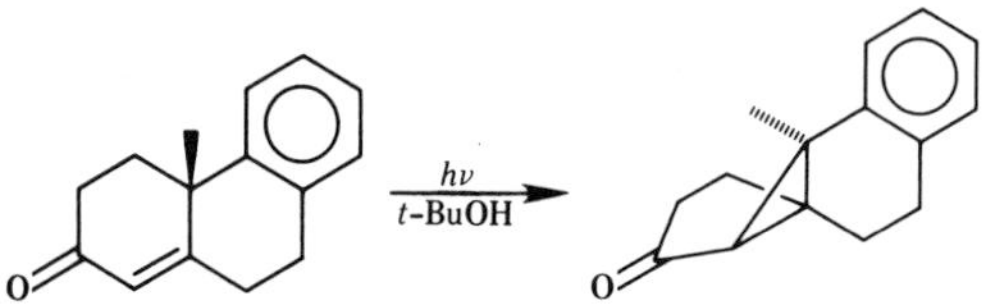

15   16

rangement. However, steric constraints imposed by the A–B ring fusion in 13 and 15 could prejudice the stereochemical course of reaction, virtually insuring inversion at C-4 (enone numbering) (25). Thus, the diradical 17, generated by cleavage of the C-1—C-10 bond, would not, according to molecular models, be planar since it appears that C-1 must lie either above or below the trigonal center generated at C-10. The angular methyl at C-10 would then direct subsequent bonding of C-1 to C-5 from the rear face of the molecule, since swinging of the chain containing C-1 around the angular methyl to the front face of the molecule (18) would appear to be energetically prohibitive in competition with ring closure of the initial diradical species. Thus, it was argued that stereospecific rearrangement

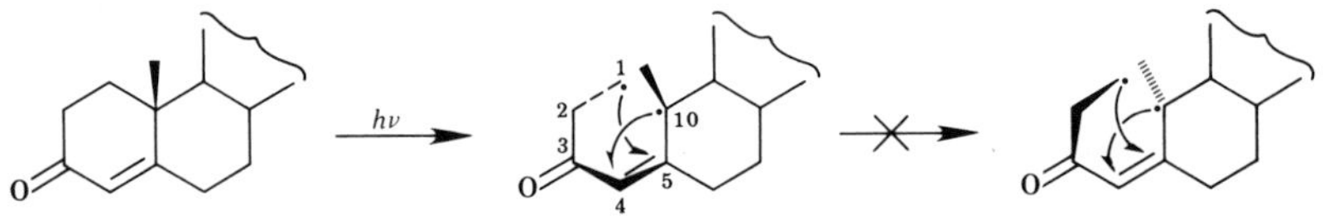

17   18

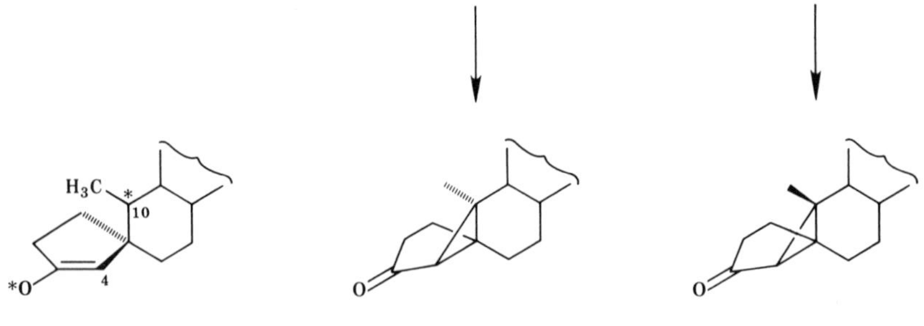

19

with inversion at the chiral center in the cases of **13** and **15** was not inconsistent with a stepwise reaction mechanism. Other workers (*26*) concur that the stereospecific character of the rearrangement does not require a concerted reaction mechanism and go further in proposing that the reaction could proceed via an explicit intermediate (**19**), which can afford only one stereoisomer of the lumiketone on subsequent bonding between C-10 and C-4 because of the constraints of the ring system. They also suggest that reversion of **19** to the ground state of the starting enone could be the source of some or all of the observed inefficiency noted in these photorearrangements.

The stereochemistry of rearrangement of two simple monocyclic chiral cyclohexenones of known absolute configuration has been studied (*25*). In these, steric constraints are minimized, if not eliminated, affording the enone molecule the opportunity to rearrange with either retention or inversion at C-4, an opportunity not available in **13** and **15**. The stereochemical course of reaction for (*R*)-(+)-**20** and (*R*)-(+)-**24,** shown below, indicates that the lumiketones are formed in both cases with absolutely no loss in optical purity within experimental error. The reactions take place

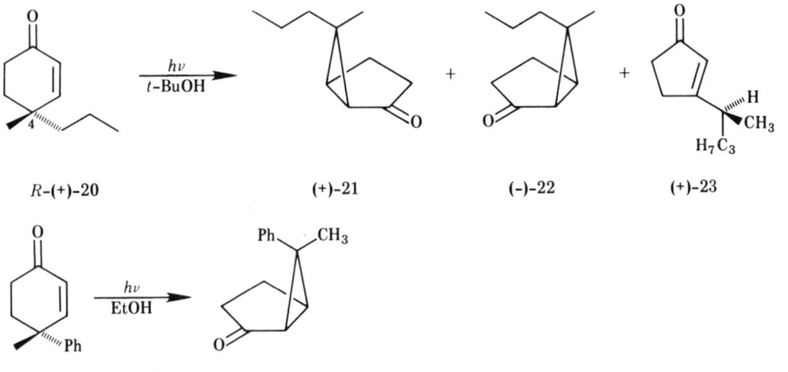

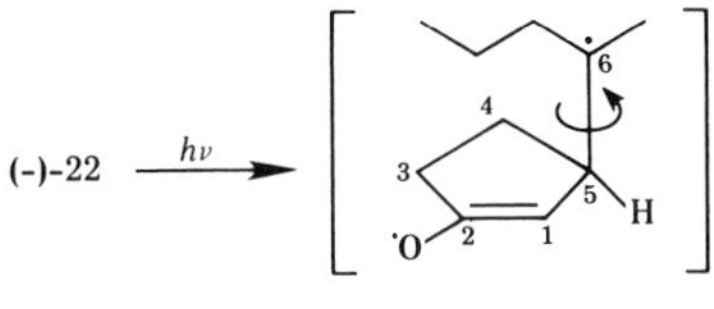

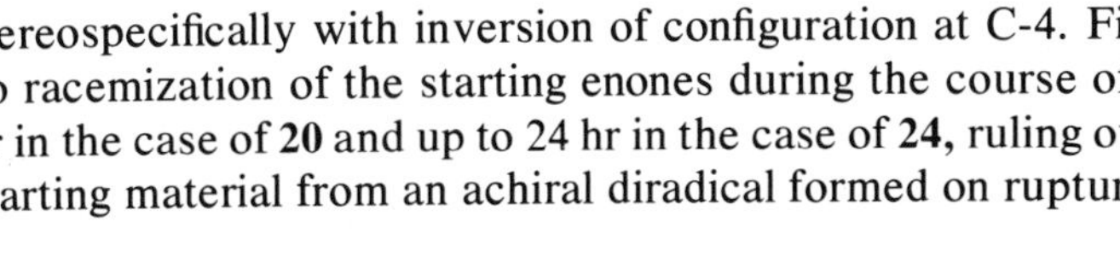

stereospecifically with inversion of configuration at C-4. Finally, there is no racemization of the starting enones during the course of reaction, 325 hr in the case of **20** and up to 24 hr in the case of **24,** ruling out reversion to starting material from an achiral diradical formed on rupture of the enone ring, a conceivable pathway for energy wastage competitive with the photorearrangement. In addition, it was shown that photoexcitation of (−)-**22** gave (−)-**21**, a process that must occur by cleavage of the C-1—C-6 bond to give **26**, rotation around C-5—C-6, and bonding of C-1 to C-6 on the opposite face of the trigonal center at C-6. (The quantum yield of lumiketone photoisomerization was comparable to that of the enone photorearrangement.) Since photoexcitation of enone (+)-**20** originally gave (−)-**22** and (+)-**21** without any loss of optical purity, intermediate **26** (analogous to the proposed intermediate **19**) is unequivocally excluded from the reaction pathway leading to the lumiketones; if **26** had been generated, (−)-**21** would have formed to some extent, resulting in at least partial loss of optical purity in the rearrangement.

Thus, the enone–lumiketone photorearrangement has all the appearance of a concerted reaction, and the observed stereochemistry is consistent with its designation as a $_\sigma 2_a + _\pi 2_a$ cycloaddition, as proposed some time ago by Woodward and Hoffmann (27). Thus, antarafacial attack by the π system on the C-4—C-5 σ bond occurs with inversion at C-4 and retention at C-5, whereas addition to the C=C bond must occur in an antarafacial manner, according to molecular models. The steric course of reaction in monocyclic enones is summarized in Scheme 1. The reaction is stereospecific on each face of the cyclohexenone ring system, affording diastereomeric lumiketones of opposite chirality. In the case of the ring-fused enones, reaction is possible on only one face of the cyclohexenone ring,

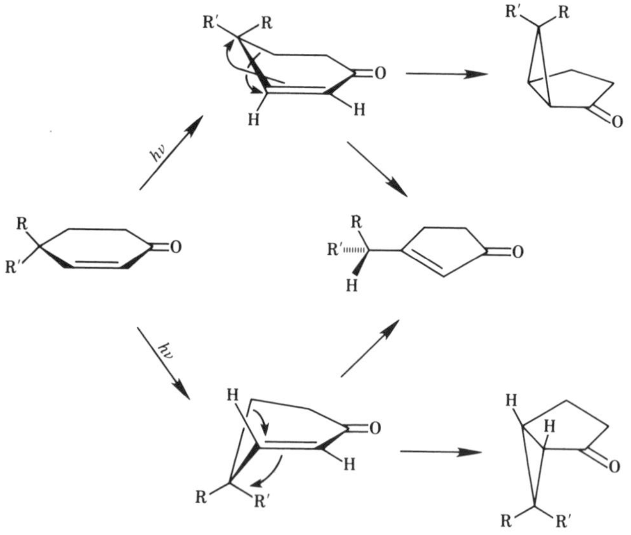

Scheme 1. Stereochemistry of cyclohexenone photorearrangements.

necessarily affording a single lumiketone product. Other mechanistic implications of these results are elaborated below.

Cyclopentenone 23, formed on photoexcitation of enone (+)-20, was also optically active (25). Since some racemization could have occurred during the oxidative reactions used to establish its configuration and optical purity, it is not yet certain whether the cyclopentenone is formed with total or only partial stereospecificity. The predominant, if not exclusive, stereochemical course of reaction is as shown in Scheme 1 and is consistent with its description as a $_\sigma 2_a + _\sigma 2_a$ cycloaddition (27) of the C-4—C-5 σ bond across the C-3—H bond, i.e., migration of the hydrogen atom from C-3 to C-4, leading to inversion of configuration at C-4. This appears to occur synchronously with ring contraction and not via a discrete diradical of type 26. The formation of racemic cyclopentenone 23 on photoexcitation of (−)-22 does appear to proceed via diradical 26, providing additional evidence against the involvement of such diradicals on the pathways from cyclohexenones to rearrangement products.

3. Mechanism of the Lumiketone Rearrangement

a. General Considerations. The lumiketone rearrangement of cyclohexenones is formally analogous to the photochemical rearrangement of 2,5-cyclohexadienones to bicyclo[3.1.0]hex-3-en-2-ones, also popularly known as a lumiketone rearrangement and discussed elsewhere in this volume (28). It is typified by the photoisomerization of 4,4-diphenyl-cyclohexa-2,5-dien-1-one (27) shown below (29). Both enone and dienone

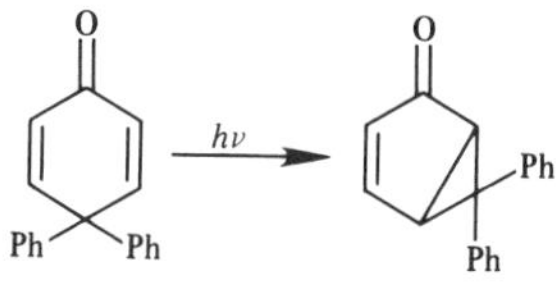

27

rearrangements (known as "type A" rearrangements) (30) can be classified in the manner of Woodward and Hoffmann (27) as $_\sigma 2 + _\pi 2$ cycloadditions, and in all cases studied sensitization and quenching experiments indicate that these isomerizations proceed from triplet excited states. Both reactions also appear to be stereospecific and proceed with inversion of configuration at C-4 (see Section II,A,2) (28). At this point, however, the similarity evaporates. Whereas the dienone rearrangements proceed with quantum efficiencies (QE) of 0.8–1.0 in a variety of polar and nonpolar media (3,4,28), the enone photorearrangements are notoriously inefficient. Thus, the QE for formation of the rearranged products from 2 in *t*-BuOH is only 0.0065 and 0.0077, respectively (4), whereas the formation of lumiketone from phenanthrenone **15** in t-BuOH has QE of 0.0084 (*30*). Similarly, small quantum yields have been measured for other enones (*17,21,31,32*). The critical role of the second double bond in the dienone rearrangement, which is undoubtedly related to the high QE of the reaction, is clear from the large body of evidence that virtually requires that zwitterions of structure **28** be key intermediates on the way to the lumiketones and other dienone rearrangement products (*2,33*). Obviously, no such bicyclic zwitterionic intermediates can be envisaged for the seemingly analogous rearrangement of cyclohexenones.

In 1963, Chapman (*1*) attempted to link the enone and dienone photorearrangements mechanistically in terms of a "polar state concept" based on a previous demonstration (*29,34*) that the course of the complex 2,5-cyclohexadienone photorearrangements, which had stubbornly resisted adequate mechanistic analysis, could be understood on the basis of the intermediacy of zwitterions of structure **28**. It was suggested that **28** was

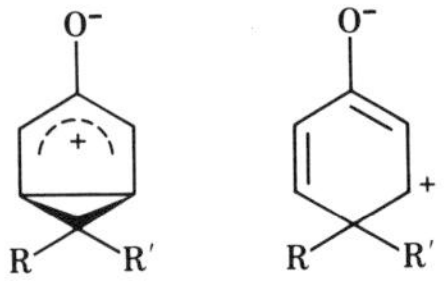

28   29

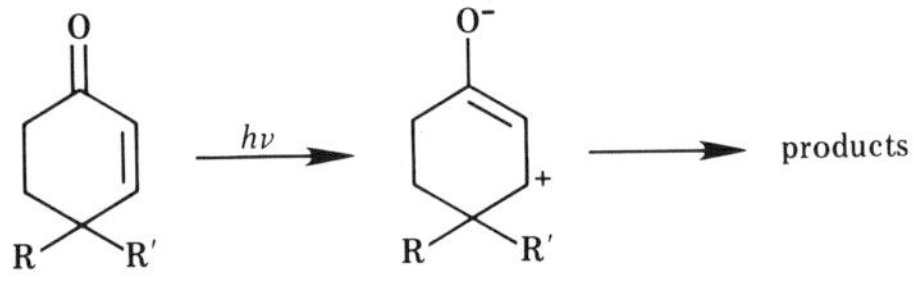

30

derived from dipolar structures of type **29**, a pathway to **28** that was different from that proposed earlier (*29,34*), although it was not specified whether **29** represented an excited state or ground state molecular species. Analogous dipolar species (**30**) derived from cyclohexenones were shown (*1*) to be a handy means of accounting for lumiketone formation, as well as formation of ring-contracted products, as shown below. At that time, it was thought (*1,12*) that 3-alkylcyclopentenones were derived exclusively by secondary photolysis of the lumiketone, although it is now known (*17,23,31*) that the cyclopentenones are primary enone photolysis products as well as products of lumiketone photolysis. Again, there was no specification as to whether the proposed dipolar intermediate (**30**) represented an excited state or a ground state species somehow distinct from the starting material and formed on electronic excitation. In fact, the dipolar structure **30** probably represents a very high energy singlet excited state, inaccessible by ultraviolet excitation of enones at wavelengths above 250 nm (35,36).

Schuster and Brizzolara (21) specifically sought to test the "polar state concept" by studying the photochemistry of the 10-hydroxymethyl-octalone **31**. If, as suspected, the lumiketone rearrangement occurred

from an excited state with diradical and not dipolar character, in the case of **31** rearrangement was expected to be competitive with a radical fragmentation pathway involving explusion of the hydroxymethyl radical. Competition between radical fragmentation and rearrangement pathways had been used profitably in the elucidation of mechanistic details in earlier studies of the photochemistry of cyclohexadienone **32** (33,37). Indeed, in addition to rearrangement of **31** to lumiketone **33** there was a second reaction path leading to ketones **34** and **35** in chloroform, toluene, cumene, and benzene; typically, **33** was the sole product in *t*-BuOH. The fragmentation reaction involved H abstraction from the solvent, as demonstrated by the formation of characteristic products derived from solvent radicals. The intermediacy of hydroxymethyl radical was evident from the formation of formaldehyde, methanol, and ethylene glycol. Ketones **36** and **37** are secondary photolysis products of **34** and **35**, respectively (*38*). Quenching of formation of **33** and **34** by piperylene in benzene and toluene established that these products originate from the same excited state, within an experimental error of ~10%. These results can be readily interpreted in terms of competitive rearrangement and abstraction–fragmentation from an excited state with diradical character. Clearly, it would be difficult to account for these results in terms of direct formation and reaction of a dipolar intermediate (*36*). However, polar intermediates must be considered in accounting for the formation of products of type **4** in acidic solvents. Another possibility is that such products can arise from excitation of protonated enones, as demonstrated by recent studies (*38a*).*

Zimmerman proposed a mechanism (outlined in Scheme 2) for the

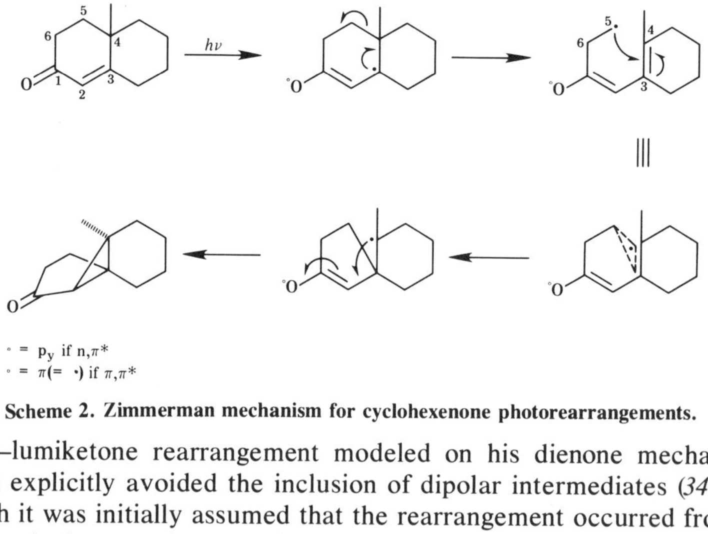

° = p_y if n,π*
° = π(= ·) if π,π*

Scheme 2. Zimmerman mechanism for cyclohexenone photorearrangements.

enone–lumiketone rearrangement modeled on his dienone mechanism, which explicitly avoided the inclusion of dipolar intermediates (*34*). Although it was initially assumed that the rearrangement occurred from an n,π* excited state, a later version of the mechanism (*30,39*) can accommodate either n,π* or π,π* excitation in that the odd electron on oxygen can be either in a (predominantly) nonbonding p orbital on oxygen orthogonal to the π system, or in an orbital that is part of the enone π system, leaving a filled nonbonding p orbital on oxygen. Scission of the 4,5 bond is envisioned to give a diradical species in which the new radical center at C-5 (equivalent to C-1 in the steroid and phenanthrenone systems) does not

* See Note Added in Proof, p. 270.

become completely free, but rather remains bound to the developing ethylenic group at C-3—C-4 (C-5—C-10 in the steroid numbering). The rearrangement should then take place stereospecifically, since neither C-4 nor C-5 ever achieves a completely flat geometry, and rotation around C-5—C-6 as well as C-3—C-4 is inhibited. There is a slight, perhaps only semantic, distinction between such a mechanistic description and one in which formation of the bond between C-5 and C-3 is synchronous with bonding between C-4 and C-2, that is, a concerted cycloaddition mechanism in which formation of one bond may slightly precede the other but in which discrete biradical intermediates of chemically significant lifetimes are not involved at any stage.

A study of the photochemistry of 4,4,6,6-tetramethylcyclohex-2-en-1-one (38) was undertaken (31,40) to test for the possibility of reversible α cleavage of the C-1—C-6 bond as a source of energy wastage. No prod-

38

ucts attributable to such cleavage were observed, and only the normal rearrangement and reduction products were formed in a variety of solvents. The reaction kinetics were similar to those of the 4,4-dimethyl-enone 2, indicating no special pertubation as a result of bis-α' substitution. It was therefore concluded that α cleavage was not occurring in this system (for further discussion of α cleavage of cyclohexenones, see Section II,C,4).

Thus, the observed stereospecificity of the lumiketone rearrangement requires either a concerted reaction mechanism, formally described as a $_\sigma 2_a + _\pi 2_a$ cycloaddition (25), or a stepwise mechanism involving chiral "bound" diradical intermediates of the type depicted in Scheme 2; these may represent shallow minima along the reaction coordinate. Further implications of the triplet nature of these reactions are discussed in Section II,E.

b. Role of Twisted (or trans-*) Cyclohexenones.* The question that logically follows is whether the rearrangement occurs directly from an excited state of the enone or from some ground state species produced after electron demotion. The reaction course depicted in Scheme 1 indicates substantial distortion of the enone geometry from the ground state planar configuration by twisting around the C=C bond. It is well recognized that such torsional motion represents a destabilizing operation for the enone ground state but is expected to be stabilizing for at least some of the enone excited states, by analogy with the effects of twisting on the electronic states of alkenes and polyenes (41). It has been calculated (42) that twisting around the ethylene double bond of acrolein strongly destabilizes the ground state and, to a slightly lesser extent, singlet and triplet n,π^* excited states, but it stabilizes singlet and triplet π,π^* excited states. If the lowest triplet state T_1 in the planar enone geometry is T_{n,π^*} (as for acrolein), substantial mixing of the two excited triplet states will occur as the angle of twist increases, increasing the π,π^* character of the lowest triplet. In some cases a small energy barrier to twisting may exist starting from the planar T_{n,π^*} state. The barrier to twisting in the case of cyclohexenones should be either nonexistent or very small, since there is substantial spectroscopic evidence that the two lowest planar triplet states of cyclic conjugated enones are nearly isoenergetic and that the lowest planar triplet, at least for steroid enones, is T_{π,π^*} (see Section II,D,1).

The tendency of cyclic enones to twist around the C=C bond has been evident since the early 1960's, when the photochemical isomerization of cis-2-cyclooctenone and cis-2-cycloheptenone to their trans isomers was reported (43,44); these were characterized chemically and spectroscopically. These isomerizations occurred to the exclusion of all other chemical reactions of the intermediate electronic excited states, and it could be shown that photochemical dimerization and addition reactions in these systems were in fact dark (i.e., ground state) reactions of the highly reactive trans cyclic enones. It was first assumed (43) that these cis–trans isomerizations, which are of course simple molecular rearrangements, occur via triplet excited states, although quenching experiments gave negative results. It was also considered (43) that isomerization of cis-cyclopentenone and cis-cyclohexenone to their trans isomers was "probably not geometrically permissible" but that such isomerization of 1-acetylcyclohexene (39 → 40) was likely. This view was based on the similarity of the photochemical behavior of 1-acetylcycloalkenes with that of six-, seven-, and eight-membered rings (41), and of 2-cycloheptenone and 2-cyclooctenone, but not with that of 2-cyclopentenone and 2-cyclohexenone. Thus, cis–trans isomerization of the reactive (triplet) excited state of the former group of enones is faster than intermolecular (triplet) energy transfer to dienes.

39   40

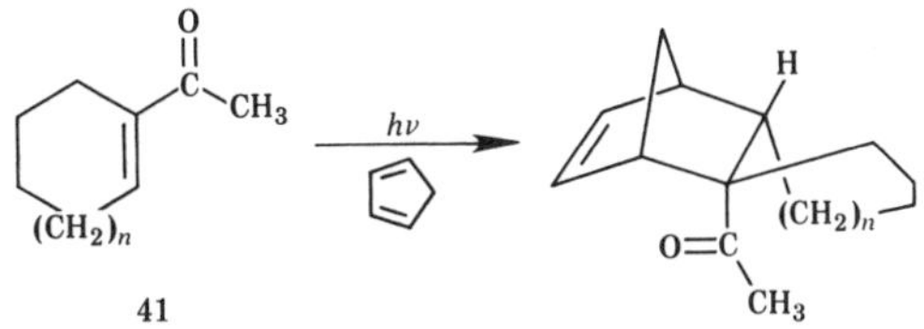

41

(n = 1, 2, or 3)

The intermediacy of *trans*-cycloalkenes in photochemical reactions has been suggested a number of times. It was proposed some time ago (*45*) that direct and sensitized photoprotonation of cyclohexenes, cyclohepntenes, and cyclooctenes involves primary formation of the *trans*-cycloalkenes, followed by protonation to give a carbocation, which then undergoes characteristic reactions. Other workers (*46,47*) have demonstrated that the trans addition of alcohols across the C=C bond of 2-cycloheptenone and 2-cyclooctenones involves initial isomerization to the *trans*-cycloalkenones, followed by syn addition of alcohol across the highly polarized and strained C=C bond, as shown below. Such reactions of 2-cyclohexenones are rare, but recently it has been established (*48*) that the stereochemistry of photoaddition of methanol to Pummerer's ketone (*42*) (*49*) is identical to that observed with the seven- and eight-membered ring enones. The authors (*48*) suggest that syn addition occurs to a molecule in an excited state or to an intermediate in which the C=C bond is twisted by more than 90°, as shown below.

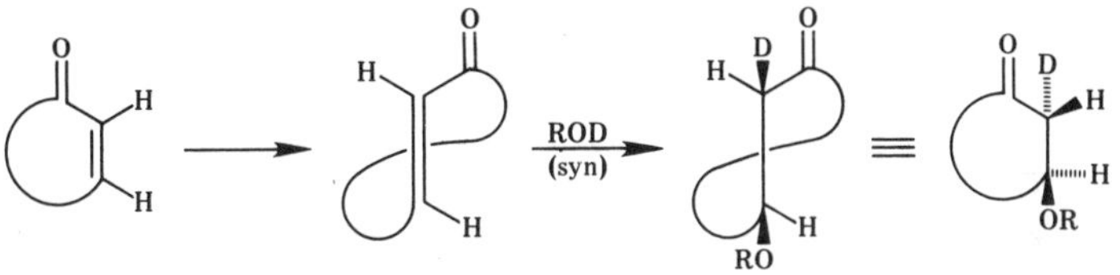

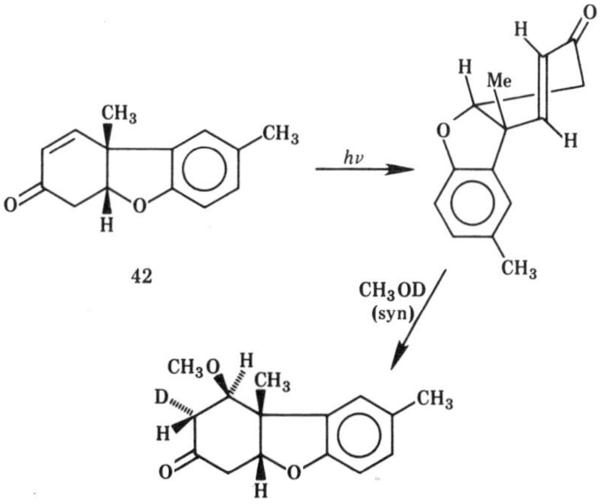

Recent flash spectroscopic studies confirm that twisting around the C=C bond of cyclohexenes and cyclohexenones occurs to a chemically significant extent upon photoexcitation. Thus, a transient intermediate (lifetime 9 μsec, λ_{max} 380 nm) was observed on 267 nm laser excitation of *cis*-1-phenylcyclohexene in fluid solution at room temperature (*50*). The transient was identified as *trans*-1-phenylcyclohexene by its spectral characteristics, lack of oxygen quenching, and kinetic identity with the intermediate in the acid-catalyzed photoaddition of methanol (comparison of kinetic parameters in flash and steady-state photolyses). More recently, independent chemical evidence for the intermediacy of *trans*-1-phenylcyclohexene has been obtained through isolation of a dimer arising from $_\pi 4_s + _\pi 2_s$ cycloaddition of the photochemically generated trans cycloalkene to the cis isomer (*50a*). Similar studies led to the characterization of *trans*-1-phenylcycloheptene (λ_{max} 300 nm), which is much longer lived because of a barrier of 20 kcal/mol to reverse thermal isomerization to the cis isomer (*51*).

Recent flash studies on cyclic α,β-enones have provided very interesting and provocative results (*52–55*). With both 2-cycloheptenone and acetylcyclohexene (**39**) two transients were observed (*52,53*): a short-lived transient (A) and a long-lived transient (B) (see Table 1). In the former case, transient B is readily identified as *trans*-cycloheptenone (λ_{max} 265 nm) by (a) its much longer lifetime in nonpolar versus alcoholic solvents (e.g., 45 sec in cyclohexane; 0.033 sec in MeOH), which is consistent with

TABLE 1

Transients Observed on Flash Photolysis of Cyclic Enones (*54*)

| | Transient A (relaxed triplet) | | | | Transient B (*trans*-cycloalkenone) |
| | Properties in deaerated cyclohexane | | Quenching rate constant (M^{-1} sec^{-1}) | | |
Enone	Lifetime (nsec)	λ_{max} (nm)	O_2	Piperylene	Lifetime λ_{max} (nm)
1-Acetylcyclohexene	16	280	3.5×10^9	$\leq 10^7$	15 μsec 345 (in CH$_3$CN)
2-Cycloheptenone	11	280	—	$\leq 10^7$	45 sec 265 (in cyclohexane)
2-Cyclohexenone	25	275	5×10^9	4×10^7	Not observed
2-Cyclopentenone	30	Not given	—	$\sim 10^7$	Not observed
Testosterone	440	300	2.2×10^9	10^9	Not observed

the previously proposed dark addition of alcohols to *trans*-cyclo-alkenones, (b) the dependence of its lifetime on enone concentration because of addition to ground state trans and cis isomers to give dimers, and (c) its spectral relationship to *trans*-cycloheptene (*51*). Similar criteria permit the assignment of *trans*-1-acetylcyclohexene (**40**) to the long-lived transient B from laser excitation of the cis isomer; its lifetime is 0.35 μsec in MeOH compared to 15 μsec in CH_3CN, and it is not quenched by oxygen (*56*). Other authors (*55*) report a transient with λ_{max} 265 nm and a lifetime of only 200 nsec which is believed to be a "higher-energy conformer" of *trans*-cycloheptenone. It would appear that this is probably the ground state *trans*-enone, the lifetime of which has been shortened by reverse trans to cis isomerization induced by the monitoring light; it has been estimated that the barrier to reversal is in excess of 17 kcal/mol (*52*).

The short-lived transients A are more difficult to identify. For **39**, transient A was demonstrated to be a direct precursor of B since the rate of decay of A matched the rate of growth of B (*53,54*). These authors found that species A for both enones could be quenched by oxygen but not by piperylene; others (*55*) reported a transient from enone **39** with a similar lifetime (37 nsec) and UV absorption (in the region 265–310 nm) which was claimed to be insensitive to both oxygen and piperylene. Since the first authors also observed a long-lived transient B for enone **39**, they argued cogently against an assignment of a ground state *trans*-enone structure for A, whereas the relatively long lifetime and sensitivity to oxygen suggest that A would have to be a triplet excited state (*53,54*). Several other enones give analogous transients with lifetimes of 10–440 nsec (see Table 1) without forming long-lived ground state trans isomers; these transients are quenched by oxygen but (with the exception of testosterone) only inefficiently quenched by piperylene (*54*). A transient with λ_{max} 280 nm and lifetime 50 nsec has also been found (*55*) in the case of cyclohexenone, but once again there is a discrepancy with respect to oxygen quenching.

The inefficient quenching of the cyclohexenone transient A by piperylene is to be contrasted with the efficient quenching of the triplet intermediate in cyclohexenone dimerization by piperylene and other dienes (*15*), corresponding to a triplet lifetime at infinite dilution in degassed acetonitrile of about 3 nsec. Therefore, transient A for cyclohexenone cannot possibly be the same triplet state implicated as a photochemical intermediate (*15*). It has been suggested that transients A are relaxed twisted triplet states, with orthogonal geometries in structurally favorable cases, the energies of which are usually too low (<60 kcal/mol) for efficient transfer of triplet excitation to piperylene (*54*). Since the lifetime of transient A for cyclohexenone is independent of cyclohexenone ground state concentration, the twisted triplet cannot be an intermediate in cyclohexenone dimerization (54). Preliminary quenching data with alkenes suggest that transient A is also not an intermediate in photocycloaddition of cyclohexenone to alkenes, in contrast to earlier suggestions (57), despite the formation of trans-fused bicyclo[4.2.0]octanes as products. It has been further suggested that the absorption maximum of the relaxed triplet A depends on its angle of twist, whereas the lifetime of A depends on the energy gap between it and the ground state with the same geometry; for testosterone, in which twisting is relatively restricted, this gap is estimated to be at 60 kcal/mol, decreasing the triplet decay rate and permitting efficient quenching by piperylene (54).

On the basis of these recent flash photolysis studies, spectroscopic studies (Section II,D,1), and analogy with the photochemistry of 2-cycloheptenone and 2-cyclooctenone, it seems reasonable to conclude that the basic process that occurs on photoexcitation of virtually all cyclohexenones after crossing to the triplet manifold is twisting about the $C\!=\!C$ bond in the manner depicted in Scheme 1 for the formation of lumiketones. The twisted triplet, or "twisted pi-bond biradicaloid" in Michl's terminology (58), serves as an ideal geometry (or "funnel") for radiationless decay from T_1 directly to S_0, since it represents the minimum in the excited triplet surface and must be close to the maximum in the ground state surface that connects enone and lumiketone ground states. The calculations for acrolein show that twisting the terminal CH_2 by 90° lowers the π,π^* triplet energy below that of the corresponding ground state (42). Even if there is no crossing of the cyclohexenone triplet and ground state surfaces at the twisted geometry, there is at least a minimum amount of energy to be converted at this stage to vibrational and rotational energy. The twisted cyclohexenone ground state, which may be a dimple or shallow minimum on the ground state potential surface, partitions between decay to starting material and progress to rearranged isomers. It is not unlikely that the triplet state minimum is lower in energy than the maximum in the ground state surface, as shown in Fig. 1 (25), in which case a small barrier remains on the path to lumiketone, so that lumiketone formation represents the minor decay route of the twisted cyclohexenone, and return to starting material is the major pathway, accounting for the low quantum efficiency of the rearrangement (25). The precise location of the potential minima and maxima in Fig. 1 should be a sensitive function of substituents on or near the enone ring, so that it is not surprising in retrospect that substituents in certain positions wipe out the rearrangement altogether, at least at room temperature. The above considerations

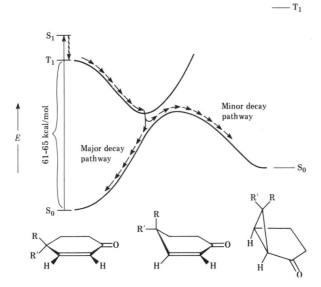

Fig. 1 Proposed potential energy surfaces for the conversion of 2-cyclohexenones to lumiketones. [From Schuster *et al.* (*25*). Reprinted with permission of the copyright holder, the American Chemical Society.]

hold as well for ring contraction to cyclopentenones, also depicted in Scheme 1.

Thus, one can account for energy wastage (i.e., low quantum efficiency) in these reactions without invoking any species, such as a diradical, in which a C—C σ bond is either fully or partially broken and which can revert to starting material in competition with formation of rearrangement products. On the basis of the results cited and also low-temperature phosphorescence data (Section II,D,1), the triplet state that is intercepted by diene quenchers must be the planar triplet ($E_T \sim 70$ kcal/mol), the lifetime of which is determined solely by the rate of twisting around the C=C bond. It is therefore meaningless to calculate rate constants for decay and isomerization from quantum yields and lifetimes of *planar* triplets as determined by quenching kinetics, as has been done many times (*4,17,21,30,39*). The twisted enone has a lifetime that depends solely on its rate of radiationless decay to the ground state surface, which in turn is a function of the angle of twist, as indicated by the data in Table 1. As a consequence, $\phi_{lumi} = \phi_{ST}F$, where ϕ_{ST} is the triplet yield, and F is the fraction of twisted enones that make it over the hump to lumiketone. Since all evidence at present is consistent with $\phi_{ST} \cong 1$ for cyclohexenones, (*4,17,30,31*) the efficiency of rearrangement ϕ_{lumi} is determined *solely* by the relative topology of triplet and ground state surfaces in the region of the twisted structure.

Two additional implications of this mechanistic description are that (a) the quantum yield for lumiketone formation should increase as the temperature is raised, as more twisted molecules make it over the barrier to lumiketones, and (b) cyclohexenones that are constrained from twisting around the C=C bond should be incapable of undergoing the lumiketone rearrangement, even if they otherwise possess all the requisite functionality. The first prediction has not yet been subjected to experimental test to our knowledge, but the second has been verified in a recent study (59).

In enone **43**, the C=C bond of 4,4-dimethylcyclohexenone has been incorporated into a five-membered ring, which severely constrains torsional motion around the C=C bond. If the lumiketone rearrangement simply involved cleavage of the C-4—C-5 σ bond and subsequent rebonding (C-4 to C-2 and C-5 to C-3), there should be no serious impediment to the rearrangement in **43**. The facts (59) are that no isomerization products

43

could be detected on photolysis of **43** in *t*-BuOH, 2-propanol, diethyl ether, acetone, benzene, or hexane when the total photolysis mixtures were subjected to gas chromatographic–mass spectrometric analysis. Reduction is the major reaction path, except in benzene in which the compound is apparently inert to UV irradiation. The observation of photoreduction of **43** in *t*-BuOH and acetone is particularly striking since these are notoriously poor hydrogen-donating solvents (20,84). Free radical addition of these solvents across the C=C bond of **43** was also observed (59). The photoreduction occurs exclusively at the C=C bond and can be quenched by 1,3-cyclohexadiene ($k_q\tau \sim 40\ M^{-1}$), implying formation of a reactive triplet state, probably $^3\pi,\pi^*$ (see Section II,C,1).

Even more intriguing is the observation that **43** fluoresces at room temperature in solution (λ_{max} 385 nm in both cyclohexane and acetonitrile; τ_F 0.24 nsec in cyclohexane), providing the first example of cyclohexenone fluorescence. The fact that lumiketone rearrangement is suppressed supports the view that substantial twisting around the C=C bond is required in the course of the rearrangement. The observation of fluorescence suggests that such torsion is also a decay mode of S_1 (n,π^*), since the enhanced singlet lifetime of this torsionally constrained enone allows fluorescence to compete with the normal singlet decay processes. Another implication is that intersystem crossing to the triplet manifold may occur preferentially in a twisted rather than a planar enone geometry; this is reasonable considering that twisting should improve spin–orbit coupling (60). Figure 1 may therefore have to be modified to include the effect of twisting in the singlet as well as triplet excited cyclohexenone. Since the energy of $^1n,\pi^*$ should increase with torsion around C=C, there may be a small energy barrier for crossing to the descending $^3\pi,\pi^*$ surface, in which case the fluorescence would be expected to be temperature dependent. This is currently under investigation.

The first reported fluorescence from a cyclic α,β-enone was that of cyclopentenone **44** (61); this emits at 350 nm in acetonitrile at room temperature and in EPA at 77 K. No fluorescence could be detected from the analogous enone **45**. The fluorescence of **44** was attributed to an unusually

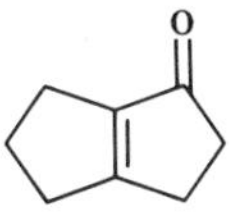

44 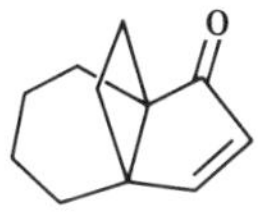   **45**

large gap (3200 cm^{-1}) between S$_1$ ($^1n,\pi^*$) and the $^3\pi,\pi^*$ state, thus inhibiting intersystem crossing and enhancing τ_s; ϕ_{ST} was not measured, however. The gap for enone **45** is only 850 cm^{-1}. One may alternatively rationalize this observation in terms of the rigidity of **44** with respect to torsion around the C=C bond, an effect that may not be as pronounced in enone **45**. However, it is not yet possible to assess the relative importance of the torsional effect and the proximity of $^3\pi,\pi^*$ to $^1n,\pi^*$ states as contributing factors affecting enone fluorescence.

B. Other Types of Cyclohexenone Photorearrangements

1. Di-π-methane Rearrangements*: 1,2-Aryl and 1,2-Vinyl Migrations

When 4,4-diarylcyclohexenones are irradiated, an aryl group migrates from C-4 to the β-carbon of the enone with formation of a three-membered ring by bonding between C-4 and C$_\alpha$. This reaction, which has been subjected to intense scrutiny (62–62b), is illustrated below for the 4,4-diphenylenone **46**. A mixture of endo and exo stereoisomers is generally formed, with the endo isomer invariably predominating.

* See Essay 16.

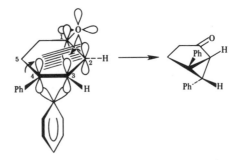

The mechanism of the transformation is fairly well understood (*62–62b*). Migratory aptitudes of substituted aryl groups establish that the aryl migration is occurring to a β-carbon, which is best described as a neutral center with odd-electron (i.e., radical) character and not as electron deficient. Once again, this is inconsistent with the "polar state concept" (*1*). Sensitization and quenching studies establish conclusively that the rearrangement occurs exclusively from triplet excited states and that the triplet yield on direct irradiation of these enones must be close to 100%.

The rearrangement is totally analogous to the di-π-methane (DPM) rearrangements studied extensively in recent years, particularly by Zimmerman and his co-workers (*63*), except that the enone rearrangements can be brought about by n → π* excitation, which is, of course, not possible in hydrocarbon systems. The formation of the major product can be rationalized in terms of a bridged intermediate, as proposed by Zimmerman and shown in Fig. 2 (*64*), in which the orbital interactions account

Fig. 2 The intermediate bridged species in the rearrangement of 4,4-diarylcyclohexenones. [From Zimmerman (*64*).]

for inversion of configuration at C-4. The fact that this is not the exclusive reaction course led to the suggestion that diradicals of type **47** may intervene at least in the minor pathway leading to 6-*exo*-aryl product, and that the rearrangement is not fully concerted. Interestingly, DPM rearrangement of the hydrocarbon analogue **48** also gives the *endo*-phenyl product predominantly, although this is a singlet and not a triplet photoreaction.

| **48** | (Major) | (Minor) |

Quantum yields for the aryl migration have been found to be as high as 0.18 but vary considerably depending on the migrating and nonmigrating groups. By the use of quantum yields and triplet lifetimes determined from quenching experiments, rate constants for unimolecular rearrangement (k_r) and decay (k_d) of the reactive triplet state have been calculated assuming that decay of the quenched triplet directly to the ground state competes with rearrangement. When this assumption is made, k_r values vary greatly depending on the migrating and nonmigrating aryl groups, whereas the k_d values show little variation from system to system (e.g., $k_d = 10.7 \times 10^8$ sec^{-1} for **46** and 15.2×10^8 sec^{-1} for the 4-p-cyanophenyl-4-phenyl analogue). It was therefore concluded that the "decay to product seems to have little in common with the decay back to reactant" (*62b*). Alternatively, these reactions may be related to the "type A" lumiketone rearrangements discussed earlier (Section II,A,3,b) in which the quenchable triplet does not itself partition between reaction and decay but in which such branching arises farther along the reaction hypersurface. If this were the case, the lifetime of the quenchable triplet (which is approximately equal to the calculated values of $1/k_d$ in these systems because of the low QE) would simply reflect the rate of formation of this geometrically distorted reaction intermediate, perhaps once again involving twisting around the C=C bond.

The direct competition between the type A and the aryl migration pathways has also been investigated (*65*) by the use of 4-methyl-4-phenyl-2-cyclohexenone (**49**); this gives five photoproducts attributable to contributions from both reaction pathways. The aryl migration products **50** and **51** are the exclusive products in benzene and ether and the dominant products in *t*-BuOH, whereas the two lumiketones (**52** and **53**) are most prominent in the more polar protic and aprotic solvents (e.g., CH_3CN, $HCONH_2$, 30% aqueous methanol). A mechanism was proposed

49   50   51

52   53   54

(65) for the formation of **54** analogous to the aryl migration pathway; however, it has been suggested (25) that this product might conceivably arise by a secondary type A rearrangement of **51**, although this would violate the generalization (18) that two alkyl groups at C-4 are required for this type of rearrangement.

The solvent dependence of the product distribution was rationalized (65) in terms of competitive reaction from the two enone triplet states, the $^3n,\pi^*$ state, which reacts by aryl migration, and the $^3\pi,\pi^*$ state, which is responsible for the lumiketone rearrangement. Increased solvent polarity and hydrogen-bonding capability are expected to stabilize the latter with respect to the former triplet; thus, an increase in the relative yield of products from the π,π^* state at the expense of products from the $^3n,\pi^*$ state is predicted, in accord with the experimental observations. Nothing definite can be concluded, however, as to which triplet is of lower absolute energy in the various solvents; only the effect of solvent polarity on the relative energies of the two triplets is predictable. A single experiment using naphthalene (E_T 61 kcal/mol) as triplet quencher in 95% ethanol indicated that formation of **50** and **52** was quenched differentially (Stern–Volmer slopes of 20 and 4 M^{-1}, respectively) (65), suggesting that these products do indeed arise from two nonequilibrating triplet excited states of different lifetimes. Additional quantitative data for this and related systems, including measurements of absolute quantum yields and quenching constants in a variety of solvents, would be very helpful in establishing the validity and generality of the "two-triplet" mechanism (see Section II,D,3).

The stereochemistry of both the lumiketone rearrangement and phenyl migration was studied (25) by the use of partially resolved enone **49** (40–50% enantiomeric excess). The formation of both **52** (in 95% EtOH) and

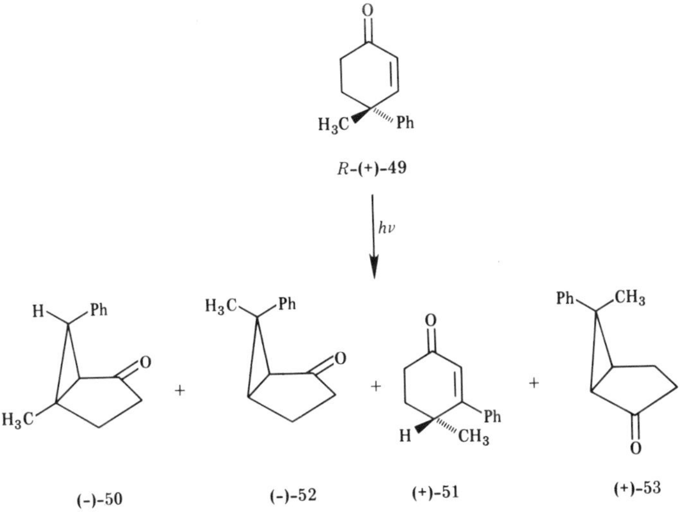

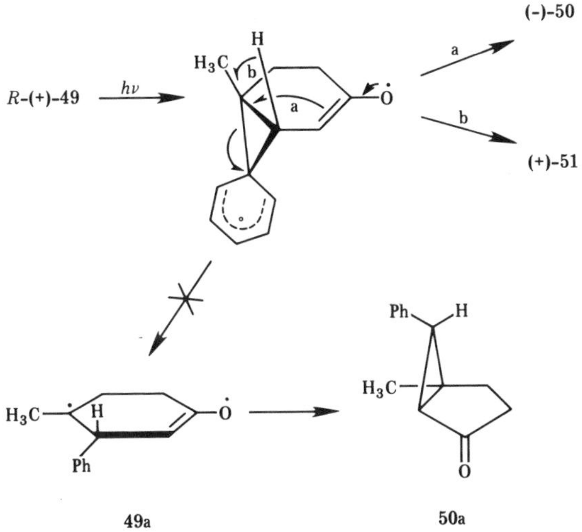

R-(+)-49

(-)-50   (-)-52   (+)-51   (+)-53

49a   50a

50 (in benzene and 95% EtOH) occurred stereospecifically with no loss of optical purity and no racemization of recovered starting material, within experimental error. By relating absolute configurations of products and starting material, it was shown that both rearrangements occurred with complete inversion of configuration at C-4. The implications of this stereochemical course for lumiketone isomerization were discussed earlier (Section II,A,2). Since the 1,2-aryl migration must occur by bonding of the aryl group to C-3 on the same face of the enone from which it was bound to C-4 (i.e., the phenonium intermediate or transition state must have a cis fusion of the three- and six-membered rings), 50 must be formed stereospecifically by either a stepwise or a concerted mechanism. The absence of the *exo*-6-phenyl ketone 50a among the products of photolysis, however, would be difficult to rationalize if diradical 49a were an intermediate, since bonding between C-2 and C-4 would appear to be possible on both ring faces of 49a, giving a mixture of 6-*exo*-phenyl and 6-*endo*-phenyl products. This specificity could be better understood if phenyl bridging and ring contraction were more or less synchronous, a mechanism that seems more attractive. The migrations of phenyl from C-4 to C-3 and of hydrogen back from C-3 to C-4, leading to 51, most likely occur on opposite faces of the cyclohexenone ring system with inversion of configuration at C-4, whether the mechanism is stepwise or synchronous. Thus, the stereochemistry of the product is almost surely that depicted, although this has not yet been established; again, it would be surprising if there were any loss of optical purity in the formation of (+)-51.

A mechanistically analogous rearrangement involving the migration of a vinyl substituent at C-4 of an enone has been reported (66). Irradiation of 55 at 254 nm gives a mixture of the 6-*endo*-propenyl ketone 56 (major product), the 6-exo epimer 57, and dienone 58. A preparative run with

(E)-55   (E)-56   (E)-57   (E)-58

(Z)-59

(E)-55 in dioxane gave 40% (E)-56, 4% (E)-57, and 6% (E)-58 based on 50% converted 55; E–Z isomerization of starting material generally competes with the rearrangements. No lumiketone product was reported. It is interesting that 55 fails to undergo a cyclization reaction, analogous to that shown by 59, on irradiation into S_2 (Section II,B,3). The authors suggest that this may be the result of an unfavorable conformation for H abstraction such that the propenyl group points away from the ring rather than toward C_α. It is likely that the observed rearrangements occur from triplet excited states, but the pertinent experimental data have not, as yet, been reported.

The ability of a cyclopropyl substituent to undergo the 1,2 migrations seen with aryl and vinyl substituents was investigated with 4-

cyclopropylenones **60** and **61** (*67,68*). The dicyclopropylenone **60** was found to undergo exclusively type A rearrangement to **62** and **63**, which in *t*-BuOH accounted for 85% of consumed **60**. Irradiation of enone **61** in nonpolar solvents gave exclusively **64**, **65**, and **66**, all products of a 1,2-phenyl migration; in polar protic solvents, the lumiketone **67** was formed in addition to the other products. Thus, the pattern of product formation as a function of solvent is reminiscent of that found for enone **49**. It was also suggested that the triplet responsible for the phenyl shift is probably $^3n,\pi^*$ and that electronic factors should favor the phenyl migration. Also, the ability of a group to migrate from C-4 to C-3 may well be dependent on its ability to assume a pseudoaxial geometry, so that if R_1 = phenyl and R_2 = cyclopropyl or methyl the extent to which **68** or **69** is populated may well determine the migratory ability of R_2 versus that of phenyl. The available data do not permit a choice between the steric and electronic explanations for the reaction course; it is probable that both play a role.

2. Rearrangement to β,γ-Unsaturated Ketones

It was found that deconjugation by rearrangement to β,γ-unsaturated ketones was a major reaction of conjugated cyclohexenones, in competition with rearrangement and dimerization (*18*). At present, there does not appear to be a sufficient pattern of reactivity to allow one to predict safely whether unstudied systems possessing one or more γ-H will or will not show this reaction.

The reaction mechanism has been studied most thoroughly (*17,32*) in the

5

$h\nu$

70   71   72

case of $\Delta^{1,9}$-10-methyl-2-octalone (**5**). In the initial study (*17*), it was found that the efficiency of conversion of **5** depended inversely on the enone concentration, suggesting a bimolecular reaction between an octalone triplet and an octalone ground state. An intermolecular hydrogen transfer was indicated from irradiation of a mixture of undeuteriated and 1,3,3,8,8-pentadeuteriated **5** in C_6F_6, which led to the formation of monodeuteriated **70**, among other products (a similar experiment was carried out earlier with testosterone acetate). Also, irradiation of testosterone in t-BuOD led to the formation of the analogous β,γ-enone, with 60% d_1 and 40% d_0, indicating the intervention of an intermediate capable of rapid deuterium–hydrogen exchange. On the basis of these results, the mechanism shown in Scheme 3 was proposed. It involves H abstraction from ground state enone **5** by the oxygen of the enone triplet to give a pair of radicals (**73** and **74**), which then disproportionate to give **5** (ground state) plus dienol **75** (or two molecules of dienol **75**); the dienol then undergoes unimolecular ketonization to a mixture of **5** and **70**. The species undergoing H–D exchange could be either radical **73** or dienol **75**.

On the basis of the earlier generalizations, it would therefore appear that this reaction proceeds from an n,π^* triplet state, and indeed this was initially suggested (*17*). It was also observed that, when the photoreactions

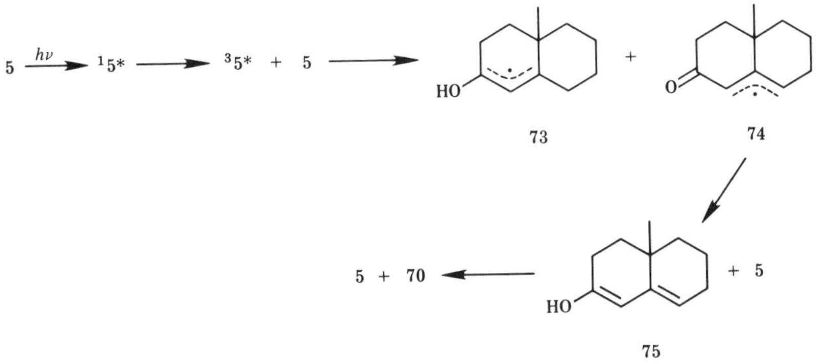

Scheme 3.

of **5** were quenched with 2,5-dimethyl-2,4-hexadiene, the efficiency of quenching of the formation of the β,γ-enone **70** was much less than that for quenching of lumiketone **71** in t-BuOH, isopropyl alcohol (IPA), benzene, and $C_6H_5CF_3$. Significantly, the kinetic quenching data in IPA for the formation of the dihydro ketone **72** fell on the same line as for **71** (Stern–Volmer slope 9.3 M^{-1}) and diverged significantly from the data for the formation of **70** (Stern–Volmer slope 1.4 M^{-1}). Assuming, as above, that the isomerization to **70** proceeds from the n,π^* triplet, one must then assign both the photoreduction and the lumiketone isomerization to the π,π^* triplet state. Later investigations (*32*) revealed that there were problems in the gas chromatographic analysis for **70** used in this study, since **70** thermally isomerizes to **5** under the conditions of the analysis. It was therefore reluctantly concluded that the kinetic data were not sufficient to *require* that these reactions proceed from different triplet states, or from triplet states that are not in thermal equilibrium at room temperature, although the two-triplet postulate is neither disproved nor inconsistent with the results. For simplicity, a mechanism for photoreaction was written (*32*) involving only one triplet excited state of unassigned configuration. This remains an unresolved problem.

3. Allylic Rearrangements and Cyclizations: Wavelength-Dependent Photochemistry

In 1971, the first report appeared (*69*) of an interesting set of reactions of cyclohexenones seen on excitation at 254 nm into the $\pi \rightarrow \pi^*$ absorption band but not seen on excitation into the n $\rightarrow \pi^*$ absorption band with light of ≥ 313 or ≥ 340 nm, depending on the system under study. These are illustrated by the reactions of compounds **76, 77,** and **78**. Thus, n $\rightarrow \pi^*$ excitation of **76** and **77** affords the usual lumiketone rearrangement and deconjugation; **78** is totally unreactive under these conditions. Upon $\pi \to \pi^*$ excitation, **76** and **77** undergo allylic rearrangement ([1,3] sigmatropic shift) of the dialkoxymethyl group from C_γ to C_α accompanied, as with **78**, by cyclization of the ether moiety to the enone β-carbon (69–72).

The allylic rearrangement was determined to be intramolecular on the basis of the failure of cross-products to be formed on irradiation of a mixture of **76** and **79**. The mechanism was further studied by means of a stereochemical probe, namely, the pair of optically active diastereomeric acetals **80** and **81** (73). Irradiation of **80** resulted in gradual epimerization of the starting material and formation of the pair of diastereomers **82** and

83 in a ratio of 1.4 : 1, extrapolated to zero conversion. Irradiation of the other diastereomer gave an inverse ratio of **82** and **83**. Epimerization was not observed on irradiation of **80** at ≥300 nm or of **82** at 254 nm, or on acetone-sensitized photolysis of **82**. Therefore, the loss of stereochemistry in the migrating group observed during the reaction must be the consequence of the reaction pathway and is not an artifact. The results indicate that the reaction must go, at least in part, via a radical pair mechanism involving an intermediate stage, depicted as **84,** in which inversion at the migrating carbon can occur before bonding at C_α or C_γ. The fact that there is some net retention of configuration implies either a competition of stepwise and concerted pathways for the reaction, or that bonding to C_α competes with rotation in the radical pair.

　　The cyclization reaction of **76** and **77** was originally thought to involve an intramolecular abstraction of hydrogen by the carbonyl oxygen (69,70), but this is impossible with **78**. Thus, the authors conclude (72) that the reaction generally involves intramolecular H transfer directly to C_α of the enone and cyclization of the radical pair at C_β.

　　It is clear that the excited state responsible for the allylic shift and cyclization is not accessible upon excitation into the enone S_1 state, but requires excitation directly into S_2. The reactive state is either S_2 or a high-lying triplet state T_3, the energy of which is between that of S_2 and S_1, since both T_1 and T_2 lie below S_1 (see Section II,D,1). The authors clearly prefer an interpretation in terms of reaction directly from S_2 competitive with internal conversion to S_1. This is yet another of the increasing number of systems displaying reactions from upper excited states (74).

　　Additional features of these reactions are illustrated by the pair of (E)- and (Z)-propenyl ketones **85** (66). Irradiation of either ketone in the n →

π^* absorption band ($\geq$300 nm) led to E–Z isomerization at the double bond, deconjugation to a mixture of (E)- and (Z)-**86**, and formation of only the (E)-lumiketone **87** [ϕ = 0.037 from (E)-**86** at low conversion]. The product distribution, as usual, was strongly solvent dependent. Acetophenone-sensitized photolysis in benzene or t-BuOH gave product distributions similar to those on direct photolysis, except that the formation of (Z)-**87** was seen after about 50% conversion; the (E)- and (Z)-lumiketones were interconverted upon acetophenone sensitization. On irradiation into S_2 ($\pi \rightarrow \pi^*$ excitation) the tricyclic compound **88** was formed in addition to the product pattern seen on irradiation at longer wavelengths. The quantum yield for formation of **88** was invariant within the $\pi \rightarrow \pi^*$ absorption band, was much larger starting with (Z)-**85** compared to (E)-**85** (0.29 versus 0.016), and decreased with increasing enone concentration. The cyclization could not be sensitized, even by means of high-energy sensitizers. There was no loss of deuterium on cyclization of (Z)-**85**-d_1 and (E,Z)-**85**-d_4, establishing the intramolecularity of the H abstraction.

These data support the conclusions reached from the earlier studies of the acetals discussed above. From the standpoint of synthesis, the cyclization to **88** (isolated yield 47%, but not optimized) affords ready access to functionalized [4.4.3]propellanes. The preferred cyclization from the (Z)- in relation to the (E)-enone could be readily rationalized in terms of conformational preferences which place the allylic hydrogen proximate to the enone α-carbon. Again, reaction directly from S_2 in competition with internal conversion to S_1 seems the simplest rationalization for the wavelength dependence.

The formation of only one lumiketone stereoisomer, (E)-**87**, directly from both the (Z)- and (E)-enones is in apparent conflict with the findings (25) of complete stereospecificity in the lumiketone rearrangement. There could be unknown factors at work in this system that interfere with the concerted process in favor of a diradical mechanism, allowing isomerization around the propenyl C=C bond. More likely, however, is the possibility that the reaction proceeds by a DPM rearrangement via the diradical **89**, which affords exactly the same product as the lumiketone rearrangement in this system. The two routes could be distinguished using enone labeled in ring B, but the results of such an experiment have not yet been reported.

C. Competitive Photoreactions of Cyclohexenones and Related Systems

Other photoreactions usually occur concurrently with photorearrangements of cyclohexenones to lumiketones and cyclopentenones. These reactions are relevant mechanistically to the rearrangements, especially with respect to the assignment of configurations to the relative excited state(s) (see Section II,D,3).

1. Photoreduction and Intramolecular H Transfer

Photoreduction of enones has been shown by means of standard sensitization and quenching techniques to involve triplet excited states in several quite different systems (75–77). Hydrogen abstraction from the solvent by the excited state acting as a radical reagent is indicated by the formation of characteristic products from solvent-derived radicals (e.g., C_2Cl_6 in $CHCl_3$, bibenzyl in toluene, biphenyl in benzene), as well as radical-coupling products. The effectiveness of the solvent in causing photoreduction is directly related to the reactivity of the solvent as an H donor toward free radicals, that is, to its C—H bond dissociation energy (20). Thus, the yields of photoreduction products competitive with rearrangement in various solvents decrease in the order 2-propanol ∼ chloroform ∼ cyclohexane > toluene > cumene ∼ ethyl ether ∼ dioxane > pyridine ∼ benzene > t-BuOH. Systems that are prone to photorearrange usually do not undergo reduction in t-BuOH. (For an exception, see the case of enone **43** in Section III,A,3,b.) Photoreduction of enones in benzene is surprising considering the very low reactivity of benzene as an H donor toward reactive free radicals such as $CH_3\cdot$, $HO\cdot$, and $H\cdot$ (78,79). The rate constant for H abstraction from benzene by benzophenone triplets, the prototype for ketone n,π^* triplets, has been determined to be $16–19\,M^{-1}$ sec^{-1} (80,81), and rate constants of this order of magnitude would not be expected to compete with the otherwise rapid decay processes of enone triplets in benzene. The rate constant for interaction of triplets of enone **31** with benzene was determined (21) to be $1.3 \times 10^5\,M^{-1}\,sec^{-1}$, which seems, by comparison, much too large for an H-abstraction process. An alternative mechanism involving initial rapid complexation of triplets of **31** with benzene was proposed (21) but has not been subjected to further mechanistic scrutiny.

The course of photoreduction of enones falls into two general categories: (a) reduction to give pinacols, solvent addition across the C=O bond, and the formation of other products attributable to initial H abstraction by the carbonyl oxygen atom; (b) reduction of the C=C bond to afford saturated ketones and solvent adducts.

Thus, irradiation of testosterone acetate (**3a**) in ethyl ether (82) afforded

2% of cyclobutane dimers **90**, originally investigated by Butenandt (*83*), 30% of pinacol **91**, and 15% of two diastereomeric adducts of structure **92**. In ethanol, a complex reaction mixture resulted, from which 20% of the saturated ketone could be isolated. A pinacol was also formed in good yield on irradiation of phenanthrenone **15** in IPA. The formation of pinacols and adducts of type **92** strongly implies a mechanism involving initial H abstraction by oxygen followed by coupling of the resulting ketyl radical with another ketyl or a solvent-derived radical. Such behavior is characteristic of ketone triplet n, π^* states (*84*). The radical fragmentation of enone **31**, which appears to be initiated by formation of a ketyl radical, also seems ascribable to a $^3n, \pi^*$ state.

The photoreduction of testosterone acetate (**3a**) in toluene takes a quite different course, leading to the dihydro ketone **93** and the toluene adduct **94** as well as **95** (*17*). This same type of behavior is also seen for octalone **5** in toluene, whereas in IPA only the saturated ketone is formed; there is no indication of pinacol formation in this system (*17*). The monocyclic enones **2** (*4,85*) and **20** (*31*) also afford only saturated ketones on reduction in IPA. The toluene adducts arise by initial H abstraction from toluene at the β-carbon atom, followed by coupling of the resulting radical and benzyl at C_α in a regiospecific but not a stereospecific manner (*17*). The manner of formation of saturated ketones in IPA is more problematical. There are three possible mechanisms, shown in Scheme 4, which have not been distinguished experimentally: (a) initial abstraction by C_β of the enone,

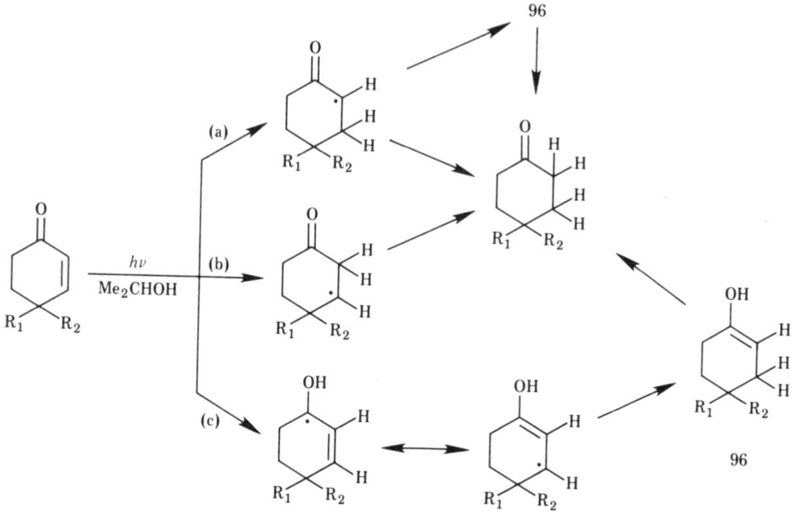

Scheme 4. Mechanisms for photoreduction in isopropyl alcohol.

followed by transfer of a second H atom to C_α from an appropriate source (IPA or $Me_2\dot{C}OH$); (b) the opposite of (a), namely, initial reaction at C_α followed by a second H transfer to C_β; (c) initial H abstraction at the carbonyl oxygen, followed by a second H transfer to C_β to afford enol **96**, which then tautomerizes to the ketone product. Studies using appropriately labeled reagents to distinguish among these mechanistic alternatives are currently in progress.* The third possibility would appear to be least likely, since the ketyl radical should undergo secondary H transfer to the carbonyl carbon as well as C_β to afford α,β-unsaturated alcohols, but such products have never been reported from enone photolysis in IPA and have been definitely excluded in the case of **20** (*31*).

It seems likely (although it is by no means proved)† that saturated ketones are formed from enones in IPA and other solvents by initial reaction at the enone β-carbon, by analogy with the intramolecular H transfers which have been studied in great detail (*86,87*). Thus, irradiation of 4-isopentyl-4-methylcyclopentenone (**97**, X = H) gives products **98, 99,**

97   101   98   99   100

102   103   104

and **100**, derivable from diradical **101** as a result of H transfer from the side chain to C_β, a route clearly demonstrated by irradiation of **97** (X = D). Similar experiments have been carried out on enones **102** and **103**. In all cases, the products arise from 1,5-H transfer to C_β via a six-membered cyclic transition state. In the case of enone **104**, in which 1,5-H transfer can occur only to C_α, reaction takes place exclusively by 1,6-H transfer to C_β (seven-membered cyclic transition state), but much more inefficiently than in the previous reactions (*86*). Stereochemical and conformational features of these reactions have been discussed (*86*). A dramatic and elegant demonstration that steric or entropic factors play little or no role in determining the specificity of these intramolecular H transfers is provided by the recent study (87) of enone **105**. Here H transfer to C_α and C_β is

$$105 \xrightarrow[\text{benzene}]{h\nu} 106 \; + \; 107$$

via **108**

equally likely on steric and conformational grounds. By means of labeling techniques it was shown that **106** and **107** are formed entirely via diradical **108**, derived from intramolecular H transfer exclusively to C_β, on irradiation at short as well as long wavelengths. Thus, one must conclude that intrinsic electronic factors in the enone excited state control the specificity of H abstraction at C_β over reaction at C_α. This is consistent with the view (86) that these are reactions of enone π,π^* states, since such selectivity is unexpected from $^3n,\pi^*$ states.†

It is tempting to generalize that those photoreductions of enones involving initial H transfer to C_β occur via $^3\pi,\pi^*$ states, whereas reactions involving initial H transfer to the carbonyl oxygen occur from $^3n,\pi^*$ states. The assignment of a π,π^* configuration to the triplet state of octalone **5** affording **72** and the toluene adduct analogous to **94** is consistent with this postulate, although it has been suggested (88) that reduction of 4,4-dimethylenone (**2**) to the saturated ketone occurs via the $^3n,\pi^*$ state (see Section II,D,3). Some other tentative assignments are of interest in this connection. The photochemical conversion of taxinine (**109**) and some

$$109 \xrightarrow{h\nu} 110$$

† See Note Added in Proof, p. 269.

analogues to compounds of structure **110,** a rare example of intramolecular H transfer to C_α of the enone chromophore, has been studied (*89*).
Models indicate that the migrating hydrogen is quite close to the C=C
bond. Since the reaction can be sensitized and quenched in ways characteristic of triplet photoprocesses, and is preferred in polar rather than
nonpolar solvents, the authors suggested that it occurs via a π,π^* triplet.
The unusual bridged cyclopentenone **111** is unique in that it undergoes
intramolecular H transfer to both C_α (to give **112**) and C_β (to give **113**) (*90*).

111   113   112

Low-temperature phosphorescence of **111** indicates that the lowest triplet
under these conditions is $^3\pi,\pi^*$ (see Section II,D,1). The formation of **112**
and **113** is quenched with markedly different efficiency by 9,10-dibromo-
anthracene, suggesting that the two reactions arise from different triplets
centered on the enone chromophore. A mechanism involving abstraction
by C_β from the $^3\pi,\pi^*$ state and by C_α from the ^{3}n,π^* state was rejected by
the authors because the ratio of **113** to **112** decreased modestly upon
increasing solvent polarity, a change that should stabilize the supposedly
lowest π,π^* triplet relative to the n,π^* triplet. However, the results would
be consistent with the proposed reactivity generalization if the lowest
triplet under reaction conditions in solution were n,π^* and not π,π^*; this is
reasonable considering the general closeness in energy of the two states in
enones (see Section II,D,1). However, one might then expect the two
states to be in thermal equilibrium since their relaxed geometries should
not differ greatly in a molecule as rigid as **111**.

2. Photodimerization

As mentioned earlier, 2-cyclohexenone itself undergoes dimerization to
a mixture of cis–anti head-to-head and head-to-tail dimers to the apparent
exclusion of all other possible photoreactions (*13–15*). Similar behavior is

shown by 2-cyclopentenone (43). Kinetic study of the cyclohexenone di-merization (15) led to the conclusion that the dimerization occurs from a quenchable triplet state formed with 100% efficiency, probably $^3\pi,\pi^*$, via two metastable dimeric species with charge-transfer character that revert to cyclohexenone ground state in competition with dimer formation. The cyclohexenone triplet that sensitized the cis–trans isomerization of piperylene was concluded to be that which led to dimers; the conclusion was based on the identity of the kinetic parameters measured for quench-ing of dimer formation and for sensitization of cis–trans isomerization of piperylene. These results must be considered in light of the recent flash studies discussed earlier (54); by default, the cyclohexenone triplet lead-ing to dimers (triplet lifetime ~3 nsec at infinite dilution) (15) must be the planar spectroscopic triplet state. Dimerization was the principal reaction of a large number of other substituted cyclohexenones and octalones (18).

3. Norrish Type II Reaction

The Norrish type II reaction (91), involving abstraction of a γ-H from the side chain of an enone by the carbonyl oxygen, may compete with normal enone reaction pathways. Thus, 6-propyl-2-cyclohexenone (114), on irradiation in t-BuOH, gave 2% of 2-propylcyclohexanone (115), 23% of cyclobutanol 116, 4% of the bicyclic ketone 117, and 3% of 2-allylcyclohexanone (118) (92). Products 116 and 117 are most reasonably derived by internal H transfer of γ-H to the carbonyl oxygen to give 119, followed by cyclization to either the carbonyl carbon or the β-carbon, respectively. Product **118** could arise by disproportionation of **119** or initial intramolecular H transfer to C_β to give diradical **120** via a seven-membered transition state, analogous to the intramolecular H transfers in 4-alkylcyclopentenones discussed in Section II,C,1, followed by a second H transfer from the methyl group to C_α (intramolecular disproportionation). Except for a small yield of photoreduction product, none of the usual cyclohexenone reaction pathways seems to operate in this system. Of course, lumiketone photorearrangement of **114** is not expected, by analogy with other systems studied by Dauben et al. (18). Although no mechanistic studies on **114** were reported, it is likely that all reactions occur via triplet states by analogy with the other enone systems discussed previously. It should be noted, however, that Norrish type II reactions in alkanones often have a substantial singlet excited state component (91).

4. α Cleavage (Norrish Type I Reaction)

Cyclic and acyclic saturated ketones readily undergo cleavage of the bond between the carbonyl carbon and an α-carbon to generate a pair of radicals in competition with other characteristic photoprocesses. The products of this Norrish Type I reaction pathway (93) in the case of cyclic ketones include the starting material, regenerated by rebonding of the radical sites, and unsaturated aldehydes and ketenes derived by H transfer in intermediate biradicals. These processes are illustrated below for the case of 2,2-dimethylcyclohexanone (**121**). The rate constant for α

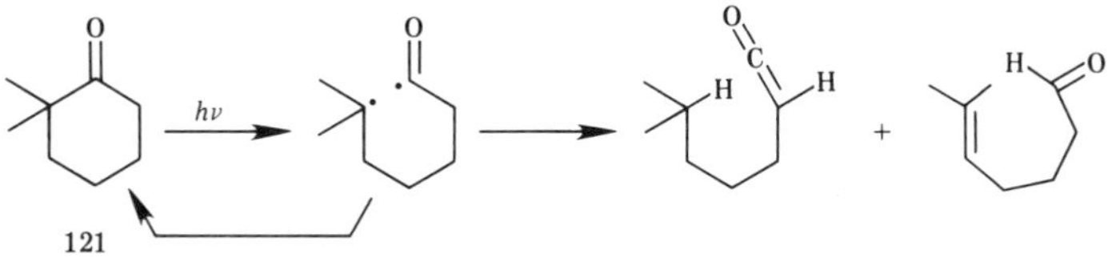

cleavage of the reactive triplet state in this case is $\sim 2 \times 10^9 \text{ sec}^{-1}$ (94), assuming that the triplet lifetime in these systems is determined solely by the rate of α cleavage and that reaction inefficiency is determined by biradical reversion to starting material, which seems reasonable. Cyclohexanone triplets are less reactive by a factor of 6 (94).

Lifetimes of quenchable triplet states of cyclohexenones are generally of the order of 10^{-8} to 10^{-9} sec on the basis of quenching kinetics, e.g., for enone **2** in IPA and t-BuOH $1/\tau_T = 1 \times 10^8$ and $3.9 \times 10^7 \text{ sec}^{-1}$, respectively (4,85); for **38** $1/\tau_T = 5.0 \times 10^8 \text{ sec}^{-1}$ in t-BuOH (31); for octalone **5**, $1/\tau_T = 5 \times 10^8 \text{ sec}^{-1}$ in benzene and $0.4 \times 10^9 \text{ sec}^{-1}$ in IPA (17). Although there is some uncertainty in deriving these values because of the assumption that the quenchers (di-t-butyl nitroxide, naphthalene, and 2,5-dimethyl-2-4-hexadiene, respectively) are quenching at a diffusion-controlled rate (95), the triplet lifetimes of these enones appear to be sufficiently long that α cleavage ought to be competitive with the other triplet decay process were it occurring at a rate similar to that in analogous cyclohexanones.

It seemed reasonable that reversible α cleavage might be responsible for at least a portion of the inefficiency generally observed in cyclohexenone photolysis and that in an appropriately substituted case characteristic products resulting from α cleavage might be detected (40). Thus, enone **38** could give dienal **122** and the ring-contracted ketene **123,** but in fact only the "normal" type A rearrangement and photoreduction products **124–126** were observed in a variety of solvents (31,40). The triplet lifetime of **38**

decreases by approximately one order of magnitude compared with enone **2** upon introduction of two α-methyl groups without any observable alteration in the rearrangement quantum yield (31), which supports the arguments given earlier that the quantum yield is determined upon decay to the ground state potential surface. These results do not absolutely rule out totally reversible α cleavage in the case of **38,** which could conceivably be detectable in a CIDNP experiment.

There are two systems of questionable relevance to the "normal" cyclohexenones discussed previously in which α cleavage has recently been reported. Photolysis of the 2-aza-2-cyclohexenones **127** gave carbamates

128 according to the mechanism shown below (96). Quenching experiments suggested that the reaction occurs via $^1n,\pi^*$ states, the lifetimes of which were not determined. Irradiation of the α-hydroxyenones **129** and **131** gave small yields of lactones **130** and **132** (97). The latter lactone is not

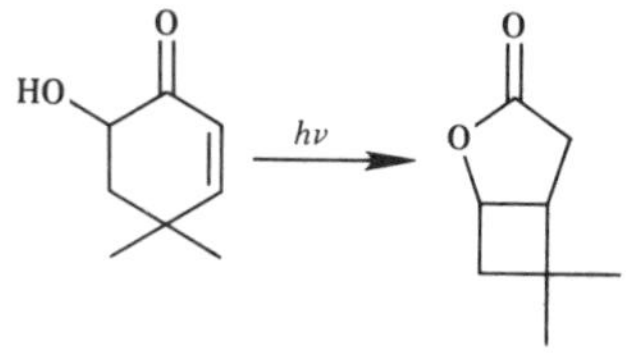

129   130

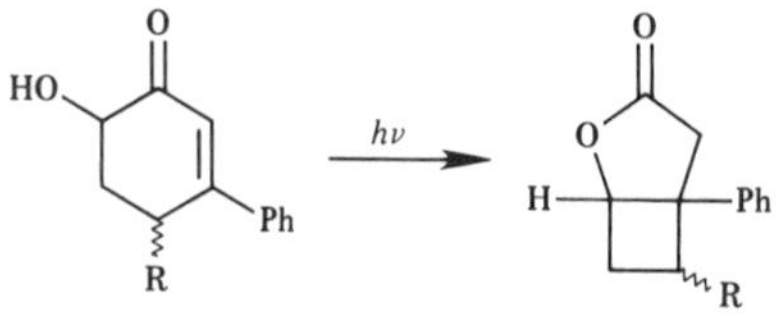

131   132

R = H or Me

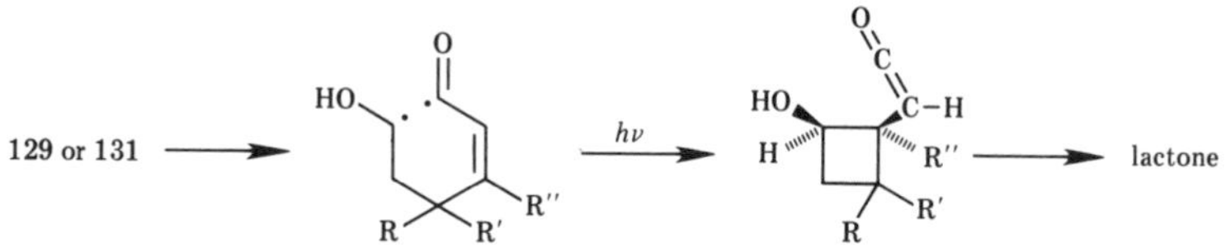

133   134

formed on acetophenone sensitization but is formed in the presence of ferrocene, which led the authors to conclude that the reaction occurs from a singlet excited state. The authors propose that the reaction proceeds via cleavage to diradical **133**, which is stabilized by the hydroxy substituent, cyclization to cyclobutyl ketene **134**, and lactonization. Hydrogen bonding of the hydroxyl group to the carbonyl in enones **129** and **131** is postulated to impart some "rigidity" to the excited state, which presumably assists the α-cleavage reaction.

The characterization of the reactive excited state in the case of the hydroxyenones (97) is incomplete. Since the lactones are formed in very low yields, the remainder of the products should be characterized so as to determine whether any typical enone photoreactions also occur. However, assuming the validity of the conclusions, these singlet-derived α-cleavage reactions occur at the expense of intersystem crossing, rather than in competition with the typical triplet enone reactions. Singlet lifetimes in these systems should be compared with those of "normal" enones to ascertain whether rates of intersystem crossing are affected in these systems or whether some other unknown factors are at work.

The problem posed earlier still remains, however: Why is α cleavage not competitive with other triplet reactions of cyclohexenones, particularly 6,6-disubstituted enones? It has been suggested that the n,π* singlet (and also presumably triplet) energies of typical α,β-enones are not high enough to provide the energy required to cleave the C-1—C-6 bonds, and to support this argument the fact has been cited that 5-substituted cyclopentenones do α-cleave (96) (see Section III,A).

Salem, Dauben, and Turro (35,98) considered the nature of the potential surfaces connecting the triplet excited states of ketones with the various diradicals formed by α cleavage and suggested that the antisymmetric n,π* states are symmetry-related to diradicals $D_{\sigma,\pi}$ (shown in Fig. 3 for cyclohexanone) (99), whereas the symmetric π,π* states are related to diradicals $D_{\sigma,\sigma}$. In the case of cyclohexanone, it was suggested that $D_{\sigma,\sigma}$ lies well below $D_{\sigma,\pi}$ in the bent geometry but that the two diradicals are of similar energy in the linear geometry (see Fig. 3). According to this diagram, neither cleavage route from the singlet can compete with intersys-

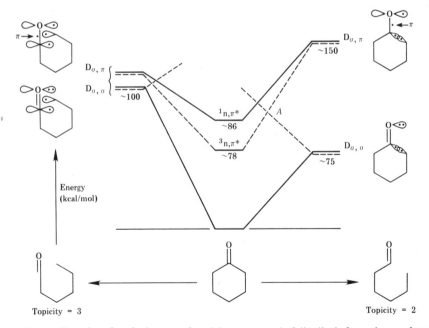

Fig. 3 Energies of excited states of cyclohexanone and of diradicals formed on α cleavage. [From Turro et al. (99).]

tem crossing while cleavage from the $^3n,\pi^*$ state is an activated pathway involving crossing at point A to a descending surface leading to $D_{\sigma,\sigma}$. However, the ketone excited state that actually correlates with $D_{\sigma,\sigma}$ is the high-energy σ,σ^* state, whereas $^3\pi,\pi^*$ correlates with a high-energy diradical or zwitterionic state (100). When a C=C bond conjugated with the carbonyl group is introduced, $D_{\sigma,\pi}$ should be stabilized much more than $D_{\sigma,\sigma}$ because of delocalization of the odd electron in the π system into the C=C bond. It is also apparent (see Section II,D,1) that the singlet and triplet π,π^* states are stabilized relative to the n,π^* states (42). Thus, the conversion of $^3n,\pi^*$ to $D_{\sigma,\pi}$ in bent or linear geometries should be a much more exothermic process for 2-cyclohexenone than for cyclohexanone, even if it still remains endothermic overall—at least, there ought to be a smaller barrier for conversion to $D_{\sigma,\sigma}$ by a surface crossing than is found for cyclohexanone. From $^3\pi,\pi^*$, which is probably the lowest triplet state for typical cyclohexenones (see Section II,D,1), the barrier to crossing to the descending surface linking $^3\sigma,\sigma^*$ to $D_{\sigma,\sigma}$ should not vary much between cyclohexenones and cyclohexanones; if anything, it should be smaller in the enones. Thus, these admittedly crude arguments suggest that rate constants for α cleavage of enones such as **2**, **5**, and **38** ought to be no smaller than for analogous cyclohexanones and should be competitive with rates of other triplet deactivation modes such as twisting and H abstraction. Since this is apparently not the case, some other factors still to be defined seem to be at work (101).

As a footnote to the above, rates of α cleavage of $^3n,\pi^*$ states of phenyl alkyl ketones are found to be generally two orders of magnitude smaller than for aliphatic ketones (102). At least part of this difference is thought to be simply a matter of energetics; that is, the 4–6 kcal/mol stabilization of phenyl ketone triplets could cause increased endothermicity in α cleavage compared to α cleavage of alkyl ketone triplets, although other factors must be considered (102). If a C=C bond in conjugation with the carbonyl has a stabilizing effect on the triplet similar to that of a phenyl group, the activation energy for α cleavage might be similarly increased.

Finally, 2,4-cyclohexadienones undergo α cleavage readily to form unsaturated ketenes, as shown for **135**. Despite the elegant symmetry arguments used to rationalize such a reaction from $^3\pi,\pi^*$ states (98), the reactions in fact appear to originate from $^1\pi,\pi^*$ states on direct photolysis of

135

such compounds (*103*) and are basically just simple electrocyclic ring openings (*27*).

D. Characterization of Excited States of Cyclohexenones and Related Compounds

1. Spectroscopic Studies

Extensive studies of absorption and emission of electronic excitation by steroidal α,β-enones have been carried out (*104–106*) at 77 and 4.2 K. Phosphorescence emission and singlet → triplet excitation were measured by direct absorption and by phosphorescence excitation techniques. The polarization of the various transitions was also measured.

In general, it was observed that the emission spectra are quite diffuse and usually do not overlap the $S_0 \to T_{n,\pi}$ absorption spectra, leading to the conclusion that at low temperatures the lowest triplets of these enones (68–73 kcal/mol above S_0) are distorted $^3\pi,\pi^*$ states, slightly below the $^3n,\pi^*$ states (73–78 kcal/mol). Interaction between these states is thought to be one factor causing the diffuseness in the $S \to T_{n,\pi}$ absorption spectra. The energy gap between the triplet states is as small as 1–2 kcal/mol (~100 cm^{-1}) for octalone **5**, testosterone acetate (**3a**), and the enedione **136** but increases to as much as 450 cm^{-1} (~7 kcal/mol) in the case of 4-

136

methyltestosterone acetate (*106*). Additional evidence for the assignment of a $^3\pi,\pi^*$ configuration to the emitting (lowest) triplet is that the observed lifetimes of 30–60 msec at 77 K are too long for $^3n,\pi^*$ states and that the radiative lifetimes estimated from the emission data are 1000–3000 times longer than the radiative lifetimes calculated from the $S \to T$ absorption spectra, indicating that the emission is not from the same state achieved on excitation. Heavy-atom effects and polarization measurements support the assignments. Triplet yields are found to be unity within experimental error (*106*).

The characteristics of the emission of testosterone acetate at 4.2 K suggest a highly Franck–Condon-forbidden transition. Furthermore, the degree of polarization of the emission with respect to either the $S_0 \to S_{n,\pi}$

(S_1) or $S_0 \rightarrow S_{\pi,\pi}$ (S_2) transitions was very low. These data led the authors (*106*) to conclude that the enone in its $^3\pi,\pi^*$ state adopts a distorted, non-planar geometry involving rotation around the C=C bond unless prevented by structural constraints (as in **136**). Subsequent analysis of the vibronic structure and polarization of highly resolved phosphorescence spectra from single crystals of several fused-ring enones at 4.2 K led to the conclusion that in fact there is little change in the geometry of the $^3\pi,\pi^*$ state relative to the ground state, especially with respect to out of plane distortion (*106a*). Furthermore, the emissive properties of these enones under these conditions could be accounted for without invoking mixing between the $^3\pi,\pi^*$ and $^3n,\pi^*$ states (*106a*). With respect to the previous cited calculations (*42*) which suggested that π,π^* states are strongly stabilized by twisting about the C=C bond, the authors (*106a*) note that these states are destabilized by twisting about the C—C bond, and that the two twisting motions are coupled in fused-ring systems, accounting for their observation that the enone chromophore remains essentially planar. Again, it must be emphasized that these conclusions derive from observations of enones in the solid state or in matrices at very low temperatures, and that at higher temperatures where photochemistry occurs pathways involving twisting may become accessible.

The main implications of these studies with respect to photochemistry (*106*) are that (a) most of the photochemistry of these enones ought to proceed via triplet excited states; (b) there is a near degeneracy of $^3n,\pi^*$ and $^3\pi,\pi^*$ states, so that both states may play a role in the room temperature photochemistry and may even exist in thermal equilibrium; (c) the known effect of solvent on the photochemistry could be due to the effect of solvent on the ordering in energy of the two states; (d) rotation around the C=C bond in the $^3\pi,\pi^*$ states may allow the enones to achieve a geometry favorable for conversion to rearrangement products; (e) effective enone triplet excitation energies as determined by energy-transfer experiments would be expected to differ from spectroscopic energies determined from the O—O band of low temperature phosphorescence emission if the enones have distorted geometries in their relaxed π,π^* triplet states at higher temperatures.

A weak emission spectrum from phenanthrenone **15** at 77 K showing "poor but discernible vibrational spacing of 1600 and 1700 cm^{-1}", was obtained (*30*); similar spectra were obtained from other cyclohexenones, but no details were provided other than that the O—O band was consistently in the range 69–71 kcal/mol.

The closeness in energy of n,π^* triplet states of 2-cyclopentenones is evident from the phosphorescence study reported by Cargill *et al.* (*107*) on a series of rigid cyclopentenones. Structured short-lived emission from compounds without substitution on the C=C bond is ascribed to lowest $^3n,\pi^*$ states, whereas the longer-lived structureless emission from compounds with alkyl substitution at C_α and C_β is ascribed to lowest $^3\pi,\pi^*$ states. The emission from the first group can be altered to that of the second group by adsorption on silica gel, which stabilizes the $^3\pi,\pi^*$ relative to the $^3n,\pi^*$ state. The β-methoxyenone 111 shows characteristic $^3\pi,\pi^*$ emission, whereas the analogous compound with hydrogen instead of methoxy shows $^3n,\pi^*$ emission (90). These authors also note the stabilization of the $^3\pi,\pi^*$ state relative to the $^3n,\pi^*$ state by torsion around the C=C bond and suggest that in solution the lowest relaxed triplet of cyclopentenones and cyclohexenones lacking substitution on the C=C bond is probably $^3\pi,\pi^*$ (107).

Configuration interaction calculations (36) on enones and cross-conjugated dienones indicated that in both systems the two triplets were close in energy, with the $^3n,\pi^*$ lowest, the gap being much smaller for dienones than for enones. The calculations also indicated that the enone β-carbon atom is electron deficient relative to the ground state in $^3\pi,\pi^*$ states (π-electron densities only) and relatively electron rich in $^3n,\pi^*$ states. This is consistent with the different reactivities of the two states in hydrogen abstraction reactions, as discussed earlier (Section II,C,1).

Fluorescence of cyclic enones is a rare phenomenon and has been observed to date only with 43 and 44 (Section II,B,3); it clearly deserves more attention.†

2. Triplet Sensitization and Quenching Studies

As discussed in the earlier sections, all of the photoreactions of enones, with the exception of the [1,3] sigmatropic rearrangements and β cyclizations discussed in Section II,B,3, can be effected using standard triplet sensitizers (benzophenone, acetophenone, acetone, etc.). The quantum efficiencies on sensitization are equal to those seen on direct photolysis at longer wavelengths (≥ 300 nm), indicating that for all enones studied the intersystem crossing efficiency is $\sim 100\%$ on excitation of the enones into the first absorption band ($S_0 \rightarrow {}^1n,\pi^*$). Of course, one must always consider the possibility of chemical sensitization as well as transfer of triplet excitation from photosensitizers (108–109a). With the possible exception of those enones discussed in Section II,B,3, which show specific reactivity on excitation into S_2 ($^1\pi,\pi^*$), it appears that the triplet yield is also unity on excitation at 254 nm. However, since the pattern of reactivity at 254 nm has not been generally established for wide classes of enones, the previous statement may need later modification.

† See Note Added in Proof, p. 269.

Triplet quenching results are much more problematical and confusing at present, and these bear directly on the question of the involvement of both $^3n,\pi^*$ and $^3\pi,\pi^*$ states in enone photochemistry. If two different photoreactions proceed from the same triplet state, then a triplet quencher should reduce the yields of both products to exactly the same extent. That is, plots of ϕ_0/ϕ_q (where ϕ_0 and ϕ_q are the quantum yields for a given reaction in the absence and presence of a triplet quencher Q, respectively) versus [Q] should be linear and have the same slope for the two reactions, which is equal to $k_q\tau_T$, where k_q is the bimolecular quenching rate constant and τ_T is the triplet state lifetime in the absence of added quencher (110). If two or more reactions occur via two different triplet states that are in thermal equilibrium under the reaction conditions [Eq. (1)] and if the quencher concentration is sufficiently small so as not to upset the equilibration (i.e., $k_q[Q] \ll k_{12}$ and only the lower-energy triplet is being quenched), a linear Stern–Volmer plot will be obtained for both reactions, as described by Eq. (2), where X_1 is the fraction of the lower (quenchable) triplet at equilibrium and τ_e is the equilibrium triplet lifetime, as given in Eq. (3) ($111,112$). If both triplets are quenchable, the same linear limiting form of the Stern–Volmer plot holds for both reactions at low quencher concentration, as described by Eq. (4). Such plots should curve upward or downward or could conceivably remain linear at higher quencher concentrations if quenching competes with equilibration, depending on the relative magnitude of the quenching rate constants and the rate constants k_{12} and k_{21} (111). If two reactions arise from two different triplet states that are not in thermal equilibrium under the quenching conditions, one should observe differential quenching, that is, linear Stern–Volmer plots with two different slopes.

$$T_1 \underset{k_{21}}{\overset{k_{12}}{\rightleftarrows}} T_2 \tag{1}$$

$$\phi_0/\phi_q = 1 + X_1\tau_e k_q[Q] \tag{2}$$

$$\tau_e = (X_1/\tau_1 + X_2/\tau_2)^{-1} \tag{3}$$

$$\phi_0/\phi_q = 1 + (X_1 k_{q1} + X_2 k_{q2})\tau_e[Q] \tag{4}$$

Thus, if the quenching data for two different reactions fall on a common straight line, the two reactions either (a) arise from the same triplet excited state, or (b) arise from different triplet states that are in rapid thermal equilibrium under the quenching conditions. In principle, one can distinguish between the two situations by quenching studies at high quencher concentrations ($111,112$). If quenching plots for two different reactions of a given enone do not coincide, the reactions must proceed from different triplet states that are not in thermal equilibrium. However, an additional factor that must be considered, but often is ignored, is that the quencher may be intercepting some reaction intermediate other than, or in addition to, the reactive triplet state. For example, it has been demonstrated that the quenching effect of dienes, nitroxyl radicals, and oxygen on the formation of p-cresol from dienone **32** involves quenching of intermediate free radicals as well as the triplet state precursor (*113*). Such an effect should be limited to those reactions involving radical intermediates (e.g., photoreduction) or other relatively long lived intermediates and would be especially magnified if a chain reaction were involved (*113*). Thus, if a quenchable intermediate were involved in only one of several reactions originating from a common triplet excited state, one would observe noncoincident Stern–Volmer plots. In principle, the plot involving quenching of a triplet, or any other reaction intermediate, should show curvature, although plots at low quencher concentrations may appear linear.

Let us now review the results of enone quenching studies in this context. It was found that the ratio of lumiketone to pinacol (isolated material) on photolysis of phenanthrenone **15** in IPA in the absence and presence of naphthalene was approximately the same, and thus it was concluded that the two reactions originate from the same triplet excited state. However, only a single naphthalene concentration was studied, and there was some variation in the product ratio in two unquenched photolyses (*30*). This quenching study, therefore, is not definitive, and the conclusion must be considered preliminary, especially in the light of conflicting data for related systems. As mentioned earlier, it was found (*17*) for octalone **5** in IPA that rearrangement to **71** and photoreduction to **72** were quenched equally by 2,5-dimethyl-2,4-hexadiene, suggesting that both reactions originate from the same triplet state (assumed to be $^3\pi,\pi^*$). Formation of the deconjugation product **70** was quenched much less efficiently in several solvents, suggesting that this reaction arose from a different triplet, $^3n,\pi^*$, although the validity of this conclusion has been questioned (*32*). Competitive quenching of rearrangement and toluene addition was not reported for **5** (*17,32*).

The lumiketone rearrangement and photoreduction to saturated ketones for enone **2** were compared (*4,85*), and it was found that the slopes of the Stern–Volmer plots were "quite different" when a variety of quenchers were used [di-*t*-butyl nitroxide (DTBN), *trans*-piperylene, isoprene, 2,5-dimethyl-2,4-hexadiene, and naphthalene). Whereas the first three quenchers quench reduction more efficiently than rearrangement, the last two do the reverse! Obviously, it is impossible to arrive at definite conclusions from such confusing results. It has been suggested (*85*) that chemical quenching involving diene addition to enone triplets may play a role and that quenching in some cases may not be diffusion controlled, but quenching of radical intermediates in the photoreduction by these triplet quench-ers does not seem to have been considered. The effects of oxygen, similar to those encountered (*113*) with dienone **32**, suggest that radical quenching in this system is a distinct possibility. Some authors (*4*) have relied on the DTBN data of Wampfler (*85*) in drawing their conclusion that rearrange-ment and reduction of **2** in IPA occur from different triplet excited states, the longer-lived one giving reduction and the shorter-lived one being re-sponsible for rearrangement. They term these $^3n,\pi^*$ and $^3\pi,\pi^*$, respec-tively, being aware of the conflict between their data and conclusions and those of other workers (*17*). Slight differences were found (*31*) in the efficiency of quenching by naphthalene of two rearrangements of **38** in *t*-BuOH to **124** and **125**, but the differences were not considered sufficient to conclude that these reactions occur from different triplet states. A somewhat larger effect of naphthalene on rearrangement versus photo-reduction (to give saturated ketone) of **20** was observed in IPA (*31*), in which reduction was quenched more efficiently, the opposite of the effect of naphthalene on enone **2** in IPA (*85*).

Focusing only on the aryl migration, Zimmerman and Lewin (*62b*) gave a conclusive demonstration that the products from irradiation of **137** in benzene (quencher 2,5-dimethyl-2,4-hexadiene) all arise from the same triplet excited state. Finally, a quenching experiment (*65*) comparing aryl

migration and lumiketone rearrangement of enone **24** in 95% EtOH was carried out, which strongly suggests that these reactions arise from different triplets. The implications of these data will be discussed in the following section.

3. Configurational Assignments to Reactive Enone Triplet States

In a perhaps foolhardy attempt to derive order and consistency from the morass of observations discussed in previous sections, we will now at-tempt to specify the nature of the reactive enone excited state responsible for each of the reactions discussed previously.

It is useful to start with photoreduction. It seems quite reasonable to assume that triplet reactions of enones involving H abstraction at the carbonyl oxygen from solvent, etc., originate from $^3n,\pi^*$ states, by anal-ogy with the well-understood mechanisms of photoreduction and Norrish type II reactions of alkyl and aryl ketones (84,91).* Therefore, one may assign pinacol formation from **15**, Norrish type II reaction of **114**, and rearrangement of **5** to **70** to reactions of ^{3}n,π* states. Similarly, it appears to be logical that reactions initiated by H transfer to the enone β-carbon are ascribable to enone $^3\pi,\pi$* states, as suggested previously; these include intramolecular H transfer reactions (86,87), toluene additions (17), and probably the reduction of enones to saturated ketones in IPA, although the mechanism of the last reaction has yet to be definitely established,† as discussed in Section II,C,1.

If one accepts the suggestion (62) that the aryl migrations proceed from ^{3}n,π* states, the quenching studies (17,65) together with the spectroscopic data (104–106) lead to the conclusion that the lumiketone rearrangement must occur from $^3\pi,\pi$* states. This conclusion is also consistent with the suggestion, again supported by spectroscopic data (106), that twisting around the C=C bond is essential for the lumiketone rearrangement (25) and that enone $^3\pi,\pi$* states are stabilized and ^{3}n,π* states destabilized by such geometric distortions (42). On this basis, photorearrangement of enones to lumiketones and cyclopentenones and reductive processes initiated by H transfer to C_β occur competitively from the $^3\pi,\pi$* state (17). Although the evidence strongly suggests that the $^3\pi,\pi$* state is usually the lowest enone triplet (65,104–106), it is conceivable that for certain molecules, particularly in nonpolar solvents, the ^{3}n,π* state may be the lowest triplet. In this case the lumiketone rearrangement, if it occurs at all, may occur via a thermally accessible π,π* triplet or by surmounting an energy barrier to the descending π,π* triplet surface as the excited molecule undergoes geometric distortion. It would appear (30) that phenanthrenone **15** is a promising case of enone ^{3}n,π* and $^3\pi,\pi$* states in thermal equilibrium, but more extensive quenching data are needed. We believe that the differential quenching, observed for enones **2** (4,85) and **20** (31), is an artifact of the multifaceted behavior of triplet quenchers and that once the mechanism of photoreduction to saturated ketones is fully understood the observed differential quenching effects will become interpretable; that is, we believe that these reactions do in fact occur from one and the same π,π* triplet state.

E. Conclusions

Considering all the available evidence from photochemical, spectroscopic, and theoretical studies, it appears that the lumiketone rearrangement originates either directly from $^3\pi,\pi$* states or by crossing to the

---

† See Note Added in Proof, p. 269.

$^3\pi,\pi^*$ surface from an initially populated $^3n,\pi^*$ state and that it requires substantial twisting around the C=C bond in its initial stages. It is not possible to state whether the further changes in bonding occur while the molecule is in an electronically excited state or after decay to the ground state potential surface. At this time, the latter description is preferred. The reaction is completely stereospecific and follows, in a formal sense, the symmetry-allowed $_\sigma 2_a + {_\pi}2_a$ cycloaddition pathway predicted by Woodward and Hoffmann (27) with inversion of configuration at C-4 and retention at C-5; the reaction has all the characteristics of a concerted process, although the various bond alterations may not occur in a totally synchronous manner. Rearrangement inefficiency is attributed to competition between decay and progress to isomerization product from a relaxed twisted $^3\pi,\pi^*$ state (see Fig. 1) and, therefore, is a sensitive function of the nature and location of substituents on and near the enone chromophore.

Stereospecific triplet state rearrangements are a relative rarity (for other examples, see Section V,D; for examples of nonstereospecific triplet rearrangements, see Sections III,C and V,D). For lumiketone rearrangements and aryl migration discussed earlier, it is probably the contour of the excited and ground state surfaces and the absence of appreciable minima corresponding to diradicals along the reaction coordinate that conspire to produce stereospecificity. A theoretical rationalization for the observation that this particular triplet ketone rearrangement is stereospecific and follows the orbital symmetry allowed pathway has recently been provided (113a). Furthermore, it was suggested some time ago (27) that spin correlations may be weak in excited state rearrangements. That is, the molecular gyrations dictated by orbital symmetry, and initiated in the excited state, may simply represent the most facile route to a particular rearrangement product and would be followed regardless of the multiplicity of the excited state; in enones, the nature of the chromophore dictates that reaction occurs in the triplet rather than singlet manifold because of rapid intersystem crossing. In this connection, one should note the existence of a singlet state rearrangement that is apparently nonstereospecific (Section II,B,3).

The general importance of wavelength effects in enone photochemistry has yet to be fully explored, but it is now clear that in suitable cases reaction from S_2 (66,69–73) can compete with internal conversion to S_1. Additional types of enone photoreactions may yet be uncovered upon exploration in the shorter-wavelength region. Much more work on the effects of the variation of enone concentration, irradiation wavelength, reaction temperature, and competitive quenching is necessary, as are further spectroscopic studies of α,β-enones at ambient and reduced temperatures.

III. REARRANGEMENTS OF 2-CYCLOPENTENONES AND RELATED COMPOUNDS

A. Ring Contraction to Cyclopropyl Ketenes

The photoconversion of 5-substituted cyclopentenones **138** to cyclopropyl ketenes **139**, isolated as esters **140**, was discovered independently by two groups (*114,115*). The reaction was observed for X = Y = CH_3 or Ph,

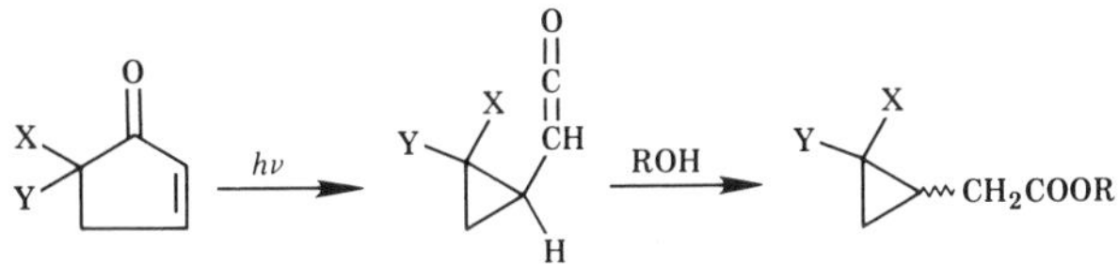

| 138 | 139 | 140 |

and X = C_2H_5, n-C_3H_7, and OCH_2CH_3 with Y = H, but it did not occur with cyclopentenone itself or its 4,4-dimethyl derivative. The observation of a typical ketene band in the infrared at 2110 cm^{-1} upon irradiation in pentane and its disappearance on treatment with methanol at room temperature confirm the intermediacy of a ketene. Although it was found (*114*) that the rearrangement can be sensitized by propiophenone and quenched by 2,3-dimethyl-1,3-butadiene, the authors were reluctant to conclude that the reaction is definitely a triplet reaction, since they could not rule out thermal population of the excited singlet from the triplet in these systems, in which the energy gap may be only 1–2 kcal/mol (*61,109a*). The occurrence of α cleavage in these systems is in striking contrast with its almost complete absence in analogous cyclohexenones (see Section II,C,4).

B. Rearrangement to Bicyclo[2.1.0]pentan-2-ones and Ketenes

4-Acyl-2,5-di-*t*-butylcyclopentenones rearrange (*116*) to bicyclo[2.1.0]-pentan-2-ones, as illustrated below with the 4-pivaloyl derivative (**141**, X = H; R = *t*-butyl). Two mechanisms are theoretically available for this

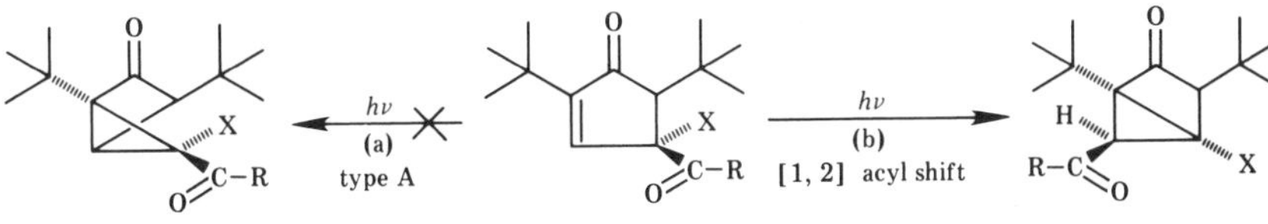

| 142 | 141 | 142 |

R = *t*-Bu, Ph; X = H, D

reaction: (a) a bond-switching mechanism analogous to the type A rearrangement of cyclohexenones discussed in Section II,B and (b) a mechanism involving migration of the acyl group to C-3 with bonding between C-2 and C-4, analogous to the aryl migration pathway utilized in 4-arylcyclohexenones (see Section II,C,1). A clear decision in favor of path (b) was provided by studies using the *trans*-4-deuterio compound (**141**, X = D). A similar course of reaction was demonstrated for the 4-benzoyl derivative (**141**, R = Ph) (*117*). The reaction course is stereospecific, giving only 5-endo-substituted products of structure **142**, consistent with a photochemically allowed concerted $_\sigma2_a + _\pi2_a$ cycloaddition process (see further discussion in Section V,D). In this sense, the reaction seems to be directly analogous to the cyclohexenone rearrangements discussed in Section II,C,1. There have been no further mechanistic studies reported in this system, including determination of reactive excited state multiplicity.

A related rearrangement (*118*) involves the acylcyclopentenone **143**, which was converted to the butenolide **144**. The reaction pathway was suggested to involve formation of the bicyclo[2.1.0]pentanone **145** and then ketene **146**, which, upon cyclization with H migration, gives the observed product. The intermediacy of ketene **146** was supported by the formation of methyl ester **147**, in addition to **144**, on irradiation of **143** in methanol. A similar rearrangement was seen with a steroid analogue.

The above rearrangements are actually examples of oxadi-π-methane

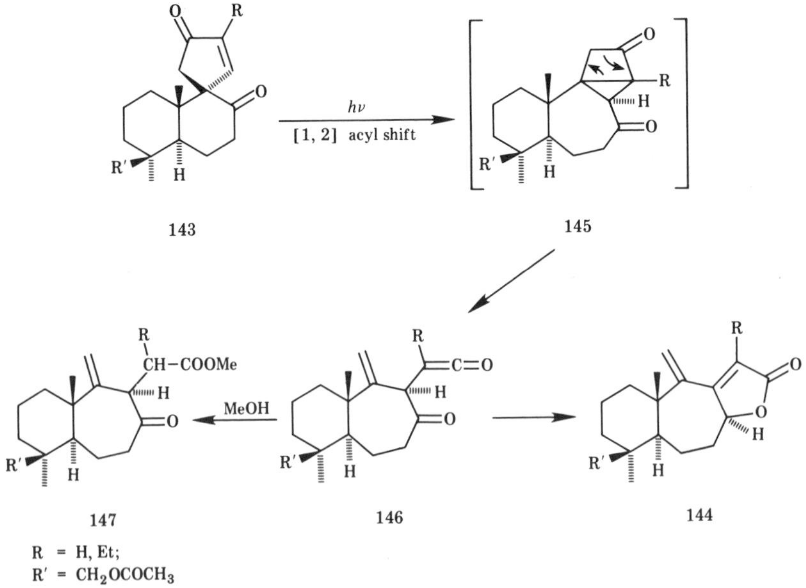

143

145

147   146   144

R = H, Et;
R' = CH₂OCOCH₃

rearrangements, which are well known in the photochemistry of β,γ-enones and which will be discussed later in depth (Section V,D). Assuming that **141** and **143** are behaving as typical β,γ-enones, it is likely that their rearrangements involve triplet excited states as reactive intermediates.

A similar rearrangement is observed starting with 4,4-diphenyl- and 4-methyl-4-phenylcyclopentenones (**148**), affording products of ketene **149** (*119,120*). In these cases, bicyclo[2.1.0]pentan-2-ones ("housones") (**150**)

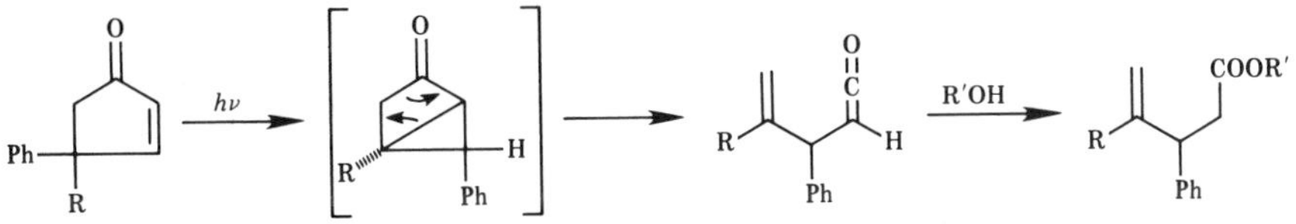

148   150   149

R = Ph, CH₃

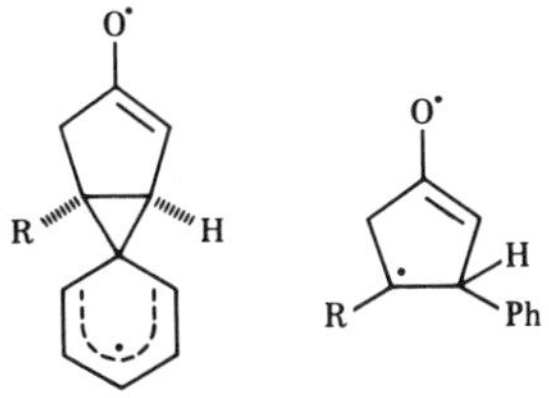

151   152

were not isolated, although a reaction intermediate observed at $-140°C$ was tentatively assigned such a structure. Since nonphotochemical routes to such ketones gave thermally unstable products, which reacted with methanol to give the same acyclic esters formed photochemically from **148,** it was concluded that the reaction probably proceeds via the "housone." However, direct fragmentation to the ketene of bridged or fully rearranged diradicals **151** and **152** at room temperature could not be ruled out. The mechanistic analogy to the aryl migrations in cyclohexenone photochemistry (Section II,C,1) is strengthened by observations (*119*) that the quantum yield is the same on direct or acetophenone-sensitized photolysis and that the reaction can be quenched by 1,3-cyclohexadiene.

C. [1,3] Sigmatropic Rearrangements with Alkyl Migration

1. Verbenone–Chrysanthenone Rearrangement

The best known example of this class of sigmatropic rearrangements is the photoisomerization of verbenone (**153**) to chrysanthenone (**154**)

(*121,122*). The reaction mixtures are generally very complex because of secondary reactions (including rearrangements) of **154** and the other products (see Section V). By appropriate choice of irradiation wavelength and solvent (e.g., 350 nm in acetic acid), these secondary reactions can be minimized, and **154** becomes the almost exclusive low molecular weight product, in yields up to 67% (*122*). In alcohols, one obtains esters **155** in addition to **154**.

The amount of racemization that occurs on formation of **154** from optically active **153** varies with the solvent and the extent of irradiation, but racemization can never be completely eliminated (*122*). This suggested that there are two routes for the formation of **154**: (a) a pathway precluding racemization via intermediate species that retain chirality and (b) a pathway that leads to racemization. Under optimal conditions, path (a) could account for 80% of the total reaction. It was suggested that path (a) proceeds via an intermediate diradical, depicted as **156**, whereas path (b) involves ring opening to ketene **157**, which recyclizes to form racemic **154;** further racemization of **154** on absorption was attributed to reverse formation of ketene **157**. Attempts to generate **157** independently and demonstrate its cyclization to **154** were unsuccessful; however, infrared spectra of crude reaction mixtures in nonalcoholic solvents showed a band at 2120 cm^{-1} attributable to a ketene. Because of the small tendency of α,β-enones to undergo α cleavage reactions (Section II,C,4), it was suggested (*122*) that the ketene **157** was probably formed from the diradical **156** in competition with direct closure to **154**. Product **158** could arise directly from verbenone by migration of the methylene as opposed to the isopropylene bridge, but it seems more likely that it is a [1,3]-acyl rearrangement product of the β,γ-enone **154**.

Some further aspects of this rearrangement were clarified in later studies. On the basis of quenching and sensitization experiments (*123*), it was demonstrated that the rearrangement arises from a triplet excited state with a lifetime of the order of 1 nsec and an excitation energy above 70 kcal/mol, an observation consistent with data for other 2-cyclopentenones (*109a*). It was suggested that the reaction was probably not concerted, as was later demonstrated (*124*) by a study of the deuterium-labeled derivative **159**; this afforded a 1 : 1 mixture of the two rearrangement products **160** and **161**. These data show that rotation around the isopropyl–ring bond leading to scrambling of the methyl groups occurs in competition with ring closure in a species such as the triplet diradical **156**. Quenching experiments (*123*) showed that esters **155** arise from the same triplet state which is a precursor of **154**, indicating that there is only one reactive triplet state, or perhaps two thermally equilibrated triplets, in this system.

2. Rearrangements of Bicyclic Ketones

The [1,3] sigmatropic photorearrangement of **162** to **164** has been shown to proceed in a nonconcerted manner via a reversibly formed diradical intermediate (**163**) (*125,126*). Thus, irradiation of 6,7-*exo*-dideuterio-**162b** led to a mixture of the cis and trans dideuteriated products **164b** and **164c,** and the 1 : 1 product ratio was independent of the extent of reaction; the stereochemistry at C-6 of the starting enone was gradually lost because of

162a X = Y = H   163   164a X = Y = Z = H
162b X = Y = D   164b X = H; Y = Z = D
                                      164c Z = H; X = Y = D

scrambling of the exo and endo protons, which was complete at 70%
conversion. The stereochemistry at C-7 is totally preserved, as shown by
stereospecific isomerization of the *exo-* and *endo*-7-methylenones. These
results are readily rationalized in terms of formation of the intermediate
diradical **163**, which undergoes rotation around the C-6—C-7 bond competitively with reversion to **162** and cyclization to **164**. Although no multiplicity determination experiments were reported, it is likely that this
reaction is analogous to that of verbenone (above) and originates from a
triplet excited state.

A second photorearrangement of compounds of type **162** leads to tetra-
hydrobenzoic esters **165**. Evidence has been presented in support of a

mechanism that involves initial photoisomerization by a [1,3] sigmatropic
shift of the internal C-1—C-5 bond to give a cyclopropanone **(166)**. This
then reacts with methanol or methoxide, and the reaction is followed by
thermal reorganization to give the observed product (*125,127*). The intermediacy of zwitterions **167** on the route to the cyclopropanones was ruled
out as a major pathway because of the observed stereoselectivity of reaction; starting with the epimeric 7-methylenones, markedly different ratios
of cis and trans esters were obtained. The authors suggested that cyclopropanone formation is a totally concerted [2 + 2] cycloaddition. The
excited state responsible for this rearrangement was not characterized.

Several analogous examples of rearrangements to cyclopropanones by
[1,3] shift of the internal bond in bicyclic ketones have been uncovered
(*128,129*) using low-temperature matrix isolation techniques. Irradiation of
168 in a glass at − 190°C (a relatively high temperature in this sort of study)
afforded cyclopropanone **169**, which was characterized by its IR band at

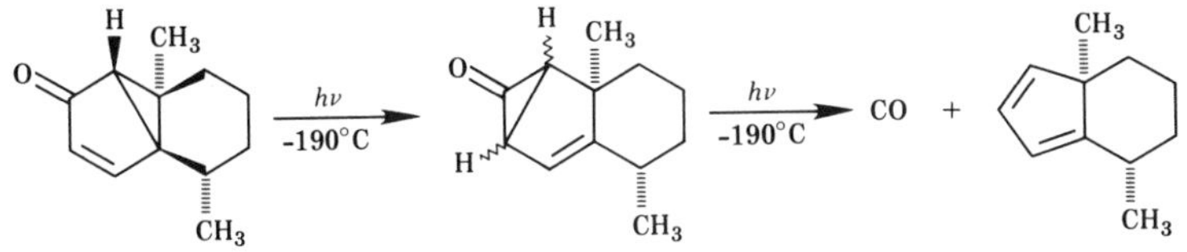

168   169   170

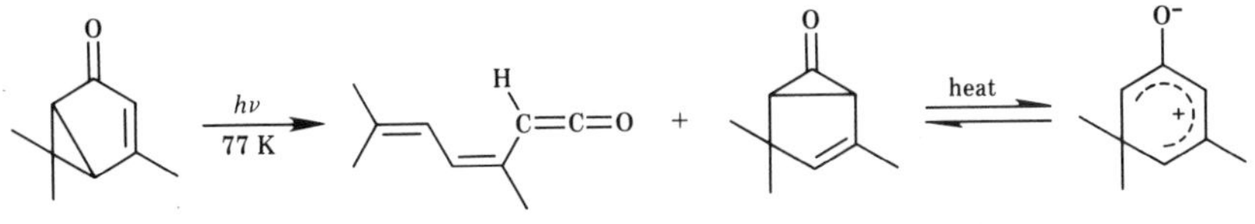

171   172   173

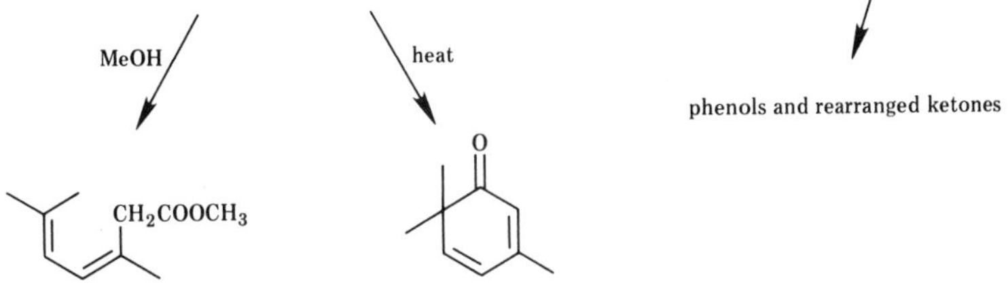

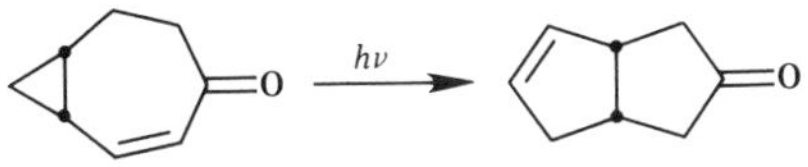

phenols and rearranged ketones

174

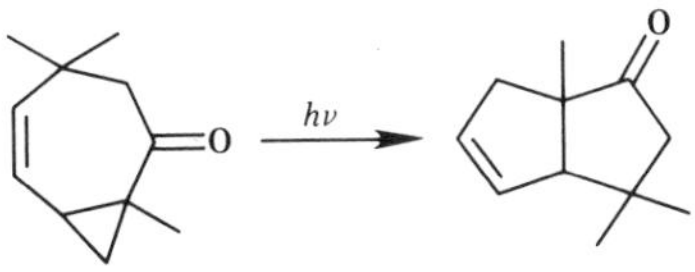

175

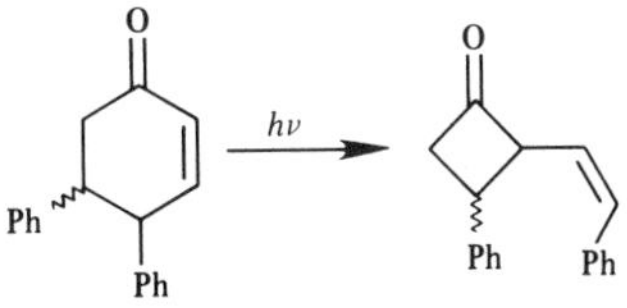

176   177

1812 cm^{-1}, formation of a Diels–Alder adduct with furan, and loss of CO on further irradiation to give 170 (*128*). Similarly, irradiation of 171 as a thin film at 77 K gives ketene 172 (IR band at 2107 cm^{-1}) and cyclopropanone 173 (IR band at 1810 cm^{-1}) (*129*). The relevance of these low-temperature isomerizations to the photochemical rearrangements of bicyclo[3.1.0]hexen-2-ones observed at room temperature has been discussed (*129*).

Examples of [1,3] sigmatropic rearrangements in other types of bicyclic systems are provided by the cases of 174 and 175 (*130*) and the unusual conversion of 176 to 177 (*62a*). The multiplicity of the reactive excited state is uncertain in the first two cases, but a triplet precursor seems certain in the third reaction.

These reactions are of interest in terms of the scope, mechanism, and stereochemistry of photochemical allylic rearrangements, as discussed recently (*131*).

D. Rearrangement of Bicyclo[3.2.0]hepta-3,6-dienones and Related Compounds

Compound 178, which is structurally an α,β- as well as a β,γ-enone, undergoes a facile photorearrangement to 179 (*132*). Although other

mechanisms could, in principle, be envisaged, it was discovered that at $-190°C$ the only product formed from 178 was ketene 180 (IR band at 2118 cm^{-1}), which was stable below $-180°C$ but which disappeared rapidly in the dark above $-70°C$ to give a mixture of 178 and 179 (*133*). A steady state involving 178, 179, and 180 can be reached starting with either 178 or 179. The conversion of 178 to 180 is a [3,3] sigmatropic (Cope) rearrangement and, not surprisingly, occurs from a singlet excited state by what is probably a concerted electronic reorganization. The triplet state of **178** generated by photosensitization undergoes [1,3] sigmatropic rearrangement to **181**, depicted (*4*) as involving a biradical intermediate (**182**). This reaction is of interest in comparison with other [1,3] sigmatropic rearrangement of β,γ-enones, which usually, but not always, proceed via singlet excited states (see Section V,C). These photochemical rearrangements are in contrast to the thermal rearrangement of **178** to **183** (*134*), which proceeds by an unusual symmetry-allowed antarafacial–antarafacial pathway.

Photoisomerization to ketenes was shown (*135,136*) to be general for bicyclo[3.2.X]dienones **184** and can be synthetically useful. In every case,

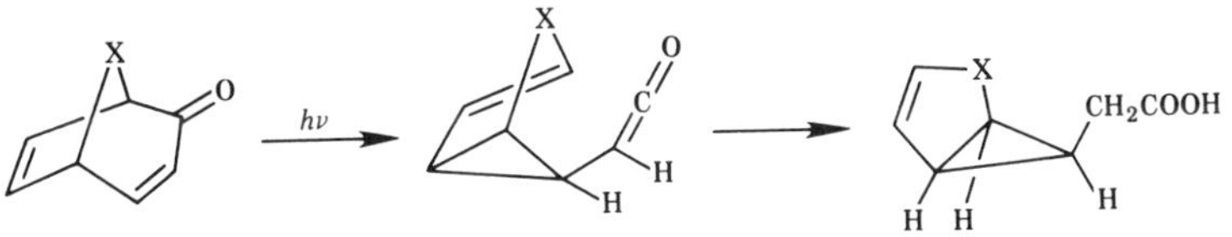

184

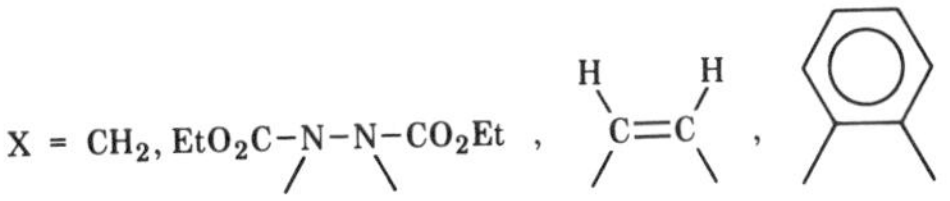

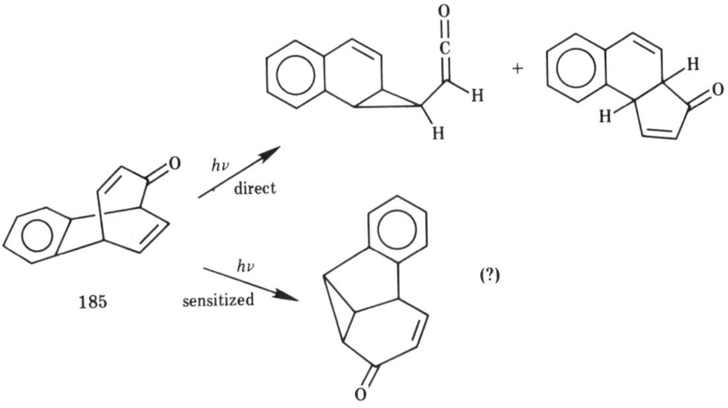

$$X = CH_2, EtO_2C-N-N-CO_2Et \ , \ \underset{/}{\overset{H}{\underset{}{\;}}}C=C\underset{\backslash}{\overset{H}{\underset{}{\;}}} \ , \ \begin{array}{c} \end{array}$$

185

186

ketene intermediates could be detected in low-temperature studies. For **185**, both [1,3] and [3,3] rearrangements apparently occur from S_1 since triplet sensitization gives a different, unidentified product (*136*), most likely the oxadi-π-methane rearrangement product **186** (see Section V,D).

Recently, the photochemical behavior of **187** (*137*) was studied. This is a by-product of the photochemistry of dienone **32** (*138*). On direct or triplet-sensitized irradiation, **187** undergoes a [1,3] sigmatropic rear-

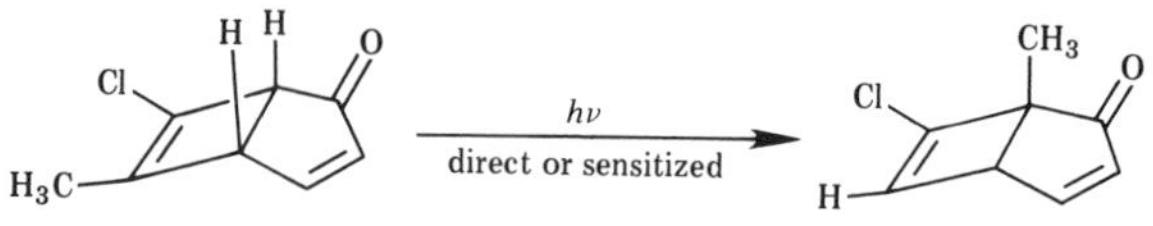

187   188

rangement to **188**, which can be quenched by CHD. Thus, a triplet precursor is indicated for this reaction; in contrast to the cases discussed above intersystem crossing is very efficient for **187**. Photolysis of **187** in methanol does not give an ester (indicative of no ketene formation), but rather gives a methanol adduct, the structure of which has not yet been elucidated, indicating that ketene formation is not a totally general photochemical reaction of bicyclo[3.2.0]hepta-3,6-dienones.

E. Competitive Photoreactions of 2-Cyclopentenones

As mentioned previously, cyclopentenone itself undergoes exclusively photodimerization to a mixture of head-to-head and head-to-tail dimers, a reaction also shown by most 2- and 3-substituted derivatives. Irradiation of several 3-alkylcyclopentenones (**189**) in toluene leads to the generation

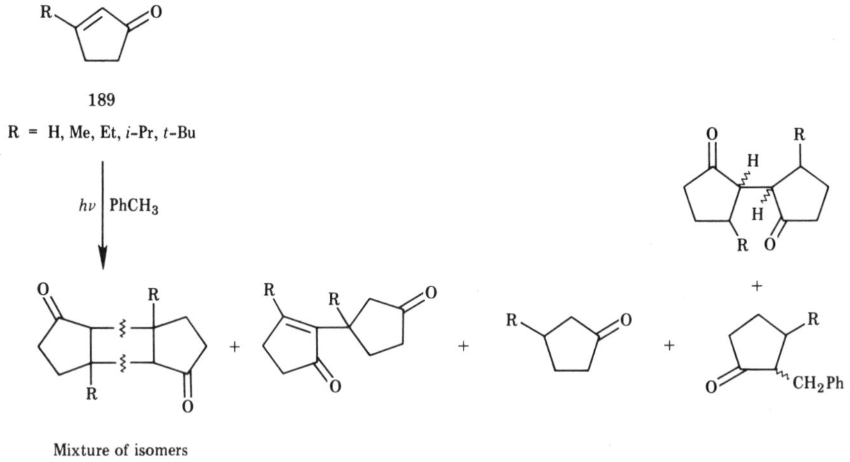

189

R = H, Me, Et, *i*-Pr, *t*-Bu

$h\nu$ | PhCH$_3$

Mixture of isomers

of radicals resulting from H abstraction at the β-enone carbon, a reaction that is analogous to the behavior of several cyclohexenones (Section II,C,1), as is evinced by the formation of α-benzyl ketones as well as α-radical dimers; these radicals could also be intermediates on the way to saturated ketones (*139*). Quenching experiments with naphthalene indicate that the various enone photodimers (as many as four from 3-methylcyclopentenone) arise via a common triplet excited state which is not the species leading to α-benzyl ketones and saturated ketones. The authors tentatively conclude, in part by analogy with the photochemistry of cyclohexenones previously discussed, that dimerization occurs from n,π^* triplets and H abstraction at C_β from π,π^* triplets; these triplets are apparently not kinetically equilibrated in these systems. Intramolecular H abstraction followed by cyclization and disproportionation is discussed in Section II,C,1.

IV. MISCELLANEOUS REARRANGEMENTS OF α,β-ENONES

The photochemistry of α-methylene ketones of type **190** with an exocyclic ene moiety have been studied (*140*). Acyclic analogues are known to undergo mainly intramolecular H abstraction on oxygen or the β-carbon (*141*). It was anticipated that dissipation of the excitation energy in **190** might occur by isomerization around the double bond, the so-called free rotor effect (*142*). In fact, **190a** undergoes a novel photorearrangement

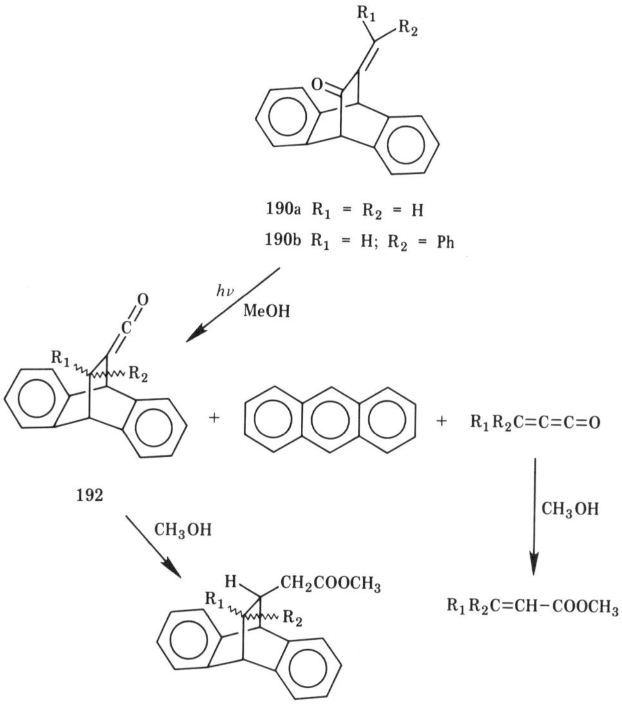

190a $R_1 = R_2 = H$
190b $R_1 = H; R_2 = Ph$

192

191

in methanol to give ester **191a,** presumably involving Norrish type I
cleavage to a diradical, structural alteration to allow electron delocalization into the methylene group, 180° rotation, and then cyclization to give
ketene **192a,** which finally is trapped by MeOH. This reaction competes
with cleavage to give anthracene and ketene. Similarly, irradiation of **190b**
gives a mixture of *cis-* and *trans-*methyl cinnamates and cis and trans
bicyclic esters **191b.** An interesting wavelength dependence was noted,
rearrangement being favored over fragmentation at longer excitation
wavelengths, which suggests that the two reactions originate from different excited states. No further mechanistic studies were reported. The
suggestion was made that in this system α-cleavage competes effectively
with isomerization around C=C because of stabilization of the odd electron by the two adjacent aromatic rings (*140*). The generation of anthracene presumably assists the novel ketene extrusion.

Acyclic α,β-enones respond to photochemical excitation mainly by rotation around the C=C bond, thus equilibrating (*Z*) and (*E*) diastereomers, a well-known process discussed extensively elsewhere (*143,144*).
However, in the presence of another double bond some interesting rearrangements occur. This is best illustrated by citral **193,** which was reported some years ago (*145*) to undergo photochemical cyclization to a
mixture of **194** and **195** via diradical **196.** Recent reinvestigation (*146*) led
to the isolation of three additional products, **197, 198,** and **199,** on irradiation of citral in aromatic solvents at various temperatures up to 190°C and
the discovery of a most unusual variation of product distribution with
increasing temperature; yields of **198** and **199** increased at the expense of
194 and **195.** The product distribution was the same on acetophenone
sensitization and in the presence of 2,3-dimethylbutadiene, suggesting one
and the same triplet precursor (or more than one triplet in thermal equilibrium) for all products. Product **198** most likely arises from diradical **200** by

migration of a formyl group and cyclization; the formation of **199** from diradical **196** can be rationalized similarly. It appears that cyclization to the more sterically congested diradical **200** becomes more feasible the higher the temperature, whereas formyl migration in diradical **196** becomes increasingly competitive with cyclization and disproportionation. The rearrangement of the formyl group in what is probably a ground state diradical appears to be unique and may bear only a formal resemblance to the acyl migrations discussed in Section V,D.

This intriguing observation points up the need for studies of temperature effects in many of the other systems discussed in this essay.

V. PHOTOCHEMICAL REARRANGEMENTS OF β,γ-ENONES

A. Introduction

As mentioned in Section I, there has been a great deal of research during the last two decades on the photochemistry of β,γ-enones, stimulated initially by spectroscopic studies (5–9) that indicated extensive interaction of the alkene and carbonyl chromophores in these compounds and by an observation (147) of the then novel photochemical equilibration of bicyclo[3.2.0]heptenones **201** and **202** by what was subsequently (148)

201   202

203   204

termed a [1,3] sigmatropic acyl shift. Shortly thereafter (149) there was the report of an analogous isomerization of dehydronorcamphor (**203**). Many types of photoreactions have since been discovered in β,γ-enones, some characteristic of the alkene chromophore (cis–trans isomerization, dimerization to cyclobutanes, electrocyclic ring closure of a dienyl moiety), others characteristic of the carbonyl chromophore (decarbonylation, reduction, efficient intersystem crossing from singlet to triplet states, Norrish type I and II reactions), and still others that are peculiar to these bifunctional molecules. The most important of the latter group are the molecular rearrangements involving [1,3] and [1,2] acyl shifts, which are the main subject of this section.

The literature through 1974 dealing with the photochemistry and spectroscopy of β,γ-unsaturated carbonyl compounds was exhaustively and critically reviewed in 1976 (10), and a second critical review, restricted to β,γ-enone photochemistry, appeared at nearly the same time (150). The present review concentrates on the significant advances made in the last few years in understanding the mechanisms of the sigmatropic photorearrangements, the most characteristic reactions of β,γ-enones.

B. Background on Photorearrangements of β,γ-Enones

The [1,3] and [1,2] sigmatropic acyl rearrangements that occur on photoexcitation of β,γ-enones are depicted schematically below. The

[1,2]-acyl rearrangement to a cyclopropyl ketone is structurally analogous to the well-studied DPM rearrangements (63) and is known as the oxadi-π-methane (ODPM) rearrangement (151).

In early studies, only the [1,3]-acyl shift was observed on direct photolysis of several enones (147,149), but later (152,153) it was found that triplet-sensitized photolysis of enones 201 and 203 gave the ODPM rear-

rangement products 205 and 206, respectively. Tricyclic ketone 205 is formed on direct photolysis of 201, as indicated by NMR spectra of crude reaction mixtures (154), but was not detected earlier (155) on gas chromatographic analysis because of its rapid thermal isomerization to the [1,3] rearrangement product 202.

The competition between the two rearrangement pathways depends subtly on molecular structure, as illustrated with octalones 207, 208, and 209 (156). The unmethylated compound 207 shows only the ODPM rearrangement on direct and sensitized photolysis. The dimethylated compound 209 undergoes only the [1,3] shift on direct photolysis but gives exclusively the ODPM rearrangement upon triplet sensitization. The monomethyloctalone 208 gives both reactions on direct photolysis but only the ODPM rearrangement on triplet sensitization. Measured quantum yields are given in parentheses, with values under arrows for the disappearance of starting material.

In the case of **201, 203, 208,** and **209** and many other enones that undergo the [1,3]-acyl shift on direct photolysis, the rearrangement is not affected by a variety of typical triplet quenchers (e.g., dienes, naphthalene, and nitroxyl radicals) (153–156), whereas the ODPM rearrangement is readily quenched, as demonstrated by studies of enones **201, 207,** and **208** (154,156). The latter rearrangement occurred almost invariably on triplet sensitization, suggesting a simple mechanistic interpretation (mechanism A in Fig. 4), in which the [1,3]-acyl shift occurs directly from S_1, whereas the [1,2]-acyl shift occurs from a triplet state, presuma-

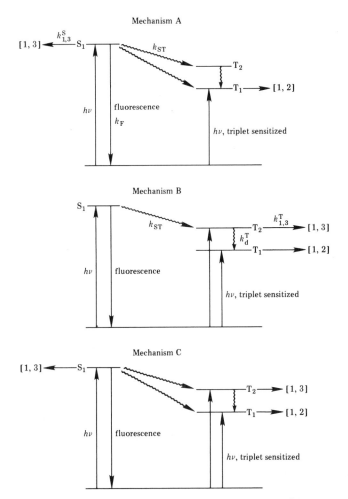

Fig. 4   General mechanisms for sigmatropic rearrangements of β,γ-enones.

bly T_1 (*10,150–156*). If this is the correct mechanism, the efficiency of intersystem crossing (ϕ_{ST}) in β,γ-enones must vary over the full range from approximately 1.0 (in the case of **207**) to effectively zero (in the case of **203** and **209**), whereas other enones (such as **201** and **208**) should possess intermediate values. In mechanism A, the [1,3]-acyl shift (rate constant $k^S_{1,3}$) competes directly with intersystem crossing to the triplet manifold (rate constant k_{ST}), in which case $k^S_{1,3}/k_{ST}$ must vary from very small values (~0) to values ≥ 100, although these data allow no firm statement about absolute values of either rate constant (*156*).

A second series of enones, which illustrates a number of features of β,γ-enone photochemistry, is that of the acetonylcycloalkenes **210–215,** the study of which (*157*) was as close to a systematic investigation of the relationship of structure and reactivity as can be found in this field. Quantum yields are indicated as before. The main features are as follows: (a) the absence of ODPM rearrangement products on direct photolysis, except in the case of enone **212,** which lacks α-methyl substitution; (b) the occurrence of [1,3]-acyl shifts only with **210, 211,** and **212;** (c) the occurrence of Norrish type II reaction leading to cyclobutanols in all cases except **210;** (d) the formation of products from **210,** attributable to the combination of free radicals formed by α cleavage; (e) the absence of rearrangement products from the medium-ring cycloalkenyl ketones **213–215** in favor of Norrish type II reaction and cyclization to oxetanes; and (f) the occurrence of [1,3]-acyl shifts on acetone sensitization in the case of **210** and **211.** As with the octalones discussed above, a great effect of α-methyl substitution is observed. Only **212** gives triplet excited states and ODPM product on direct photolysis, only the formation of **219** is quenched to any appreciable extent on direct photolysis in the presence of 2,2,6,6-tetramethylpiperidine-1-oxyl, a potent singlet and triplet quencher, and only enone **212** sensitizes dimerization of 1,3-cyclohexadiene, indicating that all reactive excited states in this series with the unique exception of the precursor to **219** are very short lived. Many factors influence selectivity in this series, and these are discussed in detail in the original paper (*157*) and the review cited (*10*). They include the following: (a) the general observation that ODPM rearrangement is generally much more efficient in rigid than in nonrigid systems, manifested in this series by the inhibition of rearrangement in those systems capable of rotation around the C=C bond; (b) the favoring of oxetane formation in systems in which the olefin is relatively electron rich (as measured by ionization potentials) and sufficiently flexible to allow the rotation necessary for ring closure; (c) the enhancement of α cleavage in relatively electron poor olefins, as indicated by the fact that **210** has the highest ionization potential in this series; (d) the enhancement of intersystem crossing to the triplet manifold relative to other singlet decay processes in the absence of α-methyl substitution, assuming the validity of mechanism A; and (e) the observation of [1,3]-acyl shifts from enone triplet states in the cases of **210** and **211**, a phenomenon discussed later in this section.

In the context of mechanism A, the question naturally arose as to the origin of the completely different modes of behavior of the S_1 and T_1 states of these β,γ-enones. The first discussion of this problem in print *(158)* suggested that these divergent courses of reaction could be rationalized in terms of different spin density distributions in enone singlet and triplet states. Structure **220** depicts the polarization of the olefinic π electrons

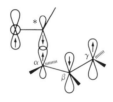

220

* = π^* electron
singlet state polarization ↓
triplet state polarization ↑

predicted from interaction with the nonbonding electron on oxygen (arbitrarily assigned α spin) through the C_{CO}—C_α σ bond. In the singlet excited state, the π^* electron on the carbonyl carbon (not depicted) would be spin-paired with the p_y electron on oxygen and would have opposite spin to the electron on C_γ, thereby directing bonding between these carbons upon cleavage of the C_{CO}—C_α σ bond. Similarly, in the triplet excited state where the π^* electron has β spin, bonding should be directed between C_{CO} and C_β upon cleavage of the C_{CO}—C_α bond *(159)*. This argument assumes an electronic description of both of these excited states as n,π^* states. It is generally agreed that the lowest singlet excited state is best described as a n,π^* state with some mixing in of higher excited configurations *(10,150,158,160)*. However, CNDO/S calculations *(160)* indicate that the lowest triplet state of β,γ-enones is best described as a π,π^* state, with some limited contribution of other configurations. This led (*10,160*) to the discussion of the divergent behavior of β,γ-enone singlets and triplets in terms of the basic difference in reactivity of $^1n,\pi^*$ and $^3\pi,\pi^*$ states. Calculations indicated that the former have a tendency to undergo α cleavage and formation of a bond between the carbonyl carbon and C_γ; the latter may or may not occur in a synchronous manner. On the other hand, calculations indicated little weakening of the α bond in the $^3\pi,\pi^*$ state but strong bonding interactions between C_{CO} and C_β, leading to diradical structures of type **221**, either as bona fide reaction intermediates or as

221

structures along a concerted reaction surface. Structure **221** is directly analogous to proposed intermediates in DPM rearrangements (*63*). Similar conclusions were reached (*58*) from considerations of optimal "tight" and "loose" geometries for intermediate structures along singlet and triplet reaction surfaces, respectively.

Although the assignments to S_1 and T_1 (*10,160*) seem reasonable and are generally accepted (*10,157*), there is very little experimental evidence supporting the $^3\pi,\pi^*$ assignment to T_1 of simple β,γ-enones. A report (*161*) of broad phosphorescence from a series of β,γ-enones in support of such an assignment was irreproducible with purified enone samples (*162,163*). Indirect support is available from studies of the efficiency of triplet energy transfer into some β,γ-enones, which place the lowest triplet at about 74–78 kcal/mol above the ground state, while estimates of the n,π^* singlet–triplet splitting with S_1 (~86–87 kcal/mol above S_0) place the $^3n,\pi^*$ state within 2 kcal/mol of acetone triplet (E_T 78 kcal/mol) (*163*). To the extent that twisting around the C=C bond is important along the reaction surface leading to rearrangement products, the $^3\pi,\pi^*$ state should be increasingly stabilized relative to $^3n,\pi^*$ and the ground state, as for α,β-enones (Section II,A,3,b). Nonetheless, it would be gratifying to have some direct spectroscopic data on simple enones supporting the T_1 assignment. The only reliable phosphorescence data available other than for β-phenylenones (discussed later) are the data for **136** (*106*), which is simultaneously an α,β- and β,γ-enone and which, not surprisingly, has a lowest π,π^* triplet at reduced temperatures.

Recently, however, it became apparent that mechanism A was an inadequate description of the behavior of at least some β,γ-enones and that alternative mechanisms merited serious consideration. There were, first of all, some isolated reports of [1,3]-acyl shifts on triplet sensitization, usually in which acetone was used as photosensitizer, as already mentioned for enones **178, 210,** and **211** (*157*) but also noted with **203** (*162,163a*) and **222** (*164*). A good case was made (*157*) that the photosensitized con-

222

version of **211** to **217** could not involve direct or indirect population of the S_1 state of **211**. The most crucial points of the argument were as follows: (a) The ratio of the ODPM and [1,3] rearrangement products **217** and **218** was not altered, although their yields were sharply reduced, in the presence of the triplet quencher biphenyl; and (b) the cyclobutanol produced on direct photolysis of **211** by a Norrish type II reaction was not observed on acetone sensitization. Since direct light absorption by **211** seemed unlikely under the reaction conditions, one is left with no apparent alternative to the conclusion (*157*) that **217** is a bona fide product of a triplet excited state of **211**. The question of whether this triplet is the same as that leading to the ODPM rearrangement product **218** was left open.

An additional problem with mechanism A was the fact that in certain situations the supposedly singlet-derived [1,3]-acyl shift was not able to compete with other intramolecular reactions of the $^1n,\pi^*$ state, such as oxetane formation and Norrish type II γ-H abstraction, as illustrated by **213–215** (*157*). An even more dramatic example is enone **223**, which gives a variety of intramolecular reactions, but no [1,3]-acyl shift (*165*). It is

223

particularly striking that in the conformation of **223** with the acetyl group axial, which would provide an excellent opportunity for α cleavage leading to [1,3] rearrangement because of instant stabilization of the incipient allyl radical, only γ-H abstraction is observed (*165*).

The assignment of the [1,3]-acyl shift to a reactive singlet excited state was derived originally from the observation that in general the reaction is not quenchable by typical triplet quenchers and is not observed on triplet sensitization. An alternative proposal (*166,167*) is that the [1,3]-acyl shift arises from the T_2 ($^3n,\pi^*$) state, a state too short lived to be intercepted efficiently by triplet quenchers, and that reaction from T_2 can compete with decay to the T_1 ($^3\pi,\pi^*$), which is responsible for ODPM rearrangement. One would also have to postulate that *direct* photolysis of β,γ-enones results in efficient and selective intersystem crossing to the $^3n,\pi^*$ state (T_2) in order to account for the absence of ODPM rearrangement in many cases. Such a preference for population of the $^3n,\pi^*$ state on intersystem crossing would be in violation of the generally accepted rules (*168*), which state that $S(n,\pi^*) \rightarrow T(\pi,\pi^*)$ is usually preferred over $S(n,\pi^*) \rightarrow T(n,\pi^*)$ because of spin–orbit coupling. However, one cannot exclude relaxation of these rules in systems, such as β,γ-enones, in which there is extensive configurational mixing (*169*). If one considers the [1,3]-acyl shift as basically an α cleavage process, a point discussed in detail in Section V,C, the occurrence of such a reaction from a $^3n,\pi^*$ state (with rate constant $k_{1,3}^T$) is in accord with Norrish type I reactions of many other ketone n,π^* triplets (*93*) and should be facilitated by α-methyl substitution in competition with radiationless decay (rate constant k_d^T) to the slightly lower lying $^3\pi,\pi^*$ state, in qualitative accord with other findings (*156,157*). It is necessary to realize that $k_{1,3}^T/k_d$ must then vary from ~0 to ≥ 100 in order to account for the findings with enones 207–215, a range that seems probable to some (*166*) and improbable to others (*170*) but that at present cannot be objectively assessed on the basis of either theory or experiment.

There are two versions of mechanisms incorporating the [1,3]-acyl shift from T_2. In mechanism B of Fig. 4, as originally proposed (*166,167*), direct population of S_1 by light absorption is followed by efficient ($\phi_{ST} \sim 1$) crossing to T_2, the origin of the [1,3]-acyl shift upon both direct and sensitized photolysis; this reaction competes with decay to T_1 ($^3\pi,\pi^*$), the source of the ODPM rearrangement. Furthermore, competitive population of T_1 and T_2 must take place upon transfer of triplet excitation from triplet photosensitizers. The fact that some competitive photoreactions of enones, such as oxetane formation and γ-H abstraction, have not been seen on triplet photosensitization indicates that these reactions must originate from S_1 (*157*). This implies that intersystem crossing is reduced in enones that display such behavior (e.g., 211–215) compared with those that do not (e.g., 207–210). This aspect has yet to be explored.

There is a third alternative, mechanism C in Fig. 4, in which the [1,3]-acyl shift occurs from S_1 competitively with intersystem crossing to T_2 and T_1. Therefore, on direct photolysis there may be contributions to the [1,3]-acyl shift from *both* S_1 and T_2, in a manner analogous to the contributions of both $^1n,\pi^*$ and $^3n,\pi^*$ states to Norrish type I and type II photoreactions of alkanones (*171*). Photosensitized [1,3]-acyl shifts then occur from T_2 and ODPM rearrangements from T_1, the relative population of these states in a particular enone depending on their energies relative to that of the triplet state of the photosensitizer.

Several kinds of recent experiments which bear directly on the validity of mechanisms A, B and C will be discussed in the following section. It is, of course, possible that no single unifying mechanism governs the behavior of all β,γ-enones and that reasoning by analogy may be particularly dangerous in this field, as noted elsewhere (150). As will be seen, however, these new data directly implicate mechanism C and convince at least this author that this mechanism may be sufficient to rationalize *all* the data on β,γ-enone photochemistry available at present.

C. Mechanism of the [1,3]-Acyl Rearrangement

1. Cyclic β,γ-Enones

In a review of the photochemical behavior of 1-acyl-2-cyclopentenes in 1976, it was noted that a correlation of the efficiencies of fluorescence and the [1,3]-acyl shift would be a valuable probe for the multiplicity of the reactive excited state in this reaction (167). Qualitatively, one might expect that the lifetime of S_1 would decrease as the efficiency of the [1,3] shift increased if the reaction occurred from S_1. Quantitatively, however, the situation is not that simple. The lifetime of the S_1 state is given by Eq. (5) and the efficiencies of the [1,3] shift and of intersystem crossing are given by Eqs. (6) and (7), respectively, within the framework of mechanism A, where $k_{1,3}^S$ and k_{ST} are as defined previously, k_F is the rate constant for prompt fluorescence, and k_i is the sum of rate constants for all other processes proceeding from S_1 (radiationless decay, oxetane formation, Norrish type II reaction, etc.). An additional assumption is that the [1,3] shift does not proceed via an intermediate, such as a radical pair, which partitions between formation of product (probability F) and return to starting material (probability $1 - F$). If such a mechanism operates (see later discussion), the quantity $k_{1,3}^S$ must be replaced by $k_\alpha F$, where k_α is the rate constant for formation of the intermediate.

$$\tau_{S_1}^{-1} = k_{1,3}^S + k_{ST} + k_F + k_i \tag{5}$$

$$\phi_{1,3}^S = k_{1,3}^S \tau_{S_1} \tag{6}$$

$$\phi_{ST} = k_{ST} \tau_{S_1} \tag{7}$$

It was discovered by two groups (166,170,172–174) that many, if not all, β,γ-enones fluoresce in solution at ambient temperatures under reaction conditions, thus providing a probe into the details of reactions proceeding from S_1. The fluorescence lifetimes of enones 207–215 were measured

TABLE 2

Fluorescence Lifetimes and Quantum Yields of β,γ-Enones (*170,173,174*)

Compound	$\phi_F \times 10^4$ [a]	τ_F (nsec) [b]
207		1.7 ± 0.1 (1.8) [c]
208		2.4 ± 0.1 (2.6) [c]
209		3.4 ± 0.1 (4.0) [c]
210	21	1.56 ± 0.05
211	9.6	0.41 ± 0.05
212	5.4	0.66 ± 0.05
213	4.6	0.33 ± 0.05
214	9.2	0.61 ± 0.05
215	6.9	0.47 ± 0.05
201	35	5.0 ± 0.1
i	72	4.91 ± 0.05
ii	53	4.47 ± 0.05
iii	46	4.16 ± 0.05
iv	20	2.25 ± 0.05
187		1.8 ± 0.1
245	32	0.97 ± 0.05
v	12.5	1.05 ± 0.05
vi	3.2	0.11 ± 0.05
vii	6.7	0.82 ± 0.05
viii	6.7	1.29 ± 0.05
ix		(1.9) [c]
x		(2.2) [c]
xi		(2.6) [c]

[a] Fluorescence quantum yields at 313 nm in cyclohexane solution at room temperature. The primary standard was N,N,N',N'-tetramethyl-p-phenylenediamine (ϕ_F 0.18), and i was the secondary standard.

[b] Fluorescence lifetimes in cyclohexane by single-photon counting with data treatment by computer-assisted convolution.

[c] From ref. *166*.

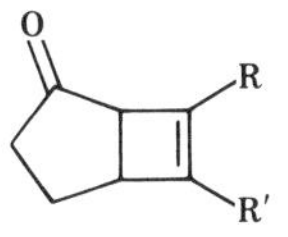

i: $R' = R' = Me$
ii: $R = t$-Bu; $R' = H$
iii: $R = H; R' = t$-Bu

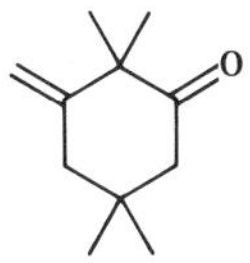

iv

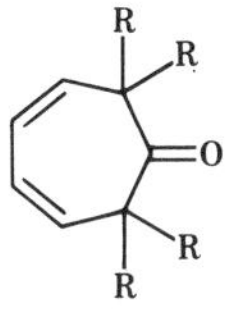

v: $R = H$
vi: $R = Me$

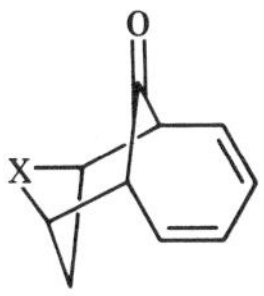

vii: $X = -CH=CH-$
viii: $X = -CH_2CH_2-$

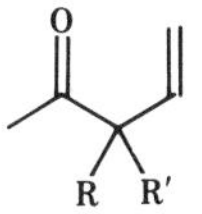

ix: $R = R' = H$
x: $R = Me; R' = H$
xi: $R = R' = Me$

(*170,173*) as were those of a number of other enones and 3,5-cycloheptad-
ienones (*173,174*). These data are shown in Table 2 along with the data of
other workers (*166*) for **207–209** and three other enones. The agreement of
the data for **207–209** between the two groups is gratifying, and the same
trend clearly emerges, namely, that α-methylation increases both τ_{S_i} and
$\phi_{1,3}$. A similar but quantitatively smaller effect of α-methylation is seen
with Dalton's enone series (*166*), but not with **211** versus **212**. From absolute values of ϕ_F (*170,173*) it was determined that values of k_F differ very
little over the whole series and agree very well with values calculated
from enone absorption spectra.

In interpreting their fluorescence data, Dalton and co-workers (*166*)
made two assumptions, one reasonable and the other controversial. The
first was that k_i is relatively unimportant in these enones, and the second
was that k_{ST} either is not affected by α-methylation or else decreases
slightly, as noted previously for alkanones (*175*) and 3-cyclopentenones
(*176*). Therefore, the observation that α-methylation causes an increase
rather than a decrease in τ_{S_i} in **207–209** concomitant with an increase in
$\phi_{1,3}$ was concluded to be inconsistent with S_1 as the source of the [1,3]
shift but consistent with T_2 as the reactive state (mechanism B). Schuster
and Eriksen (*170*) took a more conservative view of their data and made
no assumptions about the effect of α-methylation on k_{ST} in β,γ-enones
on the grounds that the limited data on k_{ST} for alkanones and 3-cyclo-
pentenones (*175,176*) did not provide a sufficiently general and trust-
worthy correlation to be accepted without question in the present context. Although the data are not inconsistent with mechanism B, it was
concluded that they can also be interpreted within the context of mechanism A. If rate constants $k_{1,3}^S$ and k_{ST} are calculated (*170,173*) from the
singlet lifetimes and relevant quantum yields, assuming the validity of
mechanism A, it is discovered that $k_{1,3}^S$ increases on α-methylation by at
least one order of magnitude in **207–209**, concomitant with a comparable
decrease in k_{ST}, a not unreasonable result. It was concluded (*170*) that an
objective choice between mechanisms A and B was not possible on the
basis of these data and that both mechanisms must be considered hence-
forth in interpreting β,γ-enone photoreactivity.

Thus, fluorescence techniques have not as yet provided an unequivocal
solution to this mechanistic dilemma, although these contributions have
defined the issues much more sharply.

It was reported some time ago (*177*) that direct irradiation of
acetylcyclopentene (**224a**) results mainly in the [1,3]-acyl shift (detected
by racemization of optically active enone **224a**) and a complex mixture of
products in low yield (including the trimethylcyclopentenyl dimer **225**)
attributable to reactions of acetyl- and trimethylcyclopentenyl radicals

224a X = Y = H
224b X = D; Y = H
224c X = H; Y = D

formed by α cleavage of 224. Irradiation of a 1:1 mixture of the deuteriated analogues 224b and 224c did not give any cross-products (i.e., undeuteriated and hexadeuteriated ketones) after 50% consumption of starting materials (controls showed that there was a negligible kinetic isotope effect due to introduction of deuterium into 224), indicating the rearrangement is entirely intramolecular and proceeds either by a concerted or a tight biradical mechanism. A photo-CIDNP (chemically induced dynamic nuclear polarization) study (167) did not indicate any polarization, further evidence that racemization does not proceed via an α-cleavage–recombination pathway. (Later CIDNP studies described below gave somewhat different results.) Naphthalene and piperylene had no effect on the isomerization, but 1 M tri-n-butylstannane could intercept the reactive excited state, causing reduction to the secondary alcohol to compete with all other photoreactions (177); this important observation indicates that the reactive excited state is sufficiently long lived to undergo bimolecular reactions. Since the two diastereomeric ODPM rearrangement products 226 and 227 are observed exclusively on triplet sensitization using acetone or acetophenone, it is clear that the T_1 state is not generated on direct photolysis of 224. The fact that radicals sufficiently "free" to undergo dimerization are produced on excitation of 224 implicates two independent pathways: a completely intramolecular [1,3] shift and α cleavage to radical pairs. Similar behavior was subsequently demonstrated for some related enones lacking methyl substituents (178).

The results of irradiation of a series of steroidal enones and model compounds can be similarly explained (179). The epimeric deuterium-labeled enones 228 and 229 (R = H or CH₃) rearrange stereospecifically without scrambling of α-methyl groups to 230 and 231, a result rationalized in terms of a solvated "intimate" allyl–acyl radical pair in

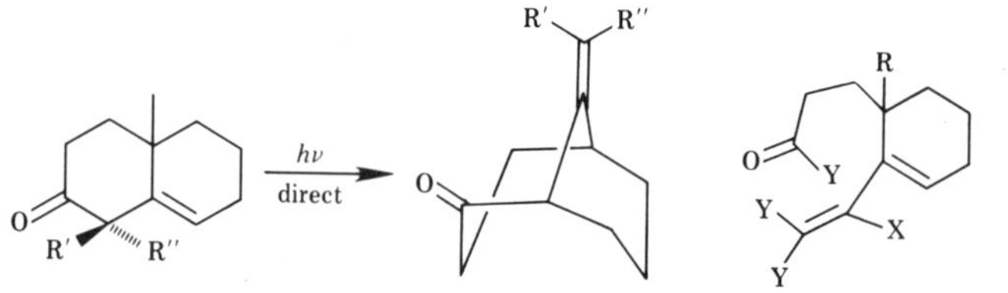

228 R = H, CH$_3$; R' = CD$_3$; R'' = CH$_3$ 230   232a X = CD$_3$; Y = H
229 R = H, CH$_3$; R' = CH$_3$; R'' = CD$_3$ 231   232b X = CH$_3$; Y = D

228 or 229 (R = H) ⟶ 232a + 232b
228 (R = CH$_3$) ⟶ 232a
229 (R = CH$_3$) ⟶ 232b

which rotation around the C=C bond is prevented or, alternatively, in terms of a concerted $_\sigma 2 + _\pi 2$ cycloaddition (s + s or a + a). A competitive intramolecular H transfer to give aldehydes **232** was nonstereospecific in the case of R = H but stereospecific for R = CH$_3$, which implicates a radical pair in which rotation is free for R = H but sterically inhibited for R = CH$_3$. Once again, two competitive pathways are indicated from one or more short-lived excited states (reactions neither sensitized by aceto-

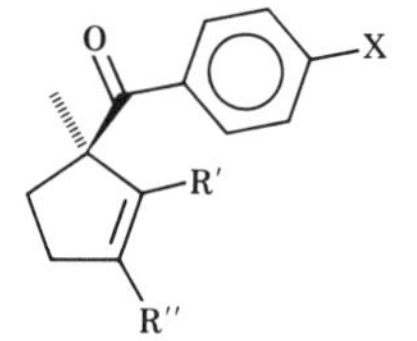

233a R' = R'' = CH$_3$; X = H
233b R' = R'' = CH$_3$; X = OCH$_3$
233c R' = CH$_3$; R'' = X = H
233d R' = CD$_3$; R'' = CH$_3$; X = H

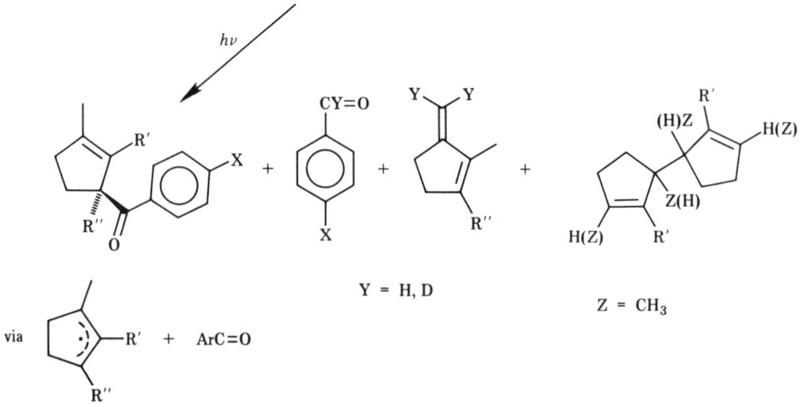

Y = H, D

Z = CH$_3$

phenone nor quenched by piperylene), totally analogous to the situation with enones **224** (*177*).

A quite different picture emerges from studies on aroylcyclopentenones **233** (X = H or OCH$_3$) (*180*). Once again there is competition between the [1,3] shift (leading to racemization in the case of **233a**) and to formation of products of "free" aroyl and cyclopentenyl radicals. An experiment employing a mixture of (+)-**233b** (X = OCH$_3$) and racemic **233d** gave extensive cross-products, indicating predominant α cleavage to a "free" radical pair, which recombines randomly to enones of type **233** in competition with formation of dimers and disproportionation products. This time, strong CIDNP effects were seen for all products of the reaction (*167,180*). A quantitative analysis based on chiroptical, mass spectrometric, and CIDNP measurements indicated that for X = H the product enones are derived 60 ± 5% from random free-radical recombination and 40 ± 5% via geminate free-radical recombination, whereas for X = OCH$_3$ these values are 85 ± 5% and 15 ± 5%, respectively (*180*). On the basis of the effects of CCl$_4$ on CIDNP intensities due to radical scavenging, it was further estimated that pair formation occurs about 30% from singlet and 70% from triplet excited states for both X = H and X = OCH$_3$. Pathways for the [1,3] shift not involving polarizable radical intermediates are of minor importance in these systems. Finally, triplet-sensitized photolysis of these ketones does *not* lead to ODPM rearrangement; it leads only to α cleavage. These results would appear to require the generation of both ^{1}n,π^* and ^{3}n,π^* states on direct photolysis, although the authors (*167,180*) do not make such an explicit statement; conceivably, the $^3\pi,\pi^*$ state could be involved, but inexplicably undergoes α cleavage in preference to the customary ODPM rearrangement. The phosphorescence of these enones strongly resembles that of acetophenone and *p*-methoxyacetophenone, respectively, with respect to spectral shape, lifetime, and quantum yields (*167*), indicating that these enones most likely have lowest-lying n,π^* triplet states with the excitation localized on the aroyl portion of the enone; this might well affect their photochemical behavior.

234a R = R' = H; R'' = Ph
234b R = CH$_3$; R' = H; R'' = Ph
234c R = H; R' = CH$_3$; R'' = Ph
234d R = CH$_3$; R' = Ph; R'' = H

When a phenyl group is introduced onto the alkene portion of these cyclopentenyl ketones (*178*), as in **234**, the situation reverts for the most part to that described for the methyl ketones **224**; that is, the "normal" intramolecular [1,3]-acyl shifts occur, without the formation of cross-products on excitation of appropriately labeled mixtures of enones, and is explained by either a concerted $_\sigma 2 + _\pi 2$ cycloaddition or reaction via a "tight-geometry" pericyclic biradical. Curiously, two phenyl-substituted enones **234c** and **234d** were recovered unchanged after twice the time needed for complete isomerization of **234a** and **234b**; no firm explanation for this was suggested, although it was noted (*178*) that homoconjugation in **234c** and **234d** may be inhibited because of steric crowding.

Heavy-atom effects on the photochemical behavior of bicyclo[3.2.1]-oct-2-en-7-ones were studied (*181*) in the hope that induced changes in ϕ_{ST} would lend insight into the origin of the [1,3]-acyl and ODPM rearrange-

X = H, Cl, Br   237

ments. However, direct irradiation of **235** and its [1,3]-acyl migration product **236** with X = H, Cl, and Br led only to the reversible [1,3] shift, which was detected for X = H by racemization of optically active starting material. On sensitized photolysis in acetone, under conditions in which the enones quenched acetone phosphorescence, all five enones gave a mixture of products of ODPM (**237**) and [1,3]-acyl rearrangement. It was considered that these products arise from different excited states, since piperylene quenched the acetophenone-sensitized ODPM rearrangement but not the [1,3] shift, and the product ratio was a function of the triplet energy of the sensitizer. Quantum yields for reaction fell off considerably on introduction of Cl and even further for X = Br. It was concluded that the ODPM rearrangement occurs from T_1 ($^3\pi,\pi^*$) and the sensitized [1,3] shift from a higher-energy n,π^* state, most likely a triplet state (T_2). Since heavy atoms did not promote intersystem crossing to T_1 from S_1 (*182*), as would have been evinced by formation of **237**, most likely the [1,3] shift arises from S_1 on direct excitation of these enones; the data, however, do not unequivocally rule out intersystem crossing to T_2, which reacts or decays to ground state to the exclusion of internal conversion to T_1. For enones **235**, ϕ_F decreases in the order $X = H \gg Cl > Br$, leading to the conclusion (*181*) that heavy atoms enhance radiationless decay processes from both S_1 and T_1, conceivably including intersystem crossing. Since thermal [1,3]-acyl migration in enone **235** $(X = H)$ has been observed (*183*) the possibility was thrown out for consideration (*181*) that the excited state merely funnels the reactant molecules onto the ground state surface where the rearrangement actually occurs, presumably via vibrationally excited ground state molecules. Such a possibility has not heretofore received serious consideration.

A major advance is represented by a recent study (*184*) on enone **238**, which undergoes [1,3]-acyl shift to **239** as well as ODPM rearrangement to

240 on both direct and triplet-sensitized photolysis. The ratio of **239** to **240** was 2.73 on direct excitation of **238** at 313 nm in acetonitrile, and 0.031 on 254 nm excitation of an acetone solution of **238** in which acetone absorbed nearly all the light. The [1,3] shift clearly dominates in direct photolysis and the ODPM in acetone-sensitized photolysis. These ratios were compared with the product ratio from *thermal* decomposition in acetonitrile of the mixture of diastereomeric dioxetanes **241**. It is well established (*185,186*) that dioxetanes decompose thermally to give ketone excited states, detectable by their characteristic luminescence and chemical reactivity, and that triplet excited states are generated preferentially to

singlets by a factor of at least 10:1, with rare exceptions (*187*). It has also been suggested that these reactions result in selective formation of n,π^* ketone triplets (*188*). The observed ratio of 0.70 for **239/240** from decomposition of **241** could be explained (*184*) a priori by simultaneous formation of S_1 and T_1 in relative yields of 88 and 12%, with subsequent production of **239** and **240** from each state in the ratios and quantum yields determined under direct and triplet-sensitized photolytic conditions, respectively. Indeed, chemiluminescence identical to the fluorescence of **238** was detected during the dioxetane decomposition, but a quantitative measurement of the fluorescence yield using luminol as a chemiluminescence standard indicated that the yield of the S_1 state of enone **238** from dioxetane **241** was ≤15% (*184*), which is insufficient to account for the relative yields of **239** and **240** by the above mechanism. The bulk of the [1,3] shift seen on thermal decomposition of **241** must originate from an enone excited state other than S_1 (^{1}n,π^*) or T_1 ($^3\pi,\pi^*$), and it would seem only logical to identify this state as T_2 (^{3}n,π^*). The ratio of products from the dioxetane decomposition also indicates that the [1,3] shift and internal conversion to T_1 occur at comparable rates, assuming that the T_2 state (^{3}n,π^*) is preferentially generated initially (*188*). The T_2 state therefore appears to be responsible for the [1,3] shift on triplet-sensitized photolysis, but the fact that the [1,3] shift dominates on direct excitation of enone **238** *requires* that it originate predominantly from S_1 before, and in competition with, intersystem crossing.†

The dual origin of the [1,3] shift was further demonstrated in recent CIDNP studies of several acetonylcyclopentenes (*189*). The polarization of the [1,3]-acyl migration products changes with temperature in a manner which indicates that the predominant pathway at lower temperatures (25°C for **238** and **242**; −50°C for **224a**) involves a triplet excited state

238 X = Y = H
242 X = CH$_3$; Y = H
224a X = Y = CH$_3$

precursor, whereas at higher temperatures (130°C for **238** and **242**; 25°C for **224a**) reaction from a singlet excited state predominates. These results strongly suggest that α cleavage from the S_1 state is an activated process which competes directly with intersystem crossing; the latter presumably

† See Note Added in Proof, p. 270.

experiences no activation barrier (*190*). Thus, at lower temperatures the predominant pathway involves intersystem crossing to T_2 and α cleavage from that state, whereas at higher temperatures α cleavage directly from S_1 becomes increasingly important. For **242** and **224a** the magnitude of the CIDNP effects in C_6D_{12} at 25°C was not affected by the presence of triplet quenchers (1,3-cyclohexadiene and naphthalene) or tributylstannane, although the latter substantially reduced the yield of dimers. These data provide direct evidence that the polarization effects seen under these conditions derive from triplet radical pairs rather than from "free" radicals, and that α-cleavage of the T_2 state is too fast to compete with diffusion-controlled quenching. The fate of the triplet radical pair also appears to depend on the temperature and the solvent as indicated by variations in product ratios. It is noteworthy that it is the enone with the shortest singlet lifetime at room temperature (**224a**), as measured by fluorescence decay, which reacts most extensively from S_1; i.e., the activation barrier for α cleavage from S_1 is presumably the smallest in this case. Thus, the totality of results for these acetonylcyclopentenes would seem to require mechanism C, with both n,π^* states, S_1 and T_2, as sources of the [1,3] acyl rearrangement but with the relative role of the two states dependent on the reaction conditions. It is tempting to extend this mechanism to other enones using the principle of analogy, but that may be premature and dangerous (*150*). At the very least, these results demonstrate the viability of the hypothesis (*166,167*) that the T_2 state of β,γ-enones *can* be chemically reactive, but they do not define the conditions under which the T_2 state *will* play a significant role for a given enone under direct as well as triplet-sensitized electronic excitation.

The authors (*189*) further note that several claims in the literature (*171,175*) for α-cleavage from S_1 states of ketones could not be substantiated by photo-CIDNP studies (*190a*), and that the experimental evidence generally cited to indicate α-cleavage from S_1 (i.e., failure to sensitize using standard triplet sensitizers, failure to quench using standard triplet quenchers) is just as compatible with reaction from a vibrationally excited triplet state. The strong evidence that has now been obtained indicating that T_2 states of β,γ-enones can be reactive in competition with decay to energetically proximate T_1 states requires that the criteria for identifying S_1 reactivity in ketone photochemistry in general need to be critically reexamined.

2. Acyclic β,γ-Enones

There has been much less work on the photochemistry of acyclic β,γ-enones than on the cyclic systems discussed above. These systems are particularly prone to *Z–E* isomerization (*143*) and to intramolecular reactions such as oxetane formation and γ-H abstraction in appropriate situations (*10*). More recent studies indicate a strong mechanistic relation to the bicyclic enones, at least with respect to the [1,3]-acyl migration.

A series of acyclic enones have been studied (*191*), of which **243** and **245**

are good examples. Direct photolysis of these compounds gave a mixture of [1,3]-acyl migration, biacetyl, and C_{10} hydrocarbons, which can all be ascribed to intermediate acetyl and 1,1-dimethylallyl radicals produced by α cleavage of the reactive excited state. There was no reaction of **243** on triplet sensitization other than *Z–E* isomerization (observed with a labeled derivative), whereas **245** underwent intramolecular cycloaddition. Thus, subject to the usual caveat that T_2 reactivity has not been unequivocally ruled out by these data, the reactions seen on direct photolysis appear to originate from the S_1 state. Products **247** and **248** were isolated from irradiation of **243** in the presence of the nitroxyl radical **246,** confirming the intermediacy of "free" acetyl and dimethylallyl radicals. The yield of **244** was reduced to 57% of its value in the absence of **246;** similar data were obtained using thiocresol as the radical trap. Nitroxyls do not trap acyl radicals **245b** derived from **245,** nor do they reduce the yield of **245a,** suggesting that the lifetime of **245b** is very short indeed, which is not surprising considering its expected ease of decarbonylation (*20*). Although the data do not rule out a more or less concerted intramolecular rearrangement path for the formation of at least part of the [1,3]-acyl migration product in these systems, the authors (*191*) prefer an interpretation involving completely efficient α cleavage to an acyl–allyl radical pair, which partitions between recombination to a mixture of starting material and [1,3]-acyl migration product and formation of "free" radicals; the latter also combine to give these cross-products in competition with dimerization and trapping by radical scavengers. All the reaction inefficiency (energy wastage) is attributed (*191*) to cage recombination of the initially formed radical pair.

The extension of this study to acetylenic ketone **249** indicated that allenic products can also be formed by [1,3]-acyl migration.

Further details have emerged from other recent studies (*192–194*). The quantum yields of enone disappearance (ϕ_{-E}), [1,3]-acyl migration ($\phi_{1,3}$), and formation of allyl radical dimers (ϕ_{DIM}) from enones **250** were mea-

250a X = H; Y = CH$_3$
250b X = CH$_3$; Y = CH$_3$
250c X = CH$_3$; Y = (CH$_3$)$_2$CH

251a X = Y = CH$_3$
251b X = H; Y = (CH$_3$)$_3$C
251c X = CH$_3$; Y = (CH$_3$)$_3$C

sured. As solvent viscosity increased, a decrease in ϕ_{-E} and an increase in $\phi_{1,3}$ at the expense of ϕ_{DIM} was observed; this is consistent with a competition between recombination of radicals within the solvent cage (to give starting enone and [1,3]-acyl migration product) and escape from the cage, the latter becoming relatively less important in solvents of higher viscosity. Added tri-n-butylstannane (TBS) increased ϕ_{-E} markedly with **250a** and **250b**, indicating that some "free" radicals also recombine in these cases to regenerate starting material. No such effect is seen with **250c**, consistent with the expected rapid loss of CO from isobutyryl radicals precluding recombination of the acyl–allyl radical pairs in this case, although sufficient TBS suppresses decarbonylation of the isobutyryl radical. These results strongly implicate radical pairs as reaction intermediates, but, once again, they do not rigorously exclude formation of at least some of the acyl migration product by a concerted pathway.

CIDNP data for these compounds (*193,194*) show that regeneration of starting material and acyl migration occur at room temperature, at least in part, from radical pairs generated predominantly from *triplet* excited states. In line with the results outlined above, radical pair recombination to give starting enone is much less pronounced for **250c** than for **250a** and **250b**. With γ-phenylenones **251**, however, the CIDNP data indicate that α cleavage at room temperature occurs mainly from *singlet* excited states, again leading to starting material, [1,3]-acyl migration, and other radical recombination products. The results were interpreted (*192,194*) in terms of an "isolated chromophore" model in which exothermic quenching of carbonyl triplet excitation by the alkene moiety is efficient for the phenylenones, thus suppressing α cleavage from the triplet, whereas such "intramolecular triplet energy transfer" is energetically unfavorable for the alkylenones and does not compete effectively with α cleavage from the n,π* triplet state (T₂). The results can also readily be interpreted in terms of the model outlined above (*189*). Thus, it is expected that α cleavage to give the stabilized γ-phenylallyl radicals from the phenylenones **251** would proceed readily from S_1 at room temperature, competing effectively with intersystem crossing, whereas the barrier for α cleavage from S_1 of the alkylenones **250** might be sufficiently high that at room temperature this reaction would not compete with intersystem crossing to T_2, which therefore becomes the predominant source of radical pairs. The obvious prediction follows that the phenylenones **251** should demonstrate triplet excited state polarization effects at low temperatures, whereas the alkyl enones **250** should show singlet excited state polarization effects at elevated temperatures.

Thus, both singlet and triplet n,π* states (S_1 and T_2) appear to play a role in the photochemistry of acyclic β,γ-enones, and specifically in [1,3]-acyl migration, in a manner consistent with the pattern for cyclic enones discussed earlier and all within the general framework of mechanism C (Section V,B). Once again, the quantitative contribution of each state cannot yet be evaluated for any given system from available data, but some trends are becoming apparent.

D. The Oxadi-π-methane Rearrangement: Mechanism and Stereochemistry

Early studies (*10,63,150*) demonstrated that under conditions of triplet photosensitization β,γ-enones commonly rearrange to cyclopropyl ketones by what is formally a [1,2]-acyl migration to C_β, accompanied by ring closure between C_α and C_γ, the so-called oxadi-π-methane rearrangement. The studies and theoretical calculations cited in Section V,B led to the conclusion that this reaction occurs from an alkene-like triplet state (T_1, $^3\pi,\pi^*$) located several kilocalories below the $^3n,\pi^*$ state. For enones such as **209–211**, **224**, **235**, and **236**, in which the reaction is observed only on triplet sensitization, one must conclude that the T_1 state is not populated to a significant extent from S_1, although it does not necessarily follow that $\phi_{ST} = 0$, as discussed at length in the previous section. With enones such as **201**, **207**, **208**, **212**, and **238**, in which the rearrangement is observed under both direct and triplet-sensitized irradiation conditions, T_1 can be populated directly from the enone S_1 state as well as by transfer of triplet excitation. In these systems, selective quenching of the ODPM rearrangement by typical triplet quenchers is observed. An ODPM rearrangement that appears to arise from the S_1 state of an enone is mentioned only once in the literature (*195*), but this merits independent confirmation. The fact that the S_1 states are inactive toward ODPM rearrangements is in accord with the general description of S_1 as an n,π* state with excitation localized largely on the carbonyl group (*10,160*), whereas the ODPM reaction would appear to require excitation of the alkenyl moiety by analogy with the DPM rearrangement (*63*) (See Essay 16).

These features are well demonstrated by a recent study of the γ-phenylenone **234a** (*178*). The lowest triplet state of this enone was clearly

234a   252   253

254 X = H, CH₃; Y = Ph
255 X = Ph; Y = H

identified as a localized styrene π,π^* state with $E_T = 59$ kcal/mol by comparison of its phosphorescence at 77 K with that of 1-phenyl-cyclopentene; the data also indicate that $\phi_{ST} \sim 1.0$ at 77 K. The two emissions were superimposable, and the excitation and absorption spectra agreed in each case. Triplet sensitization with a variety of sensitizers gave an approximately 3:1 mixture of acetylbicyclo[2.1.0]pentanes **252** and **253**. Quantum yields were similar when sensitizer triplet excitation energies were ≥ 61 kcal/mol but fell off sharply with sensitizer $E_T \leq 59$ kcal/mol (α- and β-acetonaphthone), virtually proving that the phosphorescent $^3\pi,\pi^*$ state is indeed the state responsible for the ODPM photorearrangement. Interestingly, direct photolysis of **234a** at ambient temperature results only in [1,3]-acyl migration and no detectable formation of **252** and **253**, despite the efficient population of T_1 at 77 K. Moreover, no detectable quantity of any photoproduct was formed from **234a** on irradiation with $\lambda > 300$ nm for prolonged periods at 77–173 K, suggesting that small but significant barriers exist on the respective energy surfaces leading to both ODPM rearrangement from T_1 and [1,3]-acetyl migration from S_1 (*178*). Curiously, enones **254** and **255** fail to undergo an acetone-sensitized ODPM rearrangement. This result is especially surprising for **255** since it is the [1,3]-acyl migration product of **234a** and should form the same ODPM products as that compound.

In enones in which the C=C bond is unconstrained, i.e., in most acyclic systems and medium- or large-ring cycloalkenyl ketones, the main, if not exclusive, pathway for dissipation of the excitation of the T_1 state involves Z–E isomerization by rotation around the C=C bond (*10,143,150,191,196*). This "free-rotor" effect (*142*) often completely suppresses the enone ODPM rearrangement on either direct or triplet-sensitized photolysis, as illustrated by the behavior of **243** (*191*) and **256** (*196*). Thus, the ODPM rearrangement occurs with cyclopentenyl ketones **211** and **212** but not with the cyclohexenyl ketone **213** (*157*).

	R_1	R_2	R_3	R_4	R_5
257	Ph	H	H	Me	i-Pr
258	Ph	H	H	Et	Me
259	H	H	Ph	Me	Me
260	Ph	Ph	H	Me	Me

The [1,2]-acyl shift occurs only when it can compete with the free-rotor effect (150), and this is suggested to be dependent on the degree of orbital mixing in the T_1 state, as reflected by the enhancement of the intensity of the n → π^* absorption. This correlation was used to rationalize the occurrence of the ODPM rearrangement from 257 (ϵ_{293} = 376) and 258 (ϵ_{290} = 350) but not from 259 (ϵ_{291} = 11) and 260 (ϵ_{295} = 120) (197), although the contribution of steric inhibition of rotation around the C=C bond in 259 and 260 cannot be discounted.

Three types of mechanisms, each with variations differing in mechanistic details, can be envisaged for the ODPM rearrangement: (A) Norrish type I cleavage to an acyl–allyl radical pair, followed either by recombination at the center carbon of the allyl system and subsequent cyclization, or by combination of the acyl radical with a previously cyclized cyclopropyl radical; (B) a concerted rearrangement following either a $_{\sigma}2_a$ + $_{\pi}2_a$ or a $_{\sigma}2_s$ + $_{\pi}2_s$ pathway, both of which are symmetry-allowed as excited state processes (27); or (C) a stepwise pathway of the DPM type, in which initial bridging between the carbonyl carbon and C_β is followed either by a concerted rearrangement to the cyclopropyl ketone, or by ring opening to a 1,3 diradical, which then closes to the product. These mechanistic alternatives are depicted in Scheme 5.

Mechanism (A) has generally been considered to be unlikely on energetic grounds as well as on the grounds that it does not reflect the typical behavior of allyl radicals (10,150). Accordingly, we will not consider it further. The $_{\sigma}2_s$ + $_{\pi}2_s$ variation of mechanism (B) can often be discounted on grounds of steric strain, since this pathway requires retention of configuration at the tetrahedral carbon (C_α) and leads to products involving trans fusion of the new three-membered ring to either a five- or six-membered ring, starting with cyclopentenyl or cyclohexenyl ketones, respectively. In acyclic systems, however, both concerted reaction pathways are structurally possible. Ultimately, the question is whether the diradicaloid structures B and C shown in mechanism (C) represent true intermediates with discrete lifetimes or merely points along the hypersurface of a concerted rearrangement pathway.

An attempt was made (198) to distinguish between synchronous and stepwise mechanisms for the triplet-sensitized ODPM rearrangement of benzobicyclic enone 261 to 262. A stepwise mechanism for this rearrangement would involve diradical structures 263 and 264. In an attempt to generate 264 by an independent route and characterize its modes of reaction, lactone 265 was irradiated in benzene. Decarboxylation accompanied the formation of 261, 262, naphthalene, and enone 266; the latter is the [1,3]-acyl migration product of 261 formed from 261 on direct irradiation. On the basis of quenching data, it was argued that all reactions

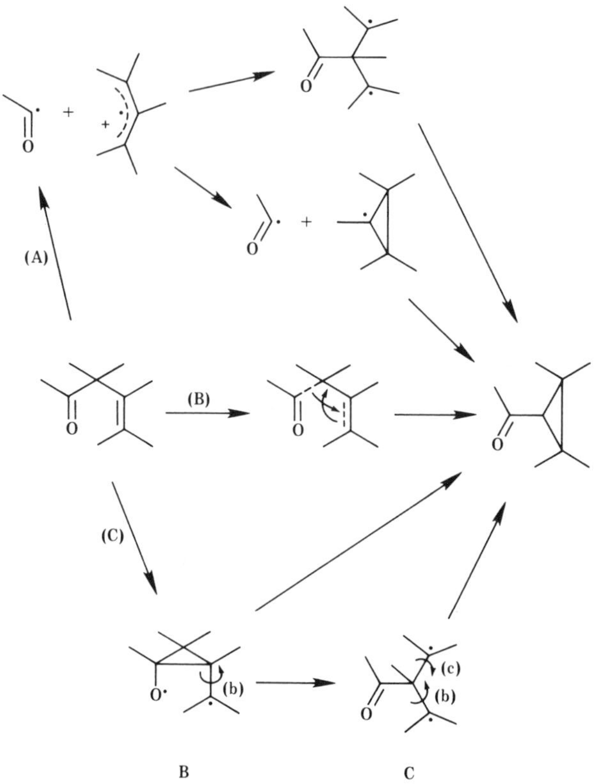

Scheme 5. Mechanistic possibilities for the [1,2]-aryl migration (ODPM rearrangement).

of lactone **265** occur via the same triplet excited state, that this triplet loses CO_2 to generate **264**, and that **264** is the precursor of all the products, including **266**.

The fact that **266** was *not* formed on triplet-sensitized photolysis of **261** was therefore taken as evidence that diradical **264** is not generated under these conditions and is thus not an obligatory intermediate on the way to the ODPM product **262** (*198*). However, this conclusion depends on the assumption that there is no experimental problem associated with the failure to detect **266** on triplet-sensitized photolysis of **261** (note that its yield is only 1% from lactone **265**) and that **266** is stable to the sensitization conditions. Even if there were no such problem, this result still does not *require* the authors' conclusion that the ODPM rearrangement is necessarily concerted, since there remains the possibility that intermediates of type B (**263**) can proceed directly to product (**262**), bypassing intermediates C (**264**), as previously pointed out (*167*).

Most efforts directed toward differentiation of synchronous and step-wise mechanisms for the ODPM photorearrangement have been devoted to studies of the stereochemistry of the reaction. Specifically, if diradicals B and C have sufficient lifetimes, rotations around bonds (b) and (c) may occur in competition with progress along the reaction coordinate to the cyclopropyl ketone product, leading to loss of stereochemistry at the former α- and γ-carbons of the original β,γ-enone. However, the experimental observations that bear on this question are in apparent conflict.

The ODPM rearrangements of **267** (*179*) and **268** (*199*) occur with complete scrambling of the methyl groups. In the latter case, there was no methyl scrambling in recovered starting material, ruling out reversible opening and closure of ring A as a pathway for loss of stereochemistry at C-4. The loss of stereochemistry is most reasonably attributed (*199*) to the

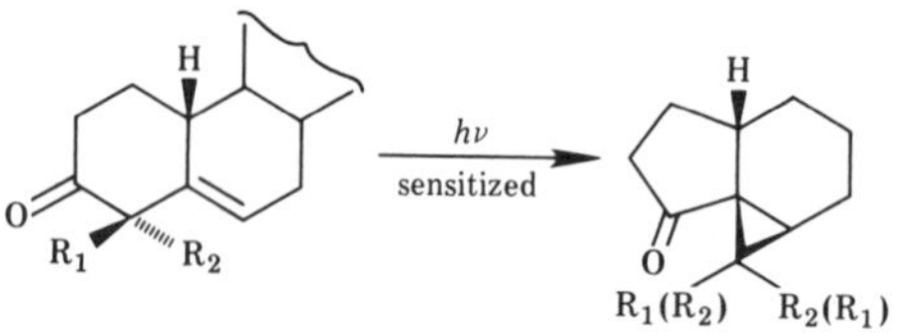

$$\text{(267a, 267b)} \xrightarrow[\text{sensitized}]{h\nu}$$

267a $R_1 = CH_3$; $R_2 = CD_3$
267b $R_1 = CD_3$; $R_2 = CH_3$

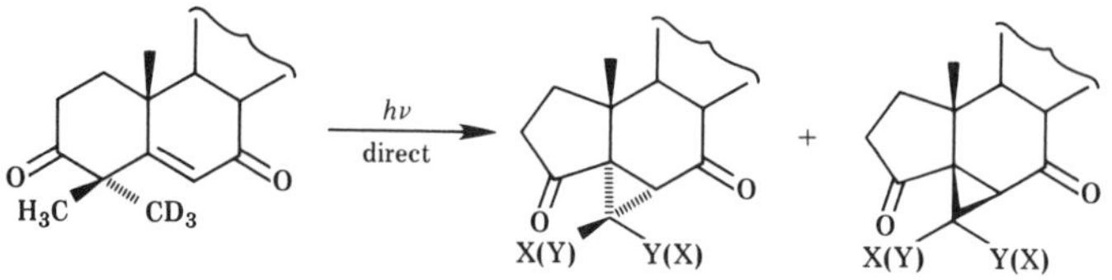

$R_1(R_2)$ $R_2(R_1)$

$$\text{268} \xrightarrow[\text{direct}]{h\nu} \quad + \quad$$

$X(Y)$ $Y(X)$ $X(Y)$ $Y(X)$

268

$X = CH_3$;
$Y = CD_3$

via   and

H_3C CD_3 H_3C CD_3

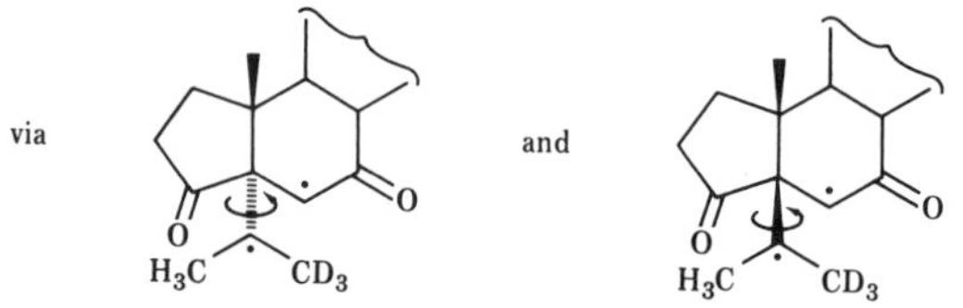

269   270

formation of epimeric diradicals **269** and **270** of type C, which undergo rotation around bond (c) before ring closure. An unlikely alternative would be fortuitous concerted rearrangements at the same rate by $_\sigma 2_a + _\pi 2_a$ pathways, with both inversion and retention of configuration at C-4; the $_\sigma 2_s + _\pi 2_s$ pathway is eliminated since it would lead to trans fusion of the cyclopropane ring to ring B.

Similarly, sensitized irradiation of **224** and **234** and related acetonyl-cyclopentenes (*167,178*) gives a mixture of *exo*- and *endo*-bicyclopentanes, which are not interconvertible on either direct or triplet-sensitized photolysis. This result is compatible with concomitant operation of two concerted pathways, the major route to the endo product involving a $_\sigma 2_a + _\pi 2_a$ or antidisrotatory mechanism and the minor route to the exo product involving a $_\sigma 2_s + _\pi 2_s$ or syn disrotatory pathway [terminology given in ref. (*200*)]. Alternatively, a stepwise route involving diradicals **271** and **272** of type B and C, respectively, can account for the formation of the products by either backside (to give endo) or frontside (to give exo) radical displacements (paths m and n in structure **271**) and/or by ring opening to **272** followed by "up" or "down" disrotatory ring closure. The endo/exo product ratio, which is markedly different from that achieved on

$$_\sigma 2_a + {}_\pi 2_a$$

$$_\sigma 2_s + {}_\pi 2_s$$

mixture of exo and endo products

thermal equilibration of the bicyclopentanones, must reflect kinetic control in the final ring closure. Although the pathway via mechanism (C) is conceptually more attractive, the results in these systems do not exclude participation of mechanism (B).

A related observation is that diketones **141** afforded exclusively *endo*-bicyclopentanes **142** in quantitative yield (*116,117*). This course of reaction is again consistent with either a concerted $_\sigma 2_a + {}_\pi 2_a$ pathway or a stepwise pathway in which the behavior of diradicals of types B and C is under the steric influence of the large acyl groups. The unlikely possibility of thermodynamic control of product formation has not been explicitly ruled out in this case.

In contrast with all the above examples is the totally stereospecific rearrangements of the epimeric enones **273** and **274** (*201*). First, it is curious that the ODPM rearrangement in this system competes so well with isomerization around the presumably unconstrained double bond, in contrast with the behavior of other unconstrained enones discussed earlier.

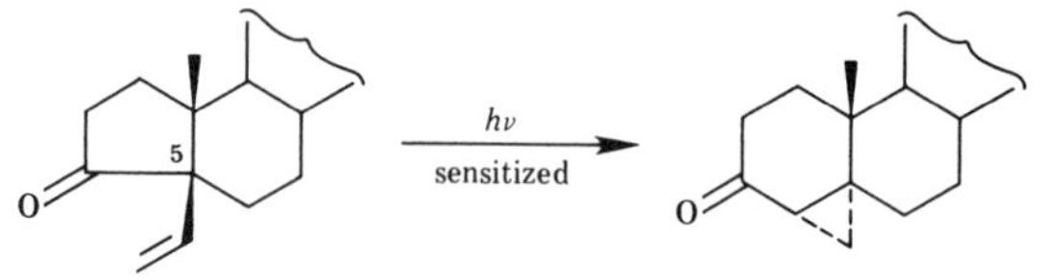

273
275

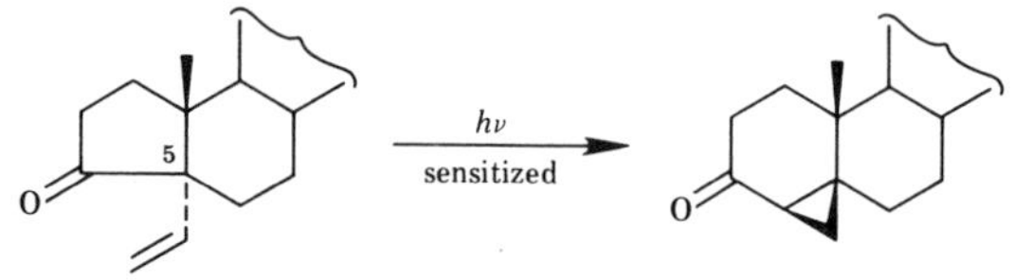

274
276

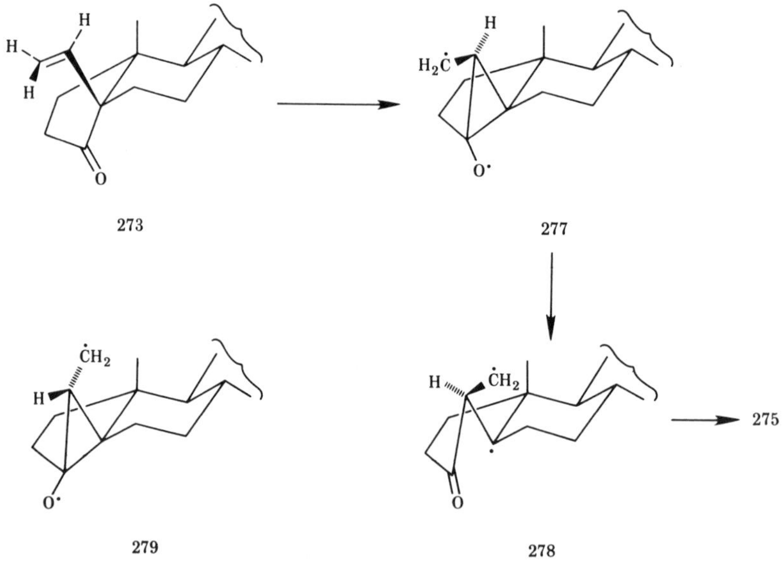

273
277

279
278

Second, the observation that the 5-β-vinyl enone **273** affords the α-methano product **275** whereas the 5α-vinyl enone **274** affords the β-methano product **276** rules out a common intermediate in the two pathways and demonstrates that these rearrangements proceed with *retention* of configuration at C-5, the α-carbon of the β,γ-enone system. Two alternative mechanisms can again accommodate the observations: a concerted $_\sigma2_s + _\pi2_s$ pathway, or a stepwise route leading to products via intermediates **277** and **278** in which bonding occurs between C_{CO} and C_β only in that conformation in which the vinyl group is directed away from the steroid

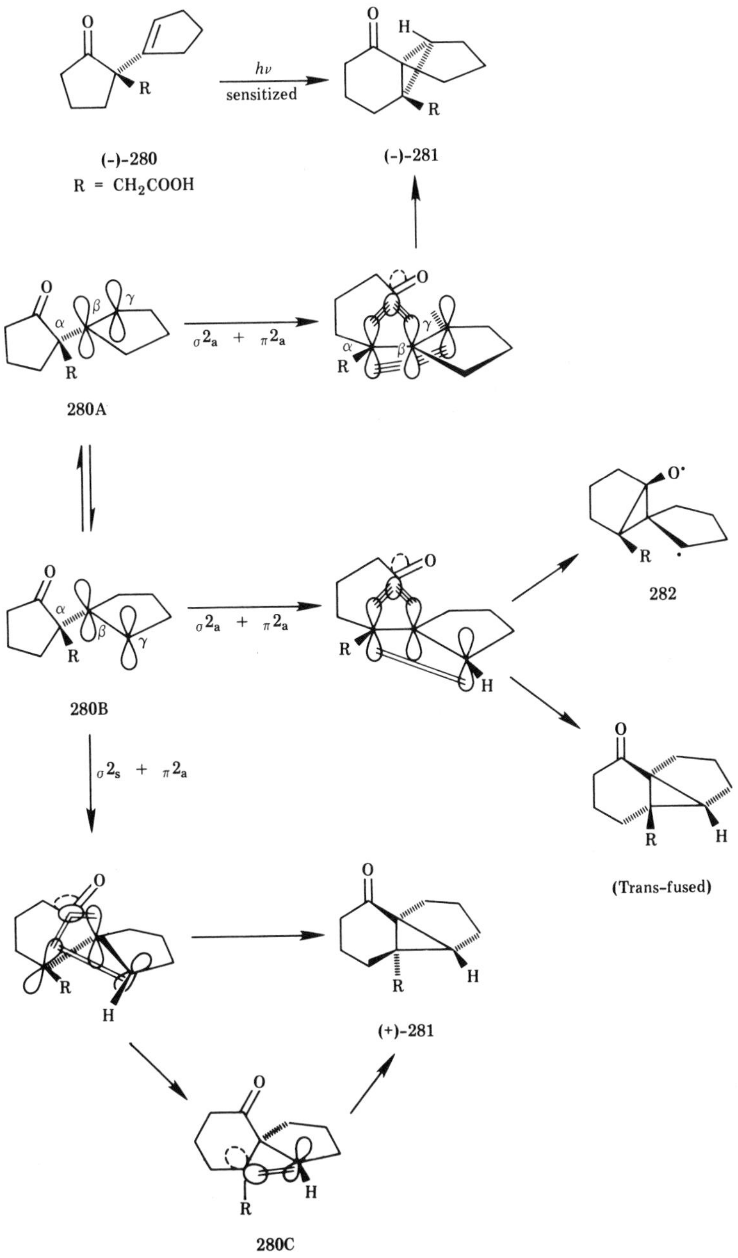
hν
sensitized
(-)-280
R = CH_2COOH
(-)-281
$_{\sigma}2_a + _{\pi}2_a$
280A
$_{\sigma}2_a + _{\pi}2_a$
280B
282
$_{\sigma}2_s + _{\pi}2_a$
(Trans-fused)
(+)-281
280C

nucleus. The latter mechanism requires that the alternative dia-stereomeric intermediates **279**, if formed, revert to starting material (**273**) rather than proceed to product, to account for the lack of inversion at C-5. However, the absence of a label at the γ-carbon precludes a decision as to the concertedness of this rearrangement.

The ODPM rearrangement of enone **280** (*202*) is also totally stereo-specific, but the correlation of absolute configurations of product **281** and starting enone established that in this case the rearrangement proceeds completely (within experimental error) with *inversion* of configuration at C_α. Assuming that the stereochemical assignment is correct (*203*), few mechanistic pathways can account for the observed reaction course. There are two conformations of enone **280**, depicted as A and B, in which the overlap of the p orbitals on the carbonyl carbon and C_β is maximized. Microwave data fail to indicate a unique conformational preference in **280** and related compounds (*202*). In conformation A, a concerted $_\sigma 2_a + _\pi 2_a$ rearrangement involving suprafacial [1,2]-acyl migration and closure of the ring on the opposite face of the system between C_α and C_γ with inversion at C_α is perfectly feasible, according to molecular models. A stepwise process that accomplishes the same molecular changes in two or three steps via biradicals is also attractive. Other concerted or stepwise alternatives from conformation A that involve retention of configuration at C_α (such as $_\sigma 2_s + _\pi 2_s$ or $_\sigma 2_s + _\pi 2_a$) are structurally impossible, since they lead to trans fusion of the cyclopropane ring in the product. From confor-mation B, both concerted $_\sigma 2_a + _\pi 2_a$ as well as $_\sigma 2_s + _\pi 2_s$ pathways are excluded, since these also lead to trans-fused ring systems. The only pathway that does not lead to a trans-fused ring system from conformation B involves a suprafacial [1,2]-acyl migration to a biradical **280C** of type C, which then must close to (+)-**281** with *retention* of configuration at C_α and inversion at C_γ, i.e., by what is essentially a $_\sigma 2_s + _\pi 2_a$ symmetry-forbidden pathway. This pathway is ruled out by the experimental results. It is therefore not surprising that, experimentally, complete inversion of con-figuration at C_α, is observed (*202*), since that appears to be the most favorable route in **280** because of these structural constraints. This path-way also seems the most favorable on least motion considerations, based on examination of molecular models. All of the ODPM reaction of **280** appears to occur only from conformer A, even though there seems to be no structural impediment to the formation of diradical intermediates of the ODPM type (**282**) from conformation B; if formed, **282** must totally revert to starting material since it apparently has no low-energy route to a stable product. It would be most interesting to determine whether an increase in temperature leads to racemization of **281** by pro-moting the energetically less favorable pathway to (+)-**281**. Another example of a stereospecific ODPM rearrangement that appears to occur with inversion of configuration at C_α has been reported (204a). This substrate is particularly interesting since it had the option of reacting as a 2,4-cyclohexadienone (cleavage to a diene ketene) or a tautomeric 2,5-cyclohexadienone in competition with the observed pathway characteristic of β,γ-enone triplets.

The stereochemical fate of the α- and γ-carbons in the course of ODPM rearrangement of the optically active enone (S)-283 to a mixture of endo and exo products 284 and 285 was studied (205) (stereochemical designations $1S,9S$ and $1S,9R$ respectively). The enantiomeric purity of the start-

ing enone changed from 54% to 42% after 90% conversion, and the products were 48% enantiomerically pure. This partial racemization was attributed to reversible α cleavage of (S)-283 which was competitive with its acetone-sensitized rearrangement. In this system, a concerted $_\sigma 2_a + _\pi 2_a$ reaction pathway on both faces of the ring system would yield a mixture of 285 (observed) and 286, the latter being the enantiomer of the observed product 284. A $_\sigma 2_s + _\pi 2_s$ route can be ruled out since it leads to impossibly strained products. The reaction course could be rationalized in terms of a concomitant symmetry-allowed $_\sigma 2_a + _\pi 2_a$ reaction to give 285 and a symmetry-forbidden $_\sigma 2_s + _\pi 2_a$ reaction to give 284, but this seems highly unlikely on energetic grounds (205). Inspection of molecular models reveals that overlap of the carbonyl p orbitals with alkene p orbitals is extremely poor in this system, inhibiting, if not totally suppressing, concerted reaction pathways, compared with very favorable orbital overlap in such systems as **273** and **280**. The results seem best understood in terms of a stepwise mechanism proceeding from the favored conformation of **283**, which has the dimethoxymethyl group in a pseudoequatorial position, leading to a diradical **287** (of type C) in which rotation around bond (b) competes with cyclization to form the three-membered ring (205). The interaction between C-5 and C-9 is relatively poor even in the proposed diradical intermediates, enhancing the probability of loss of stereochemistry at C-9 (formerly C_α). This situation is to be contrasted with the structurally facile ODPM routes in **273** and **280** discussed above.

Thus, in each of the systems described above, there are configurational and/or conformational features, often of a very subtle nature, which enhance one or another possible pathway for the ODPM rearrangement relative to others. It is therefore impossible to arrive at a decision from these studies as to which mechanistic pathway is energetically most favorable in a system completely free from structural constraints. The closest to a definitive study of this problem reported to date is probably the examination (206) of the stereochemistry of the ODPM rearrangement of an optically active acyclic enone **288**, in which all possible reaction pathways are structurally permissible. The styrene-like chromophore in **288** permitted sensitization by chrysene (E_T 57 kcal/mol). The optically active *trans*-enone (+)-**288**, optical purity 90%, gave the two ODPM rearrangement products **289** and **290** in addition to *cis*-enone and some [1,3]-acyl migration product. None of the two other possible ODPM products (**291** and **292**) were detected (<1%). The upper limit of the optical purity

(+)-288   (-)-289   (+)-290

291   292

Et Me

Ph — Me

Ph — (b)

H O·

H O

295 293 (+)-290 + (-)-289

(+)-288

Et Me

Et

H Me

H — (b)

Ph — Me

Ph —

Ph — O·

O

296 294 (+)-289 + (-)-290

of **290** was 10%, as determined by direct comparison of its rotation with that of an optically pure sample prepared independently. The optical purity of **289** was not established directly but was assumed to be approximately the same as **290** from the similar magnitudes of their optical rotations. Thus, these rearrangements appear to proceed with extensive loss of configuration at the α-carbon. Photoracemization of both the *trans*- and *cis*-enones was much less extensive ($\sim 13\%$), and the products were stable to the reaction conditions, showing that the extensive loss in optical purity of the products was a consequence of the ODPM rearrangement itself and was not due to other factors. The results were analyzed by considering each possible pathway from both s-cis and s-trans conformations of **288**. In order for racemic **290** to be formed by symmetry-allowed concerted processes, there would have to be concomitant reaction at nearly identical rates via a $_\sigma 2_a + _\pi 2_a$ mechanism from the s-cis conformer of **288** and a $_\sigma 2_s + _\pi 2_s$ mechanism from its s-trans conformer. A similar description of pathways pertains to the formation of racemic **289**. The view (*206*) that "such a fortuitous matching of reaction rates of the opposite orbital process, of opposite conformations, and of the opposite stereochemistry of the double bond seems to be a very untenable explanation for the observed racemization results" appears to be acceptable. If symmetry-forbidden pathways are allowed to compete with the allowed pathways, one can also account for the formation of racemic **290** by concomitant $_\sigma 2_s + _\pi 2_a$ and $_\sigma 2_a + _\pi 2_a$ pathways from the different conformers, which once again seems improbable. A much more reasonable picture involves a stepwise reaction mechanism in which the enantiomeric 1,3-diradicals **293** and **294** are produced and undergo rotation around bond (b) in competition with final closure of the three-membered ring to give both enantiomers of **289** and **290**. However, the enantiomeric intermediates **293** and **294** would not be expected to be formed in equal amounts from the chiral enone **288** because of asymmetric induction (note that **295** and **296** are diastereomers), resulting in a slight preference for formation of one of the intermediates (**293**) and therefore to an excess of one enantiomer of each of the products. The authors presented a "least-motion" argument to rationalize the lack of total racemization as well as the absolute configuration of that isomer of product formed in excess (*206*). The failure to produce **291** and **292** is rationalized in terms of the preferred conformations of the "diradicaloid" intermediates in which the least crowded conformer yields only products with the phenyl and acetyl groups trans, as observed experimentally.

Thus, the "ODPM" mechanism (C) invoking "diradicaloid" intermediates provides the simplest and most satisfying explanation for the behavior of (+)-**288** on triplet sensitization. Considering all the ODPM rearrangements studied to date, as summarized above and in earlier reviews (*10,150*), it would appear that mechanism (C) is capable of rationalizing *all* the stereochemical data, provided that conformational and configurational constraints are recognized which may favor one set of molecular motions over another, resulting in completely stereospecific rearrangements or to total or partial loss of stereochemistry. In no case do the data *require* a concerted pathway, although such a pathway cannot be rigorously ruled out (enones **273** and **280**). In such cases, the opportunities for continuous orbital overlap make a distinction between concerted and stepwise pathways very difficult as the two begin to merge. When overlap of the carbonyl and alkene orbitals is poor and the diradical intermediates are capable of stabilization by conjugating substituents, the features that distinguish a stepwise reaction mechanism become especially prominent.

E. Photorearrangements of 3,5-Cycloheptadienones

These cyclic $\beta,\gamma,\beta',\gamma'$-dienones undergo photorearrangements that are analogous in many ways to those of the β,γ-enones discussed in previous sections. These include ODPM rearrangements from their lowest triplet states and, at least in one case (*207*), [1,3]-acyl migration. These reactions are competitive with ring opening accompanied by loss of carbon monoxide, electrocyclic ring closure of the dienyl moiety, and dimerization. There is an excellent summary of the photochemical behavior of these compounds, including some attempts at mechanistic rationalization (*10*). Recently, fluorescence from these compounds in solution at room temperature (*173,208*) has been observed, as well as wavelength-dependent pathways in some systems (*207*), but a number of important mechanistic problems remain unsolved (*209*).

Note Added in Proof

1. Photochemistry of Cyclohexenones

Since the lack of photochemical reactivity of 6 and 7 reported some time ago (18,210) has not proved readily interpretable, we decided to reinvestigate the photochemistry of these systems (211). In both cases, the enones were rigorously purified and identified spectroscopically; this is pertinent since in the case of 7 it is possible that the material investigated earlier (18) may well have been 3,6,6-trimethyl-2-cyclohexenone, which is the main product of the synthetic pathway utilized. We find that both 6 and 7 indeed produce the corresponding lumiketones (identified spectroscopically) on irradiation in t-BuOH at 254 or 300 nm. Quantum efficiencies have not yet been measured, but qualitatively they appear similar to that found for enone 2. We attribute the earlier failure to observe these photorearrangements (18,210) to differences in analytical procedures from those used in our study (211). Thus, contrary to the earlier conclusion (18), methyl substitution on the double bond of 4,4-disubstituted cyclohexenones does not necessarily inhibit the lumiketone photorearrangement.

These observations are also relevant to the discussion (p. 186) of the photochemistry of 43, where the observed lack of reactivity toward the lumiketone rearrangement (59) could have been ascribed to inhibitory effects of alkyl substitution on the C=C bond rather than to the conformational constraints of the system. The former interpretation now seems highly unlikely, strengthening the conclusion that the lumiketone rearrangement requires substantial torsion around the C=C bond and is not observable in systems such as 43 in which such torsion is either impossible or is severely inhibited.

It should also be noted that both 6 and 7 show very weak fluorescence in cyclohexane at room temperature (211); no such emission is seen from 2. These observations are in disagreement with the hypothesis (59) that only enones that are highly constrained with respect to torsion around the C=C bond (such as 43) will exhibit fluorescence. The generality of fluorescence of simple monocyclic enones is now under investigation in our laboratory.

Some conclusions regarding the mechanism of photoreduction of cyclohexenones in IPA can be drawn from recent studies (212). Gas chromatography–mass spectroscopic (GCMS) analysis of the products of irradiation of enone 2 in IPA-OD at 254 nm indicates that 25% of the photoreduction product, 4,4-dimethylcyclohexanone, contains one deuterium; there was no D incorporation into 2 or into the concomitantly formed lumiketone. 4,4-Dimethyl-2-cyclohexen-1-ol, another possible photoreduction product, is not formed from 2 in IPA. Deuterium incorporation from IPA-O-D most likely occurs on ketonization of intermediate enols rather than by radical abstraction pathways. The failure to observe carbonyl reduction suggests that such enols are not formed via path (c) in Scheme 4 as a result of initial H-abstraction on oxygen. The simplest interpretation is that reaction is initiated at C_β of the enone by path (a), and the intermediate radical subsequently abstracts a second hydrogen either at C_α to give the product directly (75%) or at oxygen to give the intermediate enol (25%) which then ketonizes. When the photoreduction of 2 was carried out in $(CD_3)_2CHOH$, GCMS analysis indicated the saturated ketones contained no deuterium. This indicates that the second H-transfer to carbon does not take place to a detectable extent from the methyl group of the intermediate radical $(CD_3)_2\dot{C}OH$, the main pathway followed when these radicals disproportionate (213), but probably involves the carbinol hydrogen of a second IPA molecule. Also, $(CH_3)_2\dot{C}OH$ radicals produced thermally do not react with enone 2 (214), precluding the operation of a chain mechanism in photoreduction, a pathway demonstrated for cyclohexadienone

32 (*33*). Reaction to some extent by path (b) cannot as yet be absolutely excluded for **2** in IPA, although irradiation of **2** in toluene gives exclusively 2-benzyl-4,4-dimethylcyclohexanone (*212*). Experiments using $(CH_3)_2CDOH$ would obviously be helpful, but the yield of photoreduction products dramatically decreases, indicating a substantial kinetic isotope effect on the H-abstraction reaction. As a footnote to the above, we have found (*212*) that cyclohexenone itself is cleanly photoreduced to cyclohexanone in IPA.

Irradiation of protonated cyclohexenones **2** and **5** in FSO_3H at -60 to -85 C results in formation of protonated lumiketones and protonated cyclopentenones (*38a*). The protonated lumiketone formed from **2H** was also found to rearrange to protonated 3-isopropylcyclopentenone thermally at -60 C or photochemically at -80 C. Although the multiplicity of the excited states involved in these transformations is not known, it is likely on spectroscopic grounds that these reactions involve π,π^* states. It is striking that the photochemical course in these strong acid solutions at low temperatures completely parallels the behavior of these enones in neutral media at ambient temperatures.

Finally, a comparison of the course of photoreactions of epimeric 4-hydroxycyclohexenones **297** and **298** in solution and the solid state has been made (*215*). In solution, irradiation results exclusively in [2 + 2] cycloaddition, while in the solid state products arise as a result of intramolecular H-transfer to the β-carbon of the enone system. The results can be understood in terms of different preferred conformations of the starting materials in the crystal lattice versus solution, which results in different groups being brought into proximity and ultimately determines the reaction course. These results emphasize the importance of molecular conformation as a controlling feature in determining photochemical reaction pathways, a subject which has in general been insufficiently explored.

297   298

R = H, CH₃

2. β,γ-Enones

Additional evidence supporting the involvement of T_2 ($^3n,\pi^*$) states in [1,3]-acyl shifts of β,γ-enones is provided by a recent study using **211** as a model substrate (*216*). It had previously been reported (*156*) that both [1,2]- and [1,3]-acyl shifts occurred on acetone sensitization of **211**, and that the ratio of products remained constant in the presence of biphenyl, acting as a triplet quencher. We find that under these same conditions there is definitely better quenching of the [1,2]- than of the [1,3]-rearrangement, and that the ratio of quantum yields for the two processes ($\phi_{1,3}/\phi_{1,2}$) increases as the triplet state energy of the sensitizer increases. These data indicate that under triplet sensitization the two products arise from different triplet states, with the [1,2]-rearrangement occurring from the triplet of lower energy, presumably $^3\pi,\pi^*$. Studies in which triplets of **211** were generated from thermal decomposition of tetramethyl dioxetane (*185*) provided support for this conclusion (*216*). Novel confirmation of the participation of the T_2 state under direct excitation of **211** came from studies in the presence of two atmospheres of Xenon, which reproducibly resulted in a 20% *decrease* in the fluorescence intensity of **211** in cyclohexane at room temperature and a similar *increase* in $\phi_{1,3}$; however, **218** was not detectable in the photolysate when Xenon was present. Thus, at least in the case of **211**, it appears that intersystem crossing from S_1 occurs exclusively to T_2 ($^1n,\pi^* \rightarrow {}^3n,\pi^*$), in apparent violation of El-Sayed's rule (*217*), and that internal conversion from T_2 to T_1 does not compete with reaction from T_2 by α-cleavage to generate **217**. The high quenching constant for Xe on the fluorescence of **211**, similar to that for Xe on fluorescence of polynuclear aromatic hydrocarbons (*218*), is much greater than the effect of Xe on acetone fluorescence, and suggests that certain types of $^1n,\pi^*$ states may be susceptible to heavy atom effects (*219*). This is currently under further scrutiny.

An interesting case of divergence of rearrangement pathways of a β,γ-enone in the solid state versus solution has been shown recently (*220*). Both direct and benzophenone-sensitized excitation of **299** in solution give a single photoproduct, **300**, while **301** is formed from **299** on excitation in the crystalline state. The formation of **300** is thought to occur via **302**, the expected initial intermediate of an ODPM rearrangement, but rather than continuing along the ODPM hypersurface the reaction takes a different course because of the proximity of the second C=C bond, leading to **303** and then to **300**. The molecular conformation in crystals of **299** is shown as **304** (from X-ray data), which by a variety of mechanisms can proceed to **301**; one likely intermediate is **305**, but other alternatives have not been excluded. The authors (*220*) suggest that both rearrangements arise from $^3\pi,\pi^*$ states, and that the divergence in pathways reflects the different preferred molecular conformations in solution versus the crystalline state.

301   299   300

302   303

304   305

REFERENCES

1. O. L. Chapman, *Adv. Photochem.* **1**, 323–420 (1963).
2. K. Schaffner, *Adv. Photochem.* **2**, 81–112 (1966).
3. P. J. Kropp, *Org. Photochem.* **1**, 1–90 (1967).
4. O. L. Chapman and D. S. Weiss, *Org. Photochem.* **3**, 197–288 (1973).
5. H. Labhart and G. Wagniere, *Helv. Chim. Acta* **42**, 2212 (1959).
6. R. C. Cookson and N. S. Wariyar, *J. Chem. Soc.* p. 2302 (1956).
7. J. N. Murrell, "The Theory of the Electronic Spectra of Organic Molecules," pp. 164–168. Wiley, New York, 1963.
8. A. Moscowitz, K. Mislow, M. A. W. Glass, and C. Djerassi, *J. Am. Chem. Soc.* **84**, 1945 (1962).
9. E. Bunnenberg, C. Djerassi, K. Mislow, and A. Moscowitz, *J. Am. Chem. Soc.* **84**, 2823 (1962).
10. K. N. Houk, *Chem. Rev.* **76**, 1 (1976).
11. W. W. Kwie, B. A. Shoulders, and P. D. Gardner, *J. Am. Chem. Soc.* **84**, 2268 (1962); B. A. Shoulders, W. W. Kwie, W. Klyne, and P. D. Gardner, *Tetrahedron* **21**, 2973 (1965).
12. O. L. Chapman, T. A. Rettig, A. A. Griswold, A. I. Dutton, and P. Fitton, *Tetrahedron Lett.* p. 2049 (1963).
13. P. E. Eaton and W. S. Hurt, *J. Am. Chem. Soc.* **88**, 5038 (1966).
14. E. Y. Y. Lam, D. Valentine, and G. S. Hammond, *J. Am. Chem. Soc.* **89**, 3482 (1967).
15. P. J. Wagner and D. J. Bucheck, *J. Am. Chem. Soc.* **91**, 5090 (1969).
16. A. Butenandt, L. Karlson-Poschmann, G. Failer, U. Schiedt, and E. Biekert, *Justus Liebigs Ann. Chem.* **575**, 123 (1952).
17. D. Bellus, D. R. Kearns, and K. Schaffner, *Helv. Chim. Acta* **52**, 971 (1969).
18. W. G. Dauben, G. W. Shaffer, and N. D. Vietmeyer, *J. Org. Chem.* **33**, 4060 (1968).
19. H. Wehrli, R. Wenger, K. Schaffner, and O. Jeger, *Helv. Chim. Acta* **46**, 678 (1963).
20. C. Walling, "Free Radicals in Solution." Wiley, New York, 1957; W. A. Pryor, "Free Radicals." McGraw-Hill, New York, 1966.
21. D. I. Schuster and D. F. Brizzolara, *J. Am. Chem. Soc.* **92**, 4357 (1970).
22. For a discussion concerning the chemical consequences of addition of ketone triplets to benzene and substituted benzenes, see D. I. Schuster, *Pure Appl. Chem.* **41**, 601 (1975).
23. B. Nann, D. Gravel, R. Schorta, H. Wehrli, K. Schaffner, and O. Jeger, *Helv. Chim. Acta* **46**, 2473 (1963).
24. O. L. Chapman, J. B. Sieja, and W. J. Welstead, Jr., *J. Am. Chem. Soc.* **88**, 161 (1966).
25. D. I. Schuster, R. H. Brown, and B. M. Resnick, *J. Am. Chem. Soc.* **100**, 4504 (1978); for earlier communications, see D. I. Schuster and B. M. Resnick, *ibid.* **96**, 6223 (1974); D. I. Schuster and R. H. Brown, *J. Chem. Soc., Chem. Commun.* p. 28 (1976).
26. O. L. Chapman and D. S. Weiss, *Org. Photochem.* **3**, 214 (1973).
27. R. B. Woodward and R. Hoffmann, "The Conservation of Orbital Symmetry." Academic Press, New York, 1970 (esp. pp. 89–100).
28. K. Schaffner and M. Demuth, Essay 18 of this volume.
29. H. E. Zimmerman and D. I. Schuster, *J. Am. Chem. Soc.* **83**, 4486 (1961); **84**, 4527 (1962); H. E. Zimmerman and J. S. Swenton, *ibid.* **89**, 906 (1967).
30. H. E. Zimmerman, R. G. Lewis, J. J. McCullough, A. Padwa, S. W. Staley, and M. Semmelhack, *J. Am. Chem. Soc.* **88**, 1965 (1966).
31. D. I. Schuster and B. M. Resnick, unpublished observations; B. M. Resnick, Ph.D. Dissertation, New York University (1974).
32. P. Margaretha and K. Schaffner, *Helv. Chim. Acta* **56**, 2884 (1973).

33. For a critical review of the evidence bearing on the intermediacy of zwitterions in the dienone-lumiketone photorearrangement, see D. I. Schuster, *Acc. Chem. Res.* **11**, 65 (1978); see also Schaffner and Demuth (*28*).

34. H. E. Zimmerman, *Adv. Photochem.* **1**, 183–208 (1963).

35. L. Salem, *J. Am. Chem. Soc.* **96**, 3486 (1974).

36. See also H. E. Zimmerman, R. W. Binkley, J. J. McCullough, and G. A. Zimmerman, *J. Am. Chem. Soc.* **89**, 6589 (1967).

37. D. I. Schuster and D. J. Patel, *J. Am. Chem. Soc.* **90**, 5145 (1968).

38. J. E. Williams and H. Ziffer, *Chem. Commun.* p. 194 (1967); *Tetrahedron* **24**, 6725 (1968).

38a. D. G. Cornell and N. Filipescu, *J. Org. Chem.* **42**, 3331 (1977); R. F. Childs, K. E. Hine and F. A. Hung, *Can. J. Chem.*, **57**, 1442 (1979).

39. See also H. E. Zimmerman and D. J. Sam, *J. Am. Chem. Soc.* **88**, 4905 (1966).

40. See also D. I. Schuster, *Pure Appl. Chem.* **41**, 601 (1975).

41. See J. Saltiel, J. D'Agostino, E. D. Megarity, L. Metts, K. R. Neuberger, M. Wrighton, and O. C. Zafirou, *Org. Photochem.* **3**, 1–113 (1973), for a review and primary references.

42. A. Devaquet, *J. Am. Chem. Soc.* **94**, 5160 (1972); *Top. Curr. Chem.* **54**, 1–73 (1975).

43. P. E. Eaton, *Acc. Chem. Res.* **1**, 50 (1968).

44. P. E. Eaton, *J. Am. Chem. Soc.* **86**, 2087 (1964); **87**, 2052 (1965); E. J. Corey, M. Tada, R. LeMahieu, and L. Libit, *ibid.* p. 2051.

45. P. J. Cropp, E. J. Reardon, Jr., Z. L. F. Gaibel, K. F. Williard, and J. H. Hattaway, Jr., *J. Am. Chem. Soc.* **95**, 7058 (1973).

46. H. Hart and E. Dunkelblum, *J. Am. Chem. Soc.* **100**, 5141 (1978); H. Hart, B. Chen and M. Jeffares, *J. Org. Chem.*, **44**, 2722 (1979).

47. R. Noyori and M. Kato, *Bull. Chem. Soc. Jpn.* **47**, 1460 (1974).

48. E. Dunkelblum, H. Hart, and M. Jeffares, *J. Org. Chem.* **43**, 3409 (1978).

49. T. Matsuura and K. Ogura, *Bull. Chem. Soc. Jpn.* **40**, 945 (1967).

50. R. Bonneau, J. Joussot-Dubien, L. Salem, and A. J. Yarwood, *J. Am. Chem. Soc.* **98**, 4329 (1976).

50a. W. G. Dauben, H. C. H. A. van Riel, C. Hauw, F. Leroy, J. Joussot-Dubien and R. Bonneau, *J. Am. Chem. Soc.*, **101**, 1901 (1979); W. G. Dauben, H. C. H. A. van Riel, J. D. Robbins and G. J. Wagner, *ibid.*, **101**, 6383 (1979).

51. R. Bonneau, J. Joussot-Dubien, J. Yarwood, and J. Pereyre, *Tetrahedron Lett.* p. 235 (1977).

52. R. Bonneau, P. Fornier de Violet, and J. Joussot-Dubien, *Nouv. J. Chim.* **1**, 31 (1977).

53. R. Bonneau and P. Fornier de Violet, *C.R. Hebd. Seances Acad. Sci., Ser. C* **284**, 631 (1977).

54. R. Bonneau and P. Fornier de Violet, unpublished results reported at the VIIth IUPAC Conference on Photochemistry, Leuven, Belgium, July 1978, Abstracts, pp. 52–55 (1978).

55. T. Goldfarb, *J. Photochem.* **8**, 29 (1978).

56. For an early suggestion about the intermediacy of *trans*-1-acetylcyclohexene in photoaddition to alcohols, see B. J. Ramey and P. D. Gardner, *J. Am. Chem. Soc.* **89**, 3949 (1967).

57. E. J. Corey, J. D. Bass, R. LeMahieu, and R. B. Mitra, *J. Am. Chem. Soc.* **86**, 5570 (1964).

58. J. Michl, *Mol. Photochem.* **4**, 243 and 257 (1972).

59. D. I. Schuster and S. Hussain, *J. Am. Chem. Soc.*, **102**, 409 (1980); S. Hussain, Ph.D. Dissertation, New York University, 1979.

60. For a discussion on the effect of twisting on spin-orbit coupling in a totally different system, see N. J. Turro and P. Lechtken, *J. Am. Chem. Soc.* **95**, 264 (1973).
61. R. O. Loutfy and J. M. Morris, *Chem. Phys. Lett.* **19**, 377 (1973).
62. H. E. Zimmerman and J. W. Wilson, *J. Am. Chem. Soc.* **86**, 4036 (1964); H. E. Zimmerman, R. D. Rieke, and J. R. Scheffer, *ibid.* **89**, 2033 (1967); H. E. Zimmerman and R. L. Morse, *ibid.* **90**, 954 (1968); H. E. Zimmerman and K. G. Hancock, *ibid.* p. 3749; H. E. Zimmerman and W. R. Elser, *ibid.* **91**, 887 (1969).
62a. H. E. Zimmerman and D. J. Sam, *J. Am. Chem. Soc.* **88**, 4114 and 4905 (1966).
62b. H. E. Zimmerman and N. Lewin, *J. Am. Chem. Soc.* **91**, 879 (1969).
63. For a review, see S. S. Hixson, P. S. Mariano, and H. E. Zimmerman, *Chem. Rev.* **73**, 531 (1973).
64. H. E. Zimmerman, *Tetrahedron* **30**, 1617 (1974).
65. W. G. Dauben, W. A. Spitzer, and M. S. Kellogg, *J. Am. Chem. Soc.* **93**, 3674 (1971).
66. F. Nobs, U. Burger, and K. Schaffner, *Helv. Chim. Acta* **60**, 1607 (1977); see also J. S. Swenton, R. M. Blankenship, and R. Sanitra, *J. Am. Chem. Soc.* **97**, 4941 (1975).
67. R. C. Hahn and G. W. Jones, *J. Am. Chem. Soc.* **93**, 4232 (1971).
68. R. C. Hahn and D. W. Kurtz, *J. Am. Chem. Soc.* **95**, 6723 (1973).
69. J. Gloor, K. Schaffner, and O. Jeger, *Helv. Chim. Acta* **54**, 1864 (1971).
70. K. Schaffner, *Pure Appl. Chem.* **33**, 329 (1973).
71. J. Gloor, G. Bernardinelli, R. Gerdil, and K. Schaffner, *Helv. Chim. Acta* **56**, 2520 (1973).
72. J. Gloor and K. Schaffner, *Helv. Chim. Acta* **57**, 1815 (1974).
73. J. Gloor and K. Schaffner, *J. Am. Chem. Soc.* **97**, 4776 (1975).
74. See N. J. Turro, V. Ramamurthy, W. Cherry, and W. Farneth, *Chem. Rev.* **78**, 125 (1978), for a recent review of this subject.
75. D. O. Cowan and R. L. Drisko, "Elements of Organic Photochemistry," Chapter 5. Plenum Press, New York, 1976.
76. N. J. Turro, "Molecular Photochemistry," Chapter 5. Benjamin, New York, 1965.
77. A. A. Lamola, *Tech. Org. Chem.* **14**, 17–132 (1969).
78. M. C. Sauer and B. Ward, *J. Phys. Chem.* **71**, 3971 (1967).
79. R. Wander and L. M. Dorfman, *J. Phys. Chem.* **72**, 2946 (1968).
80. D. I. Schuster and T. M. Weil, *J. Am. Chem. Soc.* **95**, 4091 (1973).
81. J. Saltiel, H. C. Curtis, and B. Jones, *Mol. Photochem.* **2**, 331 (1970).
82. B. Nann, D. Gravel, R. Schorta, H. Wehrli, K. Schaffner, and O. Jeger, *Helv. Chim. Acta* **46**, 2473 (1963).
83. A. Butenandt, L. Karlson-Poschmann, G. Failer, U. Schiedt, and E. Biekert, *Justus Liebigs Ann. Chem.* **575**, 123 (1952), and earlier papers cited.
84. D. O. Cowan and R. L. Drisko, "Elements of Organic Photochemistry," Chapter 3. Plenum, New York, 1976; N. J. Turro, "Molecular Photochemistry." Chapter 6. Benjamin, New York, 1965.
85. G. Wampfler, Ph.D. Dissertation, Iowa State University, Ames (1970).
86. S. Wolff, W. L. Schreiber, A. B. Smith, III, and W. C. Agosta, *J. Am. Chem. Soc.* **94**, 7797 (1972); S. Ayral-Kaloustian, S. Wolff, and W. C. Agosta, *ibid.* **99**, 5984 (1977).
87. B. Byrne, C. A. Wilson, II, S. Wolff, and W. C. Agosta, *J. Chem. Soc., Perkin Trans. 1*, p. 1550 (1979).
88. O. L. Chapman and D. S. Weiss, *Org. Photochem.* **3**, 223 (1973).
89. T. Kobayashi, M. Kurono, H. Sato, and K. Nakanishi, *J. Am. Chem. Soc.* **94**, 2863 (1972).
90. W. Herz, V. S. Iyer, M. G. Nair, and J. Saltiel, *J. Am. Chem. Soc.* **99**, 2704 (1977).
91. P. J. Wagner, *Acc. Chem. Res.* **4**, 168 (1971).

92. A. B. Smith, III and W. C. Agosta, *J. Org. Chem.* **37**, 1259 (1972).
93. D. O. Cowan and R. L. Drisko, "Elements of Organic Photochemistry." Chapter 4. Plenum, New York, 1976.
94. P. J. Wagner and R. W. Spoerke, *J. Am. Chem. Soc.* **91**, 4437 (1969).
95. For a discussion of these problems, see A. A. Lamola and N. J. Turro, *Tech. Org. Chem.* **14**, 96–112 (1969).
96. T. H. Koch, R. J. Sluski, and R. H. Mosley, *J. Am. Chem. Soc.* **95**, 3957 (1973).
97. M. Jeffares and T. B. H. McMurry, *J. Chem. Soc., Chem. Commun.* p. 793 (1976).
98. W. G. Dauben, L. Salem, and N. J. Turro, *Acc. Chem. Res.* **8**, 41 (1975).
99. N. J. Turro, W. E. Farneth, and A. Devaquet, *J. Am. Chem. Soc.* **98**, 7425 (1976).
100. See J. Michl, *Top. Curr. Chem.* **46**, 50–53 (1974); see also Dauben *et al.* (*98*, footnote 15).
101. It has been suggested by Sevin that the matrix element for mixing which determines the size of the barrier for surface crossing from $^3\pi,\pi^*$ to $^3\sigma,\sigma^*$ may be unusually small for cyclohexenones; A. Sevin, Université de Pierre et Marie Curie, Paris (private communication).
102. P. J. Wagner and J. M. McGrath, *J. Am. Chem. Soc.* **94**, 3849 (1972); F. D. Lewis and T. A. Hilliard, *ibid.,* p. 3852; see also P. J. Wagner, *Top. Curr. Chem.* **66**, 1–53 (1976).
103. J. Griffiths and H. Hart, *J. Am. Chem. Soc.* **90**, 5296 (1968); H. Hart and R. K. Murray, Jr. *J. Org. Chem.* **35**, 1535 (1970); G. Quinkert, *Pure Appl. Chem.* **33**, 285 (1973).
104. D. R. Kearns, G. Marsh, and K. Schaffner, *J. Chem. Phys.* **49**, 3316 (1968).
105. G. Marsh, D. R. Kearns, and K. Schaffner, *Helv. Chim. Acta* **51**, 1890 (1968).
106. G. Marsh, D. R. Kearns, and K. Schaffner, *J. Am. Chem. Soc.* **93**, 3129 (1971).
106a. C. R. Jones and D. R. Kearns, *J. Am. Chem. Soc.,* **99**, 344 (1977).
107. R. L. Cargill, W. A. Bundy, D. M. Pond, A. B. Sears, J. Saltiel, and J. Winterle, *Mol. Photochem.* **3**, 123 (1971).
108. For a general discussion, see P. S. Engel and B. M. Monroe, *Adv. Photochem.* **8**, 245–313 (1971).
109. For a specific example of chemical sensitization in enone photochemistry, see R. O. Loutfy and P. de Mayo, *Chem. Commun.* p. 1040 (1970).
109a. See also Wagner and Bucheck (*15*) and R. L. Cargill, A. C. Miller, D. M. Pond, P. de Mayo, M. F. Tchir, K. R. Neuberger, and J. Saltiel, *Mol. Photochem.* **1**, 301 (1969).
110. See Lamola (*77*), Cowan and Drisko (*75*), and Turro (*76*).
111. P. J. Wagner, *Mol. Photochem.* **3**, 23 (1971); P. J. Wagner, *in* "Creation and Detection of the Excited State" (A. A. Lamola, ed.), Vol. 1, Part A, Chapter 4. Dekker, New York, 1971.
112. For a discussion of equilibration of triplet states in phenyl ketones with reaction primarily from the higher energy state, see P. J. Wagner, A. E. Kemppainen, and H. N. Schott, *J. Am. Chem. Soc.* **95**, 5604 (1973).
113. D. I. Schuster, G. C. Barile, and K. Liu, *J. Am. Chem. Soc.* **97**, 4441 (1975); D. I. Schuster and G. C. Barile, *Tetrahedron Lett.* p. 3017 (1976); see also Schuster (*33*).
113a. S. Shaik, *J. Am. Chem. Soc.,* **101**, 2736, 3184 (1979).
114. W. C. Agosta and A. B. Smith, III, *J. Am. Chem. Soc.* **93**, 5513 (1971).
115. W. C. Agosta, A. B. Smith, III, A. S. Kende, R. G. Eilerman, and J. Benham, *Tetrahedron Lett.* p. 4517 (1969).
116. T. Matsuura and K. Ogura, *J. Am. Chem. Soc.* **89**, 3850 (1967); *Chem. Commun.* p. 1247 (1967); *Bull. Chem. Soc. Jpn.* **43**, 3187 (1970).
117. D. A. Plank and J. C. Floyd, *Tetrahedron Lett.* p. 4811 (1971).
118. F. G. Burkinshaw, B. R. Davis, and P. D. Woodgate, *Chem. Commun.* p. 607 (1967); *J. Chem. Soc. C* p. 1607 (1970).

119. H. E. Zimmerman and R. D. Little, *J. Am. Chem. Soc.* **96**, 4623 (1974).
120. S. Wolff and W. C. Agosta, *J. Chem. Soc., Chem. Commun.* p. 226 (1972).
121. J. J. Hurst and G. H. Whitham, *J. Chem. Soc.* p. 2864 (1960).
122. W. F. Erman, *J. Am. Chem. Soc.* **89**, 3828 (1967).
123. D. I. Schuster and D. Widman, *Tetrahedron Lett.* p. 3571 (1971).
124. G. W. Shaffer and M. Pesaro, *J. Org. Chem.* **39**, 2489 (1974).
125. R. L. Cargill, B. M. Gimarc, D. M. Pond, T. Y. King, A. B. Sears, and M. R. Willcott, *J. Am. Chem. Soc.* **92**, 3809 (1970).
126. R. L. Cargill, A. B. Sears, J. Boehm, and M. R. Willcott, *J. Am. Chem. Soc.* **95**, 4346 (1973).
127. R. L. Cargill and A. B. Sears, *J. Am. Chem. Soc.* **92**, 6084 (1970).
128. L. L. Barber, O. L. Chapman, and J. D. Lassila, *J. Am. Chem. Soc.* **91**, 3664 (1969).
129. O. L. Chapman, J. C. Clardy, T. L. McDowell, and H. E. Wright, *J. Am. Chem. Soc.* **95**, 5086 (1973).
130. L. A. Paquette, G. V. Meehan, and R. F. Eizember, *Tetrahedron Lett.* p. 995 (1969).
131. R. C. Cookson, *Q. Rev., Chem. Soc.* **22**, 423 (1968).
132. W. G. Dauben, K. Koch, S. L. Smith, and O. L. Chapman, *J. Am. Chem. Soc.* **85**, 2616 (1963); **83**, 1768 (1961).
133. O. L. Chapman and J. D. Lassila, *J. Am. Chem. Soc.* **90**, 2449 (1968).
134. T. Miyashi, M. Nitta, and T. Mukai, *J. Am. Chem. Soc.* **93**, 3441 (1971).
135. O. L. Chapman, M. Kane, J. D. Lassila, R. L. Loeschen, and H. E. Wright, *J. Am. Chem. Soc.* **91**, 6856 (1969).
136. A. S. Kende, Z. Goldschmidt, and P. T. Izzo, *J. Am. Chem. Soc.* **91**, 6858 (1969).
137. D. I. Schuster and A. B. Gupta, unpublished results; A. B. Gupta, Ph.D. Dissertation, New York University (1975).
138. D. J. Patel and D. I. Schuster, *J. Am. Chem. Soc.* **90**, 5137 (1968).
139. R. Reinfried, D. Bellus, and K. Schaffner, *Helv. Chim. Acta* **54**, 1517 (1971); K. Schaffner, *Pure Appl. Chem., Suppl.* **1**, 412 (1971).
140. H. Hart, D. L. Dean, and D. N. Buchanan, *J. Am. Chem. Soc.* **95**, 6294 (1973); D. L. Dean and H. Hart, *ibid.* **94**, 687 (1972).
141. A. B. Smith, III, A. M. Foster, and W. C. Agosta, *J. Am. Chem. Soc.* **94**, 5100 (1972); S. Wolff, W. L. Schreiber, A. B. Smith, III, and W. C. Agosta, *ibid.* p. 7797.
142. H. E. Zimmerman and A. C. Pratt, *J. Am. Chem. Soc.* **92**, 1409 (1970).
143. For a review, see W. M. Horspool, *Photochemistry* **3**, 430–437 (1972); see also J. Saltiel, this volume, Essay 14.
144. For examples, see H. Morrison and O. Rodriguez, *J. Photochem.* **3**, 471 (1975); B. R. von Wartburg, H. R. Wolf, and O. Jeger, *Helv. Chim. Acta* **59**, 727 (1976).
145. R. C. Cookson, J. Hudec, S. A. Knight, and B. R. D. Whitear, *Tetrahedron* **19**, 1995 (1963); G. Büchi and H. Wuest, *J. Am. Chem. Soc.* **87**, 1589 (1965).
146. F. Barany, S. Wolff, and W. C. Agosta, *J. Am. Chem. Soc.* **100**, 1946 (1978).
147. G. Büchi and E. M. Burgess, *J. Am. Chem. Soc.* **82**, 4333 (1960).
148. R. B. Woodward and R. Hoffmann, "The Conservation of Orbital Symmetry," Chapter 7. Academic Press, New York, 1970.
149. D. I. Schuster, M. Axelrod, and J. Auerbach, *Tetrahedron Lett.* p. 1911 (1963).
150. W. G. Dauben, G. Lodder, and J. Ipaktschi, *Top. Curr. Chem.* **54**, 73 (1975).
151. W. G. Dauben, M. S. Kellogg, J. I. Seeman, and W. A. Spitzer, *J. Am. Chem. Soc.* **92**, 1786 (1970).
152. J. Ipaktschi, *Tetrahedron Lett.* p. 3179 (1970); *Chem. Ber.* **105**, 1996 (1972).
153. J. Ipaktschi, *Tetrahedron Lett.* p. 2153 (1969); *Chem. Ber.* **105**, 1840 (1972).
154. D. I. Schuster and J. T. Diehl, unpublished results, New York University.

155. D. I. Schuster and D. H. Sussman, *Tetrahedron Lett.* p. 1661 (1970).
156. P. S. Engel, M. A. Schexnayder, H. Ziffer, and J. I. Seeman, *J. Am. Chem. Soc.* **96**, 924 (1974).
157. P. S. Engel and M. A. Schexnayder, *J. Am. Chem. Soc.* **97**, 145 (1975); **94**, 2252 (1972).
158. D. I. Schuster, G. R. Underwood, and T. P. Knudsen, *J. Am. Chem. Soc.* **93**, 4304 (1971).
159. Experimental support for this description comes from recent studies of G. R. Underwood and K. El-Bayoumy at New York University (to be published shortly).
160. K. N. Houk, D. J. Northington, and R. E. Duke, Jr., *J. Am. Chem. Soc.* **94**, 6233 (1972).
161. K. G. Hancock and R. O. Grider, *Chem. Commun.* p. 580 (1972).
162. M. A. Schexnayder and P. S. Engel, *Tetrahedron Lett.* p. 1153 (1975).
163. P. S. Engel, M. A. Schexnayder, W. V. Phillips, H. Ziffer, and J. I. Seeman, *Tetrahedron Lett.* p. 1157 (1975).
163a. S. D. Parker and N. A. J. Rogers, *Tetrahedron Lett.* p. 4389 (1976).
164. R. K. Murray and K. A. Babiak, *Tetrahedron Lett.* p. 319 (1974).
165. J. C. Dalton and H.-F. Chan, *Tetrahedron Lett.* p. 3351 (1974).
166. J. C. Dalton, M. Shen, and J. J. Snyder, *J. Am. Chem. Soc.* **98**, 5023 (1976).
167. K. Schaffner, *Tetrahedron* **32**, 641 (1976).
168. M. A. El-Sayed, *Acc. Chem. Res.* **1**, 8 (1968).
169. See W. Amrein, I. M. Larsson, and K. Schaffner, *Helv. Chim. Acta* **57**, 2519 (1974).
170. D. I. Schuster, J. Eriksen, P. S. Engel, and M. A. Schexnayder, *Helv. Chim. Acta* **98**, 5025 (1976).
171. N. C. Yang and E. D. Feit, *J. Am. Chem. Soc.* **90**, 504 (1968); N. C. Yang, S. P. Elliott, and B. Kim, *ibid.* **91**, 7551 (1969).
172. D. I. Schuster and C. W. Kim, *J. Am. Chem. Soc.* **96**, 7437 (1974).
173. J. Eriksen, Ph.D. Dissertation, New York University (1976).
174. J. Eriksen and D. I. Schuster, *Mol. Photochem.* **9**, 83 (1978–79).
175. N. C. Yang, E. D. Feit, M. H. Hui, N. J. Turro, and J. C. Dalton, *J. Am. Chem. Soc.* **92**, 6974 (1970); J. C. Dalton, D. M. Pond, D. S. Weiss, F. D. Lewis, and N. J. Turro, *ibid.* p. 2564.
176. T. R. Darling, J. Pouliquen, and N. J. Turro, *J. Am. Chem. Soc.* **96**, 1247 (1974).
177. E. Baggiolini, K. Schaffner, and O. Jeger, *Chem. Commun.* p. 1103 (1969).
178. H-U. Gonzenbach, I.-M. Tegmo-Larsson, J.-P. Grosclaude, and K. Schaffner, *Helv. Chim. Acta* **60**, 1091 (1977); I. M. Tegmo-Larsson, H.-U. Gonzenbach, and K. Schaffner, *ibid.* **59**, 1376 (1976).
179. H. Sato, N. Furutachi, and K. Nakanishi, *J. Am. Chem. Soc.* **94**, 2150 (1972), and earlier references cited; see also H. Sato, K. Nakanishi, J. Hayashi, and Y. Nakadaira, *Tetrahedron* **29**, 275 (1973).
180. H.-U. Gonzenbach, K. Schaffner, B. Blank, and H. Fischer, *Helv. Chim. Acta* **56**, 1741 (1973).
181. R. S. Givens and W. K. Chae, *J. Am. Chem. Soc.* **100**, 6274 (1978).
182. Generally, little or no heavy-atom enhancement of intersystem crossing has been observed from singlet n,π^* states; see D. Kearns and W. Case, *J. Am. Chem. Soc.* **98**, 5087 (1966); P. J. Wagner, *J. Chem. Phys.* **45**, 2335 (1966).
183. J. M. Janusz, L. J. Gardiner, and J. A. Berson, *J. Am. Chem. Soc.* **99**, 8509 (1977).
184. M. J. Mirbach, A. Henne, and K. Schaffner, *J. Am. Chem. Soc.* **100**, 7127 (1978); results also reported at the VIIth IUPAC Conference, on Photochemistry, Leuven, Belgium, July 1978, abstracts p. 240–244.
185. For reviews, see N. J. Turro, P. Lechtken, N. E. Schore, G. Schuster, H.-C. Stein-

metzer and A. Yekta, *Acc. Chem. Res.* **7**, 97 (1974), and T. Wilson, *in* "Chemical Kinetics" (D. R. Herschbach, ed.), Phys. Chem. Ser. II, Int. Rev. Sci. Butterworth, London, 1976.

186. E. J. K. Bechara, A. L. Baumstark, and T. Wilson, *J. Am. Chem. Soc.* **98**, 4648 (1976).

187. See F. McCapra, I. Behshiti, A. Burford, R. A. Hann, and K. A. Zaklika, *J. Chem. Soc., Chem. Commun.* p. 944 (1977).

188. D. R. Kearns, *Chem. Rev.* **71**, 395 (1971); N. J. Turro and A. Devaquet, *J. Am. Chem. Soc.* **97**, 3895 (1975).

189. A. Hemme, N. P. Y. Siew and K. Schaffner, *J. Am. Chem. Soc.*, **101**, 3671 (1979); *Helv. Chim. Acta,* **62**, 1952 (1979).

190. For a demonstration that α cleavage from S_1 states of alkanones is also an activated process, see M. F. Mirbach, M. J. Mirbach, K.-C. Liu and N. J. Turro, *J. Photochem.* **8**, 299 (1978), and references cited therein.

190a. B. Blank, A. Henne and H. Fischer, *Helv. Chim. Acta,* **57**, 920 (1974); B. Blank, P. G. Mennitt and H. Fischer, *Pure Appl. Chem. Suppl. XXIIIrd Congress IUPAC,* **4**, 1 (1971).

191. M. A. Schexnayder and P. S. Engel, *J. Am. Chem. Soc.* **97**, 4825 (1975).

192. A. J. A. van der Weerdt and H. Cerfontain, *J. Chem. Soc., Perkin Trans.* 2 p. 1357 (1977).

193. A. J. A. van der Weerdt, H. Cerfontain, J. P. M. van der Ploeg, and J. A. den Hollander, *J. Chem. Soc., Perkin Trans.* 2 p. 155 (1978).

194. A. J. A. van der Weerdt, Ph.D. Dissertation, University of Amsterdam (1978).

195. T. Eckersley, S. D. Parker, and N. A. J. Rogers, *Tetrahedron Lett.* p. 4393 (1976); Dalton has uncovered an example of an ODPM rearrangement of an acyclic enone with a γ-CN substituent which apparently does not occur from the $^3\pi,\pi^*$ state (T_1) and which he concludes arises from an n,π^* state, S_1 or T_2. Details of this study are not yet available (J. C. Dalton, unpublished results, Bowling Green State University).

196. K. G. Hancock and R. O. Grider, *Tetrahedron Lett.* p. 1367 (1972); p. 4281 (1971); *J. Am. Chem. Soc.* **96**, 1158 (1974).

197. Unpublished results of W. G. Dauben, M. S. Kellogg, J. Seeman, and W. Spitzer, University of California, Berkeley [cited in Dauben *et al.* (*150*)].

198. R. S. Givens and W. F. Oettle, *J. Am. Chem. Soc.* **93**, 3963 (1971); *Chem. Commun.* p. 1066 (1969).

199. S. Domb and K. Schaffner, *Helv. Chim. Acta* **53**, 677 (1970).

200. P. S. Mariano and J.-K. Ko, *J. Am. Chem. Soc.* **94**, 1766 (1972); **95**, 8670 (1973).

201. J. I. Seeman and H. Ziffer, *Tetrahedron Lett.* 4413 (1973).

202. R. L. Coffin, R. S. Givens, and R. G. Carlson, *J. Am. Chem. Soc.* **96**, 7554 (1974); R. L. Coffin, W. W. Cox, R. G. Carlson, and R. S. Givens, *ibid.*, **101**, 3261 (1979).

203. The configuration of the optically active cyclopropyl ketone 281 was assigned from ORD–CD data using the "inverse octant rule" for bicyclic cyclopropyl ketones, an empirical correlation that is without theoretical foundation and that could be incorrect in situations in which there is a strongly perturbing group on the three-membered ring, according to recent studies in our laboratory (*204*). For references and further discussion, see C. Djerassi, W. Klyne, T. Norin, G. Ohloff, and E. Klein, *Tetrahedron* **21**, 163 (1965); G. Snatzke, *J. Chem. Soc.* p. 5002 (1965).

204. D. I. Schuster and K. V. Prabhu, unpublished results, New York University; K. V. Prabhu, Ph.D. Dissertation, New York University (1972).

204a. D. De Keukeleire and G. M. Blondeel, *Tetrahedron Lett.*, p. 1343 (1979).

205. B. Winter and K. Schaffner, *J. Am. Chem. Soc.* **98**, 2022 (1976).

206. W. G. Dauben, G. Lodder, and J. D. Robbins, *Nouv. J. Chim.* **1**, 243 (1977); *J. Am. Chem. Soc.* **98**, 3030 (1976).
207. J. Eriksen, K. Krogh-Jespersen, M. A. Ratner, and D. I. Schuster, *Am. Chem. Soc.* **97**, 5596 (1975), D. I. Schuster and J. Eriksen, *J. Org. Chem.* **44**, 4254 (1979).
208. D. I. Schuster and J. Eriksen, *Mol. Photochem.* **9**, 93 (1978); J. Eriksen, *J. Phys. Chem.* **84**, 276 (1980).
209. See, for example, D. I. Schuster and V. A. Stoute, *Mol. Photochem.* **9**, 93 (1978).
210. T. A. Rettig, Ph.D. Dissertation, Iowa State University, Ames (1966); results cited in ref. 18.
211. D. I. Schuster and J. M. Rao, unpublished results, New York University.
212. D. I. Schuster and I. M. Nuñez, unpublished results, New York University.
213. G. P. Laroff and H. Fischer, *Helv. Chim. Acta,* **56**, 2011 (1973).
214. D. I. Schuster and C. B. Chan, unpublished results, New York University.
215. W. K. Appel, T. J. Greenhough, J. R. Scheffer, J. Trotter, and L. Walsh, *J. Am. Chem. Soc.,* **102**, 1158, 1160 (1980).
216. D. I. Schuster and L. T. Calcaterra, unpublished results, New York University.
217. M. A. El-Sayed, *J. Chem. Phys.,* **41**, 2462 (1964).
218. A. R. Horrocks, A. Kearvell, K. Tickle and F. Wilkinson, *Trans. Faraday Soc.,* **62**, 3393 (1966).
219. P. J. Wagner, *J. Chem. Phys.,* **45**, 2335 (1966).
220. W. K. Appel, T. J. Greenhough, J. R. Scheffer and J. Trotter, *J. Am. Chem. Soc.,* **101**, 213 (1979).

ACKNOWLEDGMENT

I wish to thank a number of active investigators in the field of enone photochemistry for submission of unpublished data and preprints of manuscripts in advance of publication for inclusion in this essay. These include W. C. Agosta, R. L. Cargill, C. R. Dalton, W. G. Dauben, R. S. Givens, A. Henne, K. Schaffner, and A. J. A. van der Weerdt. I am particularly indebted to Professor Kurt Schaffner for the free exchange of information and ideas over a period of many years in the best scientific tradition, which has profoundly influenced our work in the field of photochemistry and the shape and content of this review.

KURT SCHAFFNER and MARTIN DEMUTH

I. REARRANGEMENTS OF CROSS-CONJUGATED DIENONES

A. 2,5-Cyclohexadienones

1. Introduction

Cross-conjugated cyclohexadienones readily undergo structural trans-formations on ultraviolet irradiation (250–370 nm). At first sight and in the absence of appropriate reaction control, the result has often been a bewil-dering array of photoproducts. After the light sensitivity of α-santonin (**1**, Scheme 1), a sesquiterpene with a cross-conjugated cyclohexadienone chromophore, had been noted in the 1830's by Kahler and Trommsdorf (*1*), it also attracted the attention of the Italian pioneers of organic photo-chemistry, Cannizzaro, Francesconi, Sestini, and Villavecchia (*1*), around the turn of the century. The structural complexity of the natural com-pound and the photoproducts isolated, such as isophotosantonic lactone (**2**), photosantonin (**5**), and photosantonic acid (**6**), withstood elucidation at the time, and, as with most early photochemical discoveries, the field

REARRANGEMENTS IN GROUND AND EXCITED STATES, VOL. 3
Copyright © 1980 by Academic Press, Inc.

lay dormant until the mid-1950's, with the exception of one light-induced "dienone–phenol rearrangement" (7 → 8) described in 1911 by Staudinger (2).

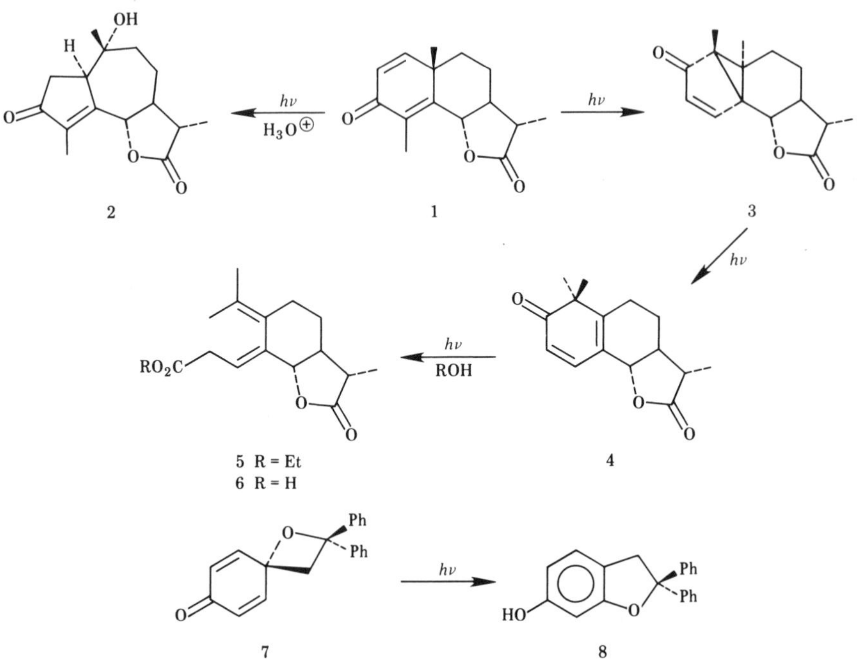

Scheme 1

It remained for Barton, Büchi, Jeger, van Tamelen, and their groups to establish the structures of the key products of α-santonin: 2 (3,4), 3 (3,5,6), and 5 and 6 (7,8). [For the stereochemical assignments of 2 and 3 by X-ray evidence see Asher and Sim (9) and Barton et al. (10), respectively]. Together with the initial results on similarly complex photorearrangements of steroid dienones (11,12), these studies stimulated rapidly expanding research activity in organic photochemistry in the following years. Several reviews (13–18) have already described in detail the investigations that unveiled the often multistep photochemical transformations of cross-conjugated cyclohexadienones and the progress in understanding the mechanisms of these reactions.

2. Major Modes of Rearrangement

In the absence of any interference by solvent or nucleophilic trapping agents, cross-conjugated cyclohexadienones normally rearrange to one or several bicyclo[3.1.0]hex-3-en-2-one isomers. The prototype of such transformations is the conversion of α-santonin (1) to lumisantonin (3) (Scheme 1) (3,5,19). However, the bicyclohexenones themselves are photochemically labile and undergo further rearrangement to 2,4- and 2,5-cyclohexadienones and phenols, depending on the substitution pattern and other structural constraints (see Section I,A,8), as exemplified by the formation of mazdasantonin (4) from lumisantonin (3) (20,21) and by an extract, given in Scheme 2 (12–20), from the plethora of rearrangement sequences branching off from the photoisomer of 1-dehydrotestosterone acetate (9) (22).

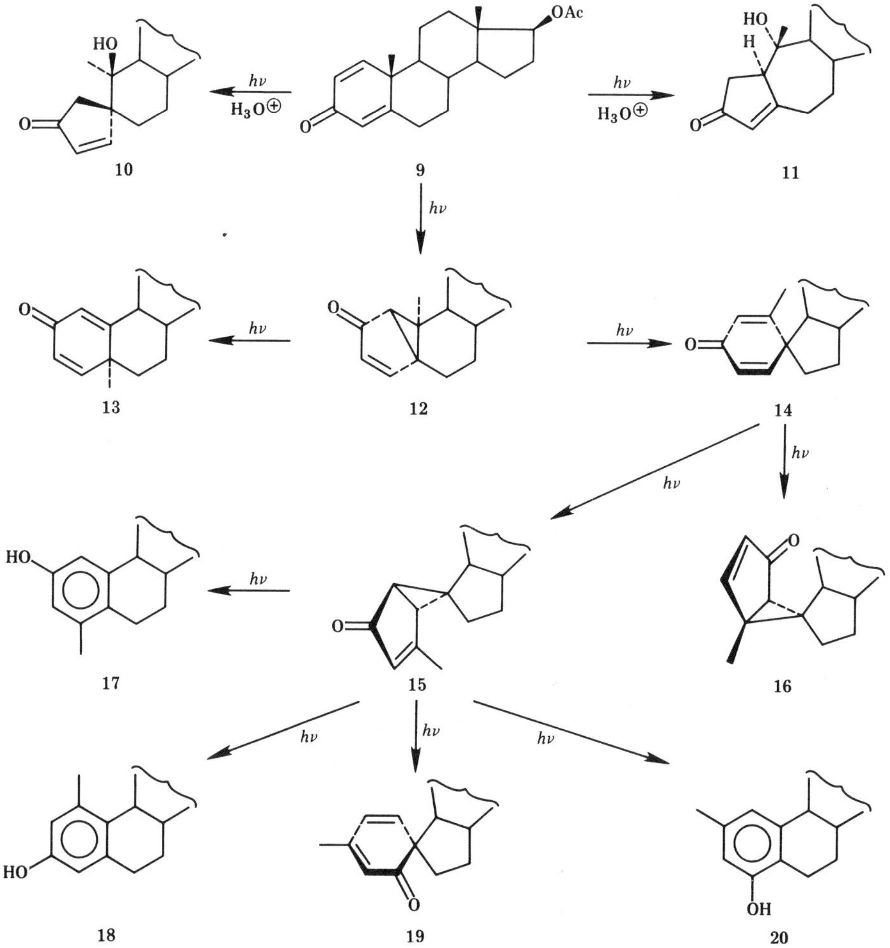

Scheme 2

The cyclohexadienone → bicyclohexenone transformation can be viewed in a *formal* manner, and without prejudicing the *actual* reaction mechanism, as a concerted $_\sigma 2_a + _\pi 2_a$ cycloaddition (Scheme 3, **21** → **23**)

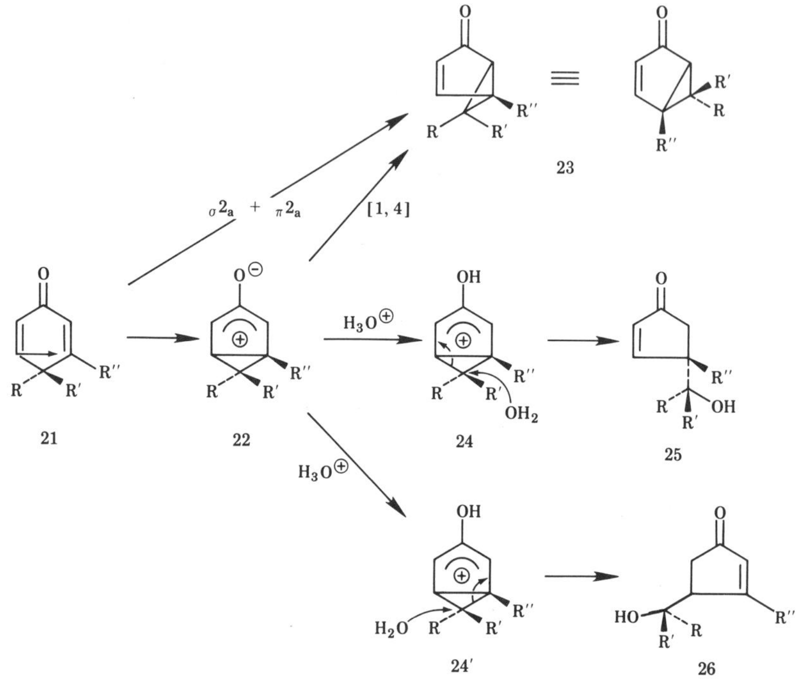

Scheme 3

(*23*). The process can be dissected into the initial formation of a new bond between the two β-carbon atoms (**21** → **22**) (for the choice of a zwitterionic intermediate see Sections I,A,3 and I,A,5), followed by a [1,4] sigmatropic shift with inversion of configuration at the migrating carbon atom (**22** → **23**).

The rearrangement of the bicyclohexenones to phenols and dienones requires the breaking of the internal cyclopropane bond (Scheme 4, **23** → **27**) and subsequent 1,2 migration of one of the geminal substituents in either direction (**27** → **28** + **29**).

In aqueous *acidic* media the rearrangement to bicyclohexenones is largely suppressed in favor of solvent incorporation and formation of spirocyclic (**10**) (*24,25*) and 5/7-fused hydroxy ketones (**2, 11**) (*3,4,25*). The structure of these products can be derived by protonation of the intermediate zwitterion **22**, opening of the three-membered ring, and nucleophilic attack of solvent (**24** → **25**; **24'** → **26**).

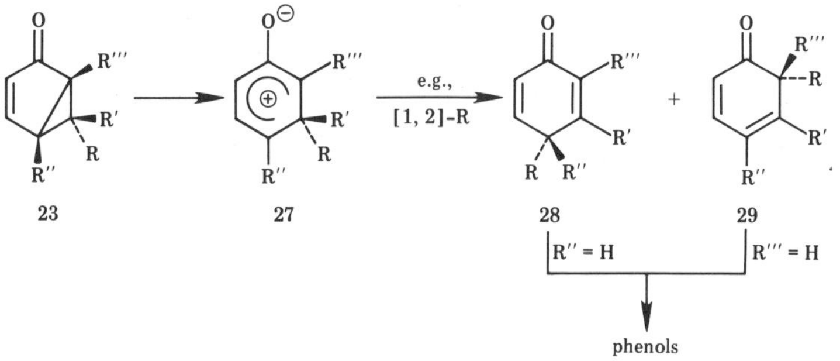

Scheme 4

3. The Zimmerman–Schuster Mechanism

In 1961 and 1962 Zimmerman and Schuster (13,26,27) postulated a unifying mechanistic concept to rationalize the nature of the primary photochemical processes that, *at ambient temperatures* (see Section I,A,8 for mechanisms at low temperature), lead to the ubiquitous skeletal rearrangements of cross-conjugated dienones and bicyclohexenones. The approach involves four steps, as delineated in Scheme 5: (a) n → π* excitation (21 → 21*; 23 → 23*); (b) electron redistribution in the n,π* excited molecules by bond alterations to give 22* and 27*, which are still electronically excited states of the n,π* type; (c) π* → n electron demotion, affording the ground state zwitterions 22 and 27; and (d) rearrangements to products.

The occasional isolation of β,δ-dienoic acids as primary photoproducts of bicyclohexenones in aqueous solvents was postulated to arise from cleavage of an alternative, external cyclopropane bond in 23*, followed by further ring cleavage to the ketene 31, either directly in the biradical 30 or in its corresponding zwitterion.

This mechanism does not specify the spin multiplicity of the reactive excited species, and in fact it is applicable to both singlet and triplet states. Predicated on an n,π* electronic configuration, interaction between the two odd electrons of the excited states (21*, 22*, 23*, and 27*) is minimal, with one electron localized in the p orbital on oxygen, which is orthogonal to the π* system containing the other electron. With regard to the precise chronology of events, the scheme retains some flexibility, except for the requirement that bond alteration occur on the excited state potential surface. The precise point of S → T intersystem crossing and the interposition of zwitterions between electron demotion and further bond changes are explicitly left to experimental testing. This also includes possible merging of certain steps. In different molecules, for example, zwitterions may range from existing as discrete intermediates to repre-

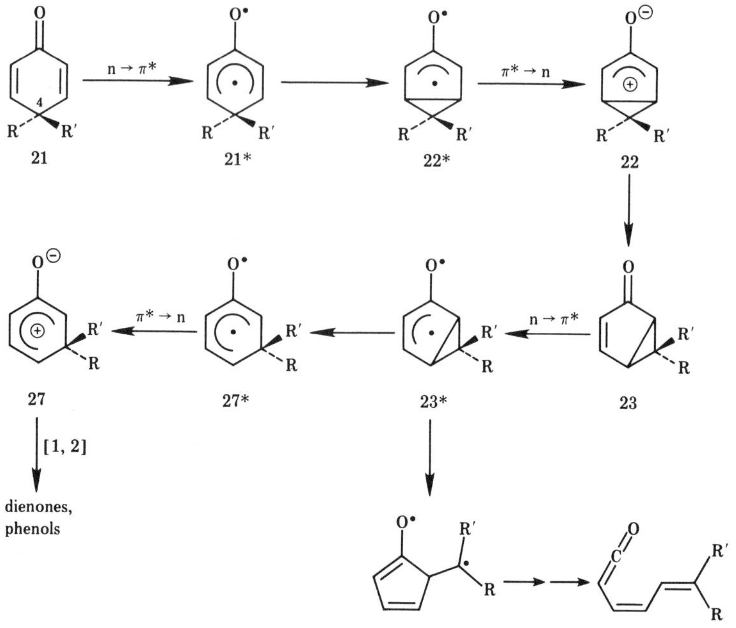

Scheme 5

senting merely a point on the downhill slope of a concerted potential energy surface. In the extreme, the entire sequence of formal steps could proceed concertedly without appreciable charge separation along the path.

The Zimmerman–Schuster formulation thus adapts the polar state concept of Chapman (14) to rationalize the mechanism of dienone photochemistry. Divergent proposals concern the chronology of electron demotion and rearrangement (28,28a) and the unsatisfactory suggestion that the rearranging zwitterions are dualistic in nature, with either positive or negative character of the β-carbon (29).

4. Nature of the Reactive Excited State

Quenching experiments with 1,3-pentadiene and 1,3-cyclohexadiene have established that the reactions of the dienones 1 (→ 2), 33 (Schemes 6 and 8), and 50 (Scheme 9) occur from a triplet excited state (18,21,30). A correlation of the yield of cyclohexadiene dimer with the reduction in yield of 2 confirmed that exclusively triplet excitation was transferred from 1 to the diene in high concentration (31). These results were complemented by benzophenone and acetophenone sensitization of 1 (21) and

33 (*32*). The quantum yields for bicyclohexenone formation were the same as on direct excitation (~0.85 to unity), requiring unity efficiency of the S → T intersystem crossing (*21,32*).

Triplet sensitization by aromatic solvents was also observed (*33*) on γ irradiation of toluene and benzene solutions of 1-dehydrotestosterone acetate (**9**), which induced rearrangement to **12** and, on further irradiation of this product, to the same mixture of ketonic and phenolic isomers as obtained photochemically (cf. Scheme 2) (*22*).

Although the quenching results established a triplet reaction path on direct irradiation, they are inconclusive with respect to the precise nature of the quenchable triplet. Thus, the energy and identity of this species remain unsolved problems. The lowest spectroscopic triplet state energies of **1**, **33**, and **50** were determined to be *ca.* 68 kcal/mol by low-temperature phosphorescence measurements in glasses (*21,32,34,35*). Triplet transfer to naphthalene (E_T = 61 kcal/mol), 1,3-pentadiene (E_T = 57–59 kcal/mol), and 1,3-cyclohexadiene (E_T = 53 kcal/mol), therefore, ought to occur at the same diffusion-controlled rate (*36*). Yet, naphthalene failed entirely to quench the rearrangement of **33** (*32*), and, with **1**, **33**, **50**, and its 3-methyl homologue (**127**), the quenching efficiency of 1,3-pentadiene was markedly lower than that of 1,3-cyclohexadiene (*18,30,31,37*). Two possible explanations for these findings have been considered (*18*): (a) A triplet exciplex mechanism might diminish the rate constants for energy transfer by factors other than the difference in donor and acceptor triplet energies and be dissimilar for different acceptors; (b) the relaxation to a lower-energy geometry might be sufficiently fast to preclude quenching of the spectroscopic dienone triplet. The β,β′-bonded triplet **22*** cannot be the species responsible for the observed quenching effects. Since its electronic ground state, zwitterion **22**, lies on the reaction path to product (reversion to **21** is symmetry forbidden), quenching would remain undetected in experiments in which only the donor is analyzed. The relaxed quenchable triplet observed would have to adopt, therefore, a geometry interposed between **21*** and **22***, e.g., with an out-of-plane twist of the dienyl radical moiety and with an energy around or below 60 kcal/mol.

A final point concerns the electronic configuration of the reactive triplet. The low-temperature phosphorescence from **50** (*34,35*), **33**, and some other monocyclic dienones (*32,34*) has been assigned to $^3n,\pi^*$ states, whereas the 3-methyl homologue of **50**, **127** (*38*), α-santonin (**1**) and some analogues (*39*), and 4-alkylated steroids (*40*) exhibited emissions characteristic of $^3\pi,\pi^*$ states. One may conclude that the two spectroscopic triplet states are energetically not very different and that their order is a subtle function of the substitution, and possibly also of the conformational flexibility, of the dienones. Irrespective of the order, however, a reactive

T_2 state could be populated thermally from an unreactive T_1 state at ambient temperature, as is the case with some aryl ketones (41) (see also Fig. 1).

Reaction, e.g., β,β' bonding (21* → 22*, Scheme 5), from an $^3n,\pi^*$ state (T_1 or T_2) is therefore still a distinct possibility. In a study of the thermal decomposition of dioxetanes of type 32 (Scheme 6), it was argued (42) that the formation of the bicyclohexenone 34, when accompanied by 2-acetonaphthone (35; $E_T = 59$ kcal/mol; $^3\pi,\pi^*$), is proof of the n,π^* configuration of the reactive triplet of 33 in solution at ambient tempera-

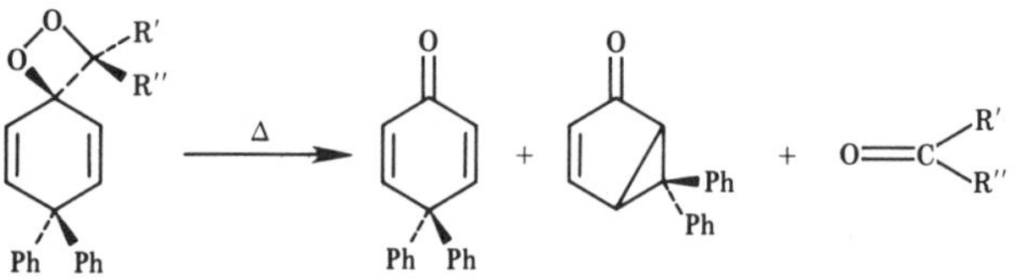

Scheme 6

ture. The conclusion is based on the postulate that the formation of n,π^* triplets is kinetically preferred over that of π,π^* triplets (42a) (and thus would override the energy gap of ca. 10 kcal between the n,π^* triplet of 33 and the π,π^* triplet of 2-acetonaphthone). Varying from an earlier caveat (18), this argument still lacks conclusive evidence against the possibility that the n,π^* triplet of 33, when formed from the dioxetane 32, is not reactive but thermally populates the higher-lying $^3\pi,\pi^*$ state before rearrangement.

That such is not the case in a reaction structurally related to the β,β'-bonding process in 21* → 22* was demonstrated recently (43) for the rearrangement 36 → 39 (Scheme 7). The overall transformation was shown to proceed along two competing rearrangement paths initiated by bridging from the olefinic β-carbon of the cross-conjugated ketone in 36 to the naphthalene moiety (→ 37) and the second double bond (→ 38). The phosphorescent triplet state of 36 is 58.2 kcal/mol above the ground state, and its phosphorescence spectrum is that of a 1,8-bridged naphthalene. Figure 1 summarizes the quantum yields for rearrangement on irradiation at several wavelengths and on sensitization with donors of different triplet energies (61.9–68.9 kcal/mol), all of which occurred at similar rates close to diffusion-controlled [(2.8–4.2) × 10^9 M^{-1} sec^{-1} in benzene]. When 36 was excited to its $^3\pi,\pi^*$ state with light of 435 nm, the quantum yield was temperature dependent in the range 5°–75°C, with an activation energy of ca. 8 kcal/mol. On irradiation with 366 nm, added 1,3-cyclo-

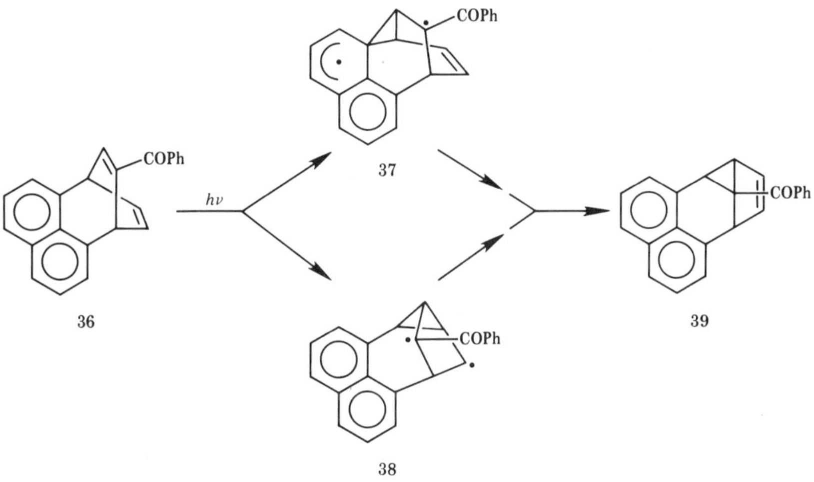

Scheme 7

hexadiene did not affect the rearrangement to **39** by diffusion-controlled triplet quenching. These results are interpreted in terms of direct formation of the biradicals **37** and **38** from both the singlet (S_1) and triplet (T_2) n,π^* states. Laser flash experiments revealed the intermediacy of a nanosecond transient at room temperature, and electron spin resonance at 77 K and IR spectroscopy in the 77–294 K range showed that two consecutive biradical intermediates (or families of biradical intermediates) are formed (*43a*). Excitation to an upper singlet (S_2) π,π^* state is followed by a highly efficient intersystem crossing and the population of T_2 (60 < E_T < 63 kcal/mol), or by direct formation of biradicals with an efficiency similar to that from T_2, or by both reaction paths. Reaction from the lowest-lying naphthalene triplet state, formed on irradiation with 435 nm or energy transfer from phenanthrene ($E_T = 61.9$ kcal/mol), proceeds either via thermal population of T_2 or along a separate inefficient path. Interestingly, the rearrangement **36** → **39** also occurs, in a reversible fashion, in the electronic ground state in competing stepwise and thermally allowed concerted processes (*43b*).

Electrochemical generation of a seven-electron π system in cross-conjugated cyclohexadienones did not afford cross-bonded products (*44*). The result was interpreted as ruling out the possibility that similar electron distribution of n,π^* states is responsible for β,β' bonding. The argument overlooked, however, the possibility that even if β,β' bonding to **22*** were endothermic and reversible, a very rapid demotion and rearrangement could still allow for a rapid overall reaction.

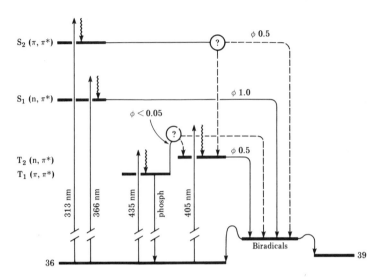

Fig. 1   State and reaction diagram of compound **36** and its di-π-methane-like rearrangement to **39**.

5. Evidence for Zwitterion Intermediates

Although the 1,2-aryl, 1,2-alkyl, and 1,2-hydrogen migrations in the photorearrangement of cyclohexadienones and bicyclohexenones are reminiscent of the ground state chemistry of electron-deficient species, the driving force for such processes should also be appreciable in biradicals (*28a,45–48*) such as **22*** and **27*** (Scheme 5). Still, numerous observations would be difficult to rationalize without recourse to the concept of the zwitterion intermediates **22** and **27**. In particular, the formation of hydroxy ketones in acidic media, such as shown in Schemes 1 and 2 [numerous analogous examples are given elsewhere (*3,4,12,24,25,49–70,70a*); see also Section I,A,7,b], at the expense of bicyclohexenones strongly suggested that a common zwitterion precursor of type **22** was intercepted (Scheme 3). The bicyclohexenones themselves are not intermediates in the dienone photoconversion to hydroxy ketones. Although acid-catalyzed transformation in the dark into the corresponding hydroxy ketones was normally possible (*5,7,24,26,27,49,71*), the reaction conditions required were more severe than in the dienone irradiations and the product distributions were not identical (*71*).

The plausibility of the zwitterion mechanism in the photochemical system was further strengthened when it was shown (*72–76*) that ground-state-generated zwitterions of types **22** and **27** indeed undergo rearrangement to bicyclohexenones and phenols, respectively, as delineated in

Schemes 3 and 5. Favorskii-type reaction of, e.g., the bromo ketone **40** (Scheme 8) gave **42,** one of the stereoisomeric photoketones of the corresponding dienone **41,** in high yield, and the phenols **44** and **45** resulted in similar ratios from the bicyclohexenone **34** and the bromo ketone **43.** Furthermore, the bromo ketones of type **40** rearranged without competition by a process reverting to dienone. This is in accord with the close to unity quantum yield of the corresponding dienones, which indicates that return from any bridged species is inefficient.

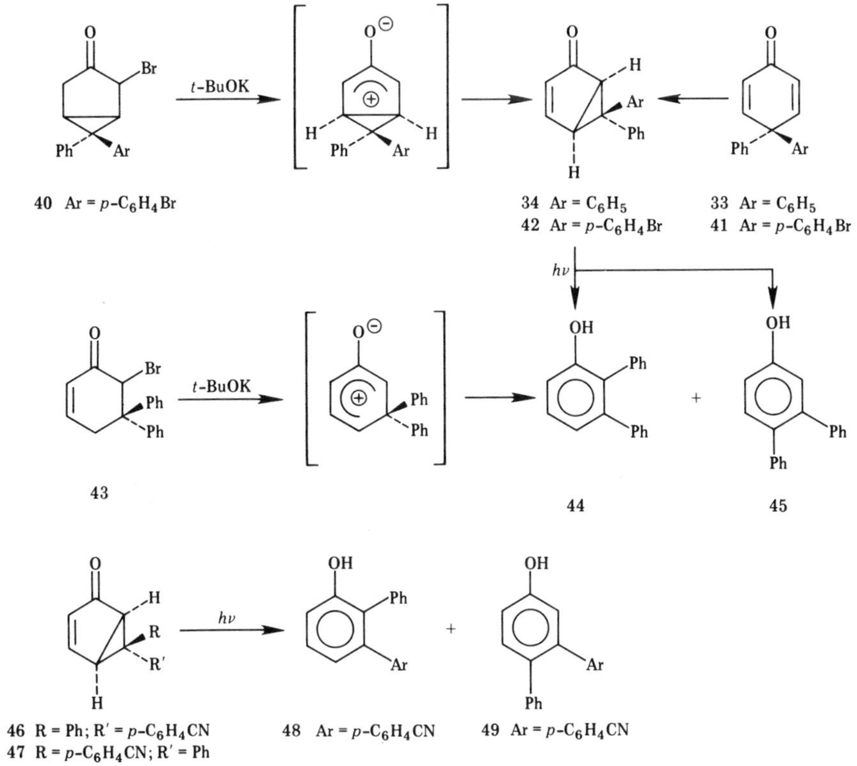

40 Ar = p-C$_6$H$_4$Br

34 Ar = C$_6$H$_5$
42 Ar = p-C$_6$H$_4$Br

33 Ar = C$_6$H$_5$
41 Ar = p-C$_6$H$_4$Br

43

44

45

46 R = Ph; R' = p-C$_6$H$_4$CN
47 R = p-C$_6$H$_4$CN; R' = Ph

48 Ar = p-C$_6$H$_4$CN

49 Ar = p-C$_6$H$_4$CN

Scheme 8

The case of the conversion **43** → **44** + **45** supplemented strong earlier evidence that the photochemical bicyclohexenone → phenol conversion proceeds via the zwitterion route: The stereoisomeric ketones **46** and **47** rearranged in aqueous t-butyl alcohol under both direct irradiation and triplet-sensitized conditions to similar ratios of phenols **48** and **49** (77). No cyanophenyl migration product could be detected. Phenyl migration must have taken place, therefore, to a positive center rather than to a radical one; hence, demotion to zwitterion must have preceded the rearrangement.

However, direct evidence for the mandatory intermediacy of zwitterions in the dienone photorearrangements *in solution* would require, e.g., their capture, when formed photochemically from dienones, by nucleophiles before any further transformation. The formation of hydroxy ketones had already indicated that the lifetime of the hydroxyallyl cations (24) derived from the dienones discussed so far was too short for any such interception at this stage. Obviously, a decrease in the propensity for undergoing the [1,4] shift in 22 or the cyclopropane cleavage in 24 would improve the succeptibility of these intermediates to nucleophilic trapping. This condition was first met by the dienone 50 (Scheme 9), as shown in an extensive study (35,78–80). The electron-withdrawing trichloromethyl substituent was responsible for the buildup of positive charge at C-4 of the transition state, making [1,4] rearrangement and cyclopropane cleavage less favorable (81), and it rendered the zwitterion 55 accessible for trapping and kinetic study. The compound 55 was found to be the common precursor of products 56, 58, 61, and 62. In acidic alcohols (methanol, ethanol, 2-propanol), protonation of 55 to give 57 and uptake of solvent afforded the alkoxy ketones 58, unique in that they are examples of dienone photoproducts in which the skeleton of the postulated zwitterion has been preserved. When an appropriate electrophile was not available, the zwitterion was still captured by nucleophiles, such as alcohol solvent and added halide ions, to give 59 and 60, respectively, which then fragmented in an anionic Grob-type process yielding 61 and 62. In 2,2,2-trifluoroethanol and methanol, the ratios 62/56 and 62/61 increased linearly as the lithium chloride concentration in the solutions was increased, and the quantum efficiency of formation of zwitterion 55 was close to unity.

Of additional interest in these studies is the indication that reversion of the zwitterion 55 to ground state dienone accounts, at least in part, for the residual quantum inefficiency of product formation from excited 50 (18). The yield of 56 in 2,2,2-trifluoroethanol, essentially the single photoproduct of 50 in this system, was lower than the total yield of 56 + 62 in the presence of added lithium chloride, and this difference increased with temperature. In fact, a temperature dependence, owing to a high activation barrier for the cycloreversion, would be anticipated since the process is forbidden by orbital symmetry (23) and zwitterions of type 22 correlate with a doubly excited state of the corresponding dienone (32).

Zwitterions derived from 4*H*-pyran-4-ones should be amenable to nucleophilic trapping and fragmentation just as is the trichloromethyl analogue 55. This expectation was confirmed by the results with, e.g.,

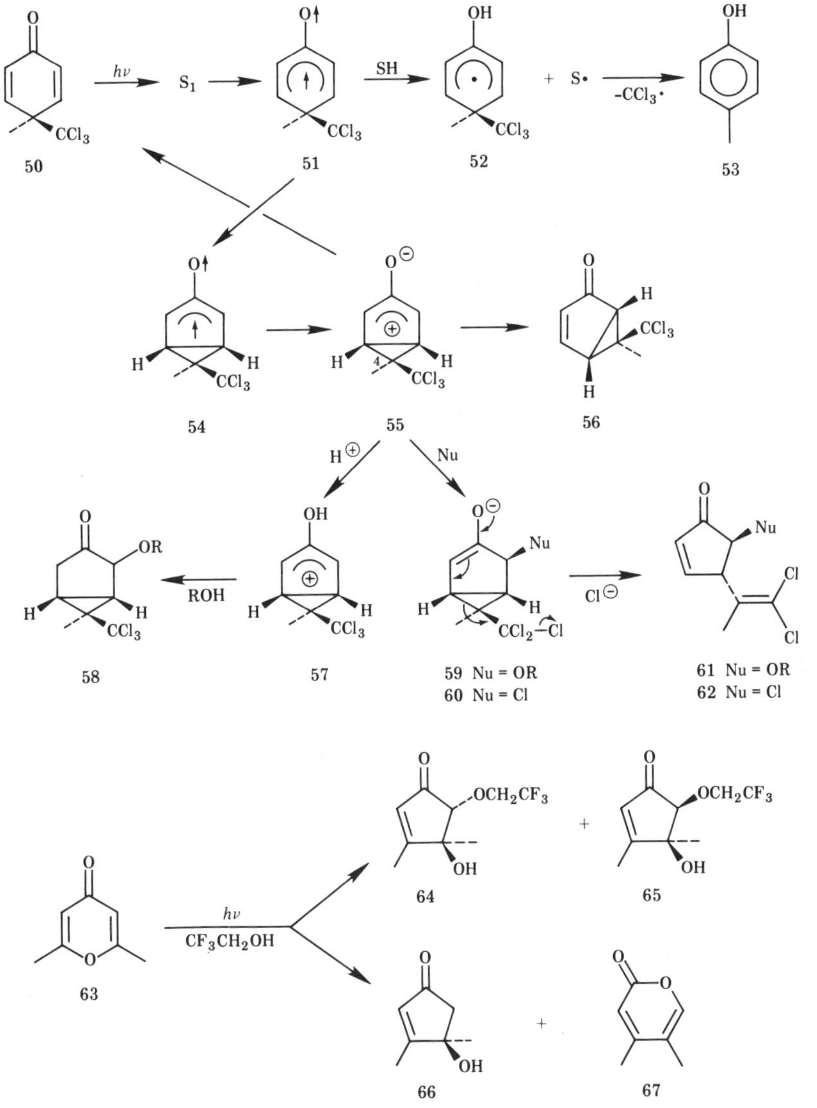

Scheme 9

2,6-dimethyl-4*H*-pyran-4-one (**63**) (*82,83*). The irradiation of **63** in 2,2,2-trifluoroethanol gave the stereoisomers **64** (major isomer) and **65** (minor), clearly trapping products of the zwitterion intermediate, in which on continued irradiation the trifluoroethoxy group was photolytically removed to give **66**. A fourth photoproduct, **67**, was isomeric with the starting material and conceivably resulted from photocleavage of the primary photoisomer corresponding to **23** (see Section I,A,8,b).

4-Hydroxycyclohexadienones photoisomerized to enediones in anhy-

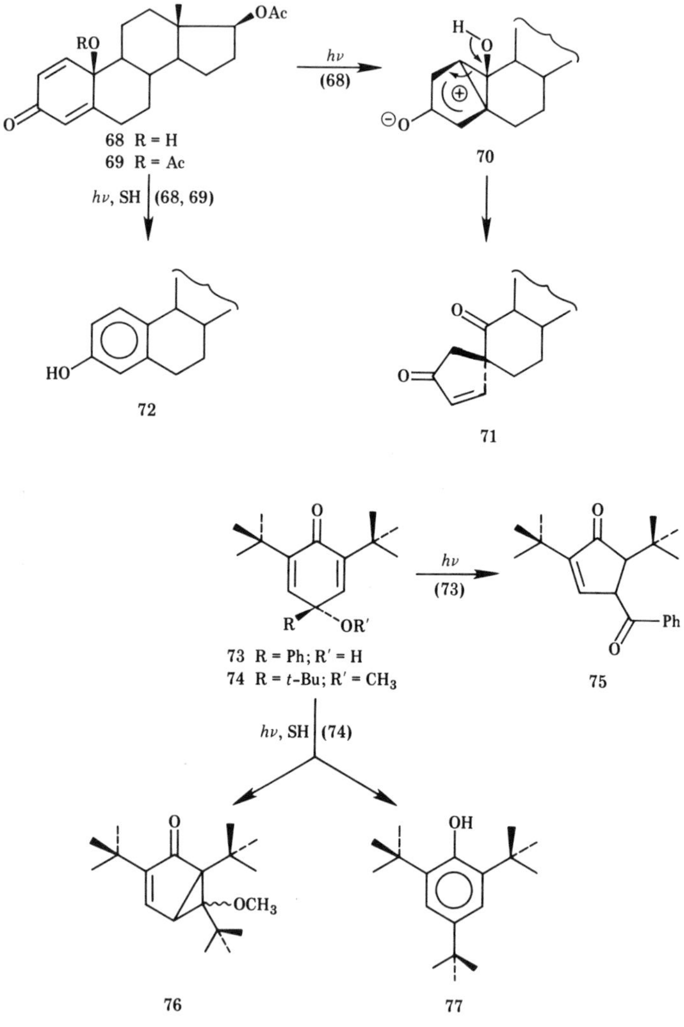

68 R = H
69 R = Ac

70

72

71

73 R = Ph; R' = H
74 R = *t*-Bu; R' = CH₃

75

76   77

Scheme 10

drous (Scheme 10, **68** → **71**) (*84*) and aqueous dioxane (**73** → **75**) (*85*). This behavior is in excellent agreement with that expected for a zwitterion intermediate (e.g., **70**) containing a cyclopropanolylcarbinyl cation moiety. The array of similar isomerizations has since been enlarged (*86–90*).

A possibly direct observation of zwitterion intermediates were reported for α-santonin (**1**), lumisantonin (**3**), and some halo derivatives (*21,91*). At 77 K, nonparamagnetic blue transients appeared; these, however, could not be trapped, so that the assignment remains tentative. Similar colors on irradiation of **50** (*18*) and lumiprednisone (*70a*) at low temperature were observed.

6. Fragmentation Reactions: The Role of Radical Intermediates

The trichloromethyldienone **50** underwent yet another primary photoreaction, in which chloroform, hexachloroethane, and *p*-cresol were formed (Scheme 9, **50** → **53**) (*18,35,92–94*). The reaction occurred only in solvents that are good hydrogen donors toward free radicals (2-propanol, diethyl ether, cyclohexane). It was shown to involve hydrogen abstraction by triplet excited dienone (**51**) and radical elimination of the substituent from the resulting ketyl radical **52**. This intermediate was identified by flash photolysis and unequivocally proves the free-radical nature of the lowest dienone triplet state. In 2-propanol, where hydrogen abstraction leading to **53** competes with the ionic route to **61**, the addition of lithium chloride selectively reduced the yield of the latter product only (*18*), establishing the sequential formation of dienone triplet state (**51**) and zwitterion **55** in conformity with the Zimmerman–Schuster mechanism.

At least one other photoelimination reaction of a cross-conjugated cyclohexadienone follows the same mechanistic route as **50** → **53**. Thus, **78** gave phenol **79** and methane (Scheme 11) when irradiated in hydrogen donor solvents (*95*).

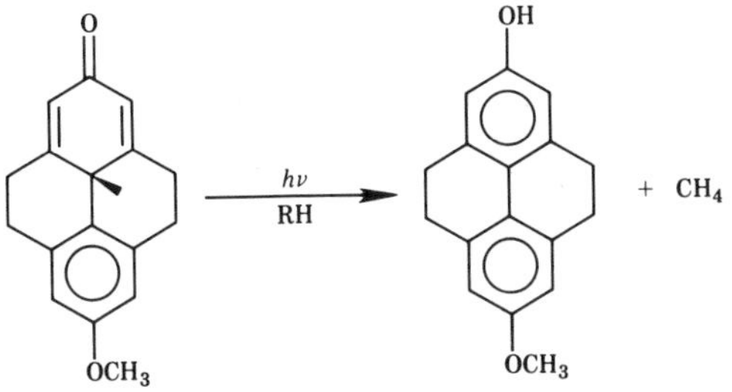

$$78 \quad \xrightarrow[\text{RH}]{h\nu} \quad 79 \quad + \quad CH_4$$

Scheme 11

This case also offers additional mechanistic information. The compound was totally unreactive in benzene, and attempts to trap a zwitterion intermediate with nucleophiles or 1,3-dipolarophiles failed. The rate constants for triplet hydrogen abstraction from 2-propanol (leading to **79**, $\phi = 0.1$) and excited state decay ($3.6 \times 10^4 \text{ M}^{-1} \text{ sec}^{-1}$ and $4.2 \times 10^6 \text{ sec}^{-1}$, respectively), were slightly smaller than those of benzophenone and very much smaller than those of the characteristically rapid rearrangement to bicyclohexenone ($>10^{10} \text{ sec}^{-1}$; $\phi = 0.73$) and decay ($>4 \times 10^9 \text{ sec}^{-1}$) of 4-methyl-4-phenylcyclohexadienone, the nonconstrained analogue of **78**. It was concluded that hydrogen abstraction by **78** takes place in lieu of an efficient and rapid rearrangement, which is sterically impeded here, rather than excluding it (to this extent, the tendency of **50** and **78** to abstract hydrogen may qualitatively have similar reasons). The reaction might occur upon thermal population of a $^3n,\pi^*$ state lying closely above the $^3\pi,\pi^*$ state; the latter appears, from its phosphorescence, to be the lowest triplet. One of the possible reasons for the failure of **78** to attain the zwitterion stage might be the need to twist about at least one of the double bonds in order to effect β,β' bonding.

In the cases of the 10-hydroxyestradienone **68** and the monocyclic methoxydienone **74** (Scheme 10), the competition between the zwitterion pathway and expulsion of the oxy substituent (presumably also radical in nature) was balanced, as in the case of the trichloromethyldienone **50** (Scheme 9), and products from both processes, **71** and **72** (*84*) and **76** and **77** (*96*), respectively, were isolated. On irradiation of the 10-acetoxy-steroid **69** in dioxane, only the fragmentation product, estradiol monoacetate (**72**), was identified (*97*).

The spirodienone **80** provides an example in which excited singlet state reactivity competes with intersystem crossing to the triplet (Scheme 12) (*46,98,99*). Of the products isolated, the major compound **81** as well as **82** were shown by quenching and sensitization studies to arise from the triplet state ($E_\text{T} = ca.$ 62 kcal/mol). The chronology of cyclopropane fission and hydrogen abstraction from diethyl ether solvent is not known. The proclivity of α,β-unsaturated β-cyclopropyl ketones (*100–102*) to undergo reversible π^*-assisted ring fission (*103*) competed with intersystem crossing in **80** (*99*). The relatively low quantum yield of disappearance of **80** (0.065) on direct irradiation was attributed to restitution of starting material from the singlet biradical **83**. 1,2-Hydrogen migration in **83** gave, furthermore, the quinone methide **84**, which then proceeded, by a subsequent photochemical step in its triplet state, to phenol **85**.

That reversible bond cleavage can lead to epimerizations was shown for appropriately substituted spiro[2.5]octa-4,7-dien-6-ones (*48,104*), e.g., **86** ⇄ **87**, on n → π^* irradiation and triplet sensitization (as well as on heating). In addition to the faster cis–trans isomerization, stereoselective methyl and hydrogen 1,2 migrations and formation of the quinone

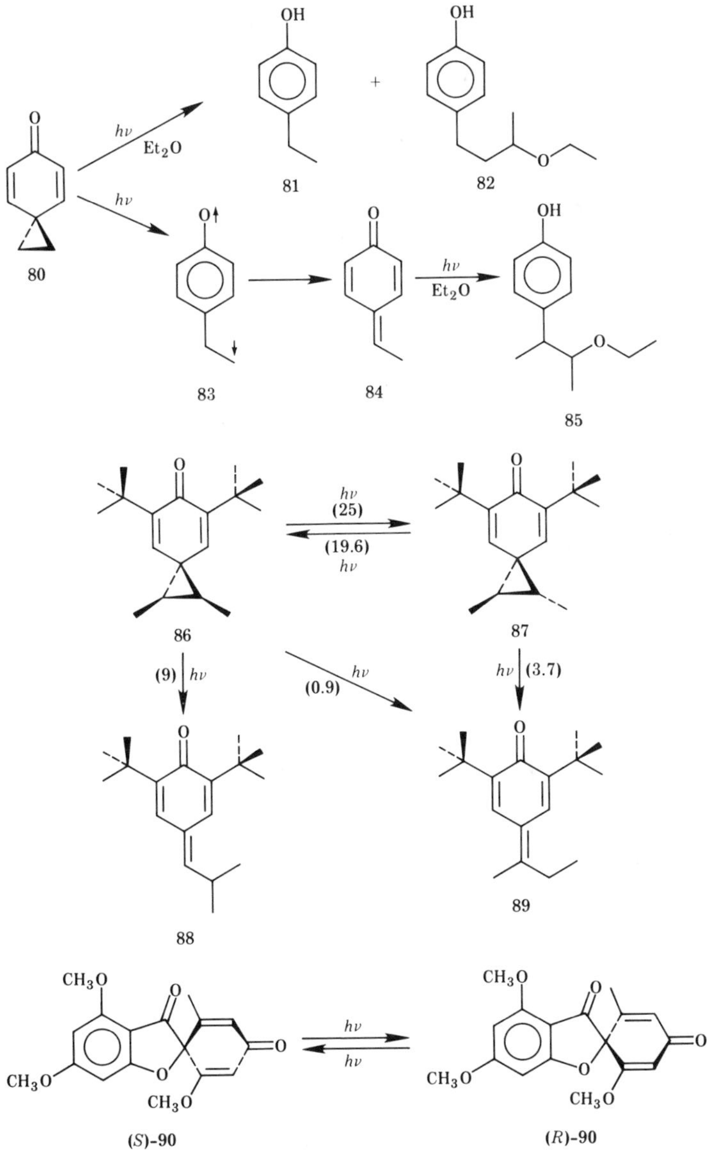

Scheme 12

methides **88** and **89** (relative quantum yields are given in parentheses in Scheme 12) were introduced when **86** and **87** were excited in the $\pi \rightarrow \pi^*$ absorption band. The nature of the intermediate(s) involved in these processes has not yet been resolved. The light-induced racemization of dehydrogriseofulvin (**90**) was obviously also due to direct and reversible cleavage of the excited dienone (*105*).

Electron spin resonance observations of radical products arising from cleavage processes at the levels of the excited dienone and bridged biradicals (Scheme 5, **21*** and **22***) have been reported for **91** and **92** (Scheme 13). The photolytic elimination of a bromine atom from **91** was followed either by hydrogen abstraction from solvent to give the corresponding phenol or, upon interception of the radical by oxygen, by the formation of 2,6-di-*t*-butyl-*p*-quinone (*106*). The transformation of **92** in methanol to product **95** included homolytic cleavage of the peroxide bond and addition of a solvent-derived radical. Here, the most likely path would seem to involve the bridged excited biradical **93** collapsing to *t*-butoxy radical and **94** the existence of which was ascertained by ESR analysis in toluene (*107*).

It has been argued (*47*) that bridged biradicals (**22***) might also be capa-

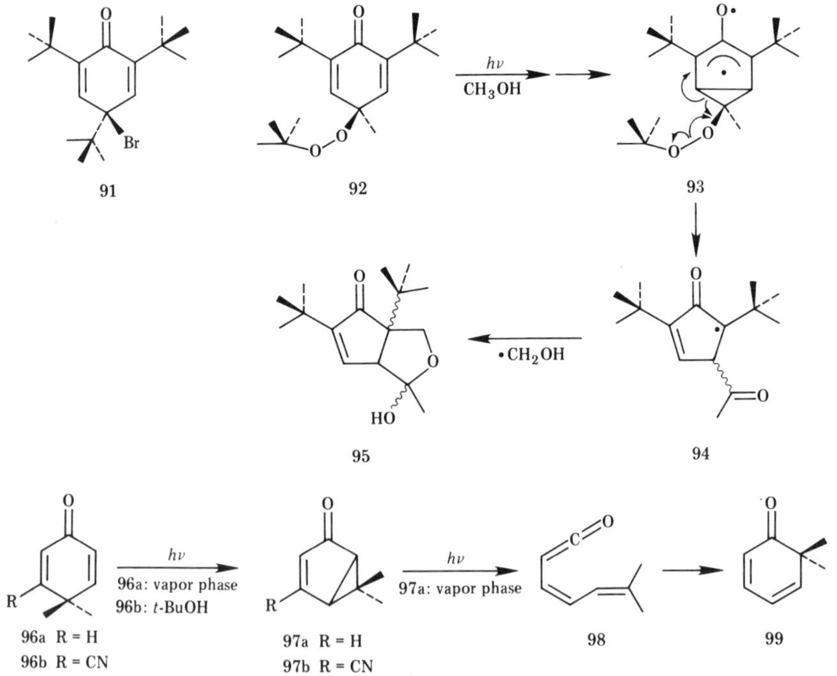

Scheme 13

ble of rearrangement to bicyclohexenone. Irradiation of the 2,5-cyclo-hexadienone **96a** in the *vapor phase* gave, in two consecutive photochemical steps, the bicyclohexenone **97a** (ϕ = 0.40) and the 2,4-dienone **99**. It is undisputed that the ionic path from **97a** to 2,3- and 3,4-dimethylphenols was followed in aqueous dioxane solution. The rearrangement to **97a** was suggested (*47*) to proceed, here, directly from the excited state level (cf. **22***) in the absence of a polar medium, which is considered necessary to facilitate unit charge separation in the formation of a zwitterion. However, this assumption has been challenged (*35*) since the available excited state energy of *ca.* 100 kcal/mol might still be sufficient to accommodate the (unknown) energy requirement for charge separation in the vapor phase. The formation of **99** was reduced in the presence of methanol vapor, which supports the intermediacy of ketene **98** in this reaction (*47*). A better case in favor of rearrangement at the biradical stage is provided by the regioselective transformation **96b** → **97b** in *t*-butyl alcohol (*28a*). A [1,4] shift in a zwitterion intermediate (Scheme 3: **22**, R″ = CN) would have been expected to give the 5-cyano isomer rather than product **97b**.

7. Scope and Limitations of 2,5-Cyclohexadienone Rearrangements

a. Formation of Bicyclo[3.1.0]hex-3-en-2-one Isomers. As discussed in Sections I,A,2 and 6, β,β' bonding **21*** → **22*** (Scheme 5) is the principal, and frequently exclusive, primary photochemical step of cross-conjugated cyclohexadienones. Following the initial reports on α-santonin (Scheme 1) (*3,5,19*) and 1-dehydrotestosterone (Scheme 2) (*11,108*), the ensuing rearrangement to bicyclohexenone photoisomers, **22** → **23**, was described for a number of other steroid ring-A dienones (*22,24,40,50,64,70a,109–111*) and bicyclic analogues (*25,56,59,71,112–115*), a steroid ring-B dienone (*116,117*), and many other mono- and polycyclic cyclohexadienones (see Schemes 8, 9, and 13) (*26,38,47,72–78,96,118–127*).

Departures from the course of the rearrangement **21** → **23** are relatively few. The case of γ-hydroxydienones (e.g., **68** and **73**, Scheme 10), in which the bridged intermediates (see **70**) collapse by way of a cyclopropanol cleavage, and the related reaction course of the γ-peroxide **92** (Scheme 13) have been mentioned in Section I,A,5 and 6.

Another modification of the zwitterion isomerization was proposed to account for the exclusive rearrangement of 1-dehydro-B-nortestosterone acetate (**100**) (Scheme 14) in dioxane to the linearly conjugated ketone **102** (*128*). The preferential fission of the 5,10 bond in **101** was attributed to the relief of the greater ring strain introduced by the five-membered ring B as compared with the analogous intermediates with a six-membered B ring. Interestingly, a similar directive effect on rearrangement was observed by crystal lattice forces on α-santonin (**1**) (*129*). Irradiation of crystalline **1** gave a dimer of **103,** an anhydro derivative of isophotosantonic lactone (**2**), rather than lumisantonin (**3**). A driving force for the conversion to the cyclopentadienone **103** could be the minimization of atomic movement in the solid state (see *130*); this may favor the opening of the β,β′-bonded intermediate to an enol similar to **108,** followed by ketonization coupled with a 1,2-hydride shift.

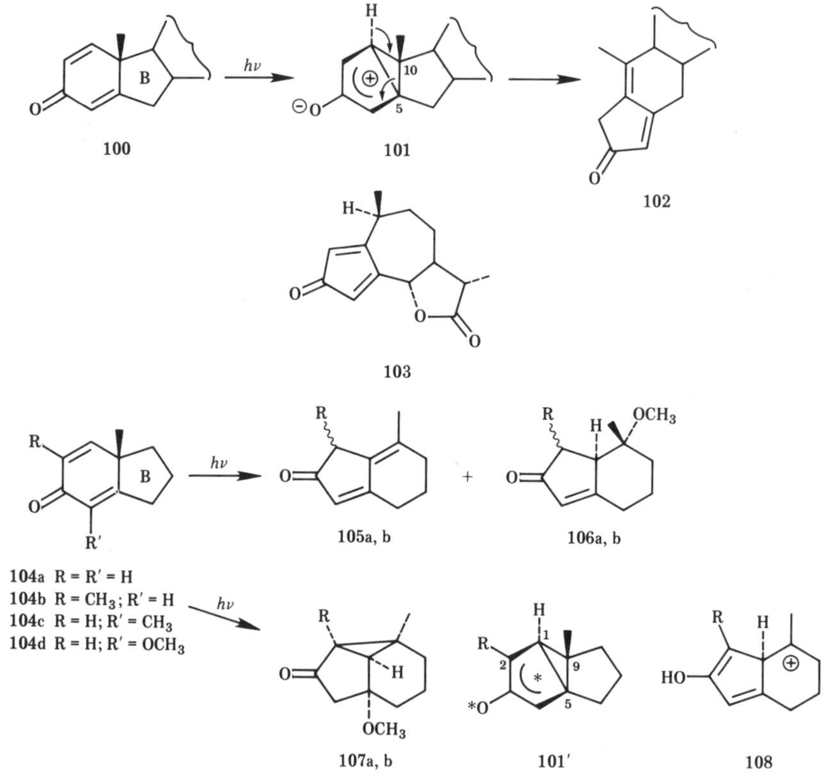

100   101   102

103

105a, b   106a, b

104a R = R′ = H
104b R = CH₃; R′ = H
104c R = H; R′ = CH₃
104d R = H; R′ = OCH₃

107a, b   101′   108

Scheme 14

The strain exerted by ring B of the 6/5-fused system of steroid **100** is further accentuated by the additional fusion with ring C. Thus, the photochemical behavior of the bicyclic analogues **104a,b** in dioxane (*131,132*) and of types **104c** and **104d** in protic solvent (*64,65,131,132*) was still predominantly similar to that of related 6/6-fused dienones, with the formation of 5/6-fused dienone products of type **105** constituting a minor path at best. However, **104a** and **104b** in methanol and methanolic acetic acid afforded only products **105–107** (*66*). Irrespective of mechanistic details, all three structures can be derived from formal 5,9 cleavage in a β,β'-bonded species of the basic type **101'**, in which preference for this cleavage over the 1,9 alternative is again due to the strain effect exerted by the five-membered ring B. This effect is seen in **104b** → **106b** also to overcome the directing force of 2-methyl substitution, which in 6/6-fused dienone favors the formation of spirocyclic hydroxy- and alkoxy ketones (see Section I,A,7,b). A singular variation of the dienone isomerization is represented by the products **107a,b**. It appears to reflect a somewhat greater conformational flexibility of the bicyclic 6/5 system of **104** in comparison with the steroid **100**, in which a structure related to **107** would undoubtedly be more highly strained. It has been postulated (66) to result from a [1,4] sigmatropic shift of the 5,9 bond to C-2 with retention of configuration at the migrating center C-9 in the excited biradical **101'** (* = ·/·), followed by addition of methanol to the double bond of the initial α,β-unsaturated ketone. As opposed to the 1,4 migration of the alternative 1,9 bond with configuration inversion on the ionic level, the rearrangement step would thus compete with n → π^* demotion to the zwitterion **101'** (* = +/−). Without further evidence on this point, an equally valid rationalization would involve collapse of the conjugate acid of **101'** (* = +/−) to cation **108**, which might in fact serve as a common precursor of **105–107**.

In order to avoid competitive nucleophilic trapping of the zwitterion intermediate (see Scheme 9) or the more frequent formation of hydroxy ketones (Scheme 3, **22** → **25** + **26**) and alkoxy analogues, anhydrous and nonhydroxylic solvents such as dioxane and ether were used preferentially. Since the bicyclohexenones are themselves photoreactive, their yields depend critically on the relative rates of the consecutive light-initiated conversions in a given system. A preparative optimization has to resort, therefore, to an appropriate selection of the excitation wavelength and irradiation period, combining an optimal conversion of dienone with a minimal light absorption by the bicyclohexenone product(s); e.g., the fraction of light absorbed by dienone over bicyclohexenone is usually higher at 254 nm than at >300 nm.

To date, the dienone ester **109** is the only compound the rearrangement to the bicyclohexenone isomer **111** of which is also known to persist in aqueous acetic acid (Scheme 15) (112). The stabilization toward hydrolytic cleavage of either the 1,10 or 5,10 bond as been ascribed to the electron-withdrawing effect of the carboethoxy substituent on the three-membered ring in the intermediate **110**.

There are numerous reports on the isolation of isomeric ketones other than the expected primary bicyclohexenone(s) and of phenols ("photochemical dienone–phenol rearrangement") (2,12,133–140). These examples would normally be expected to involve the intermediacy of the

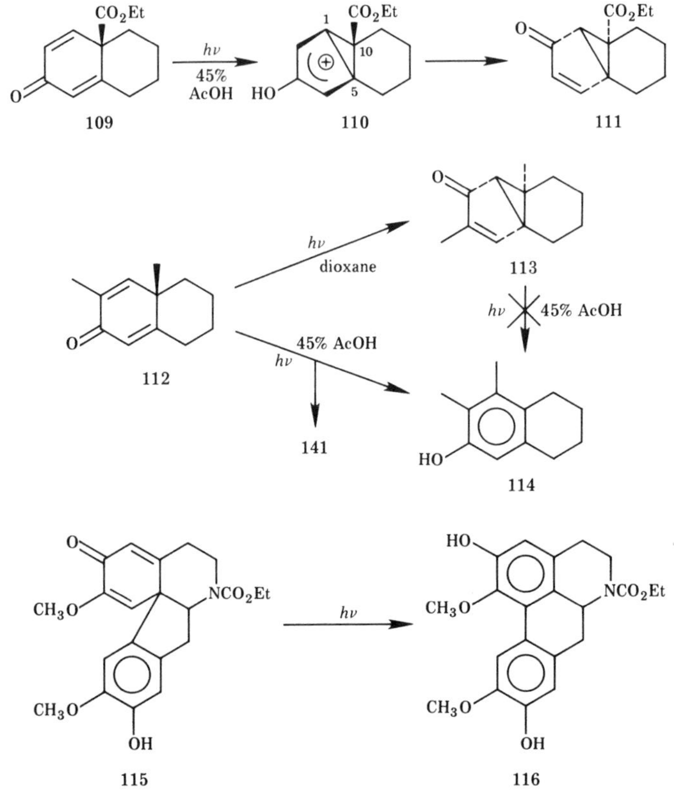

Scheme 15

ketone precursors required by the sequential structural changes delineated in Scheme 5. One possible exception is phenol **114,** which, in either methanol or aqueous 45% acetic acid, appeared to form by a methyl shift directly from the 2-methyldienone **112** rather than from the bicyclohexenone photoisomer **113** (Scheme 15) (*56*). A mechanistic interpretation of this result has yet to be given, and no analogy in the photoisomerization of the corresponding steroid, 2-methyl-1-dehydrotestosterone acetate, has been found (*22*). A similar situation appears to pertain to the photorearrangement of the spirodienone **115,** which gave a 44% yield of **116** in ethanol containing sodium acetate; this was a crucial step in a synthesis of the aporphine boldine (*141*).

Phototransformations of 4-substituted 2,6-di-*t*-butylphenols into isomeric phenols have also been interpreted in terms of intermediate dienone and bicyclohexenone photochemistry (*142,143*). The triplet excited phenols appear to tautomerize to 2,4- and 2,5-cyclohexadienones and then undergo further photorearrangements to the final phenolic products.

Although the Zimmerman–Schuster mechanism (Scheme 5) has accommodated, with persistent success, the primary processes and the constitutional changes leading to, or deviating from, the dienone → bicyclohexenone transformation, it was not set up *prima facie* to predict factors that govern the steric and regioselective course of this section, such as (a) the puckering of the ring system on β,β' bonding to 22*, (b) the configurational fate of the migrating carbon in the [1,4] shift 22(*) → 23, and (c) the direction in which this migration proceeds. Inversion of configuration [factor (b)] is predicted in the ground state rearrangement of zwitterion 22, and this has precisely been found in the reaction of bromo ketones such as 40 (Scheme 8) (*72–76*). Direct experimental evidence proving unequivocally that the light-induced rearrangement mandatorily proceeds in the same manner has not come forth as yet, except for the case of 14 → 16 (Scheme 2) (*22*). Here, inversion at the spirocarbon during migration (117 → 16; Scheme 16) is satisfactorily established if we accept the configurational assignments for 14 and 16, which are based on a chiroptical analysis of the latter (*144*) and on the conclusion that 1,2-alkyl migrations in the photoisomerization of bicyclohexenones occur stereospecifically (i.e., 12 → 14 and 16 → 9; see Section I,A,8,a). There is no obvious structural constraint in the spiro intermediate 117 that would discriminate against retention in the further transformation to 16. Such is the case, however, when the migration center is part of a fused ring system, and the resulting product stereochemistry necessarily corresponds, then, to inversion, as,

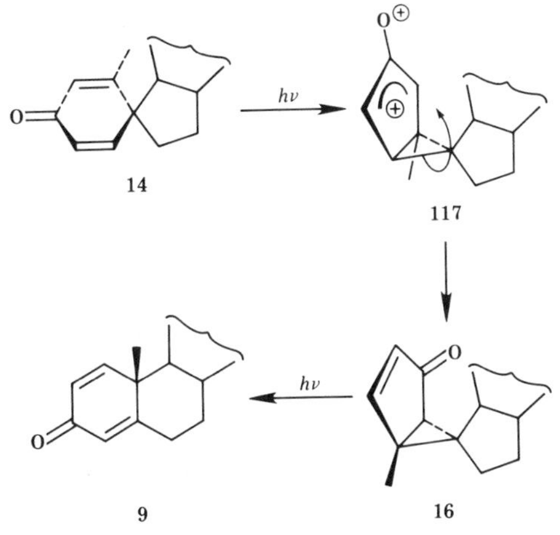

Scheme 16

e.g., in lumisantonin (3). One claim that the final [1,4] sigmatropic shift occurs with retention of configuration rests on a questionable assignment of configuration to the intermediate (96); i.e., it ignores the stereochemical factors controlling β,β' bonding, as discussed below. Another such claim concerns the transformation **104a,b** → **107a,b** (Scheme 14) (66), which, as we have seen above, may possibly find a different rationale.

Factor (a), which controls the direction of ring puckering at the outset of β,β' bonding (**118** → **119** + **120**, Scheme 17), appears to be predominantly steric in the absence of other perturbations in the system. Increased steric requirements of substituents at C-3 and C-5 may direct the

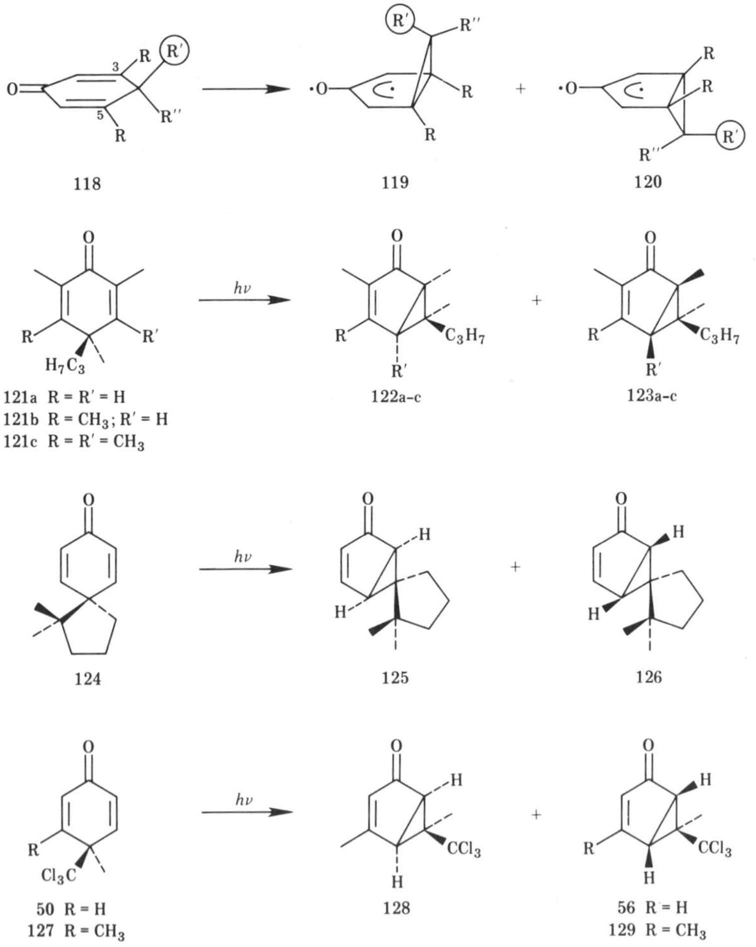

Scheme 17

bulkier of the C-4 substituents (118, R′) into the endo orientation (119) (*145*). The molecular motion leading to 120 would require the large substituent R′ to pass by the substituents R, which becomes more difficult with their increasing size. This effect was confirmed with the series 121a–c → 122a–c + 123a–c, in which the product ratios 122/123 were 44/56 (a), 68/32 (b), and 91/9 (c) (*145*), if inversion of configuration in the [1,4] shift is assumed.

It appears, however, that there is a subtle balance of this and other steric effects as well as other controlling factors. Thus, in the absence of strong repulsion by R substituents the motion leading to 120, which avoids the buildup of steric compression caused by endo R′ in 119, may become more favorable, and solvent effects of as yet unresolved nature may come into play. An example is seen with 124 the major product of which is 125 in alkane and 126 in alcoholic solvents (*121,122*). Furthermore, coulombic charge repulsion between the electron-rich trichloromethyl group and the dienone π system has been proposed to counterbalance the endo path (118 → 119) in dienones 50 and 127 and favor the exo path (118 → 120) to partial (127 → 129 > 128) or full extent (50 → 56) (*38,146*).

There are a few examples in which the [1,4] shift can occur *a priori* in two nonequivalent directions and in which the double-bond substitution in the bicyclohexenone product appears to exert a selective influence [factor (c)]. Thus, the constitutional selectivity in the product formations from 121b (→ 122b > 123b) (*145*), 127 (→ 128 < 129) (*38*), and 130 (→ 131) (*118*) (Scheme 18) reflects a preference for α,β-di- or β-monosubstituted over alternative α-mono- or unsubstituted double bonds. However, the selective rearrangement of dienone 132 to the bicyclohexenone 133 (*147*) combines preferential endo puckering [cf. (*134*) for additional examples of this type] with a [1,4] shift toward the product with an α-monosubstituted double bond. This reversion of the [1,4] shift trend may be due to less severe steric compression between methyl and *t*-butyl groups in 133 than in 134. A further example, 96b → 97b (Scheme 13), has already been discussed in Section I,A,6.

A detailed discussion of the factors that may have influenced the relative bicyclohexenone product distributions resulting from steroidal spirodienones of type 14a–c (15a/16a *ca.* 3 : 1, 15b/16b/135 *ca.* 1 : 30 : 3, 15c/16c *ca.* 5 : 1) and 136 (predominantly 137) has been given by Schaffner (*15*) (*22*). The reaction course of these cases can be fully rationalized by the steric and regioselective controls summarized in (a), (b), and (c), if one takes into account that steric hindrance by C-9 is greater than that by C-6 only on the β face of the molecule.

b. Formation of Hydroxy Ketone Products. The reports on the formation of hydroxy ketones corresponding to 22 → 25 and 22 → 26 (Scheme

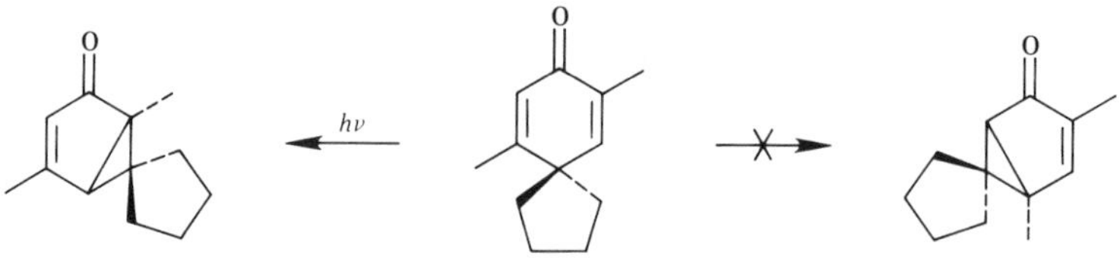

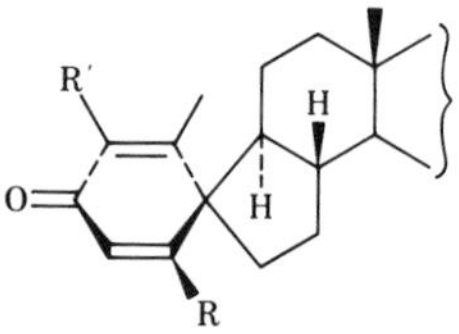

14a R = R' = H
14b R = CH$_3$; R' = H
14c R = H; R' = CH$_3$

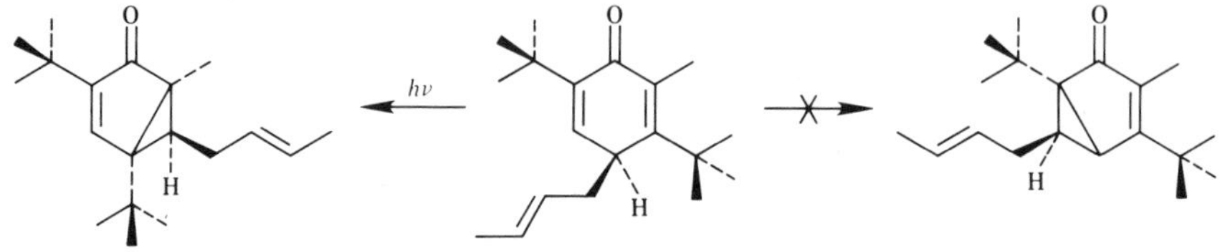

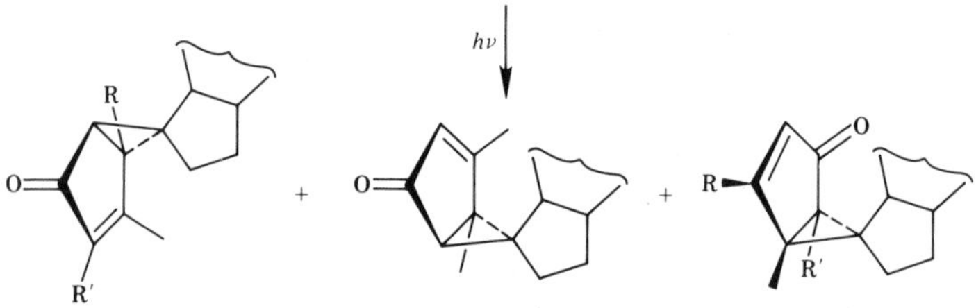

15a–c   135   16a–c

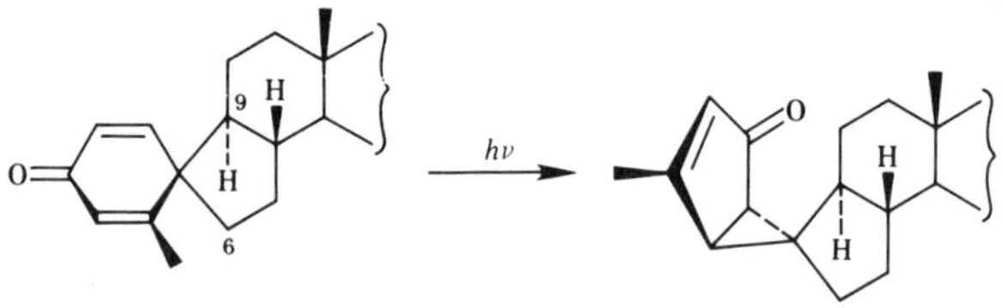

136   137

Scheme 18

3), although numerous, have been restricted to santonin-type (*3–5, 49,51,52,60*), steroid ring-A (*12,14,25,50,64,70a*), and other polycyclic dienones (*25,53–59,61–66,68–70*). The products were normally obtained in moderately acidic media, e.g., aqueous acetic acid. In glacial acetic acid, mixtures of the corresponding spiro and 5/7-fused acetoxy ketones and dienones were formed, and occasionally irradiation in methanol or ethanol afforded analogous alkoxy ketones.

Irradiation of unsubstituted dienones such as 1-dehydrotestosterone acetate (**9**, Scheme 2) (*24,25*) and the bicyclic analogue **138** (Scheme 19) (*25*) in acetic acid at room temperature gave approximately equal amounts of the spiro and the 5/7-fused hydroxy ketones (**10/11** and **139/140**, respectively). The stereochemistry of the two types of photoproducts is conson-

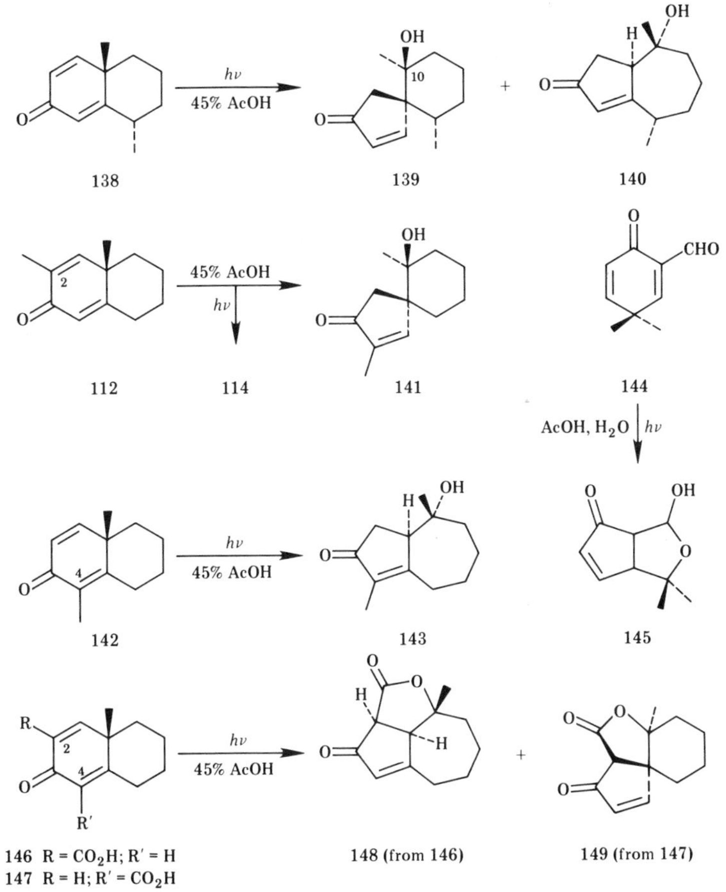

Scheme 19

ant with an S_N2-type nucleophilic displacement of either of the lateral cyclopropane bonds in the cationic intermediate (see **24** and **24′**, Scheme 3) by solvent with inversion of configuration. That the process need not be entirely concerted is seen from the fact that some of the C-10 epimer of the spiro hydroxy ketone **139** was also formed at reflux temperature (*25*).

Substitution of the dienone chromophore and steric effects can favor the predominant, if not exclusive, formation of one of the two hydroxy ketone structures. Thus, the spiro product **141** was formed exclusively from the 2-methyldienone **112** (*56*), and the 5/7-fused compound **143** was formed only from the 4-methyl isomer **142** (Scheme 19) (*54,55*). A similar directive influence was observed for α-santonin (**1** → **2**, Scheme 1) (*3,5*) and several of its isomers and related sesquiterpenes (*49,51,52,60*), and for 4-methyl-1-dehydrotestosterone acetate, which gave the spiro and 5/7-fused products in a *ca.* 1 : 6 ratio (*15*). These selectivities have been attributed (*16*) to the methyl group causing hyperconjugative stabilization of the incipient double bond being formed upon cyclopropane cleavage in **24/24′** (Scheme 3) and/or an inductive effect localizing positive charge at the more highly substituted position. A converse inductive effect by the electron-withdrawing substituents appears to control the preferred rearrangement of **144** to **145** (*67*). Irradiation of **146** and **147** selectively gave product families possessing 5/7-fused and spirocyclic systems, respectively. The structural variations within these groups depended on the solvents used, ranging from aqueous acetic acid to anhydrous dioxane, and they included anhydro derivatives (dienones) and hydroxyketone acids, which eventually cyclized to **148** and **149**. A similar 5/7 directive effect was found in 2-carboxy-4-methyl-, 2-formyl-, and 2-carbomethoxy-substituted related systems (*61,63,67,69*) and in the monocyclic dienone **144** (→ **145**) (*148*).

c. Alternatives to Photochemical β,β′ Bonding. With the possible exception of the dienone–phenol rearrangements **112** → **114** and **115** → **116** (Scheme 15) in polar media, photoreactions occasionally competing with or occurring instead of β,β′ bonding (Scheme 5, **21*** → **22***) are mostly those of hydrogen abstraction from solvent and γ elimination. A number of examples have been discussed in Section I,A,6, with compounds **50** (Scheme 9), **68, 69, 74** (Scheme 10), **78** (Scheme 11), **80, 86, 87, 90** (Scheme 12), and **91** (Scheme 13). In the case of **150** hydrogen abstraction from solvent led to the saturation of one double bond (**151**, Scheme 20) (*149*) rather than fragmentation, as had been observed for **78**, in which case rearrangement was inhibited for similar structural reasons. It is not known whether the primary hydrogen transfer occurs here onto the oxygen or the β-carbon. The latter process is characteristic of cyclohexenone π,π* triplets (*113,150*). For α,α′-bis(*t*-butyl)dienones, intramolecular hydrogen abstractions have been reported to compete with rearrangement to bicyclohexenone (*151,152*). In the case of **152**, abstraction of a methyl hydrogen is evidently followed by cyclobutanol formation and dehydration to **153** (*151*). In another case, the intramolecular conjugate addition of a hydroxy group to a 2-methoxy-2,5-cyclohexadienone was observed (*153*).

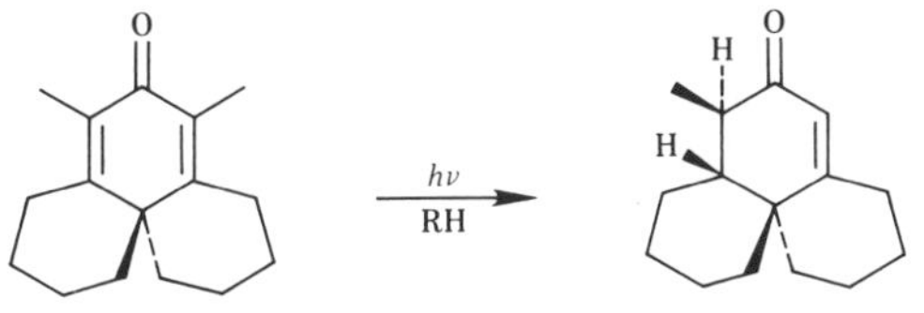

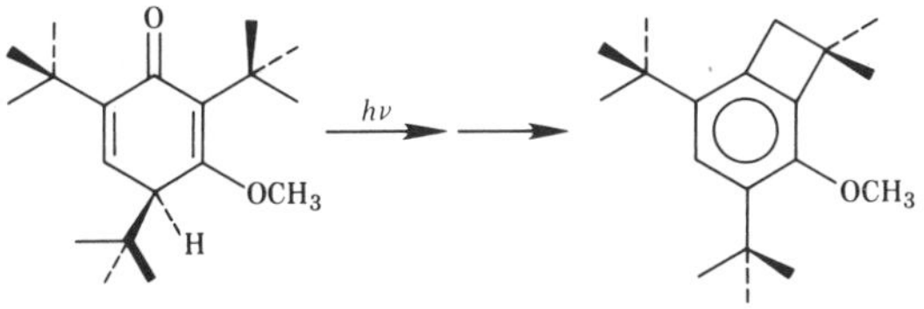

Scheme 20

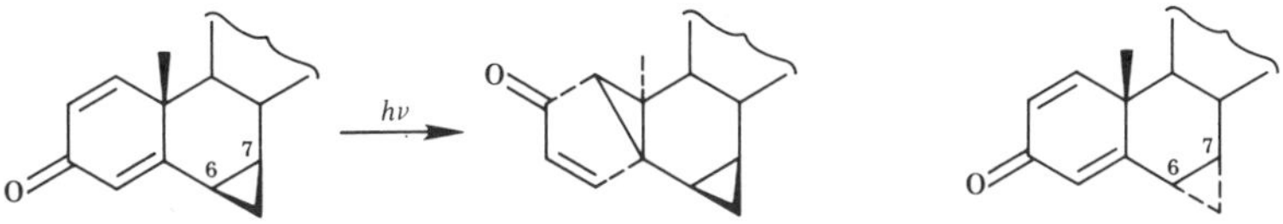

Whereas the 6β,7β-methano homologue of 1-dehydrotestosterone (**154**) rearranged readily to **155**, the 6α,7α isomer **156** proved stable on irradiation in dioxane (*101*). A similar finding was reported for a bicyclic analogue of **156** (*102*). Reversal of β,β' bonding similar to the (less efficient) process **55** → **50** (Scheme 9, Section I,A,5) has been considered as one possible explanation for the failure of **156** to rearrange. It might be caused by steric strain introduced by the two adjacent cis three-membered rings on ring B in the primary intermediate. Steric inhibition of a similar magnitude would not arise in the reaction course **154** → **155**, in which the two cyclopropyls are initially trans. It is noteworthy that 7α-methyl-1-dehydrotestosterone does rearrange (*154*).

A further departure from β,β' bonding was found in the rearrangement of the 4,4-disubstituted naphthalenones **157** and **159** (benzhomologous cyclohexadienones) to 3,4-disubstituted 1-naphthols (Scheme 21) (*155,156*). In the case of **157**, phenyl rather than methyl migration occurred, and naphthol **158** was formed exclusively. Compound **159** gave a mixture of naphthols, with a preference for p-cyanophenyl ($\rightarrow$ **160**) over phenyl migration ($\rightarrow$ **161**). Triplet-excited **159** was identified as the reactive species to the extent that identical product compositions were obtained on direct irradiation and on sensitization with benzophenone. Furthermore, the selectivity in aryl migration is most compatible with an n,π^* configuration of triplet **159** in which the electron density is reduced on oxygen and augmented on carbon.

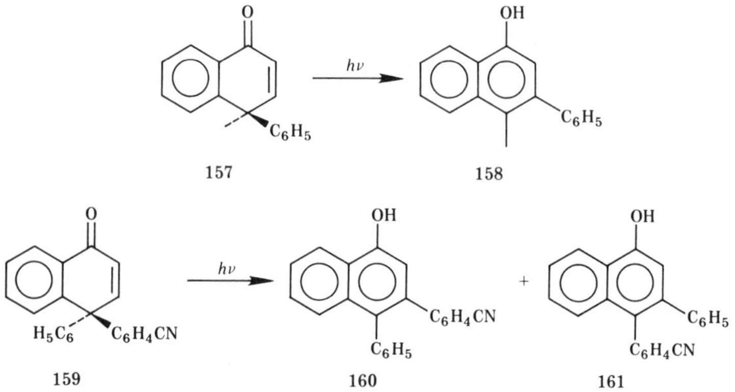

Scheme 21

8. Rearrangements of Bicyclo[3.1.0]hex-3-en-2-ones

The complexity of the photochemistry of cross-conjugated cyclohexadienones, which is often encountered in apolar solvents, is due principally to the photochemical lability of the primary bicyclohexenone product(s). As a consequence, the initial transformation of a dienone into one or two bicyclohexenones may proliferate into sequences of rearrangements that alternatingly furnish cross-conjugated dienone and bicyclohexenone photoproducts and that ultimately terminate by the formation of phenols or linearly conjugated cyclohexadienones, depending on the substitution pattern. Illustrative sequences of this kind were resolved for the bicyclic dienone **112** (*56,118*) and for 1-dehydrotestosterone acetate (**9**), its 1-, 2-, and 4-methyl homologues, and the 10α stereoisomer (*22,108,109*). The most complex and intriguing sequences were provided by the steroid work; e.g., the single primary bicyclohexenone product (**12**) of dienone **9** afforded altogether four new bicyclohexenones, three new cross-conjugated cyclohexadienones, six phenols, and three linearly conjugated cyclohexadienones in 17 discrete photochemical steps. In addition, two of the secondary bicyclohexenones rearranged, in part, back to the starting dienone (see Schemes 2, 16, 18, and 26 for some of the first steps and Schaffner (*15*) for a comprehensive review).

a. Cleavage of the Internal Cyclopropane Bond. Evidence for a zwitterionic route for the formation of phenols from bicyclohexenones (Schemes 4 and 5, **23** → **27**) is discussed in Section I,A,5, and it should plausibly also apply to rearrangements affording 2,4- (*20,21,56,109,118*) and 2,5-cyclohexadienones (*22,24,86,87,110,126,151*) in cases such as **3** → **4** (Scheme 1), **12** → **13** + **14** (Scheme 2), and **16** → **9** (Scheme 16). However, extensive *low-temperature* investigations (*157*) indicate that the direct route to zwitterion **27** by cleavage of the internal cyclopropane bond in **23*** may prevail, if at all, in high (ambient) temperature photochemistry only. At −190°C, this simple path, as given in Scheme 5, may occur to a minor extent at best, and extensive refinement is required to account for the major observations. So far, the following processes have been revealed to lead to phenolic and dienone products at −190°C: (a) cleavage of the 1,5 and 1,2 bonds, leading to a rearranged diene ketene, and (b) rearrangement to a cyclopropanone (a bicyclo[3.1.0]hex-2-en-6-one) (Scheme 22). It is, of course, conceivable that at room temperature these mechanisms do not operate or compete with the path delineated in Scheme 5.

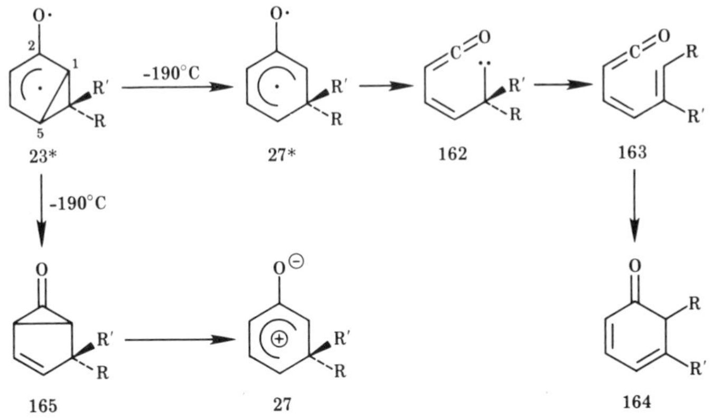

Scheme 22

In the ketene-forming process (a), **23*** → **163**, a concerted reaction and a carbene mechanism (**23*** → **27*** → **162** → **163**), as originally proposed (*8*) for the formation of photosantonic acid (**6**) from lumisantonin (**3**), are reasonable possibilities. The thermal closure of ketene **163** to 2,4-cyclohexadienone (**164**), the precursor to phenols in C-6 un- or monosubstituted cases, is a general reaction (see Scheme 23 and Section II,A). The rearrangement (b) to cyclopropanone **165** can be viewed, at least formally, as an allowed suprafacial [1,3] sigmatropic shift. Thermal σ-symmetric heterolysis can then lead, without intervention of **27*** as envisaged previously, to zwitterion **27**.

The bicyclohexenone opening to rearranged ketene [process (a)] was observed with umbellulone (**166**), lumisantonin (**3**), and the keto ester **111** (*157,158*). The smooth aromatization of **166** to thymol (**170**) in methanol at room temperature (*159,160*) proceeded at −190°C via **167**, which on warming cyclized to dienone **169**, as is characteristic for such diene ketenes (Scheme 23) (*161–163,219*). Nucleophilic trapping by added methanol (→ **168**) could compete with the cyclization only below −80°C. Lumisantonin (**3**) and mazdasantonin (**4**) gave on irradiation at −190°C the same ketene (**189**), which thermally gave **4** (Scheme 24). The cyclization was slower here than in the case of **167**, and on warming in the presence of ethanol the ketene was converted entirely to photosantonin (**5**) instead.

It is interesting that the nature of the angular substituent appears to direct the reaction course in **111** and **173** (Scheme 23). Both dienones rearrange at room temperature to a phenol: **172** (*112*) and **179** (*25*), respectively. Whereas in the former case the intermediacy of a rearranged ketene (**171**) was again established at −190°C (*157*), **173** was found to give the cyclopropanone **174** [process (b)] in the first photochemical step (*164*). Further irradiation at low temperature resulted in decarbonylation to diene **175**, whereas warming of **174** in the presence of furan gave a 2 + 4 adduct, as is characteristic of a three-membered ketone. Clearly, the room-temperature route to phenol **179** is likely to comprise heterolysis of **174** to zwitterion **176**, rearrangement to spirodienone **177**, and a subsequent two-step photochemical sequence via the spirobicyclohexenone **178**. A second example of cyclopropanone formation was encountered in the low-temperature photochemistry of **180** (*165*). The product **184** isomerized thermally via **185** to the phenols **187** and **188**, and it was trapped with methanol (→ **186**) and furan to give products that could be isolated. The unrearranged diene ketene **181**, which was formed in addition from **180**, cyclized thermally to dienone **182** and gave ester **183** in the presence of ethanol. Unlike process (a), the cleavage to this ketene must involve breaking of an external cyclopropane bond, as discussed in the Essay 19.

An intramolecular trapping of the conjugate acid of a zwitterion of type **27** has been observed with lumiprednisone acetate (*70a*). On irradiation in aqueous acetic acid, bridging of the 11-keto oxygen to C-1 occurred.

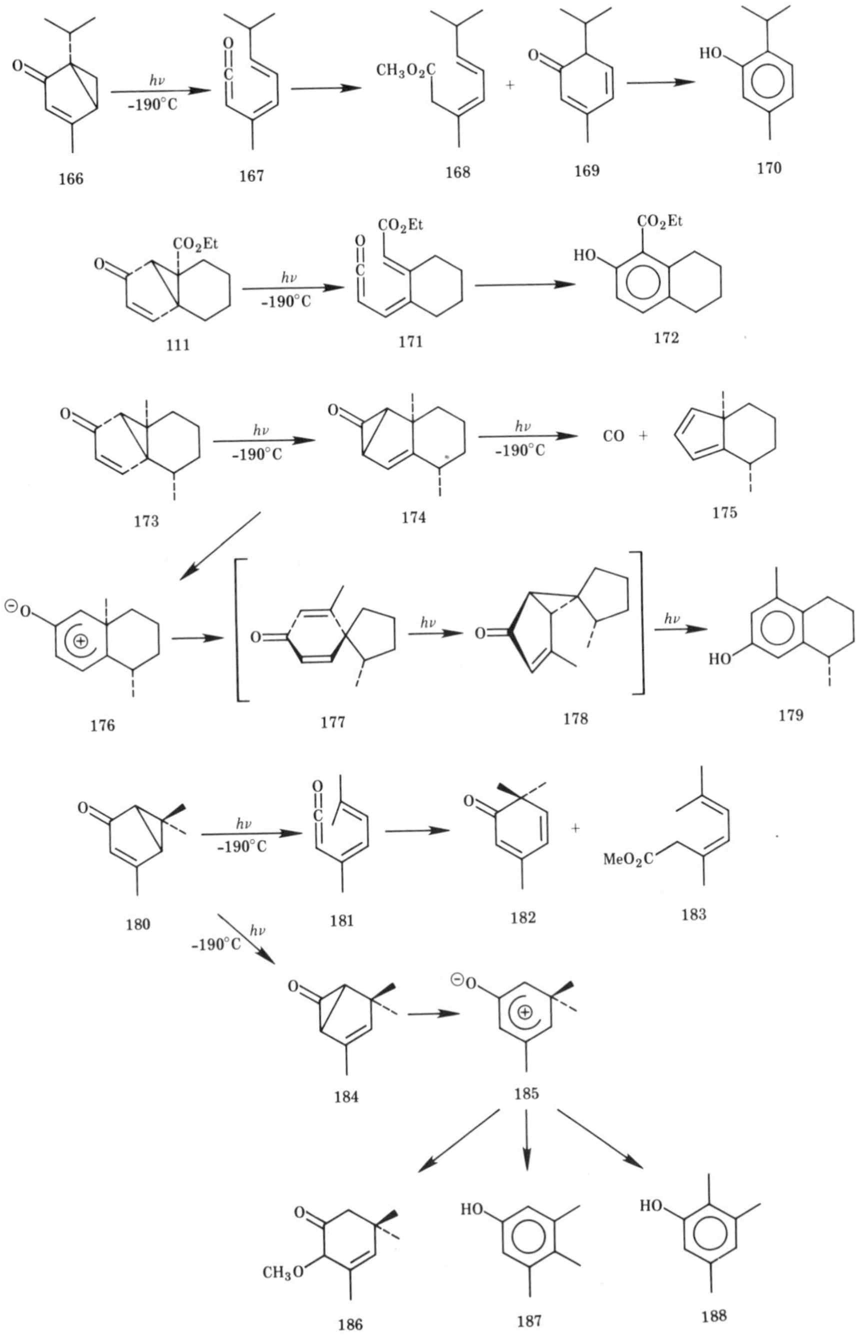

Scheme 23

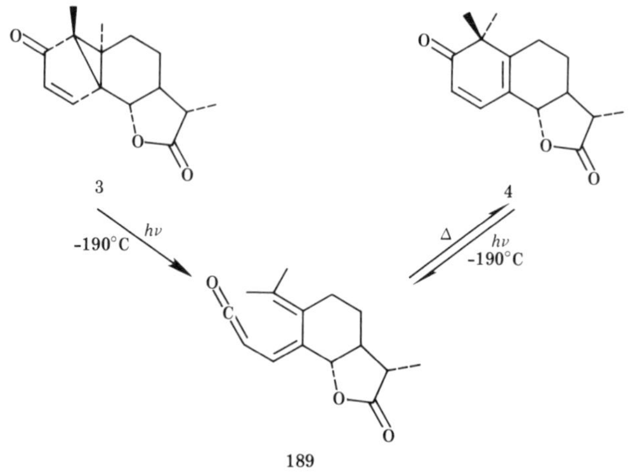

Scheme 24

Detailed mechanistic information on the photochemistry of a bicyclo-hexenone at *ambient temperature* evolved from extensive investigations of the 4,4-diphenylcyclohexadienone series (*166*). In aqueous solvents, singlet formation of acid **192** competed with S → T intersystem crossing in **34**, and the triplet again gave **192** as well as the phenols **44** and **45** (Scheme 25; see also Section I,A,5, Scheme 8). The reactions of **34** on direct irradiation were considerably less efficient than the dienone rearrangement **33** → **34**, i.e., ϕ = 0.16 versus 0.85. The difference was proposed to result from the intervention of reversible fission(s) of either cyclopropane bond(s) in triplet **34**. The phenolic product distribution was acid dependent, with **44** predominating under neutral and mildly acidic conditions but **45** predominating in strongly acidic medium, whereas the ratio of phenolic to acid product was essentially unaffected. The influence of solvent acidity on phenol formation is as would be predicted for equilibrating zwitterionic and cationic species, **193** and **194**. Considerations based on maximization of resonance stabilization (*166*) and on minimization of charge separation (*16*) in the dipolar half-migrated species favor intermediate **195**, whereas migration in the protonated form **194** would be expected to predominate via **196** toward the more positive C-4 site, according to molecular orbital calculations (*166*).

Competitive 1,2 shifts of hydride, alkyl, and aryl groups in zwitterion intermediates of type **27** (and its protonated form) should reflect migratory aptitudes characteristic of the groups involved and may be modified by structural constraints introduced by a particular ring system. A meaningful evaluation of several other examples of selectivities in the rearrange-

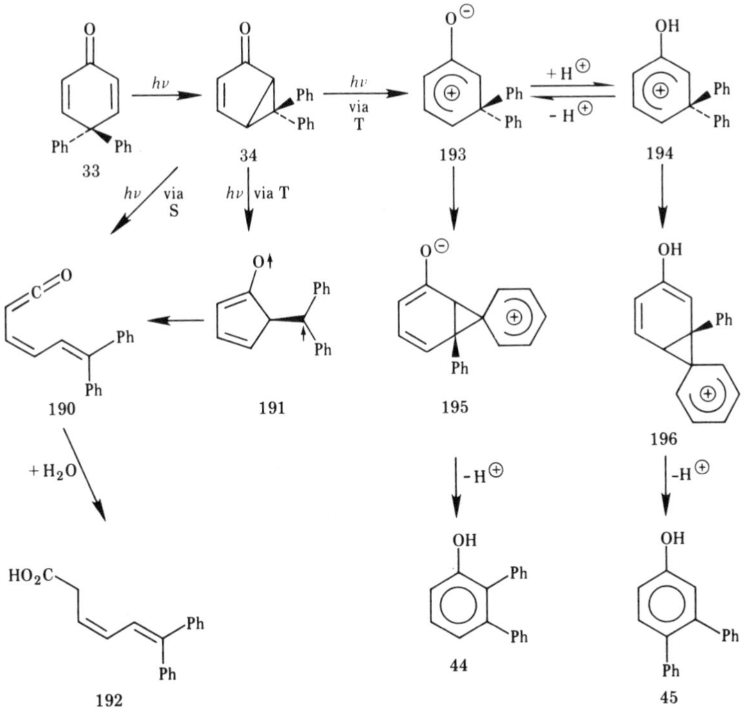

Scheme 25

ment to phenols (e.g., *16,53,55,56,118,167,168*) is presently difficult in view of the uncertainty as to which basic mechanism of the bicyclohexenone → phenol rearrangement is operating in each case. The route via rearranged diene ketene (**163**, Scheme 22) observed at −190°C (*157*) might also contribute to phenols at ambient temperature to an unknown extent.

b. Formation of Unrearranged Diene Ketenes. Direct double cleavage to unrearranged diene ketenes, first postulated (*26*) and then experimentally confirmed by a low-temperature study (*165*), is possible from both singlet and triplet excited bicyclohexenones, as recognized with **34** (*166*) (see Essay 17 and Scheme 25). The two routes have been formulated as a concerted breaking of both bonds and direct collapse of singlet excited **34** to the (*Z*)-ketene **190** and breaking of the external cyclopropane bond in triplet **34** to give the 1,4 biradical **191**, which then affords **190** by spin inversion and central bond cleavage. Reports of similar formation of dienoic acids or esters are few [see **97a** → **98** (Scheme 13) (*47,134*) and possibly analogous mechanisms for the conversion of 4*H*-pyran-4-ones to 2*H*-pyran-2-ones (e.g., **63** → **67**, Scheme 9) (*82,83,169*) and similar transformations of isoflavones and pyridones (*169–172*) (Section I,B)].

The tendency of diene ketenes to cyclize thermally may also be responsible for the formation of 2,4-cyclohexadienones with retention of the
quaternary carbon substitution. Supporting evidence is discussed in Section I,A,6 for the case of **97a** → **99**. The same mechanism could also apply
to **197** → **198** (Scheme 26) (*120*) and to the formation of spirocyclic

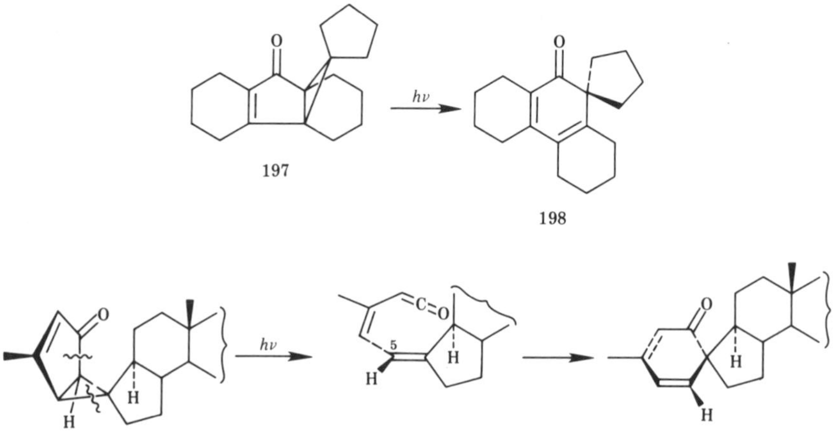

Scheme 26

dienones in the 1-dehydrotestosterone series (*22*). In the latter, the rearrangement of the spirobicyclohexenone precursors is stereospecific, as
exemplified by the set of two constitutionally identical transformations **15**
→ **19** (Scheme 2) and **137** → **200** (Scheme 26). Evidently, the epimeric
nature of the spirocarbon in the starting compounds is carried over to the
products. The diene ketene mechanism here would require a least-motion
path for the opening to the *all-Z*-diene ketene **199** and its cyclization to
200. The initial all-syn forms of **199** and of the 5,6 diastereoisomer resulting from **15** would be enforced, sterically, to remain in coiled conformations with identical helical orientations and thus to close to diastereoisomeric dienones.

A different rationale (*15,22*) envisaged a [1,4] shift of the apical cyclopropane carbon to the carbonyl carbon in the excited bicyclohexenone,
leading first to 2,4-cyclohexadienone and then, in a second photochemical
α cleavage, to unrearranged diene ketene. The [1,4] shift should proceed
with retention of configuration at the migrating center (and not with inversion, as suggested erroneously) and would thus give spirodienones of
opposite configuration, i.e., **15** → **200** and **137** → **19**. Although not directly
ruled out by experiment (the configurational bicyclohexenone–dienone re-

lationship has not been established in these cases), this mechanism finds no support in the low-temperature results on **180** (*165*).

9. Synthetic Use of 2,5-Cyclohexadienone Photoreactions

Several structural features of dienone photoproducts appear to be potentially attractive for exploitation in the synthesis of carbon skeletons not readily accessible by nonphotochemical methods alone. In the bicyclohexenones, (a) the configuration of the quaternary dienone γ-carbon is inversed, and (b) a [5.6]spirane with defined stereochemistry is preformed in decalin-derived compounds. Furthermore, (c) a one-step contraction–expansion of fused bicyclic systems, i.e. 6/6 → 5/7 and 6/5 → 5/6 ring transformations, is readily achieved.

So far, there have been few synthetic uses of the γ inversion (a) and the spiro system (b). The former served as a key reaction in a six-step synthesis (overall yield 22%) of a steroid with unnatural angular configuration, 10α-testosterone acetate, from 1-dehydrotestosterone acetate (**9**) via **12** (*173*).

The conversion of a bicyclohexenone to a spiro derivative (**201** → **202** → **203**, Scheme 27) was chosen as an efficient, short route for the synthesis of the racemic forms of the spirocyclic sesquiterpenes β-vetivone (**204**) (*174*) and α-vetispirene (**205**) (*175*).

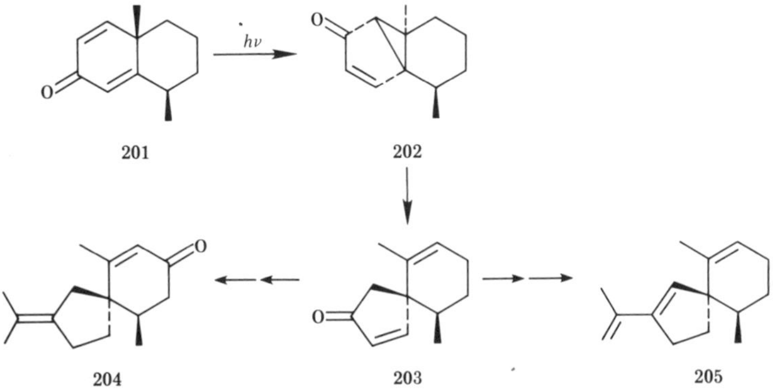

Scheme 27

Much more frequent use has been made recently of 6/6 → 5/7 ring transformations (c), which provide direct access to the basic ring skeleton of numerous natural products. A successful synthesis of the diterpene grayanotoxin II (**208**, Scheme 28) was based on the photorearrangement of dienone **206** in acetic acid to acetoxyenone **207** (80% yield), which possessed the appropriate functional groups for further transformation to **208** (*69*).

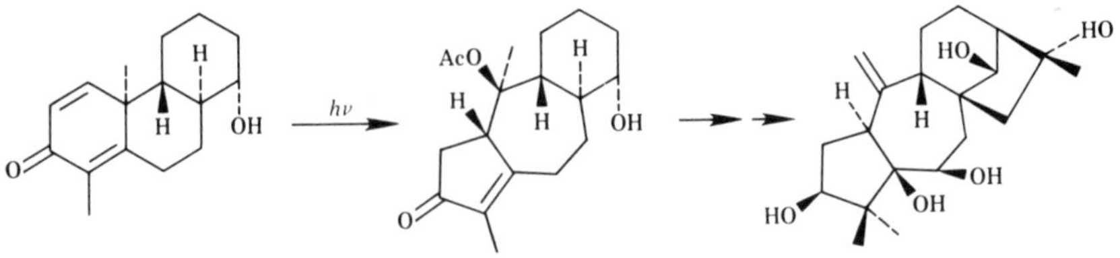

206 207 208

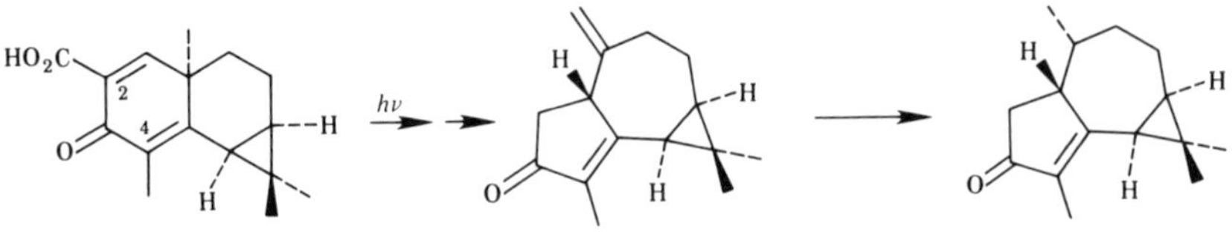

209 210 211

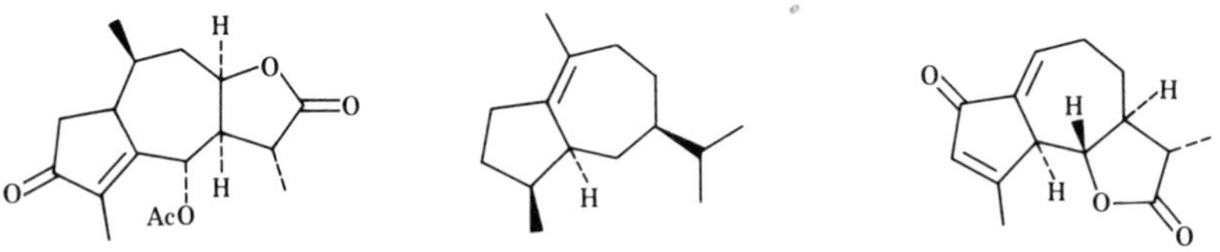

212 213 214

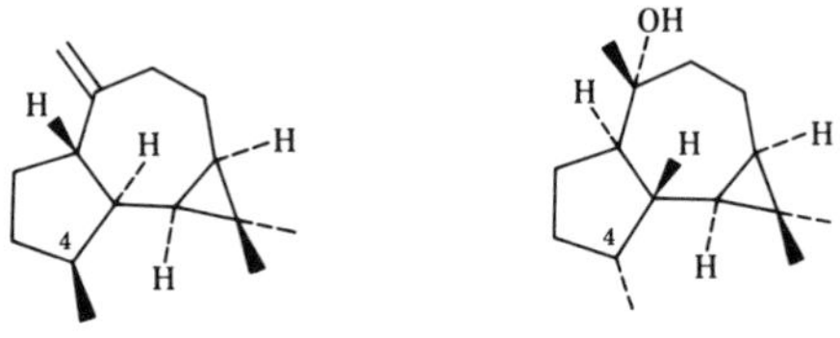

215 216

Scheme 28

A high-yield synthesis of cyclocolorenone (**211**) took advantage of the 5/7 directive influence by 2-carboxyl and 4-methyl substituents on the course of the dienone rearrangement (**209** → **210**) (*62*). Various similar schemes were employed for the synthesis of the related sesquiterpenes epicyclocolorenone (*176*), geigerin acetate (**212**) (*10*), α-bulnesene (**213**) (*61*), deacetoxymatricarine (**214**) (*177*), aromadendrene (**215**) (*178*), 4-epiaromadendrene (*68*), globulol (**216**) (*179*), and 4-epiglobulol (*68*).

The 6/5 → 5/6 ring conversion **217** → **219** (Scheme 29) in glacial acetic acid proceeded in 91% yield and was carried on to oplopanone (**221**) (*65*).

A similar rearrangement of 218 gave the appropriate intermediate 220 in a synthesis of 3-oxo-α-cardinol (222) and α-cardinol (223) (70).

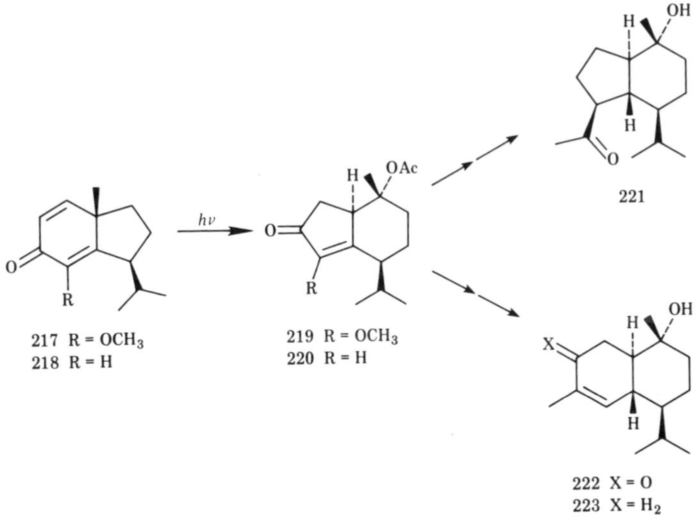

217 R = OCH$_3$
218 R = H

219 R = OCH$_3$
220 R = H

221

222 X = O
223 X = H$_2$

Scheme 29

B. Hetero-2,5-cyclohexadienones

The photochemical behavior of cross-conjugated 4-heterodienones varies markedly with the nature of the heteroatom and substitution. 4-Pyridones are unreactive, and 4H-pyran-4-ones and 4H-thiapyran-4-ones preferably undergo addition reactions and dimerization (180,181), unless β,β' bonding is favored by steric crowding or other substituent effects.

Facilitation of β,β' bonding by the hydroxy group may conceivably play a role in the smooth rearrangement of the pyranone 224 to the bicyclohexenone analogue 225 and its derivative 226 (Scheme 30) (182). Likewise, 3-hydroxyflavones were quantitatively converted to isomers corresponding in structure to 226 (183), whereas 3-methoxyflavones dimerized instead (184). Although primary photoisomers of type 228 were not isolated, the rearrangements of the pyranones 63 (Scheme 9) and 227 and of the isoflavones 230 seem to take a similar reaction course, followed by a double fragmentation–reclosure process (Section I,A,8,b) to final products, the 2H-pyran-2-ones 67 (82,83) and 229 (169,170) and the isocoumarins 231 (172).

The formation of the minor photoisomer (234) of the pyridone 232 was also attributed to an analogous route via 233 (171). The substitution pat-

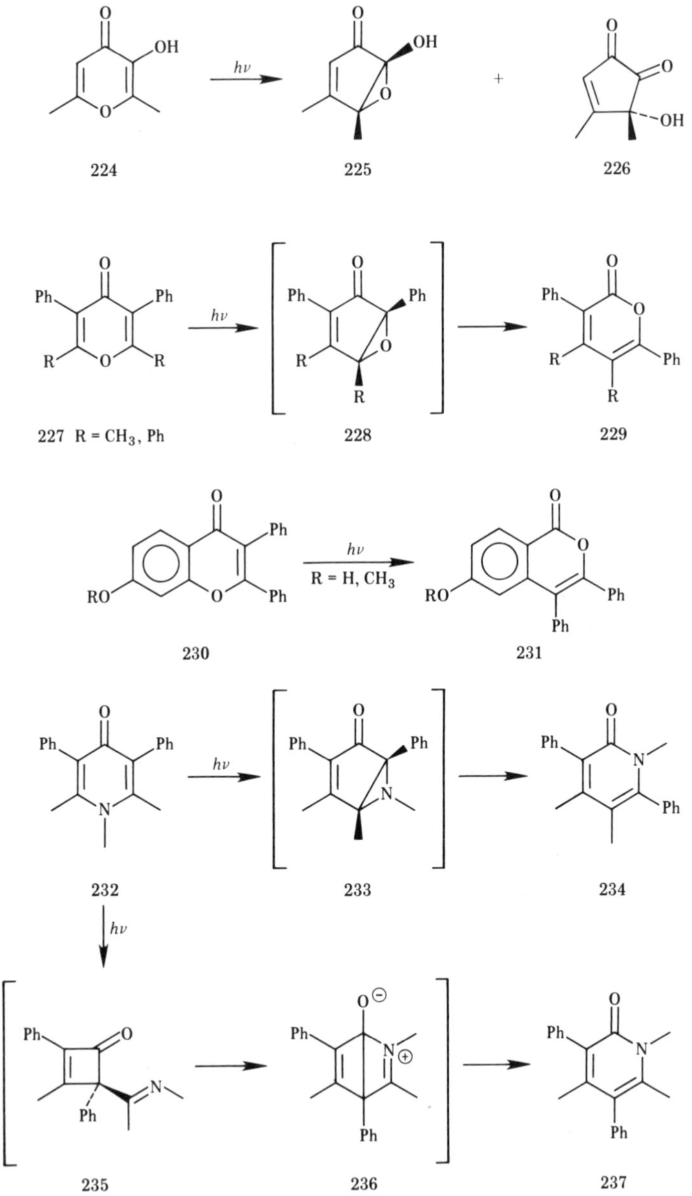

Scheme 30

tern of the major product, **237**, must result from yet another rearrangement mechanism, which was suggested to include the intermediates **235** and **236** (*171*).

Thiapyranones of type **238** (Scheme 31) were reported to yield cyclopentadienones (**239**) and sulfur, apparently as a result of photochemical β,β' bonding and subsequent decomposition (*185,186*), whereas 2,6-diphenyl-4*H*-thiapyran-4-one dimerized only (*187*), and its sulfone derivative underwent photoaddition of methanol and acetylenic cosolutes (*188,189*).

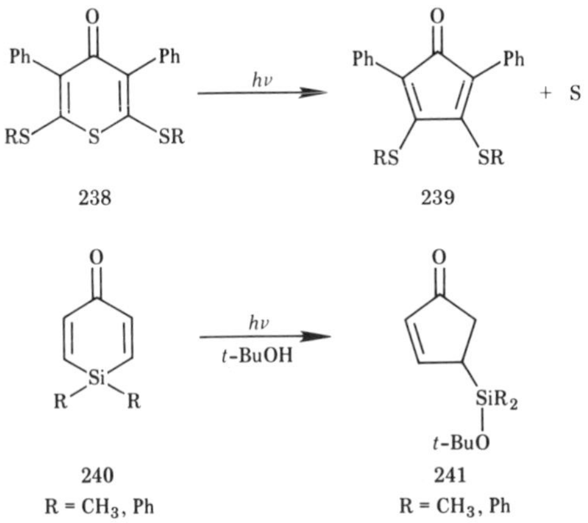

Scheme 31

Finally, the silyl compounds **240** provide yet another example in which zwitterion β,β'-bonded intermediates (see Section I,A,5) are captured by a nucleophile and opened to products **241** (*190*).

C. 2,6-Cycloheptadienone, 2,7-Cyclooctadienone, and 2,8-Cyclononadienone

All three dienones gave photoproducts of two types, **245** and *endo-* and *exo-***246** (Scheme 32) (*191–194*). It is a reasonable possibility that in each case the photoprocess was isomerization to an (*E,Z*)-dienone (**243**), which could serve as a common precursor of the final products. Direct nucleophilic addition of a solvent molecule across the strained (*E*) double bond would lead to **245**, and a thermal disrotatory cyclization to **244** and solvent uptake would give **246**. An alternative route to the bicyclic products remains possible: β,β' bonding in the excited starting dienones (**242**)—a conrotatory photocyclization analogous to the process in 2,5-cyclohexadienones—and electron demotion to zwitterion **244**.

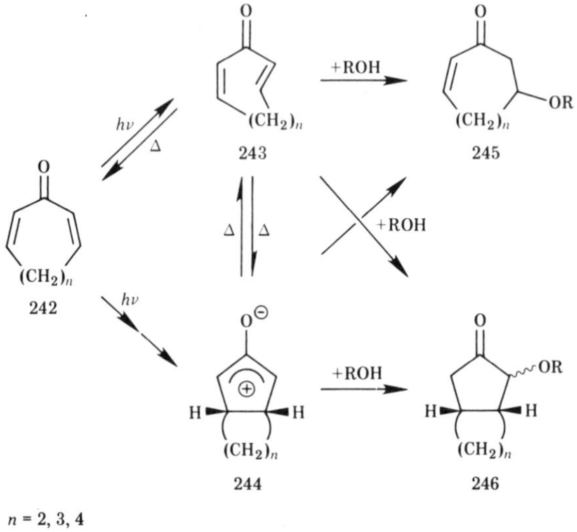

Scheme 32

The involvement of a reactive ground state intermediate in the reactions of (Z,Z)-cyclooctadienone was demonstrated at $-78°C$ in inert solvents (193). Addition of acetic acid, methanol, cyclopentadiene, or furan in the dark after irradiation and warming to room temperature gave the respective products (e.g., **245** and **246**, R = CH_3, Ac). In the absence of these reagents, the intermediate reverted thermally to **242**. Both **243** and **244** can structurally be visualized as affording the products **245** and **246**. In the case of cyclononadienone, infrared spectroscopic evidence was obtained that an (E,Z) photoisomer is indeed formed (194).

D. Cyclopentadienones

One may argue that bicyclopentenone and tricyclopentanone should be the most likely photoisomers of cyclopentadienone. Such an expectation was recently confirmed in spectacular studies of the tri- and tetra-*t*-butylcyclopentadienones, which culminated in the preparation of crystalline **256** (Scheme 33), the first stable representative of the long-sought and elusive tetrahedrane (195).

Irradiation of the trisubstituted dienone **247** in an argon matrix at 10 K gave the isomeric cyclopentadienone **251** and the cyclobutadiene **252** in wavelength-dependent proportions (196). A detailed investigation at various temperatures and excitation wavelengths showed that the bicyclopentenone **248** is, in fact, the primary photoproduct. Subsequent photo-

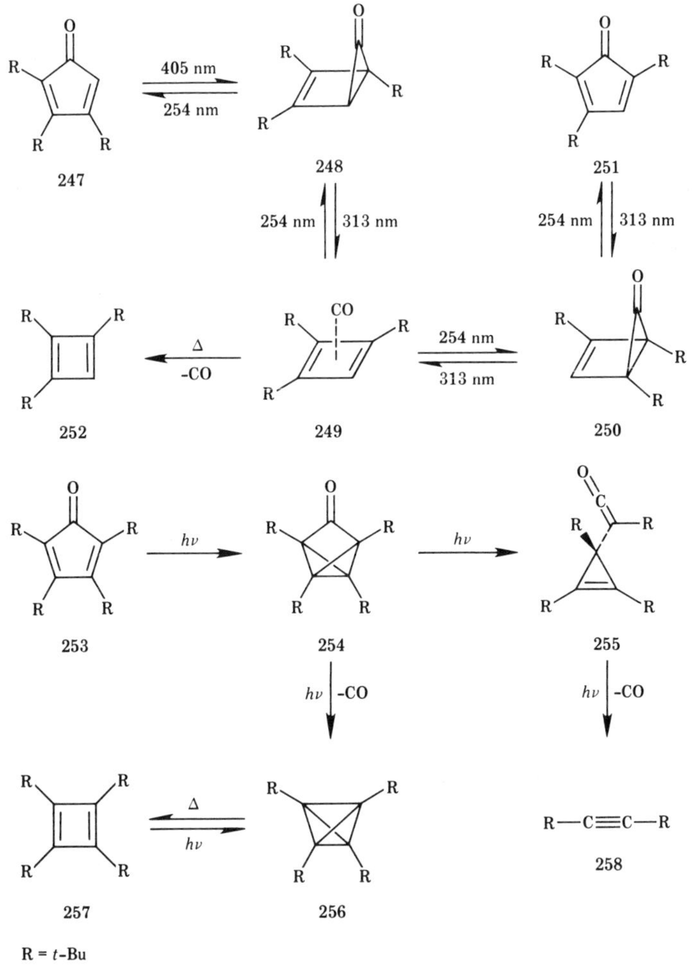

Scheme 33

lytic cleavage of **248** at 10 K afforded the cyclobutadiene–carbon monoxide complex **249**, which dissociated on warming to 35 K. The sequence **247** → **248** → **249** was photochemically reversible, and the alternative reversion via **250** was obviously responsible for the concomitant formation of **251** (*196*).

The irradiation of tetra-*t*-butylcyclopentadienone (**253**) afforded an entirely different product pattern (*197*). Apparently as a consequence of enhanced steric crowding by the fourth *t*-butyl group, the buildup of a bicyclopentenone isomer was suppressed. Instead, the tricyclopentanone

254 was formed, which photoisomerized further to the cyclopropenyl ketene **255**. This product was also photolabile and decarbonylated slowly, with desintegration to di-t-butylacetylene (**258**). At $-100°C$ and below, however, direct decarbonylation of **254** and ring closure to the tetrahedrane **256** set in and competed efficiently with the rearrangement to **255**. A 35% yield of **256** (44% based on consumed **253** and **254**) was obtained on irradiation of **253** in a rigid solvent matrix at 77 K. Thermal isomerization of **256** at 130°C gave the cyclobutadiene **257**, which in turn reformed **256** on irradiation at room temperature in solution and at 10 K in argon matrix (*197*).

Photochemical dimerization of a cyclopentadienone as a competitive alternative to unimolecular processes has been reported in only one example; the cage product **260** was obtained (*198*) from crystalline **259** in quantitative yield (Scheme 34). The dimerization appears to require the entropic facilitation available in the crystal lattice (presumably a topochemical effect), since solutions of **259** failed to show any photoreaction. Intriguingly, the thermal dimer **261** also affords, in part, product **260**

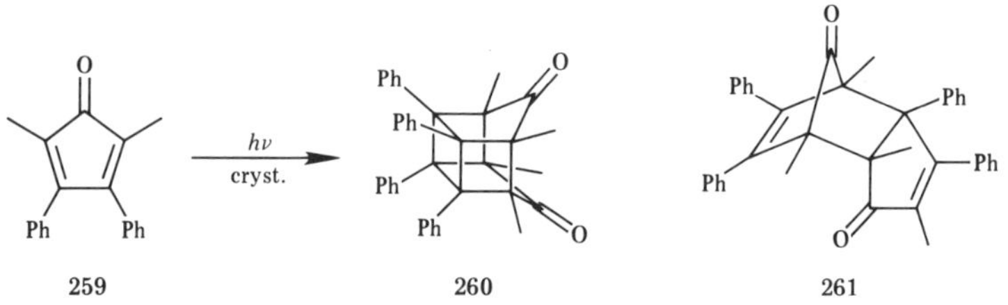

Scheme 34

in a triplet reaction (*199*). The mechanism of the transformation **261** → **260** has not yet been established (see *200*). Its "intramolecular" nature has been demonstrated by appropriate deuterium-labeling experiments (*201*). An interesting speculation is that **261** photochemically splits into a pair of monomers, which then photodimerizes. A prerequisite for such a process is that this pair of **259** be suitably oriented either in a cage of ground state molecules or in the form of an excimer.

E. Acyclic Cross-conjugated Dienones

Aliphatic cross-conjugated dienones undergo dimerizations, double-bond shifts, and $E \rightleftarrows Z$ isomerizations rather than any rearrangement initiated by β,β' bonding. Topochemically aided double [2 + 2] additions have been described for compounds such as **262** (→ **263**) (Scheme 35) in the crystalline state (*181,202*), but similar reactions were also observed in solution (*203,204*). The double-bond shift, e.g., **264** → **265** → **266** (*205,206*) and **268** → **269** (*207*), is characteristic of α,β-unsaturated ketones that possess a γ-hydrogen suitably positioned for intramolecular abstraction by the ketone oxygen and thus form an intermediate dienol ("photoenolization"). An example of an $E \rightarrow Z$ isomerization is given by **272** → **273**, which is accompanied by the formation of the cyclized product **274**, presumably due to a photochemical ring closure of **273** with loss of hydrogen bromide (*204*). Other photoproducts originating via still not fully established mechanisms are **267**, formed on irradiation of phorone (**264**) in methanol (*206*), and the cyclopentenone derivative **271**, formed from **270** (*203*).

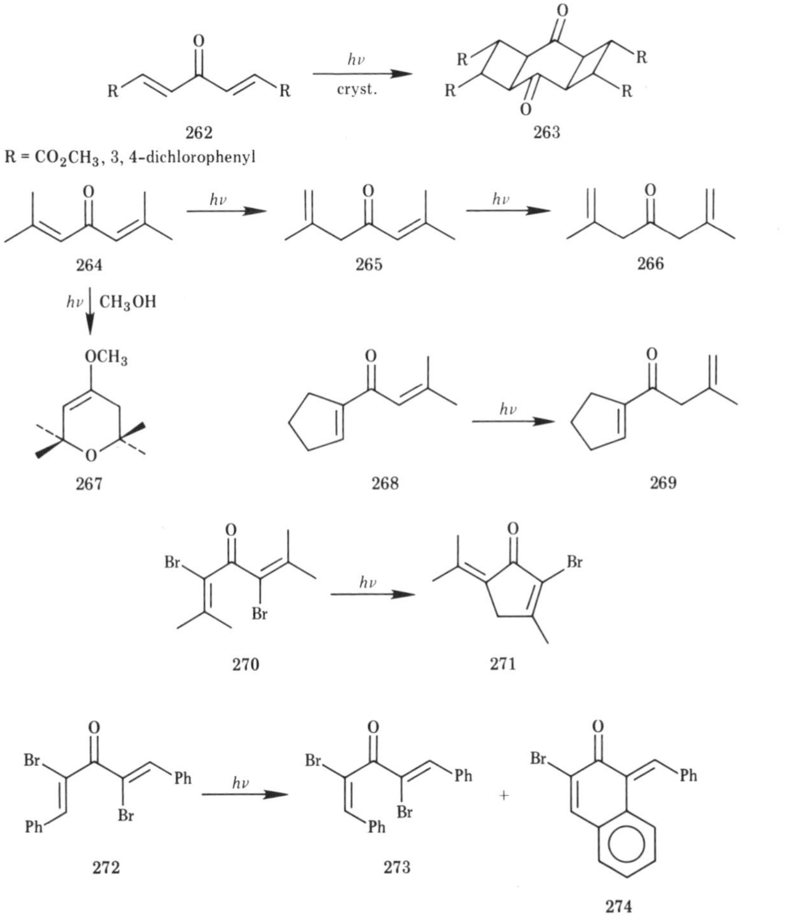

Scheme 35

The situation is changed when both double bonds are contained in rings, as, e.g., in dicyclohexenyl ketone (**275**, Scheme 36). Irradiation of this dienone gave **276** (*23,208*). The syn backbone of this tricyclic enone is in accord with a disrotatory electrocyclic photoprocess comparable to the β,β' bonding in cyclohexadienones.

Phenyl cyclohexenyl ketones undergo a similar photocyclization: **277** → **281** (*209*), **278** → **282** (*207,210*), **279** → **283** (*207*), **280** → **284** (*210*). The quantum yields were generally somewhat higher in polar media than in hydrocarbons, reaching $\phi_{-280} = 0.17$ and $\phi_{284} = 0.16$ in *t*-isoamyl alcohol (*211*). Phenyl-d_5 cyclohexenyl ketone in *t*-isoamyl alcohol gave a cyclization product with only 17% deuterium at C-9a. Alternatively, reaction of **278** in *O*-deuteriated *t*-butyl alcohol was accompanied by 58% deuterium incorporation at the same angular position along the reaction path. These

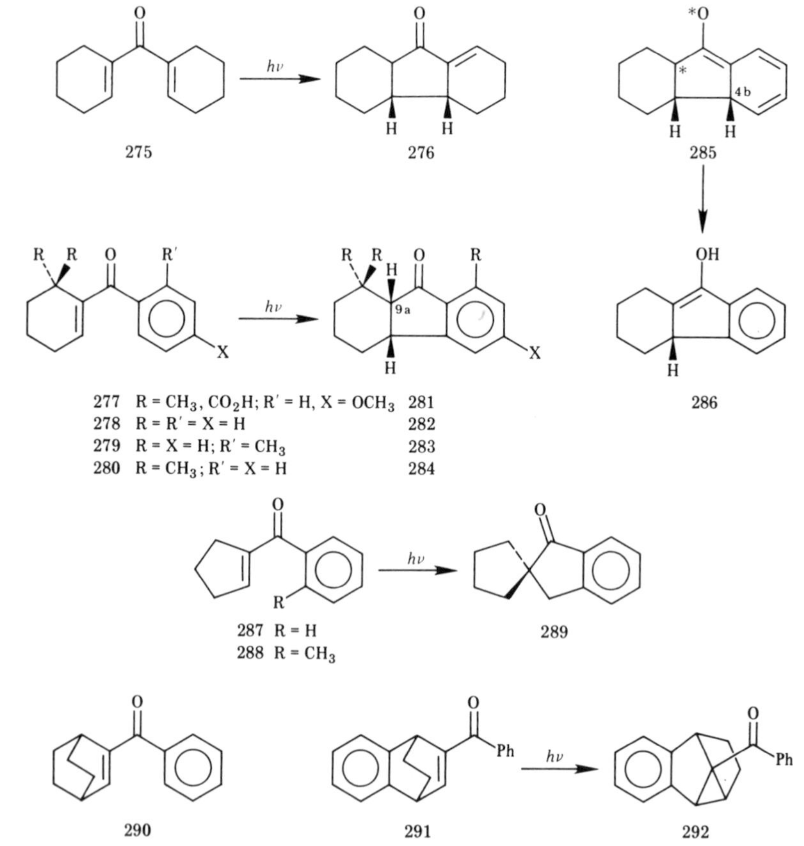

277 R = CH$_3$, CO$_2$H; R' = H, X = OCH$_3$ 281
278 R = R' = X = H   282
279 R = X = H; R' = CH$_3$ 283
280 R = CH$_3$; R' = H; X = H   284

287 R = H   289
288 R = CH$_3$

290   291   292

Scheme 36

results suggest that at least the major mechanism involves transfer of the angular hydrogen at C-4b in the primary photoproduct **285** (∗ = ·/· or +/−) to the oxygen (→ **286**), where it is subject to protic exchange with the solvent before ketonization (*211*).

The cyclopentenyl (**287, 288**) (*207*), bicyclooctenyl (**290**) (*210*), and benzobicyclooctenyl ketones (**291**) (*210,212*) failed to cyclize in any similar manner. Such structural limitation indicates that geometric distortion around the cycloalkenyl double bond is a requirement for the reactive excited state that cannot be sufficiently attained in the conformationally more rigid ring structures of **287, 288, 290,** and **291**.

Whereas **287** and **290** were slowly transformed into mixtures of as yet unidentified products, ketones **288** and **291** underwent smooth photo-isomerizations of a different nature. Ketone **288** cyclized in 94% yield to **289** (*207*). The reaction involves overall a 1,6 hydrogen transfer from the aromatic methyl group to the enone β-carbon, a process that may occur

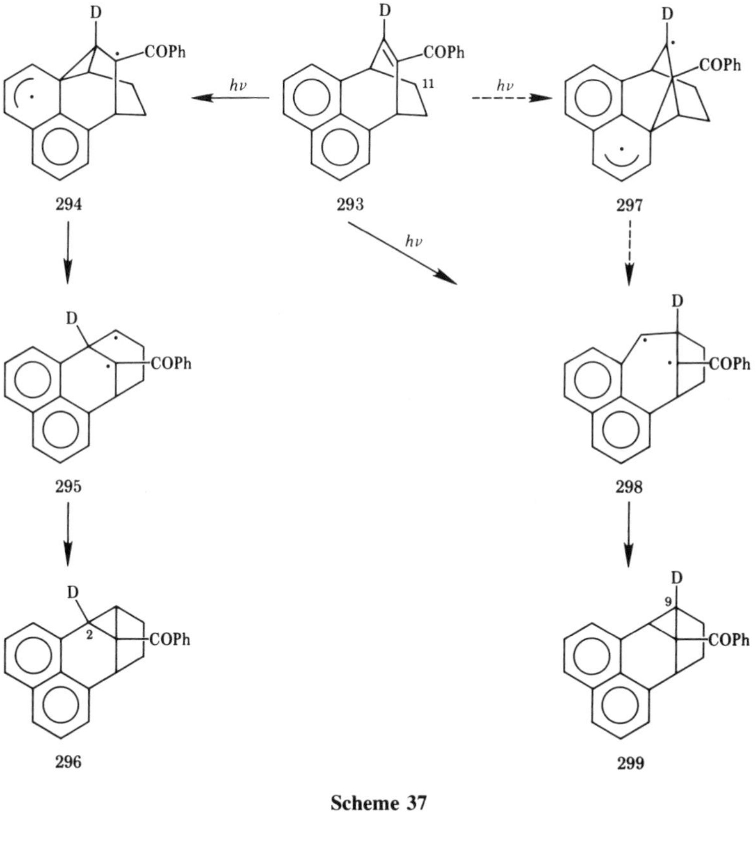

Scheme 37

directly in the primary photochemical step, in analogy to well-established hydrogen abstractions by the β-carbons of $^3\pi,\pi^*$ excited enones in intermolecular (*113,213,214*) and intramolecular (*215*) fashion. It is interesting that this hydrogen abstraction process is obviously less efficient than β,β' bonding in **279**, the cyclohexenyl homologue of **288**, so that the latter process and formation of **283** prevail (*207*).

Ketone **291** gave **292** quantitatively in a rearrangement that at first sight is reminiscent of the di-π-methane type of reactions of the naphthobarrelene-like system **36** (Section I,A,4, Scheme 7). More detailed mechanistic information was obtained with **293** (Scheme 37), a monodeuteriated dihydro derivative of **36** and naphtho analogue of **291**. Direct and triplet-sensitized irradiations of **293** gave a mixture of **296** (88%) and **299** (12%) (*216*). The formation of the major product, **296**, indeed represents a di-π-methane process initiated by naphthyl–vinyl bonding and formally proceeding via the diradical structures **294** and **295**, similar to **36** → **39** which was proven in greater detail (*43a*). However, the minor isotopomer, **299**, must arise from a 1,2 migration of the C-11 methylene group, either directly to **298** or facilitated by the alternative naphthyl–vinyl bonding to **297**, which would have to revert after the alkyl shift was completed. The closest analogy to this unusual rearrangement of a cyclohexenyl ketone is the phototransformation of 1-cyanocyclohexene to 1-cyanobicyclo[3.1.0]hexane (*217*).

II. REARRANGEMENTS OF LINEARLY CONJUGATED DIENONES

A. 2,4-Cyclohexadienones

With a very few exceptions, linearly conjugated cyclohexadienones are photochemically transformed into diene ketenes and bicyclohexenones. The two reaction modes strongly depend on the substitution and the reaction conditions and, in particular, on the nature of the solvent. That α cleavage to diene ketenes is a major photoprocess had already been recognized in 1958 (*218*) in an early entry into this field. Far-reaching quantitative understanding of the mechanisms has since been achieved, experimentally through systematic studies of the formation of intermediates and final products at variable temperatures, and interpretatively through an increasing understanding of the relationships between potential energy surfaces which determine possible paths for a molecule along an assumed reaction coordinate. Since progress has been reviewed periodically (*163*), the discussion is limited here to a brief summary of the main aspects.

6,6-Disubstituted dienones (**300**, Scheme 38) preferably undergo cleavage to diene ketenes (**301**); these have been detected spectroscopically by low-temperature irradiation (*161–163,219–223*) and have been found to revert thermally to **300** or to incorporate added nucleophiles to give **302**. The quantum yield for the transformation **300** → **302** (R = CH₃) is 0.6 (*163*) at room temperature in nonprotic solvent under optimal conditions for ketene trapping (e.g., in the presence of a strong nucleophile such as cyclohexylamine). On the other hand, **300** (R = CH₃) is almost inert in trifluoroethanol or when absorbed on silica gel (*162*).

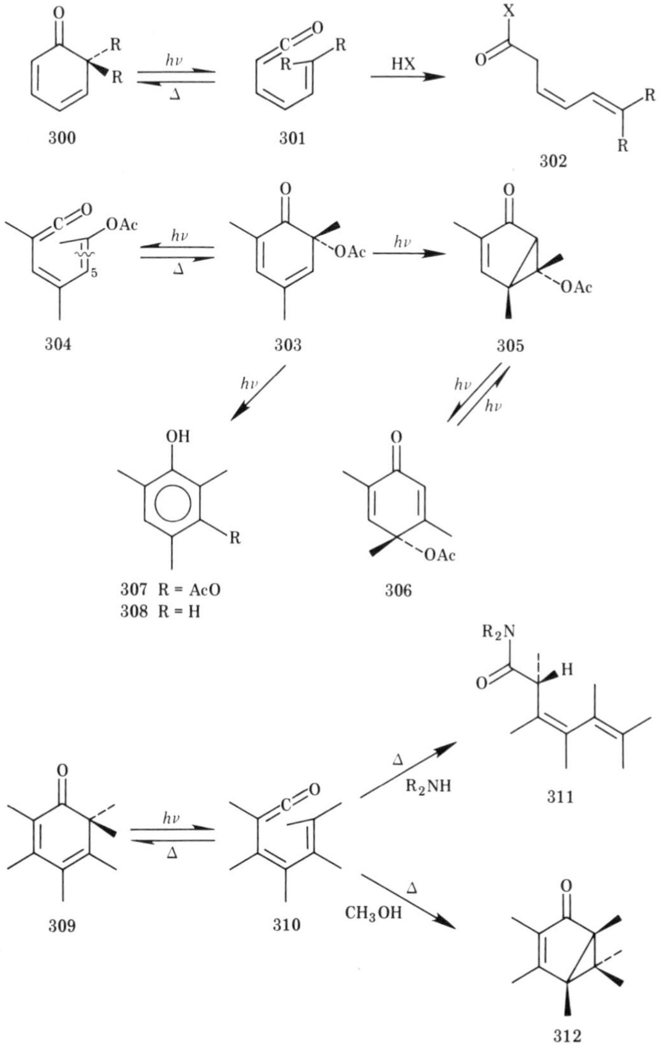

Scheme 38

The photochemical rearrangement to bicyclohexenone occurs only with somewhat more highly substituted dienones. For example, **303** still cleaved in methanol to the isomeric ketenes **304**, with a quantum yield of ≥0.42 (*163*). However, in trifluoroethanol or when **303** was adsorbed on silica gel, the picture changed dramatically. No ketene was formed. Instead, the bicyclohexenone **305** was formed in a highly stereoselective (*220*) rearrangement, followed by a reversible phototransformation to the cross-conjugated isomer **306** (see also *145,224*). Here, ketene was neither a thermal nor a photochemical precursor of bicyclohexenone. This has also been verified for some tetra- and pentamethylated 2,4-cyclohexadienones (*161,162*).

It has been shown that the photoreactivity of the fully methylated dienone **309** is again reduced to α cleavage (*124,161,225–227*). In the presence of strong nucleophiles (amines, but not in methanol alone), the ketene **310** could be trapped (→ **311**). Otherwise, **310** cyclized instead to starting material (**309**) and the bicyclohexenone **312** in *thermal* processes. The relatively low electrophilic reactivity of **310** and its enhanced tendency to reclose, in particular to **312** (formally a thermally allowed $_\pi 2_s$ + $_\pi 4_s$ addition), are obviously consequences of steric crowding. The quantum yield for ketene formation was 0.46 in methanol (with closure to **312** only), and it decreased with decreasing solvent polarity (which enhances the tendency of **310** to form **309**).

Since neither the ketene formation nor the rearrangement to bicyclohexenone could be triplet-sensitized or quenched with 1,3-dienes, these processes have been assumed by all authors to occur from excited singlet states. The quenching results alone have to be judged with caution. An inefficient ($\phi \leq 10^{-2}$) side reaction of **303** leading to acetoxymesitol (**307**) could be sensitized with donors of triplet energies as low as 42 kcal/mol (*163*). The lowest-lying triplet state of 2,4-cyclohexadienones may therefore not be amenable to exothermic energy transfer to dienes. The rearrangement **303** → **307** was shown (*218*) to be an intramolecular 1,2-acetoxyl migration, described in terms of neighboring-group participation by the acetoxyl group. It is accompanied, furthermore, by an equally inefficient homolytic cleavage of the acetoxyl group and aromatization to give phenol **308** (for an analogy, see Section I,A,5, Scheme 10, **69** → **72**).

The dependence of the reaction path selectivity on ring substitution and solvent polarity is paralleled by concomitant marked changes in the absorption spectra of the dienones. These show that the order in energy of the n,π^* and π,π^* singlet states varies as a function of the same factors. It has been concluded (*161–163,228*) that α cleavage to ketene is attributable to the n,π* singlet state, and the photochemical rearrangement to bicyclohexenone to the π,π* singlet state.

A refinement of this interpretation evolved from the treatment (229) of the α cleavage of 2,4-cyclohexadienones by means of qualitative state correlation diagrams. The ketene should originate from the biradical cleavage product with $^1D_{\sigma,\pi}$ rather than $^1D_{\sigma,\sigma}$ character. The dienone ground and excited singlet states correlate, as shown in Figs. 2 and 3, assuming a helical reaction geometry, which appears to be more plausible than the planar arrangement (163). The reaction path from a dienone with a lowest-lying $^1n,\pi^*$ state leads through a weakly avoided surface crossing to $^1D_{\sigma,\pi}$. In a case with a lowest-lying singlet with π,π* configuration, perturbation by system or solvent polarity may push the previously high-energy zwitterionic ground state Z below biradical states. Reaction of $^1\pi,\pi^*$ can then lead to Z, which has been considered a precursor of the bicyclohexenone products (163).

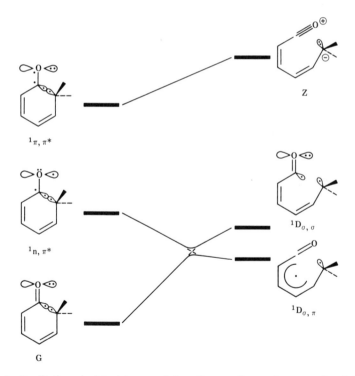

Fig. 2   Qualitative singlet state correlation diagram for α cleavage of a 2,4-cyclo-hexadienone with n,π* manifold below π,π* manifold.

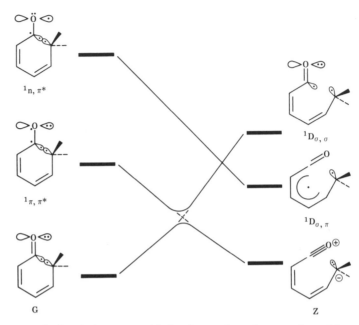

Fig. 3 Qualitative singlet state correlation diagram for α cleavage of a cyclohexadienone with π,π* manifold below n,π* manifold and a primary Z ground state product.

B. 2,4-Cycloheptadienones

Altogether four different photoreaction paths have been unraveled for 2,4-cycloheptadienone (**313a**, Scheme 39) (*230,231*) and three methyl-substituted homologues, **313b** (*230*), **313c** (*232–238*), and **313d** (*239*):

1. The bicyclo[3.2.0]heptenones **314a–d** are the only photoisomers that have been reported for all four dienones. Under the conditions of formation, the methyl homologues were normally subject to photochemical equilibration with the [1,3]-acyl-shifted isomers **318b–d** (Scheme 39), a photoreaction characteristic of β,γ-unsaturated ketones (*240*).

2. With **313a–c**, the norbornenones **315a–c** appeared additionally at the expense of **314a–c** when the irradiations were carried out in acidic solvents. Whereas only a trace of norbornenone **315a** was formed in 50% aqueous acetic acid (*230*), the percentages of **315b** and **315c** were higher, and they gradually increased with decreasing pH. The reaction to **315b** predominated in fluorosulfonic acid (*230*), and **315c** was accompanied by product **323c** (Scheme 40) in methanolic phosphate buffer solutions (*238*).

3. The product pattern of eucarvone (**313c**) contained still another isomer, **316c.** Further irradiation of this compound resulted in [1,3] sigmatropic shifts of the external allylic (→ **319**, Scheme 39) and of the

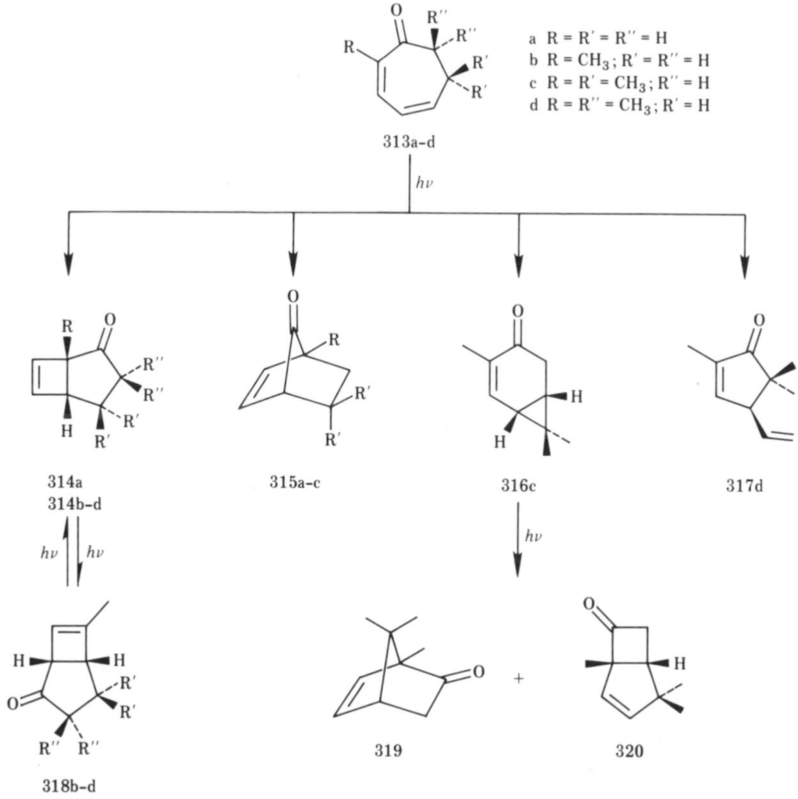

a R = R' = R'' = H
b R = CH₃; R' = R'' = H
c R = R' = CH₃; R'' = H
d R = R'' = CH₃; R' = H

313a-d

hv

314a
314b-d

315a-c

316c

317d

hv   hv

hv

318b-d

319   +   320

Scheme 39

internal cyclopropane bonds (→ 320); for analogous examples see Section I,A,8,a (Scheme 23) (*157*) and Essay 17 (*240*).

4. Finally, the predominant reaction of **313d** in cyclohexane was rearrangement to the vinylcyclopentenone **317d**. The products **314d** and **317d** formed much faster in trifluoroethanol, but no significant change in their ratio was observed. However, protonated **317d** was the sole initial photoproduct in fluorosulfonic acid at −78°C (*239*).

Triplet quenching and sensitization results with **313a** indicated that the bicycloheptenone **314a** originates from two excited states, presumably the singlet n,π* state and the π,π* triplet of an estimated energy between 65 and 70 kcal/mol (*231,235,238*). The formation of **316c** was attributed to the π,π* singlet (*236*).

The cyclization **313** → **314** seems simply to represent a photochemically allowed disrotatory closure of the diene moiety. Such a process might occur in both singlet and triplet excited state multiplicities. Nevertheless, one may also speculate that at least the triplet dienone rearranges first to either of the two possible (and not observed) ground state (E,Z) isomers, which only then would cyclize thermally to **314** in a conrotatory manner. The sequence is shown in Scheme 40 for the reaction of eucarvone (**313c**) via the arbitrarily chosen (E,Z) intermediate **321**. As a competing alternative in acidic solution, the pentadienyl cation system of protonated **321** could undergo another conrotatory electrocyclization to **322**, the obvious precursor to products **315c** and **323c** (see also **328** → **329**, Scheme 41).

The formation of both **316c** and **317d** has been formulated to occur via cleavage of the dienone 6,7 single bond (see **313c,d** → **324, 325**), although a

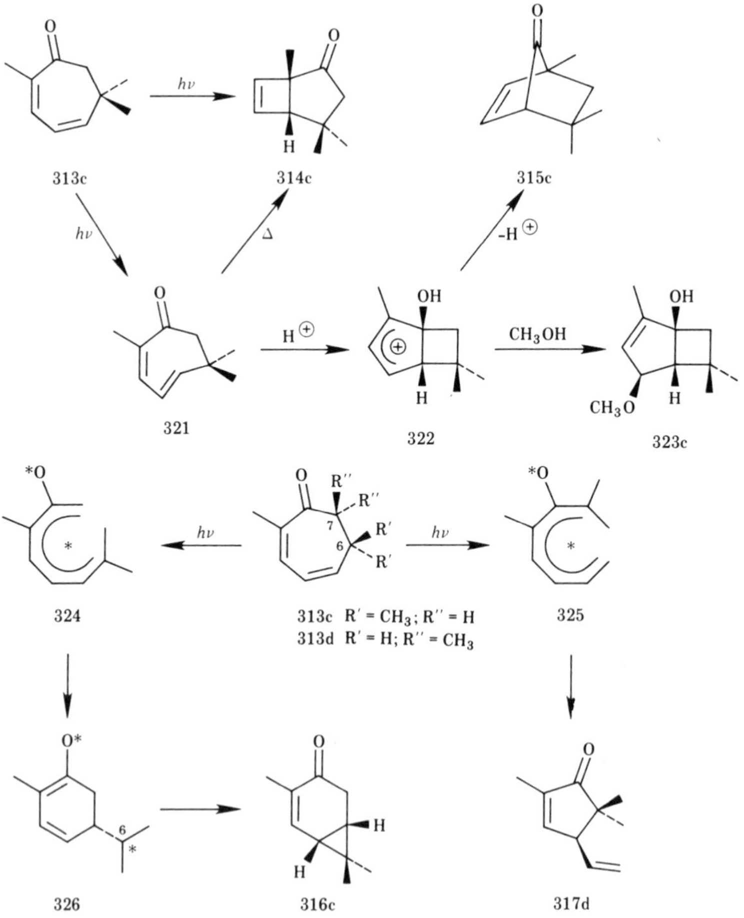

Scheme 40

direct ring contraction in a 1,2-alkyl shift to **326** remains an alternative for **316c**.

It has been shown *(241–243)* that $Z \rightarrow E$ isomerization of the double bond of triplet-excited 2,3-benzo- and 2,3-naphtho-2,4-cyclohepta-dienones is, in fact, the predominant reaction (see **327a–c** $\rightarrow$ **328a–c**, Scheme 41). The highly reactive E isomers were amenable to trapping with furan *(242)*. When formed in cyclohexane, they dimerized ($\rightarrow$ **330a,b, 333c, 334c**), whereas competitive transannular cyclization and solvent incorporation prevailed in methanol (**328a,b** $\rightarrow$ **329a,b**).

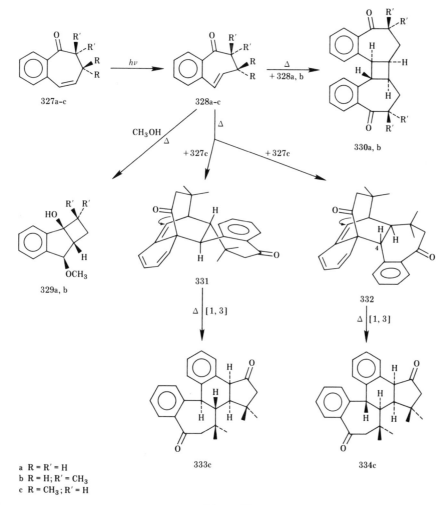

a R = R′ = H
b R = H; R′ = CH_3
c R = CH_3; R′ = H

Scheme 41

The stereochemistry of the cyclobutane dimers **330a** and **330b** is compatible with a $[_\pi 2_a + _\pi 2_s]$ addition of the two ground state (E) isomers **328**. In order to rationalize the formation of the dimers **333c** and **334c**, a thermal two-step sequence including a starting material (**327c**) and a photoproduct (**328c**) component was postulated. A $[_\pi 4_s + _\pi 2_s]$ addition of the (E) double bond of **328c** onto the styryl moiety of **327c** would be followed by a [1,3]-acyl shift in the adducts **331** and **332** (*241,242*).

C. 2,4-Cyclooctadienones

2,4-Cyclooctadienones undergo smooth $Z \rightarrow E$ isomerization of the 2,3 double bond (**335** $\rightarrow$ **336**, Scheme 42) (*244–247*). The failure of sensitization experiments with donor triplet energies ≥ 74 kcal/mol and of quenching by oxygen and 1,3-cyclohexadiene identified the excited singlet as the reactive state of **335** (*246*). It is noteworthy that an excited singlet state $Z \rightarrow E$ isomerization has also been reported for 2-cyclooctenones (*224,248*). A claim for evidence in favor of a triplet nature of the reaction **335** $\rightarrow$ **336** (*244*) may be owing to a neglect of residual direct light absorption by the dienone under sensitization conditions.

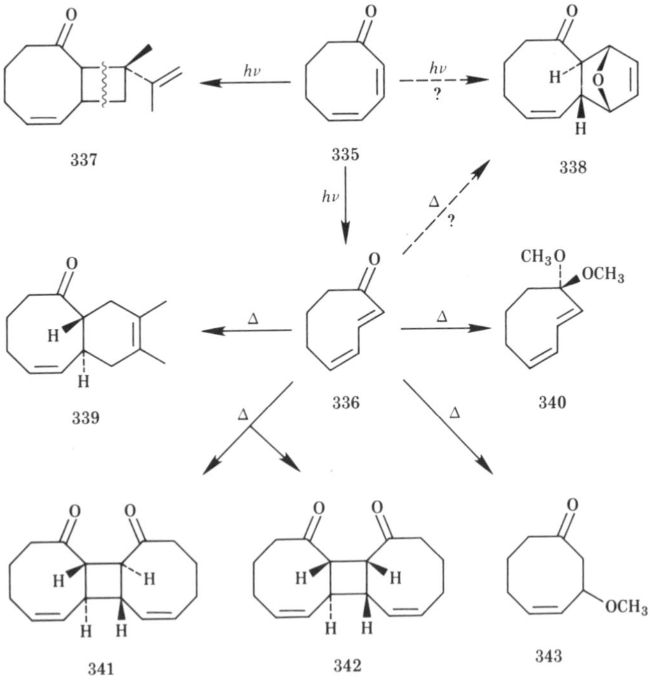

Scheme 42

The nature of the reactive photoisomer **336** was demonstrated in a number of trapping experiments. Irradiation of **335** at room temperature in the presence of an excess of 2,3-dimethyl-1,3-butadiene gave two types of adducts, **337** (head-to-head and/or head-to-tail) and **339**, and the dimers **341** and **342**. Adduct(s) **337** must have arisen from a photochemical [2 + 2] addition since it was not formed when the irradiation of **335** was carried out at −78°C and dimethylbutadiene was added afterward on warming to room temperature. Only the thermal [2 + 4] Diels–Alder adduct **339** and the dimers (**341** and **342**) were obtained in this experiment (*246*). On irradiation of **335** in methanolic solutions, the dimers were accompanied by the solvent adduct **343** and by the (*E,Z*)-ketal **340** in the presence of acid (*247*). The 44:56 ratio of the dimers **341** and **342** was independent of temperature, solvent, and concentration, but their formation competed with the addition of diene (→ **339**) when the latter was given to the low-temperature photolyzate. Products **339**, **341**, and **342** must therefore possess **336** as a

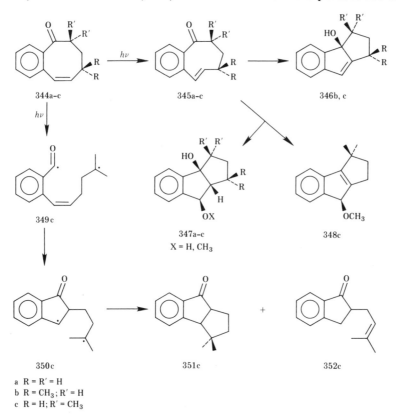

344a–c   345a–c   346b, c

349c   347a–c   X = H, CH₃   348c

350c   351c   352c

a   R = R' = H
b   R = CH₃; R' = H
c   R = H; R' = CH₃

Scheme 43

common precursor. It was concluded (246) that the dimers form in two steps from **336**—addition of two ground state dienones (**336**) and subsequent ring closure of the 1,4 biradical intermediate—rather than according to an earlier postulate (244) that triplet excited **335** adds to its ground state counterpart.

The formation of the trans-fused Diels–Alder adduct **338** on irradiation of **335** in a 1 : 1 ether–furan mixture has been observed (244). The question remains as to whether the product originates from a photochemical addition of furan (to **335**) or a thermal [2 + 4] addition (to **336**).

Similar to the 2,3-benzo-2,4-cycloheptadienones (Scheme 41), the corresponding eight-membered ring homologues **344a–c** isomerized around the 4,5 double bond to give the (E) compounds **345a–c** (Scheme 43) (249). Whereas **345a** and **345b** were sufficiently stable in ether solution to allow spectroscopic analysis, product **345c** spontaneously cyclized under any irradiation conditions (to **346c**, and to **347c** and **348c** in methanol), as did **345a** and **345b** (to **346b** and **347a,b**), depending on the solvents used in the irradiations and on the work-up conditions.

α,α-Dimethyl substitution introduced still another photoreaction mode in the benzocyclooctadienone **344c**, which had not been encountered with the cycloheptadienone analogue **327b**. The formation of the isomeric ketones **351c** and **352c**, which competed with the double-bond isomerization, was attributed to α cleavage ($\rightarrow$ **349c**) and subsequent cyclization (**349c** $\rightarrow$ **350c** $\rightarrow$ **351c**) and 1,4-hydrogen shift processes (**350c** $\rightarrow$ **352c**) (249).

D. 2,4,6-Cyclooctatrienones

The early studies of the photochemistry of the parent 2,4,6-cyclooctatrienone (**353**, Scheme 44) gave the following results (250): isomerization in pentane to the bicyclic ketone **355** and ring cleavage and formation of diastereoisomeric methyl octatrienoates (**359**) in methanol. In a subsequent study employing low-temperature techniques (251), the details of the two reaction paths were elaborated. They are initiated by competing α cleavage and $Z \rightarrow E$ isomerization of the 2,3 double bond. The resulting primary photoproducts, triene ketene **358** and (E,Z,Z)-trienone **354**, respectively, could be analyzed by infrared spectroscopy at liquid-nitrogen temperature. Each is subject to competing thermal transformations. The ketene **358** recyclized back to starting material unless it was captured nucleophilically by added methanol ($\rightarrow$ **359**). The double-bond photoisomerization to **354** was also thermally reversible, in competition with a conrotatory cyclization of the (E,Z)-diene moiety to isomer **355** and with [2 + 4] trapping of the (E) double bond by added furan, furnishing the trans-fused adducts **356** and **357**. The possibility of a photochemical dis-

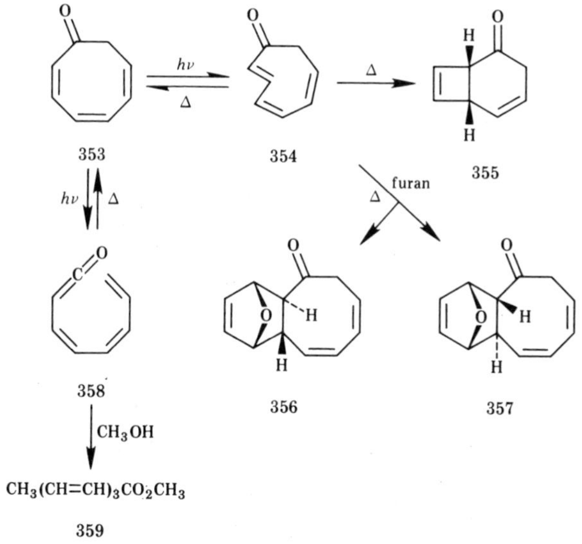

353 354 355

358

356 357

CH₃OH

$CH_3(CH=CH)_3CO_2CH_3$

359

Scheme 44

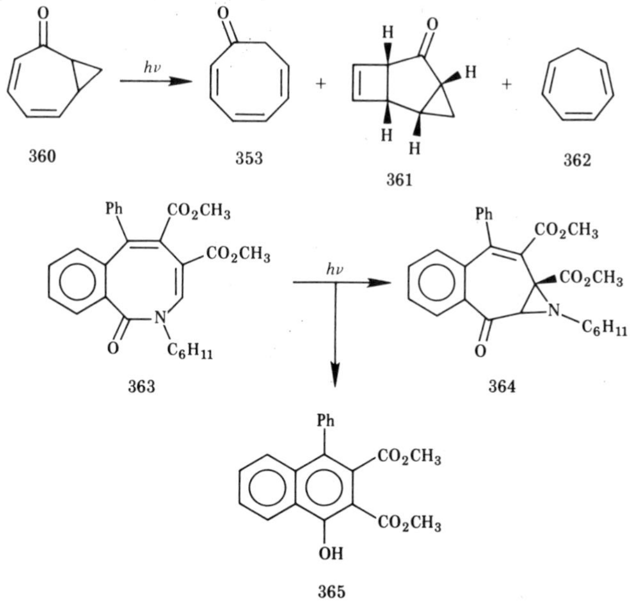

360 353 361 362

363 364

365

Scheme 45

rotatory cyclization of 353 to 355 was ruled out by the observation that the formation of 355 at room temperature was a function of furan concentration and consequently competed with the trapping reaction.

2,3-Homotropone (360, Scheme 45) could have been expected to be among the photoproducts of cyclooctratrienone 353, in analogy to the oxadi-π-methane type of rearrangements of 2,4-cyclohexadienones to bicyclohexenones (see 303 → 305, Scheme 38) and of $^3\pi,\pi^*$ excited β,γ-unsaturated ketones in general (240). The reverse reaction, 360 → 353, did take place, but with concomitant formation of other photoproducts (361, 362), which arose from homotropone (360) and were not detectable in the photolyzate of 353 (252). The major photoproduct was, in fact, 361. It has not been rigorously established yet whether this compound was derived directly from excited 360 (disrotatory cyclization) or from an undetected (E,Z) photoisomer of 360 in a thermal conrotatory closure.

The aziridine 364, a heteroanalogue of homotropone, was, however, the major photoproduct of 363 (253). N-Cyclohexylformamide and 365, formed additionally as minor components, probably resulted from α cleavage of the OC—N bond to ketene followed by cyclization and hydrolysis (on work-up).

E. Reactions from Upper Excited States

2-Cyclohexenone derivatives are among the substances that in recent years have been found to react from upper excited states in competition with relaxation to the lowest excited state(s). Such deviations from the conventional model of fast relaxation of higher excited states prior to photochemical reaction have recently been reviewed and discussed (254).

Heteroannular dienones of the basic type 366 (Scheme 46) normally do not show any notable unimolecular photoreactivity. Rather, they undergo dimerizations and addition of olefinic cosolutes [for leading references see Schaffner (154) and Horspool (255)]. The dienones 366, 368, 370, and 371 are exceptional in this respect, and they are capable of reacting from a state above the lowest singlet (n,π^*) and triplet (n,π^* and π,π^*) states. In close analogy to the corresponding α,β-unsaturated enones, they were found to undergo specifically ($\pi \to \pi^*$)-induced photochemical transformations to 367 (25% yield) (114), 369 (30%) (115), 372 (72%) (256), and 373 (17%) (256). Excitation to the lowest-lying singlet state, S_1 (n,π^*), was ineffective.

Studies with the enone analogues of 366 and 368 and with related systems (114) have shown that the lowest-lying triplet states (^{3}n,π^* and $^3\pi,\pi^*$), which are accessible through intersystem crossing from S_1, react differently and that the quantum yield of the specifically ($\pi \to \pi^*$)-induced

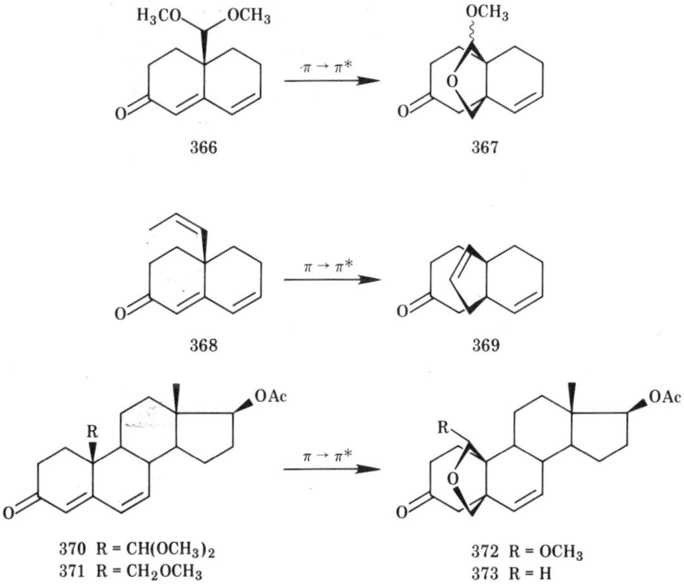

Scheme 46

product formation is not wavelength dependent within the $\pi \to \pi^*$ absorption band. The reactive excited state is therefore probably S_2 (the lowest π,π^* singlet manifold), although intersystem crossing from S_2 to a T_3 state and reaction from the latter remains, in principle, an alternative. Extrapolation of this conclusion to the case of the dienones appears to be plausible. Furthermore, in the case of dimethoxymethylenones there is evidence that the ring closure to hemicyclic acetal product involves a direct transfer of a methoxyl hydrogen to the enone α-carbon (*114,257*).

REFERENCES

1. J. L. Simonsen and D. H. R. Barton, "The Terpenes," Vol. III, pp. 292–295. Cambridge Univ. Press, London and New York. 1952.
2. H. Staudinger and S. Bereza, *Justus Liebigs Ann. Chem.* **380**, 243 (1911).
3. D. Arigoni, H. Bosshard, H. Bruderer, G. Büchi, O. Jeger, and L. J. Krebaum, *Helv. Chim. Acta* **40**, 1732 (1957).
4. D. H. R. Barton, P. de Mayo, and M. Shafiq, *J. Chem. Soc.* p. 929 (1957).
5. D. H. R. Barton, P. de Mayo, and M. Shafiq, *Proc. Chem. Soc., London* p. 205 (1957); *J. Chem. Soc.* p. 140 (1958).
6. D. H. R. Barton and P. T. Gilham, *J. Chem. Soc.* p. 4596 (1960).
7. D. H. R. Barton, P. de Mayo, and M. Shafiq, *Proc. Chem. Soc., London* p. 345 (1957); *J. Chem. Soc.* p. 3314 (1958).

8. E. E. van Tamelen, S. H. Levin, G. Brenner, J. Wolinsky, and P. E. Aldrich, *J. Am. Chem. Soc.* **81**, 1666 (1959).
9. J. D. M. Asher and G. A. Sim, *J. Chem. Soc.* p. 1584 (1965).
10. D. H. R. Barton, J. T. Pinhey, and R. J. Wells, *J. Chem. Soc.* p. 2518 (1964).
11. H. Dutler, H. Bosshard, and O. Jeger, *Helv. Chim. Acta* **40**, 494 (1957).
12. D. H. R. Barton and W. C. Taylor, *Proc. Chem. Soc., London* **96**, 147 (1957); *J. Am. Chem. Soc.* **80**, 244 (1958); *J. Chem. Soc.* p. 2500 (1958).
13. H. E. Zimmerman, *Adv. Photochem.* **1**, 183 (1963).
14. O. L. Chapman, *Adv. Photochem.* **1**, 323 (1963).
15. K. Schaffner, *Adv. Photochem.* **4**, 81 (1966).
16. P. J. Kropp, *Org. Photochem.* **1**, 1 (1967).
17. O. L. Chapman and D. S. Weiss, *Org. Photochem.* **3**, 197 (1973).
18. D. I. Schuster, *Acc. Chem. Res.* **11**, 65 (1978).
19. W. Cocker, K. Crowley, J. T. Edward, T. B. H. McMurry, and E. R. Stuart, *J. Chem. Soc.* p. 3416 (1957).
20. O. L. Chapman and L. F. Englert, *J. Am. Chem. Soc.* **85**, 3028 (1963).
21. M. H. Fisch and J. H. Richards, *J. Am. Chem. Soc.* **85**, 3029 (1963); *90*, 1547 and 1553 (1968).
22. F. Frei, C. Ganter, K. Kägi, K. Kocsiś, M. Miljković, A. Siewinski, R. Wenger, K. Schaffner, and O. Jeger, *Helv. Chim. Acta* **49** 1049 (1966).
23. R. B. Woodward and R. Hoffmann, "The Conservation of Orbital Symmetry." Academic Press, New York, 1970.
24. C. Ganter, E. C. Utzinger, K. Schaffner, D. Arigoni, and O. Jeger, *Helv. Chim. Acta* **45**, 2403 (1962).
25. P. J. Kropp and W. F. Erman, *J. Am. Chem. Soc.* **85**, 2456 (1963).
26. H. E. Zimmerman and D. I. Schuster, *J. Am. Chem. Soc.* **83**, 4486 (1961); **84**, 4527 (1962).
27. H. E. Zimmerman, *Tetrahedron* **19**, Suppl. 2, 393 (1963); *Pure Appl. Chem.* **9**, 493 (1964).
28. G. A. Taylor, *Chem. Commun.* p. 896 (1967).
28a. J. K. Stille, T. A. Rettig, and E. W. Kuemmerle, Jr., *J. Org. Chem.* **41**, 2950 (1976).
29. T. Tezuka, *Tetrahedron Lett.* p. 5677 (1968).
30. D. I. Schuster, A. C. Fabian, N. P. Kong, W. C. Barringer, W. V. Curran, and D. H. Sussman, *J. Am. Chem. Soc.* **90**, 5027 (1968).
31. D. I. Schuster and A. C. Fabian, *Tetrahedron Lett.* p. 1301 (1968).
32. H. E. Zimmerman and J. S. Swenton, *J. Am. Chem. Soc.* **86**, 1436 (1964); **89**, 906 (1967).
33. J. Hoigné, K. Schaffner, and R. Wenger, *Helv. Chim. Acta* **48**, 527 (1965).
34. H. E. Zimmerman, R. W. Binkley, J. J. McCullough, and G. A. Zimmerman, *J. Am. Chem. Soc.* **89**, 6589 (1967).
35. D. I. Schuster and D. J. Patel, *J. Am. Chem. Soc.* **90**, 5145 (1968).
36. A. A. Lamola, *Tech. Org. Chem.* **14**, 81 (1969).
37. D. I. Schuster and N. K. Lau, *Mol. Photochem.* **1**, 415 (1969).
38. D. I. Schuster and K. V. Prabhu, *J. Am. Chem. Soc.* **96**, 3511 (1974).
39. G. Marsh, D. R. Kearns, and M. H. Fisch, *J. Am. Chem. Soc.* **92**, 2252 (1970).
40. D. I. Schuster and W. C. Barringer, *J. Am. Chem. Soc.* **93**, 731 (1971).
41. P. J. Wagner and J. Nakahira, *J. Am. Chem. Soc.* **95**, 8474 (1973), and references cited.
42. H. E. Zimmerman, G. E. Keck, and J. L. Pflederer, *J. Am. Chem. Soc.* **98**, 5574 (1976).
42a. N. J. Turro and A. Devaquet, *J. Am. Chem. Soc.* **97**, 3859 (1975), and references cited.
43. M. Demuth, C. O. Bender, S. E. Braslavsky, H. Görner, U. Burger, W. Amrein, and K. Schaffner, *Helv. Chim. Acta* **62**, 847 (1979).

43a. M. Demuth, D. Lemmer, and K. Schaffner, *J. Am. Chem. Soc.* **102**, in press (1980).
43b. M. Demuth, U. Burger, H. W. Mueller, and K. Schaffner, *J. Am. Chem. Soc.* **101**, 6763 (1979).
44. A. Mazzenga, D. Lomnitz, J. Villegas, and C. J. Polowczyk, *Tetrahedron Lett.* p. 1665 (1969).
45. G. W. Griffin, J. Covell, R. C. Petterson, R. M. Dodson, and G. Klose, *J. Am. Chem. Soc.* **87**, 1410 (1965), and subsequent papers.
46. D. I. Schuster and I. S. Krull, *J. Am. Chem. Soc.* **88**, 3456 (1966).
47. J. S. Swenton, E. Saurborn, R. Srinivasan, and F. I. Sonntag, *J. Am. Chem. Soc.* **90**, 2990 (1968).
48. W. H. Pirkle, S. G. Smith, and G. F. Koser, *J. Am. Chem. Soc.* **91**, 1580 (1969).
49. D. H. R. Barton, *Proc. Chem. Soc., London* p. 61 (1958); *Helv. Chim. Acta* **42**, 2604 (1959).
50. K. Weinberg, E. C. Utzinger, D. Arigoni, and O. Jeger, *Helv. Chim. Acta* **43**, 236 (1960).
51. D. H. R. Barton, J. E. D. Levisalles, and J. T. Pinhey, *J. Chem. Soc.* p. 3472 (1962).
52. D. H. R. Barton, T. Miki, J. T. Pinhey, and R. J. Wells, *Proc. Chem. Soc., London* p. 112 (1962).
53. P. J. Kropp, *J. Am. Chem. Soc.* **85**, 3779 (1963).
54. D. Caine and J. B. Dawson, *J. Org. Chem.* **29**, 3108 (1964).
55. P. J. Kropp, *J. Org. Chem.* **29**, 3110 (1964).
56. P. J. Kropp, *J. Am. Chem. Soc.* **86**, 4053 (1964).
57. D. Caine and J. F. DeBardeleben, Jr., *Tetrahedron Lett.* p. 4585 (1965).
58. W. E. Hymans and P. J. Kropp, cited in Schuster (*18*).
59. J. Streith and A. Blind, *Bull. Soc. Chim. Fr.* p. 2133 (1968).
60. K. Schaffner-Sabba, *Helv. Chim. Acta* **52**, 1237 (1969).
61. E. Piers and K. F. Cheng, *Chem. Commun.* p. 562 (1969); *Can. J. Chem.* **48**, 2234 (1970).
62. D. Caine and P. F. Ingwalson, *J. Org. Chem.* **37**, 3751 (1972).
63. M. Shiozaki, K. Mori, M. Matsui, and T. Hiraoka, *Tetrahedron Lett.* p. 657 (1972).
64. J. P. Pete and J. L. Wolfhugel, *Tetrahedron Lett.* p. 4637 (1973).
65. D. Caine and F. N. Tuller, *J. Am. Chem. Soc.* **93**, 6311 (1971); *J. Org. Chem.* **38**, 3663 (1973).
66. D. Caine, J. T. Gupton, III, K. Ming, and W. J. Powers, III, *Chem. Commun.* p. 469 (1973).
67. D. Caine, P. F. Brake, J. F. DeBardeleben, Jr., and J. B. Dawson, *J. Org. Chem.* **38**, 967 (1973).
68. D. Caine and J. T. Gupton, III, *J. Org. Chem.* **40**, 809 (1975).
69. S. Gasa, N. Hamanaka, S. Matsunaga, T. Okuno, N. Takeda, and T. Matsumoto, *Tetrahedron Lett.* p. 553 (1976).
70. D. Caine and A. S. Forbese, *Tetrahedron Lett.* p. 3107 (1977).
70a. J. R. Williams, R. H. Moore, R. Li, and J. F. Blount, *J. Am. Chem. Soc.* **101**, 5019 (1979); J. R. Williams, R. H. Moore, R. Li, and C. M. Weeks, *J. Org. Chem.* **45**, in press (1980).
71. P. J. Kropp, *J. Am. Chem. Soc.* **87**, 3914 (1965).
72. H. E. Zimmerman, D. Döpp, and P. S. Huyffer, *J. Am. Chem. Soc.* **88**, 5352 (1966).
73. H. E. Zimmerman and D. S. Crumrine, *J. Am. Chem. Soc.* **90**, 5612 (1968).
74. H. E. Zimmerman, D. S. Crumrine, D. Döpp, and P. S. Huyffer, *J. Am. Chem. Soc.* **91**, 434 (1969).
75. H. E. Zimmerman and G. A. Epling, *J. Am. Chem. Soc.* **94**, 7806 (1972).
76. T. M. Brennan and R. K. Hill, *J. Am. Chem. Soc.* **90**, 5614 (1968).

77. H. E. Zimmerman and J. O. Grunewald, *J. Am. Chem. Soc.* **89**, 3354 and 5163 (1967).
78. D. J. Patel and D. I. Schuster, *J. Am. Chem. Soc.* **90**, 5137 (1968).
79. D. I. Schuster and V. Y. Abraitys, *Chem. Commun.* p. 419 (1969).
80. D. I. Schuster and K.-C. Liu, *J. Am. Chem. Soc.* **93**, 6711 (1971).
81. D. I. Schuster, *Pure Appl. Chem.* **41**, 601 (1975).
82. E. B. Keil and J. W. Pavlik, *J. Heterocycl. Chem.* **13**, 1149 (1976).
83. J. W. Pavlik and L. T. Pauliukonis, *Tetrahedron Lett.* p. 1939 (1976).
84. C. Ganter, R. Warszawski, H. Wehrli, K. Schaffner, and O. Jeger, *Helv. Chim. Acta* **46**, 320 (1963).
85. E. R. Altwicker and C. D. Cook, *J. Org. Chem.* **29**, 3087 (1964).
86. A. Rieker and N. Zeller, *Tetrahedron Lett.* p. 463 (1968).
87. T. Matsuura and K. Ogura, *Tetrahedron* **24**, 6167 (1968).
88. K. Ogura and T. Matsuura, *Bull. Chem. Soc. Jpn.* **43**, 3187 (1970).
89. G. F. Burkinshaw, B. R. Davis, and P. D. Woodgate, *Chem. Commun.* p. 607 (1967); *J. Chem. Soc. C* p. 1607 (1970).
90. A. Nishinaga, T. Itahara, and T. Matsuura, *Chem. Ber.* **109**, 1530 (1976).
91. M. H. Fisch, *Chem. Commun.* p. 1472 (1969).
92. D. I. Schuster and D. J. Patel, *J. Am. Chem. Soc.* **87**, 2515 (1965).
93. D. I. Schuster, G. C. Barile, and K.-C. Liu, *J. Am. Chem. Soc.* **97**, 4441 (1975).
94. D. I. Schuster and G. C. Barile, *Tetrahedron Lett.* p. 3017 (1976).
95. H. E. Zimmerman and G. Jones, II, *J. Am. Chem. Soc.* **91**, 5678 (1969); **92**, 2753 (1970).
96. T. Matsuura, *Bull. Chem. Soc. Jpn.* **37**, 564 (1964); T. Matsuura and K. Ogura, *J. Am. Chem. Soc.* **89**, 3846 (1967).
97. R. Warszawski, K. Schaffner, and O. Jeger, *Helv. Chim. Acta* **43**, 500 (1960).
98. D. I. Schuster and C. J. Polowczyk, *J. Am. Chem. Soc.* **86**, 4502 (1964); **88**, 1722 (1966).
99. D. I. Schuster and I. S. Krull, *Tetrahedron Lett.* p. 135 (1968); *Mol. Photochem.* **1**, 107 (1969).
100. B. Nann, H. Wehrli, K. Schaffner, and O. Jeger, *Helv. Chim. Acta* **48**, 1680 (1965).
101. J. Pfister, H. Wehrli, and K. Schaffner, *Helv. Chim. Acta* **50**, 166 (1967).
102. P. J. Kropp and H. J. Krauss, *J. Org. Chem.* **32**, 4118 (1967).
103. L. D. Hess, J. L. Jacobson, K. Schaffner, and J. N. Pitts, Jr., *J. Am. Chem. Soc.* **89**, 3684 (1967).
104. W. H. Pirkle and W. B. Lunsford, *J. Am. Chem. Soc.* **94**, 7201 (1972).
105. D. Taub, C. H. Kuo, H. L. Slates, and N. L. Wendler, *Tetrahedron* **19**, 1 (1963).
106. K. Ogura and T. Matsuura, *Bull. Chem. Soc. Jpn.* **43**, 3181 (1970).
107. H. Lind and H. Loeliger, *Tetrahedron Lett.* p. 2569 (1976).
108. H. Dutler, C. Ganter, H. Ryf, E. C. Utzinger, K. Weinberg, K. Schaffner, D. Arigoni, and O. Jeger, *Helv. Chim. Acta* **45**, 2346 (1962).
109. C. Ganter, F. Greuter, D. Kägi, K. Schaffner, and O. Jeger, *Helv. Chim. Acta* **47**, 627 (1964).
110. L. Lorenc, M. Miljković, K. Schaffner, and O. Jeger, *Helv. Chim. Acta* **49**, 1183 (1966).
111. E. Pfenninger, D. E. Poel, C. Berse, H. Wehrli, K. Schaffner, and O. Jeger, *Helv. Chim. Acta* **51**, 772 (1968).
112. P. J. Kropp, *Tetrahedron Lett.* p. 3647 (1964).
113. D. Belluš, D. R. Kearns, and K. Schaffner, *Helv. Chim. Acta* **52**, 971 (1969).
114. J. Gloor and K. Schaffner, *Helv. Chim. Acta* **57**, 1815 (1974).
115. F. Nobs, U. Burger, and K. Schaffner, *Helv. Chim. Acta* **60**, 1607 (1977).
116. D. H. R. Barton, J. F. McGhie, and M. Rosenberger, *J. Chem. Soc.* p. 1215 (1961).

117. K. Tsuda, E. Ohki, J. Suzuki, and H. Shimizu, *Chem. Pharm. Bull.* **9**, 131 (1961).
118. P. J. Kropp, *Tetrahedron* **21**, 2183 (1965).
119. J. King and D. Leaver, *Chem. Commun.* p. 539 (1965).
120. H. Hart and D. C. Lankin, *J. Org. Chem.* **33**, 4398 (1968).
121. W. V. Curran and D. I. Schuster, *Chem. Commun.* p. 699 (1968).
122. D. I. Schuster and W. V. Curran, *J. Am. Chem. Soc.* **35**, 4192 (1970).
123. D. I. Schuster, K. V. Prabhu, S. Adcock, J. van der Veen, and H. Fujiwara, *J. Am. Chem. Soc.* **93**, 1557 (1971).
124. H. Hart and R. J. Bastiani, *J. Org. Chem.* **37**, 4018 (1972).
125. H. Hart and M. Nitta, *Tetrahedron Lett.* p. 2113 (1974).
126. D. Caine and C.-Y. Chu, *Tetrahedron Lett.* p. 703 (1974).
127. W. J. Seifert, H. Perst, and W. Dannenberg, *Tetrahedron Lett.* p. 4999 (1973).
128. G. Bozzato, H. P. Throndsen, K. Schaffner, and O. Jeger, *J. Am. Chem. Soc.* **86**, 2073 (1964).
129. T. Matsuura, Y. Sata, K. Ogura, and M. Mori, *Tetrahedron Lett.* p. 4627 (1968).
130. M. D. Cohen and G. M. J. Schmidt, *J. Chem. Soc.* p. 1996 (1964), and subsequent papers.
131. D. Caine, W. J. Powers, III, and A. M. Alejandre, *Tetrahedron Lett.* p. 6071 (1968).
132. D. Caine, A. M. Alejandre, K. Ming, and W. J. Powers, III, *J. Org. Chem.* **37**, 706 (1972).
133. E. Altenburger, H. Wehrli, and K. Schaffner, *Helv. Chim. Acta* **46**, 2753 (1963).
134. B. Miller and H. Margulies, *Chem. Commun.* p. 314 (1965); *J. Am. Chem. Soc.* **89**, 1678 (1967).
135. B. Miller, *Chem. Commun.* p. 327 (1966); *J. Am. Chem. Soc.* **87**, 5515 (1965); **89**, 1684 (1967).
136. D. H. Hey, G. H. Jones, and M. J. Perkins, *Chem. Commun.* p. 47 (1971).
137. Z. Horii, M. Aoi, and Y. Hayashi, *Chem. Commun.* p. 210 (1972).
138. D. G. Hewitt and R. F. Taylor, *Chem. Commun.* p. 493 (1972).
139. P. Margaretha, *Helv. Chim. Acta* **59**, 661 (1976).
140. J. J. Houser, M.-C. Chen, and S. S. Wang, *J. Org. Chem.* **39**, 1387 (1974).
141. S. M. Kupchan, C.-K. Kim, and K. Miyano, *Chem. Commun.* p. 91 (1976).
142. K. Ogura and T. Matsuura, *Bull. Chem. Soc. Jpn.* **43**, 2891 (1970).
143. T. Matsuura, Y. Hiromoto, A. Okada, and K. Ogura, *Tetrahedron* **29**, 2981 (1973).
144. K. Schaffner and G. Snatzke, *Helv. Chim. Acta* **48**, 347 (1965).
145. T. R. Rodgers and H. Hart, *Tetrahedron Lett.* p. 4845 (1969).
146. D. I. Schuster, K. V. Prabhu, S. Adcock, J. van der Veen, and H. Fujiwara, *J. Am. Chem. Soc.* **93**, 1557 (1971).
147. B. Miller, *J. Am. Chem. Soc.* **89**, 1690 (1967).
148. H. V. Secor, M. Bourlas, and J. F. DeBardeleben, Jr., *Experientia* **27**, 18 (1971).
149. W. L. Mock and K. A. Rumon, *J. Org. Chem.* **37**, 400 (1972).
150. K. Schaffner, *Pure Appl. Chem., Suppl.* **1**, 405 (1971).
151. K. Ogura and T. Matsuura, *Tetrahedron* **26**, 445 (1970).
152. I. V. Khudyakov, I. Y. Aliev, and V. A. Kuz'min, *Izv. Akad. Nauk SSSR, Ser. Khim.* p. 2598 (1975); *Chem. Abstr.* **84**, 58225 (1976).
153. R. E. Harmon and B. L. Jensen, *J. Heterocycl. Chem.* **7**, 1077 (1970).
154. K. Schaffner, *in* "Organic Reactions in Steroid Chemistry" (J. Fried and J. A. Edwards, eds.), Vol. II, p. 288. Van Nostrand-Reinhold, Princeton, New Jersey, 1972.
155. H. E. Zimmerman, R. C. Hahn, H. Morrison, and M. C. Wani, *J. Am. Chem. Soc.* **87**, 1138 (1965).
156. H. E. Zimmerman, R. D. Rieke, and J. R. Scheffer, *J. Am. Chem. Soc.* **89**, 2033 (1967).

157. O. L. Chapman, *Pure Appl. Chem., Suppl.* **1**, 311 (1971).
158. L. Barber, O. L. Chapman, and J. D. Lassila, *J. Am. Chem. Soc.* **90**, 5933 (1968).
159. J. W. Wheeler, Jr. and R. H. Eastman, *J. Am. Chem. Soc.* **81**, 236 (1959).
160. R. Jacquier and J. Soulier, *Bull. Soc. Chim. Fr.* p. 1284 (1962).
161. J. Griffiths and H. Hart, *J. Am. Chem. Soc.* **90**, 3297 (1968).
162. J. Griffiths and H. Hart, *J. Am. Chem. Soc.* **90**, 5296 (1968).
163. G. Quinkert, *Photochem. Photobiol.* **7**, 783 (1968); *Angew. Chem.* **84**, 1157 (1972); **87**, 851 (1975); *Angew. Chem., Int. Ed. Engl.* **11**, 1072 (1972); **14**, 790 (1975); *Pure Appl. Chem.* **33**, 285 (1973).
164. L. L. Barber, O. L. Chapman, and J. D. Lassila, *J. Am. Chem. Soc.* **91**, 3664 (1969).
165. O. L. Chapman, J. C. Clardy, T. L. McDowell, and H. E. Wright, *J. Am. Chem. Soc.* **95**, 5086 (1973).
166. H. E. Zimmerman, R. Keese, J. Nasielski, and J. S. Swenton, *J. Am. Chem. Soc.* **88**, 4895 (1966).
167. M. Hirakura and M. Yanagita, *J. Org. Chem.* **27**, 2948 (1962).
168. A. M. Small, *Chem. Commun.* p. 243 (1965).
169. N. Ishibe, M. Odani, and M. Sunami, *Chem. Commun.* p. 1034 (1971).
170. N. Ishibe, M. Sunami, and M. Odani, *J. Am. Chem. Soc.* **95**, 463 (1973).
171. N. Ishibe, and J. Masui, *J. Am. Chem. Soc.* **95**, 3396 (1973); **96**, 1152 (1974).
172. N. Ishibe, S. Yutaka, J. Masui, and Y. Ishida, *Chem. Commun.* p. 241 (1975).
173. R. Wenger, H. Dutler, H. Wehrli, K. Schaffner, and O. Jeger, *Helv. Chim. Acta* **45**, 2420 (1962).
174. J. A. Marshall and P. C. Johnson, *J. Org. Chem.* **35**, 192 (1970).
175. D. Caine, A. A. Boncugnani, and W. R. Pennington, *J. Org. Chem.* **41**, 3632 (1976).
176. G. Büchi, J. M. Kauffman, and H. J. E. Loewenthal, *J. Am. Chem. Soc.* **88**, 3403 (1966).
177. E. H. White, S. Eguchi, and J. N. Mark, *Tetrahedron* **25**, 2099 (1969).
178. G. Büchi, H. Hofheinz, and J. V. Pankstelis, *J. Am. Chem. Soc.* **91**, 6473 (1969).
179. J. A. Marshall and J. A. Ruth, *J. Org. Chem.* **39**, 1971 (1974).
180. N. Sugiyama, Y. Sato, and C. Kashima, *Bull. Chem. Soc. Jpn.* **43**, 3205 (1970).
181. J. W. Hanifin and E. Cohen, *J. Org. Chem.* **36**, 910 (1971).
182. M. Shiozaki and T. Hiraoka, *Tetrahedron Lett.* p. 4655 (1972).
183. T. Matsuura, T. Takemoto, and R. Nakashima, *Tetrahedron* **29**, 3337 (1973).
184. S. C. Gupta and S. K. Mukerjee, *Tetrahedron Lett.* p. 5073 (1973).
185. N. Ishibe and M. Odani, *Chem. Commun.* p. 702 (1971).
186. N. Ishibe, M. Odani, and R. Tanuma, *J. Chem. Soc., Perkin Trans. I* p. 1203 (1972).
187. N. Sugiyama, T. Sato, H. Kataoka, C. Kashima, and K. Yamada, *Bull. Chem. Soc. Jpn.* **42**, 3005 (1969).
188. H. Aoyama, Y. Sato, T. Nishio, and N. Sugiyama, *Bull. Chem. Soc. Jpn.* **46**, 1007 (1973).
189. N. Ishibe, K. Hasimoto, and M. Sunami, *J. Org. Chem.* **39**, 103 (1974).
190. T. H. Koch, J. A. Sonderquist, and T. H. Kinstle, *J. Am. Chem. Soc.* **96**, 5576 (1974).
191. H. Nozaki, M. Kurita, and R. Noyori, *Tetrahedron Lett.* p. 3635 (1968).
192. R. Noyori and M. Katô, *Tetrahedron Lett.* p. 5075 (1968).
193. J. K. Crandall and R. P. Haseltine, *J. Am. Chem. Soc.* **90**, 6251 (1968).
194. R. Noyori, Y. Ohnishi, and M. Katô, *Tetrahedron Lett.* p. 1515 (1971).
195. J. F. Liebman and A. Greenberg, *Chem. Rev.* **76**, 311 (1976), and references cited.
196. G. Maier, U. Schäfer, W. Sauer, H. Hartau, R. Matusch, and J. F. M. Oth, *Tetrahedron Lett.* p. 1837 (1978).

197. G. Maier, S. Pfriem, U. Schäfer, and R. Matusch, *Angew. Chem.* **90**, 552 (1978); *Angew. Chem., Int. Ed. Engl.* **17**, 520 (1978).
198. B. Fuchs and M. Pasternak, *Chem. Commun.* p. 537 (1977).
199. B. Fuchs, *J. Am. Chem. Soc.* **93**, 2544 (1971).
200. K. N. Houk, *Chem. Rev.* **76**, 1 (1976).
201. B. Fuchs and M. Pasternak, unpublished results.
202. B. S. Green and G. M. J. Schmidt, *Tetrahedron Lett.* p. 4249 (1970).
203. C. W. Shoppee and Y. Wang, *J. Chem. Soc., Perkin Trans. I* p. 1595 (1975).
204. C. W. Shoppee and Y. Wang, *J. Chem. Soc., Perkin Trans. I* p. 695 (1976).
205. K. J. Crowley, R. A. Schneider, and J. A. Meinwald, *J. Chem. Soc. C* p. 571 (1966).
206. P. J. Kropp and T. W. Gibson, *J. Chem. Soc. C* p. 143 (1967).
207. A. B. Smith, III and W. C. Agosta, *J. Am. Chem. Soc.* **95**, 1961 (1973).
208. R. B. Woodward, *Chem. Soc., Spec. Publ.* **21**, 217 (1967).
209. L. M. Jackman, E. F. M. Stephenson, and H. C. Yick, *Tetrahedron Lett.* p. 3325 (1970).
210. W. Amrein, Ph.D. Thesis, ETH, Zürich (1974).
211. W. Amrein and K. Schaffner, unpublished results.
212. W. Amrein and K. Schaffner, *Helv. Chim. Acta* **58**, 380 (1975).
213. R. Reinfried, D. Belluš, and K. Schaffner, *Helv. Chim. Acta* **54**, 1517 (1971).
214. K. Schaffner, *Pure Appl. Chem. Suppl.* Vol. 1, p. 405 (1971).
215. A. B. Smith, III, A. M. Forster, and W. C. Agosta, *J. Am. Chem. Soc.* **94**, 5100 (1972).
216. M. Demuth, C. O. Bender, W. Amrein, and K. Schaffner, unpublished results.
217. C. Manning and J. J. McCullough, *Chem. Commun.* p. 75 (1977).
218. D. H. R. Barton and G. Quinkert, *Proc. Chem. Soc., London* p. 197 (1958); *J. Chem. Soc.* p. 1 (1960).
219. J. D. Hobson, M. M. Al'Holly, and J. R. Malpass, *Chem. Commun.* p. 764 (1968).
220. M. R. Morris and A. J. Waring, *Chem. Commun.* p. 526 (1969); *J. Chem. Soc. C* p. 3269 (1971).
221. O. L. Chapman and J. D. Lassila, *J. Am. Chem. Soc.* **90**, 2449 (1968).
222. O. L. Chapman, M. Kane, J. D. Lassila, R. L. Loeschen, and H. E. Wright, *J. Am. Chem. Soc.* **91**, 6856 (1969).
223. G. Quinkert, P. Bronstert, D. Egert, P. Michaelis, P. Jürges, G. Prescher, A. Syldark, and H.-H. Perkampus, *Chem. Ber.* **109**, 1332 (1976).
224. H. Hart and D. W. Swatton, *J. Am. Chem. Soc.* **89**, 1874 (1967).
225. H. Hart, P. M. Collins, and A. J. Waring, *J. Am. Chem. Soc.* **88**, 1005 (1966).
226. A. J. Waring, M. R. Morris, and M. M. Islam, *J. Chem. Soc. C* p. 3274 (1971).
227. A. D. Dickinson, A. T. Hardy, and H. Hart, *Org. Photochem. Synth.* **2**, 62 (1976).
228. H. Hart and R. K. Murray, *J. Org. Chem.* **35**, 1535 (1970).
229. W. G. Dauben, L. Salem, and N. J. Turro, *Acc. Chem. Res.* **8**, 41 (1975).
230. K. E. Hine and R. F. Childs, *Chem. Commun.* p. 145 (1972).
231. D. I. Schuster and M. A. Tainsky, *Mol. Photochem.* **4**, 437 (1972).
232. G. Büchi and E. M. Burgess, *J. Am. Chem. Soc.* **82**, 4333 (1960).
233. J. J. Hurst and G. H. Witham, *J. Chem. Soc.* p. 710 (1963).
234. D. I. Schuster, M. J. Nash, and M. L. Kantor, *Tetrahedron Lett.* p. 1375 (1964).
235. D. I. Schuster and D. H. Sussman, *Tetrahedron Lett.* p. 1657 (1970).
236. H. Hart and T. Takino, *Chem. Commun.* p. 450 (1970); *J. Am. Chem. Soc.* **93**, 720 (1971).
237. K. E. Hine and R. F. Childs, *J. Am. Chem. Soc.* **93**, 2323 (1971).
238. K. E. Hine and R. F. Childs, *J. Am. Chem. Soc.* **95**, 6116 (1973).
239. H. Hart and A. F. Naples, *J. Am. Chem. Soc.* **94**, 3256 (1972).

240. D. I. Schuster, this volume.
241. H. Hart, T. Miyashi, D. N. Buchanan, and S. Sasson, *J. Am. Chem. Soc.* **96**, 4857 (1974).
242. E. Dunkelblum, H. Hart, and M. Suzuki, *J. Am. Chem. Soc.* **99**, 5074 (1977).
243. H. Hart, *Pure Appl. Chem.* **33**, 247 (1973).
244. T. S. Cantrell and J. S. Solomon, *J. Am. Chem. Soc.* **92**, 4656 (1970).
245. G. Lange and E. Neidert, *Tetrahedron Lett.* p. 4215 (1971); p. 1349 (1972).
246. G. Lange and E. Neidert, *Can. J. Chem.* **51**, 2207 (1973).
247. G. Lange, and E. Neidert, *Can. J. Chem.* **51**, 2215 (1973).
248. R. Noyori, A. Watanabe, and M. Katô, *Tetrahedron Lett.* p. 5443 (1968).
249. M. Suzuki, H. Hart, E. Dunkelblum, and W. Li, *J. Am. Chem. Soc.* **99**, 5083 (1977).
250. G. Büchi and E. M. Burgess, *J. Am. Chem. Soc.* **84**, 3104 (1962).
251. L. L. Barber, O. L. Chapman, and J. D. Lassila, *J. Am. Chem. Soc.* **91**, 531 (1969).
252. L. A. Paquette and O. Cox, *J. Am. Chem. Soc.* **89**, 5633 (1967).
253. A. Padwa, P. Sackman, E. Shefter, and E. Vega, *Chem. Commun.* p. 680 (1972).
254. N. J. Turro, V. Ramamurthy, W. Cherry, and W. Farneth, *Chem. Rev.* **78**, 125 (1978).
255. W. M. Horspool, *Photochemistry* **8**, 262 (1977).
256. M. Karvaš, F. Marti, H. Wehrli, K. Schaffner, and O. Jeger, *Helv. Chim. Acta* **57**, 1851 (1974).
257. We wish to thank Professor David I. Schuster for a most profitable exchange of information and ideas and for constructive criticism of parts of this manuscript, and Professor Benzion Fuchs for the disclosure of results in advance of publication.

D. BRYCE-SMITH and A. GILBERT

I. INTRODUCTION

In this essay, we are concerned principally with rearrangements of benzene rings not forming part of condensed polycyclic aromatic systems. The emphasis is on reactions in which the benzene ring itself undergoes isomerization to a nonaromatic species. Reactions that merely involve the migration of substituents are not covered, except for such photochemical processes that occur by transposition of ring carbon atoms.

In view of the well-known aromatic stabilization energy of the benzene ring, it is not surprising that most known rearrangements, leading as they do, in most cases, to nonaromatic isomers, have large energy requirements. By far the greatest number of known examples occur under the influence of ultraviolet radiation, and this essay is, naturally enough, concerned principally with processes of this type. Among other examples, there are a few in which rearrangement occurs under γ irradiation, and, although the rearrangement of benzyl-type carbocations to the corre-

REARRANGEMENTS IN GROUND AND EXCITED STATES, VOL. 3

sponding tropylium ions has long been thought to occur in mass spectrometry, much early work in this area is now being questioned.

A few processes are, however, known to occur by (thermal) pathways of relatively low energy, notably the ketonization of phenols. The presence of fluorine substituents can greatly modify the properties normally associated with the benzene ring, and a few examples of the thermal rearrangement of polyfluorinated benzenes are discussed. Many thermal rearrangements of substituted benzenes to give aromatic products have been suggested to proceed by way of transient nonaromatic isomers, and in a small number of cases such intermediates have been trapped. In most cases, however, the proposed intermediates are merely speculative, and their identification by suitable trapping procedures remains a potentially rich field for future research. The following section is concerned with thermal rearrangements of the benzene ring, but, owing to the heterogeneity of the subject matter, it is intended to provide a source of leading references and of illustrative examples rather than to be a comprehensive account.

II. NONPHOTOCHEMICAL REARRANGEMENTS OF THE BENZENE RING

A. Rearrangement of Benzyl Carbocations and Related Species

Since the original proposal (*1*) that the $C_7H_7^+$ ion from toluene was the ring-expanded tropylium ion 1 rather than the benzyl carbocation 2, the

structures of the corresponding ions from a considerable number of sources have been extensively studied, and structures have sometimes been assigned from rather tenuous evidence. This is currently an active field of research, but there is a general feeling among the workers concerned that much of the early evidence was misinterpreted. The chemical activation methods employed by McLafferty (*2*) appear to be placing the subject on a sounder basis and have provided evidence, for example, that the equilibrium between benzyl and tropylium species principally, if not exclusively, involves the C_7H_8 radical cations rather than the C_7H_7 carbocations. The isomeric *o-, m-,* and *p*-tolyl carbocations, and possibly, to a lesser extent, the 7-norbornadienyl carbocation, are also apparently formed by fragmentation of the C_7H_8 radical cations, but it remains uncertain whether they themselves are directly involved in the equilibria. Although caution is necessary when one is comparing the results of studies carried out under different experimental conditions and involving species of different energies, there does seem at present to be a lack of hard evidence for direct interconversions between the C_7H_7 carbocations. Any interconversions of this type seem likely to require highly activated species. For recent studies in this area, Dunbar *et al.* (*2a*) may be consulted (see also Essay 2).

Tropylium ions are formed in the radiolysis of toluene, but the results are not entirely analogous to those from electron impact studies (*3*). It has been reported that γ irradiation of aniline gives the isomeric picolines, possibly via a corresponding azatropylium species (*4*). The foregoing reports concern gas-phase studies, so it is interesting that tropylium salts have also been found to react with anisole in the liquid phase to give both tropyl- and benzylanisoles (*5*).

B. Phenol–Cyclohexadienone Tautomerism

Simple phenols exist almost exclusively in the enol forms, doubtless because ketonization involves loss of the aromatic stabilization energy. Although keto forms of simple benzenoid phenols have only rarely been obtained [see Garbisch (*5a*) for the diketo tautomer of *p*-quinol] and the physical evidence for the presence of keto forms in solution is rather uncertain, many reactions of phenols can be reasonably understood only if it is assumed that they involve tautomeric keto forms. In general, the tendency to react in keto forms increases with the number of hydroxyl groups on the benzene ring and with the size of the aromatic system in condensed benzene derivatives. The tendency for polyhydric phenols to behave in this way is readily understood, for in the first-formed monoketo tautomer there is no aromatic stabilization and this barrier to ketonization of any remaining enol groups is therefore absent.

The classic example of the reaction of a phenol in a keto form is the formation of a trioxime (**3**) from 1,3,5-trihydroxybenzene (**6**). Likewise,

3

the catalytic hydrogenation of 1,3-dihydroxybenzene to cyclohexane-1,3-dione can readily be understood only in terms of an intermediate keto form (**7**). (This reaction is noteworthy as an example of the formation of a ketone by *reduction* of a hydroxy compound.) Even monohydric phenols can sometimes react as if they existed in a keto form; thus, *o*-cresol gives a proportion of the ketone **4** under the conditions of the Reimer–Tiemann reaction (*8*).

It has been shown that 1,4-dihydroxybenzene undergoes thermal addition of maleic anhydride under forced conditions to give the 1 : 1 adduct **5** (*9*). This reaction, which was the first example of a thermal cycloaddition to a benzene derivative, can be rationalized as involving an addition of the Diels–Alder type to a monoketo tautomer **6,** although one might have expected the diketo tautomer to be a preferred species at equilibrium. Phenol tautomerism is the subject of an early, but still informative, review (*10;* see *11*).

To our knowledge, no evidence has yet been obtained for a tautomeric equilibrium involving aromatic amines analogous to that which appears to occur with phenols, but the possibility should be borne in mind, especially for polyamino compounds and higher condensed aromatic systems.

C. *Thermal Rearrangement of Polyfluoroaromatic Compounds*

Although the Claisen rearrangement of allyl phenyl ethers to isomeric 2-allylphenols has long been known to proceed via the intermediacy of cyclohexadienones, the latter normally tautomerize to the phenol too rapidly to permit their isolation. As an exception, it has been found that the dienone **7** is obtained in 32% yield as a thermally stable product from the pyrolysis of pentafluorophenyl allyl ether in the vapor phase at 365°C (*12*). This was, in fact, the first example to be reported of the thermal isomerization of a benzene derivative to a nonaromatic product, although a previous example had been reported in the naphthalene series, namely, the thermal rearrangement of 1-allyl-2-allyloxynaphthalene to the naphthalenone **8** (*13*).

Subsequently a quite different type of rearrangement was reported, namely, the thermal isomerization of hexakis(trifluoromethyl)benzene into its para-bonded (Dewar) isomer **9** (*14*). This remarkable reaction occurs in a flow system at 400°C with a contact time of 1 sec. The same

group has extended this reaction to other polyfluoroaromatic compounds
(*15*). These processes and the Claisen-type reaction described by Brooke
(*12*) appear to represent the only examples in the literature of the thermal
isomerization of uncondensed benzene derivatives to thermally stable and
isolable nonaromatic products.

D. *m-Cyclophane Rearrangements*

It has been shown (*16*) that the *m*-cyclophane **10** undergoes thermal and
photochemical reversible valence tautomerization to the nonbenzenoid
(*14*) annulene **11**. The resulting relief of overcrowding and the formation of
a new aromatic system undoubtedly provide a driving force for this process. It is interesting that this rearrangement is in some ways analogous to
the initial step in the photochemical conversion of stilbenes to phenanthrenes (see Section III,B,7). It has subsequently been shown (*17*) that only
the anti isomer of **10** undergoes the above thermal isomerization; the cis
isomer has been shown (*17*) to give only **12**, which is not in equilibrium with
the *syn*-cyclophane, even though the thermal reaction would be allowed as
a concerted process; the observed thermal transformation between **11** and
the anti form of **10** should be correspondingly forbidden.

10   **11**   **12**

E. *Rearrangements of Benzocyclobutenes*

Many thermal reactions of benzocyclobutenes can be rationalized in
terms of intermediate *o*-quinodimethanes, and these can be trapped in
suitable systems. Thus, it was shown (*18*) that cis- and *trans*-7,8-diphenyl-
benzocyclobutenes undergo stereospecific conrotatory thermal isomeriza-

13   **14**   **15**

16   **17**

tion to intermediate quinodimethanes (13), which can be trapped by an N-alkylmaleimide as adducts of type 14. The corresponding tetraphenyl-benzocyclobutene undergoes thermal isomerization to the quino-dimethane 15, which isomerizes to 16; the quinodimethane 15 was also trapped in a hydrocarbon matrix at −190°C and was shown to reform the benzocyclobutene at −120°C (19). The absence of an ESR spectrum indicated that the species is not a diradical. The intermediacy of an acylquinodimethane (17) was invoked (20) to account for the formation of chromenes 18 by pyrolysis of the 7-acylbenzocyclobutene. 7-Vinyl-benzocyclobutenes undergo thermal rearrangement to the corresponding o-quinodimethanes (19), which, depending on the natures of R and R′, either undergo a 1,7-hydrogen shift to give o-tolylbutadienes or cyclize to 1,2-dihydronaphthalenes (21).

F. Rearrangements of Arylcarbenes and Arylnitrenes

Phenylcarbene (20) undergoes ring contraction at temperatures of 600°C and above to give fulvenallene (21) and ethynylcyclopentadiene (22) (22). Interestingly, the use of ^{13}C-labeled phenylcarbene leads to the fulvenal-lene in which the label is uniformly distributed over all the carbon positions, probably as a result of a degenerate rearrangement of the bicyclic and monocyclic intermediates 23 and 24, respectively.

The sequence 25 → 26 → 27 → 28 appears to exemplify a different type of arylcarbene rearrangement; the overall yield is 89% (23).

Phenylnitrene (**29**) undergoes a related ring contraction to cyanocyclo-pentadiene (**30**) (*24*). On the other hand, the generation of phenylnitrene in the presence of diethylamine gives the ring-expanded product *N,N*-diethyl-2-amino-3*H*-azetine (**31**), consistent with the trapping of the intermediate **32** (*25*). 2,6-Dimethylphenylnitrene (**33**), generated by gas-phase pyrolysis of the corresponding azide, appears to rearrange to the corresponding carbenes **34** and **35** and then to 2-methyl-6-vinylpyridine (**36**) (*26*). For further discussion, see Essay 3.

G. *Miscellaneous Thermal Rearrangements*

It has been suggested that the *o*-thiomethylation of aromatic amines proceeds via the rearrangement of a sulfur ylid of type **37** to the nonben-zenoid species **38** (*27*).

A carbon analogue of the Claisen rearrangement appears to be involved in the base-catalyzed isomerization of 4-phenylbut-1-ene to *o*-allyltoluene at 350°C (*28*); the nonaromatic isomer **39** has been suggested as a likely intermediate. The Claisen-type thermal rearrangement of phenyl propar-gyl ether (**40**) to the indanone **41** at 460°C appears to proceed via initial rearrangement to the allenylcyclohexadienone **42** followed by an intramo-lecular Diels–Alder addition to give **43** and then the ketene **44** (*29*). Others (*30*) have shown that pyrolysis of 2-ethynylbiphenyl at 700°C/0.03 mm gives the benzazulene **45** together with phenanthrene. A somewhat similar process has been described in the thermal rearrangement of the isonitrile **46** to the aza-azulene **47** (*31*).

III. PHOTOCHEMICAL REARRANGEMENTS OF THE BENZENE RING

A. Unsubstituted Benzene

Before 1957, it was widely believed that benzene was stable to ultraviolet irradiation. In that year, Blair and Bryce-Smith reported that
irradiation of liquid benzene at 50°C and 254 nm gave the isomer fulvene
(**48**) (*32*). It was subsequently shown that the highly strained isomer benzvalene (tricyclo[3.1.0.0²,⁶]hex-3-ene) (**49**) (*33–33b*) is also formed. Some

of the fulvene appears to arise by isomerization of benzvalene, but it is
still uncertain whether all of it is formed in this way. The quantum yields
are *ca.* 0.01–0.03 for each isomer. The formation of both isomers from
neat benzene is favored by an increase in temperature, and at 50°–60°C
limiting concentrations of *ca.* 300–500 mg/liter of each can be obtained.
The chemical yields of both isomers tend to increase with increased dilution of the benzene with an alkane such as hexadecane (*33*), although the
limiting concentration of fulvene is approached the more slowly; this is
consistent with the formation of at least some of it via benzvalene.

Reports on the temperature effect in the isomerization of benzene in
dilute solutions are conflicting. Thus, it has been reported (*34*) that the
quantum yield (0.18) for the formation of benzvalene from benzene in
oxygen-free, dilute hexane solution is independent of temperature over

the range 9°–50°C; this is in contrast with the findings for undiluted benzene. However, others (35) have observed definite temperature effects: In cyclohexane, the quantum yields at 9°, 25°, and 50°C were 0.035, 0.05, and 0.08 respectively; the corresponding values in water were 0.06, 0.07, and 0.07.

Although fulvene is fairly stable in dilute solutions, it has such a strong tendency to polymerize in more concentrated solutions that it is difficult to isolate in the pure state (36). The ultraviolet absorption spectrum is, however, very characteristic (λ_{max} 365, 242 nm; tailing of the former peak into the visible accounts for the marked yellow color) and permits unambiguous detection at very low concentrations.

Benzvalene is more sensitive to acid than is fulvene, but it is less sensitive to bases; its marked sensitivity to the alumina used in chromatograph columns should always be borne in mind. The photochemical reversion to benzene is strongly sensitized by triplet benzene (33a), and slow thermal rearomatization occurs at room temperature ($t_{1/2}$ ca. 10 days). The sensitivity to rearomatization by triplet benzene may account, in part at least, for the favorable effect of dilution on formation of benzvalene; the yield of triplet benzene increases greatly with increasing concentration (37).

Benzvalene readily reacts thermally with methanolic hydrogen chloride to give methoxy[3.1.0]bicyclohexenes, mainly 50 together with minor amounts of 51 (33b). These adducts may also conveniently be prepared by direct irradiation of benzene in acidic methanol (33), although they are really thermal adducts of benzvalene rather than direct photoadducts of benzene [compare also (38)]. Indeed, the quantum yield for the 1,3-photoaddition of methanol to benzene is equal within experimental error to that for the formation of benzvalene (39). The apparent benzene adducts of 2,2,2-trifluoroethanol, acetic acid, and water (as aqueous phosphoric acid) also arise by thermal addition to benzvalene (33,40). The use of D_2O gave the alcohol 52, thereby confirming the suggestion (41) that benzvalene rather than the benzenonium ion 53 (42) is the key intermediate in the acid-catalyzed 1,3 photohydration of benzene (43). The bicyclo-[3.1.0]hex-3-en-2-yl cation 54 was proposed as an intermediate in the photoadditions of methanol and other hydroxylic compounds to benzene (42), and its formation via protonation of photochemically generated benzvalene under strongly acidic conditions has since been demonstrated (33b). It is interesting that, under less strongly acidic conditions, increasing proportions of endo adducts such as 51 are formed, probably via a nondissociating ion pair such as 55; other isomeric products arise by benzene-sensitized vinylcyclopropane rearrangement of the primary exo and endo adducts.

Mechanistic and orbital symmetry aspects of the photoisomerization of the benzene ring have been discussed in detail (44). The conclusions can be broadly summarized as follows. First, the S_1 benzene, which is formed by excitation at the commonly employed wavelength of 254 nm, is incipiently meta bonding, and adiabatic transformation to the ground state of the "prefulvene" species 56 can occur as a consequence of ring distortions, which tend to bring meta carbon atoms closer than in the equilibrium regular hexagonal conformation. This vibrational excitation can arise concomitantly with the electronic excitation at short wavelengths within the $S_0 \rightarrow S_1$ absorption band, and benzvalane is, indeed, not formed at longer wavelengths within this band (45).

Second, the direct formation of benzvalene from S_1 benzene is not allowed as a fully concerted process, i.e., a process in which both the two new bonds are formed synchronously. On the other hand, benzvalene can be formed by such a process directly from S_2 benzene. The fact that S_1 benzene can be a precursor of benzvalene was considered to imply that it arises via initial symmetry-allowed meta bonding to give prefulvene 56, which species then undergoes intramolecular cyclization to benzvalene by a presumably thermal process. Benzvalene has also been shown to arise from S_2 benzene, and the implication, from the orbital symmetry considerations, that the mechanism must in this case be different from that in the case of S_1 benzene is nicely borne out by the observation that the process from S_2 benzene shows no evidence for a thermal (vibrational) activation stage (46).

Third, the orbital symmetry analysis indicates that para positions in S_2 (but not S_1) benzene should be incipiently para bonding. This conclusion accounts very nicely for the absence of Dewar benzene (57) from the

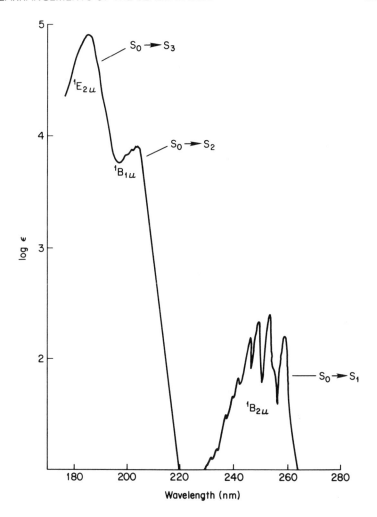

Fig. 1 Ultraviolet spectrum of benzene.

products of irradiation of benzene in its S_0–S_1 band and the production of Dewar benzene on irradiation in the liquid phase into the S_0–S_2 band (47). Dewar benzene was also produced in earlier work in which benzene was simultaneously excited into its S_2 and S_3 states (48). The positions of the bands in question are shown in Fig. 1.

The possibility that *cis,cis,trans*-cyclohexatriene ("Möbius benzene") might be an intermediate in photoreactions of benzene was raised originally by Farenhorst (49) and was more recently mentioned by Mulder (50). These workers argued that S_1 benzene and Möbius benzene should be isoenergetic in the Hückel approximation, and the latter author expressed the opinion that the Möbius benzene intermediate should correspond to a minimum on the surface of the S_1 state. This argument does not commend itself to us for several reasons: Möbius benzene would be a highly strained and buckled molecule if it were to exist, and we are by no means clear that it could properly be treated as a conjugated 6π system. The orbital symmetry analysis given in Bryce-Smith and Gilbert (*44*) suggests that the ground state of Möbius benzene could not transform adiabatically into S_1 benzene, but only into a much higher excited state. On the other hand, a concerted thermal transformation of ground state benzvalene into ground state benzene could, in principle, proceed via S_1 Möbius benzene, but one would expect this to be a very high energy species.

Hexadienynes are open-chain isomers of benzene, and these are among the products formed on irradiation of benzene vapor at very short wavelengths (185 nm) (*51*). The genesis of these is not definitely known, but it is likely that they are secondary photodecomposition products of fulvene.

The relationships among the various photoisomers of benzene are summarized in Fig. 2.

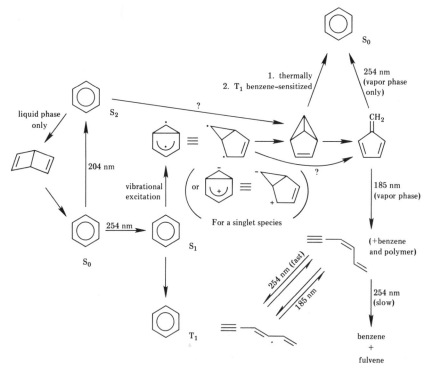

Fig. 2   Photoisomerizations of the benzene ring.

B. Photoisomerization of Substituted Benzenes

The general harmony between theory and experiment that prevails in the case of unsubstituted benzene is not always immediately apparent with substituted benzenes, yet, even for these, and allowing for gaps in our knowledge, close examination reveals little discordance. The isomerization reactions that are observed fall into two main categories: (a) formation of fulvenes, benzvalenes, Dewar benzenes, and prismanes (58) and (b) formation of positional isomers involving *apparent* migration of a substituent, as in the photoisomerization of *o*-xylene to the meta isomer. There is, in fact, evidence that benzvalenes are involved as intermediates in processes of type (b).

58

1. Hexafluorobenzene

In contrast with benzene, hexafluoro-Dewar benzene (hexafluorobicyclo[2.2.0]hexa-2,5-diene) (59) is the only isomer that has been detected following irradiation of hexafluorobenzene in the liquid or vapor phase at wavelengths over the range 212–265 nm (52). On the other hand, irradiation of solutions of hexafluorobenzene in cyclohexane and cyclooctane leads to the evolution of hydrogen fluoride and the formation of a complex mixture containing cyclohexylpentafluorobenzene (from cyclohexane) and other radical-coupling products, but no photoisomers (53).

59

Hexafluoro-Dewar benzene (59), mp 6°C, bp 52°C, is safe to handle in dilute solution but highly explosive in the pure liquid state (as is benzvalene). It rearomatizes smoothly to hexafluorobenzene in the vapor phase at 80°C.

At first sight, the formation of a para-bonded product on irradiation of hexafluorobenzene in its longest-wavelength absorption band appears to be in conflict with the orbital symmetry requirement for transformation from the S_2 state. However, the S_1 and S_2 states are much closer in the case of hexafluorobenzene than in that of benzene, and the corresponding absorption envelopes overlap to a considerable extent (Fig. 3). The exclusive formation of hexafluoro-Dewar benzene might well result from the practical difficulty of achieving selective excitation to the S_1 state. An-

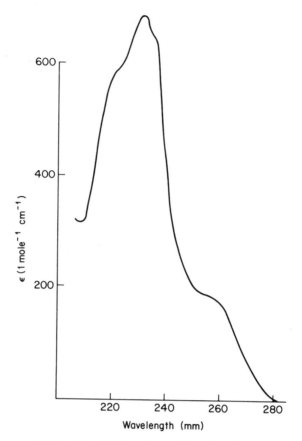

Fig. 3 Ultraviolet spectrum of hexafluorobenzene.

other possibility is that the nondetection of hexafluorobenzvalene arises from its thermal or photochemical instability and its ready transformation to the Dewar isomer by a process of the following type:

Hexafluorofulvene has not been detected, possibly because its formation would involve an unusual 1,2-fluorine shift. A more complete discussion of this matter can be found elsewhere (*44*).

2. Other Fluorobenzenes

The tendency for para rather than meta bonding that is apparent in hexafluorobenzene is also observed in a number of the lower fluoro derivatives. Thus, it was found that some, although not all, substituted penta-fluorobenzenes reacted as follows:

R = H, Me, OMe, CF$_3$

In contrast, the corresponding compound **60**, in which R = Cl or —CH=CH$_2$, gave no photoisomers (*54*). In another study, 1,2,4-trifluoro-benzene (**61**) gave two of the three possible Dewar isomers, but no ful-venes, benzvalenes, or hexadienynes (*55*). The quantum yields were very low. It is rather surprising that no photoisomers have yet been detected following irradiation of monofluorobenzene (see *56*). Irradiation of the other monohalobenzenes gives products that appear to be derived from radical reactions.

Some very interesting studies on the isomerization of perfluoroalkyl-benzenes have been reported (*57*). The thermal processes have been men-tioned in Section II,C, but photoprocesses appear to occur more readily. The photoisomerization of hexakis(trifluoromethyl)benzene gives the corresponding benzvalene, Dewar benzene, and prismane derivatives (*57*). The ratios of these isomers are time dependent owing to interconver-sions between the isomers. The Dewar isomer **62** forms the prismane directly, whereas the benzvalene **63** appears to give this indirectly via rearomatization and further photolysis. In another report, the Dewar isomer **62** is said to be produced by pyrolysis of the corresponding pris-mane **64** (*58*). It may be noted that the parent prismane has not yet been obtained as a photoisomer of benzene, although it has been synthesized indirectly by photoelimination of nitrogen from the azo compound **65** (*59*).

Irradiation of the corresponding pentafluoroethyl compound **66** was re-ported to give mainly the prismane, with traces of the Dewar isomer (presumably a precursor of the prismane), but the benzvalene isomer was not detected (57).

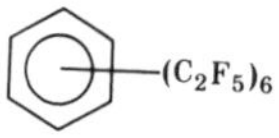

66

Extension of the foregoing photoisomerizations to the related molecules perfluoropentaethylmethylbenzene and perfluoro-1,2,3,5-tetraethyl-4,6-dimethylbenzene gave broadly similar results (15). It is clear that the introduction of perfluoroalkyl substituents greatly increases both the ease of formation and the thermal stability of Dewar and prismane isomers of benzene rings.

3. Photoisomerization Reactions of Alkylbenzenes

Although toluene and some other alkylbenzenes having at least one α-H atom can undergo C—H bond homolysis on irradiation in glassy matrices at very low temperatures, or on flash photolysis in the gas phase, to give the corresponding benzyl-type radicals (60), this process (which may involve absorption of two photons) does not appear to occur readily in the liquid phase at nearly ambient temperatures under normal experimental conditions. One or both of the following reactions can occur on irradiation at 254 nm in the gas or liquid phase: (a) ring isomerization to fulvenes, benzvalenes, Dewar benzenes, prismanes, and the ring-opened dienynes, although these are not all necessarily formed in a particular case (see Fig. 2); (b) positional isomerization of the alkyl substituents. There is general agreement that processes of type (b) occur through the intermediate formation and rearomatization of valence-bond ring isomers formed by processes of type (a), although it is fair to say that in many cases such intermediates have not yet been detected. The involvement of such valence-bond isomers has been inferred from isotopic labeling studies on [1,3,5-^{14}C]mesitylene which prove that the 1,2,4 isomer arises exclusively by transposition of ring carbon atoms and not by migration of methyl groups (61).

It has been suggested that processes of type (b) can conveniently be analyzed in terms of 12 possible ring permutation patterns (Fig. 4) (62). For example, the photoisomerization of o- to m-xylene could be regarded as a process of type P_2.

The ring transposition processes that give rise to apparent 1,2 shifts of substituents can, in principle, involve either benzvalene or prismane intermediates, whereas those that cause apparent 1,3 shifts involve either prismanes, isomerization between Dewar forms [a process that is apparently involved in the photoisomerization of pyridazine to pyrazine (63) but has not yet been established for benzene derivatives], or photoisomeriza-

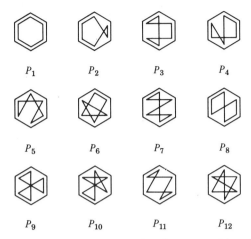

Fig. 4 Permutation patterns for ring transpositions (*62*).

tion between benzvalenes. The last-named process has been shown to occur for the interconversion of the benzvalenes **67** and **68** (*64*). The

mechanism is as yet unknown, but it appears not to involve the trivial process of aromatization and reisomerization. It may proceed directly by way of a vinylcyclopropane valence-bond isomerization of the type originally envisaged by Viehe when he named this class of compound (*65*). Photochemical interconversion of benzvalenes occurs with benzvalene-d_2 as follows (*66*):

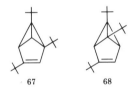

The various pathways for transposition processes in the benzene ring are summarized in Fig. 5. Pathway a normally gives rise only to 1,2 transpositions and then only to apparent 1,2 shifts of substituents. Photoisomerization of the initially formed benzvalene, as mentioned above, could, in principle, provide an apparent 1,3 shift via pathway d(ii). Pathway b involves two 1,2 transpositions [C-1–C-2 and C-3–C-4 in b(i)] and thereby can give rise to apparent 1,2 and/or 1,3 shifts depending on the modes of bond cleavage in the prismane in relation to ring substituents or isotopic labels. Since pathway c leads only to 1,3 transpositions, only

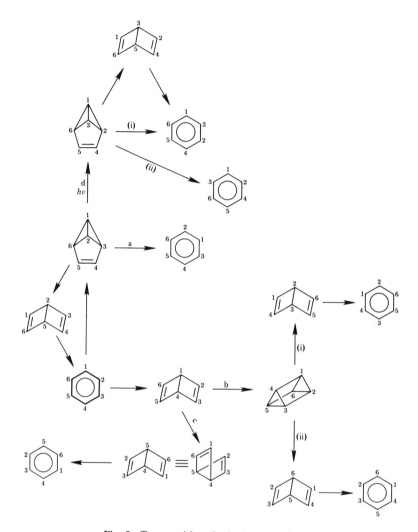

Fig. 5 Transpositions in the benzene ring.

apparent 1,3 shifts of substituents could result. It should be noted that benzvalene → Dewar benzene transformations of the type mentioned earlier introduce no new changes in the distribution pattern of carbon atoms in the final aromatic isomer.

The interconversions of perfluoro-1,3,5- and perfluoro-1,2,4-trimethyl-benzenes are summarized in Fig. 6. They appear to provide examples of

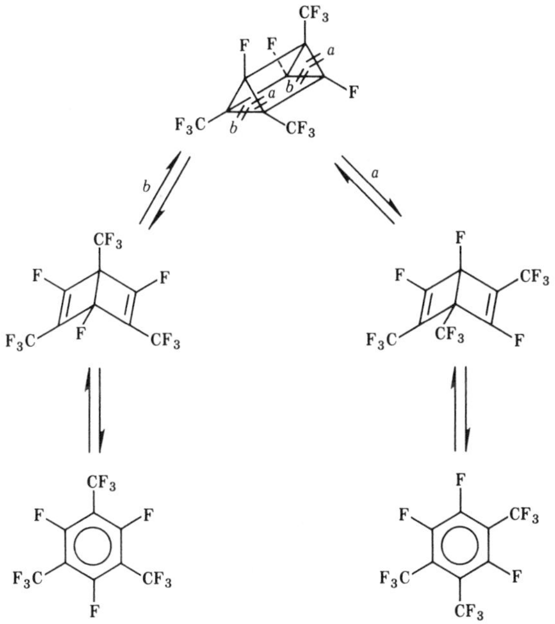

Fig. 6 Interconversions of perfluoro-1,3,5- and perfluoro-1,2,4-trimethylbenzenes.

the 1,2 mode of pathway b in Fig. 5 (67). The 1,3 mode may not have been observed because it would have produced either no apparent change or the more overcrowded 1,2,3 isomer. Although pathway c is at present known to be followed only in the cases of certain pyridines and pyridazines (63), there seems to be no reason, in principle, why it should not also be available for benzene derivatives. For example, it would provide a considerable relief of strain in cases in which C-1 and C-2 bore bulky substituent groups such as t-butyl. However, there is certainly evidence that pathway a is preferred in the photoisomerization of 1,3,5- to 1,2,4-tri-t-butylbenzene (64), and it has quite often been invoked for other systems even in the absence of specific evidence.

Wilzbach and Kaplan were the first workers to describe photochemical interconversions between isomeric xylenes (68), and Burgstahler and Chien almost simultaneously reported the photoisomerization of di-t-butylbenzenes (69; cf. 70). The xylenes underwent isomerization in the gas phase or, in the case of m-xylene, less efficiently in solution or as the pure liquid. It was demonstrated that the primary methyl shifts were exclusively 1,2 in character, and the traces of p-xylene formed on prolonged irradiation of the o isomer evidently arose by reisomerization of the first-formed m isomer. Although radicals are known to be formed in the photolysis of xylenes (71), it was demonstrated that the photoisomerization did not involve radical dissociation followed by recombination, and only traces of toluene were formed. In comparison, irradiation of o-di-t-butylbenzene in ether gave a 1 : 4 photostationary equilibrium mixture of the m and p isomers, respectively, with total disappearance of the strained o isomer; the same photostationary ratio also resulted when either of the m or p isomers was used as starting material (69). Despite the apparently major 1,3 shift in the o isomer, it is apparent that most, if not all, of the p isomer arose by a double 1,2 shift, presumably involving two photons. The situation may therefore not differ fundamentally from that with o-xylene. A further discussion of the mechanism of 1,2-methyl shifts in xylene is given elsewhere (44). The general conclusion is that processes of this type occur by singlet mechanisms, show temperature effects consistent with the previously mentioned requirement of vibrational excitation for meta bonding, and involve wholly if not exclusively 1,2 shifts in each photochemical step. If any expulsion of alkyl groups occurs, it makes only a minor contribution to the isomerization process.

We note in passing that "para" bonding and 1,3 shifts are relatively common among aromatic nitrogen heterocycles in which excited states may have $n\pi^*$ character, but such processes are beyond the scope of this essay. Numerous examples are described elsewhere (72).

The para bonding that occurs to a certain extent on irradiation of 1,2,4-tri-t-butylbenzene (69) (64) appears to constitute an exception to the general rule that S_1 benzene derivatives undergo only meta bonding as a symmetry-allowed process. If the Dewar isomer 70 is indeed a primary photochemical product and does not arise from the S_2 state of 69, the mechanistic difficulty might be overcome by postulating a nonconcerted triplet mechanism. Another odd feature is that the unstrained 1,3,5-tri-t-butylbenzene differed from the overcrowded 1,2,4 isomer in forming only a benzvalene on irradiation. It appears in general that overcrowding of substituents tends to promote the anomalous formation of Dewar isomers. A good illustration of this is provided by the observation that 1,2,4,5-tetra-t-butylbenzene gives a para-bonded isomer on irradiation (73),

69   70   71

whereas the less overcrowded silicon analogue 71 gave only meta-bonded products (74).

4. Photochemical Shifts of Substituents in Other Systems

The predominant tendency for 1,2 shifts of substituents noted in the foregoing sections has also been observed in 2-, 3-, and 4-tritylanisoles (75), bitolyls (76), monomethylbiphenyls (77), 2-, 3-, and 4-fluoro-benzotrifluorides (78), and 2,6-di-*t*-butylphenols (79). Benzvalenes have been postulated, although not isolated, as intermediates in most of these cases. Rather interestingly, photoracemization of the optically active biphenyl 72 appears to occur by two mechanisms, only one of which is thought to involve benzvalene intermediates (80).

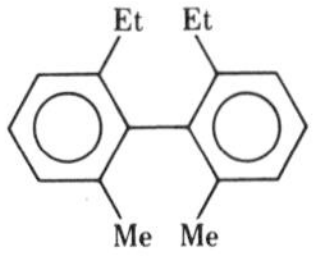

72

On the other hand, it was reported (79) that photoisomerization of the di-*t*-butylphenol 73 (→ 74 + 75) occurs by a triplet mechanism thought to involve intermediate keto tautomers of the phenol rather than benzvalenes. Thus, the use of ArOD gave a mixture of ortho- and para-

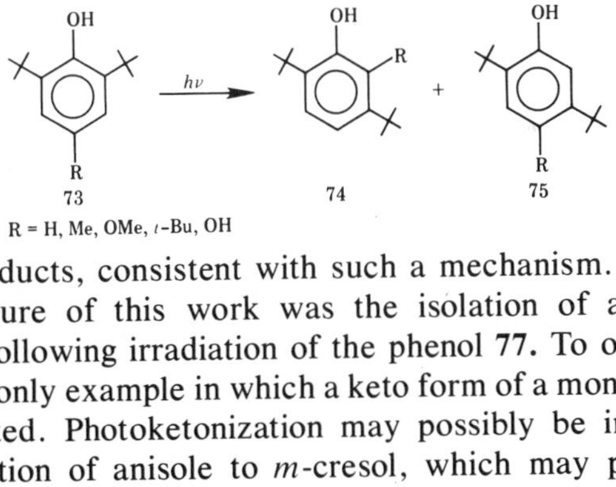

73   74   75

R = H, Me, OMe, *t*-Bu, OH

deuteriated products, consistent with such a mechanism. A particularly interesting feature of this work was the isolation of a "para" keto tautomer (76) following irradiation of the phenol 77. To our best knowledge this is the only example in which a keto form of a monohydric phenol has been isolated. Photoketonization may possibly be involved in the photoisomerization of anisole to *m*-cresol, which may proceed via an intermediate bicyclohexenone (81).

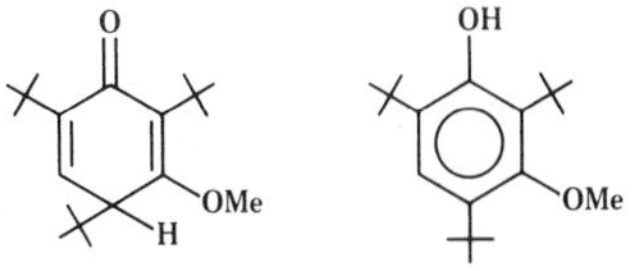

76   77

5. Photoenolization of Aryl Ketones and Related Processes

First, we draw attention to a comprehensive review (82) of photoenolization. An important photophysical study of such processes has been

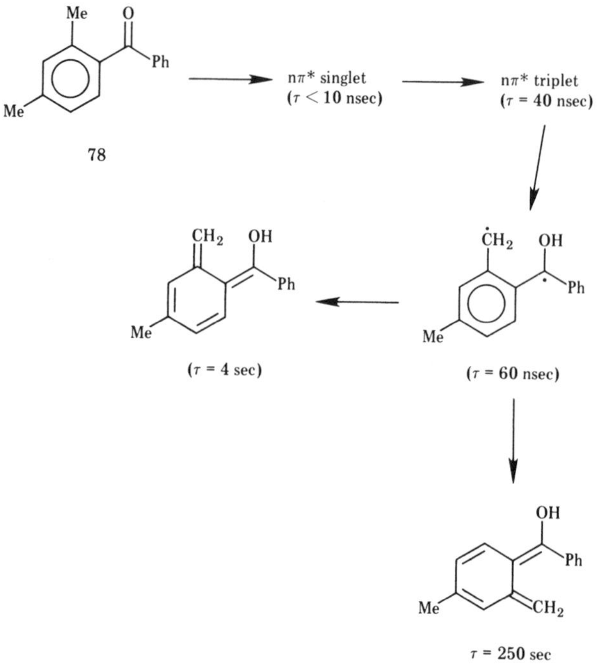

Fig. 7 Intermediates in the photoenolization of 2-methylbenzophenones (*83*).

reported for the ketone **78** (*83*); the results are summarized in Fig. 7. Conformational aspects of the reaction have been discussed (*84*), and a good example of photoenolization in which the product **79** from the ketone **80** is stabilized by hydrogen bonding has been described (*84a*).

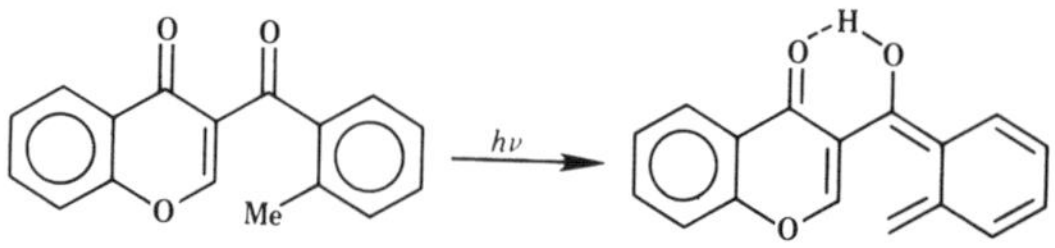

Although it is rather rare for a photoenol to be isolated, many workers have successfully trapped these by dienophiles such as maleic anhydride. A classic example is the trapping by dimethyl acetylenedicarboxylate of the photoenol **81** from 2-methylbenzophenone (*82*) (*85*) (Fig. 8). Many other dienophiles have subsequently been used by other workers (*86*). Related enols have often been proposed as intermediates in the photo-

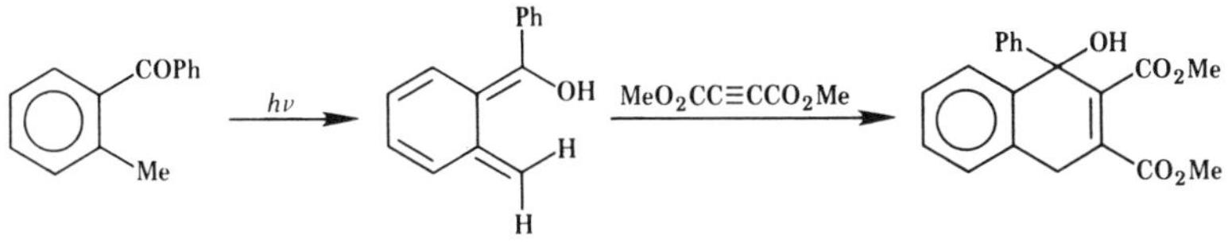

Fig. 8 Photoenolization of 2-methylbenzophenone (*85*).

chemistry of quinones, for example, **83** from duroquinone, but they have proved extremely difficult to detect [see, for example, Creed (*87*)].

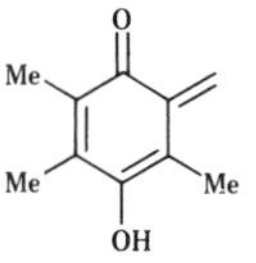

83

Aromatic aldehydes undergo analogous photoenolization reactions. For example, the photoenol (**84**) of *o*-methylbenzaldehyde was trapped by maleic anhydride as the adduct (**85**) (*88*). An interesting intramolecular example of such a process in the photoisomerization of **86**, which gives **87** and **88** as the major and minor products, respectively (*89*), has been described.

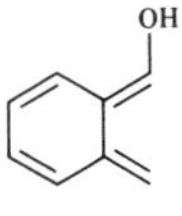

84 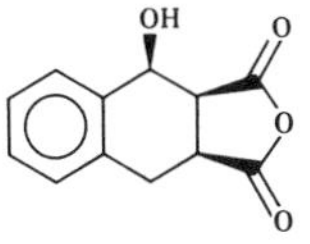   85 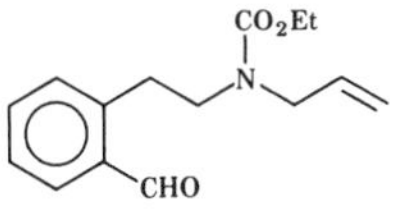   86

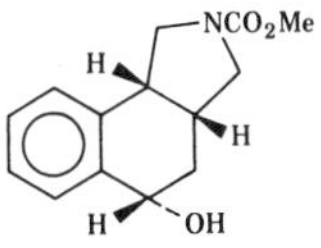

87 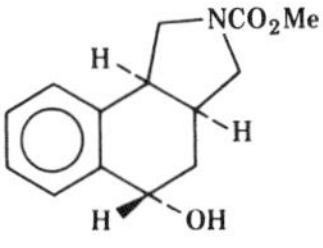   88

Irradiation of the naphthoquinone **89** gives a blue product absorbing at 550–580 nm, which is believed to be the enol **90** (*90*).

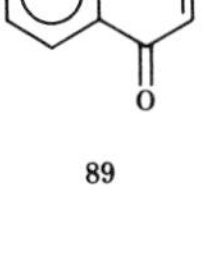

89 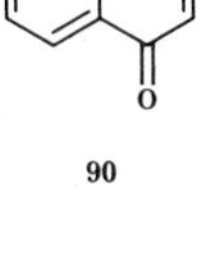   90

The photoisomerization of o-nitrobenzaldehyde to o-nitrosobenzoic acid was first observed by Ciamician and Silber in 1901 (*91*), and many related processes have been described in more recent times. It is generally considered that rearrangements of this type proceed by way of an unstable intermediate photoisomer (**91**) (*92*), as follows:

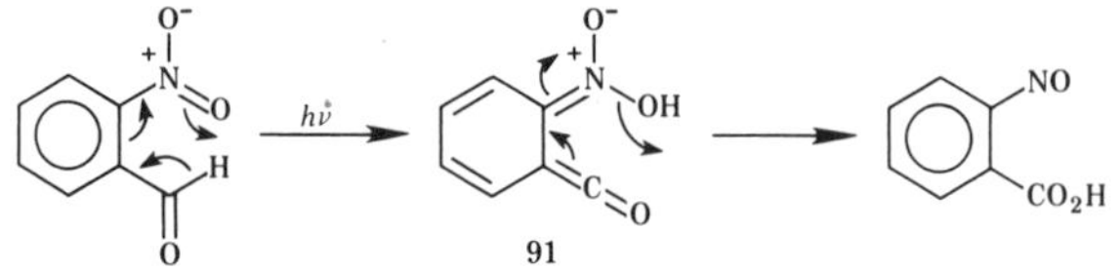

91

The photochromism of o-nitrotoluene derivatives bearing an α-hydrogen atom proceeds in an analogous manner and has been extensively reviewed (*93*). The general process is as follows:

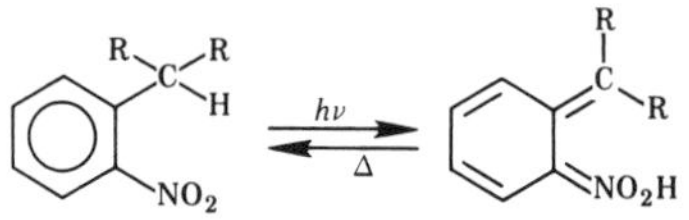

6. Photoisomerization of Styrenes

Deuterium labeling studies have indicated that an o-quinodimethane (**92**) is probably formed as an intermediate in the photoisomerization of 1,2-dihydronaphthalene (**93**) to the cyclopropane **94** (*94*), as follows:

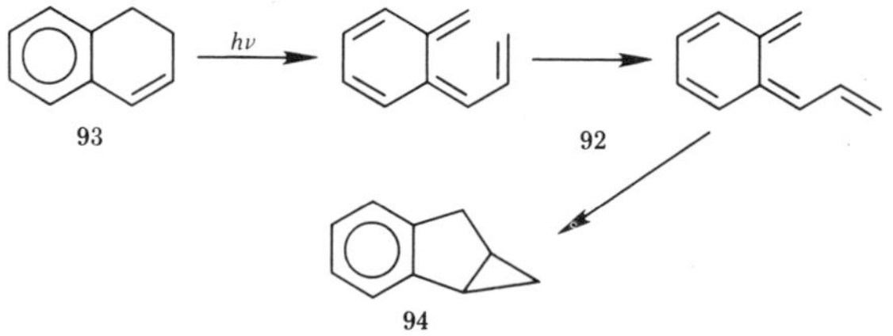

93   92

94

Photoisomerization of the substituted dihydronaphthalene **95** to the divinylbenzene **96** probably proceeds in a somewhat analogous manner, except that the intermediate o-quinodimethane (**97**) undergoes a photo-

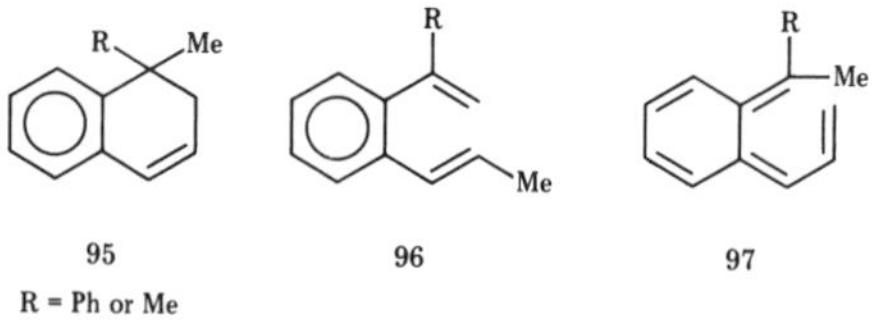

95   96   97
R = Ph or Me

chemical [1,7] sigmatropic hydrogen shift (*95*). One group (*96*) successfully trapped an intermediate quinodimethane (**98**) by means of maleic anhydride.

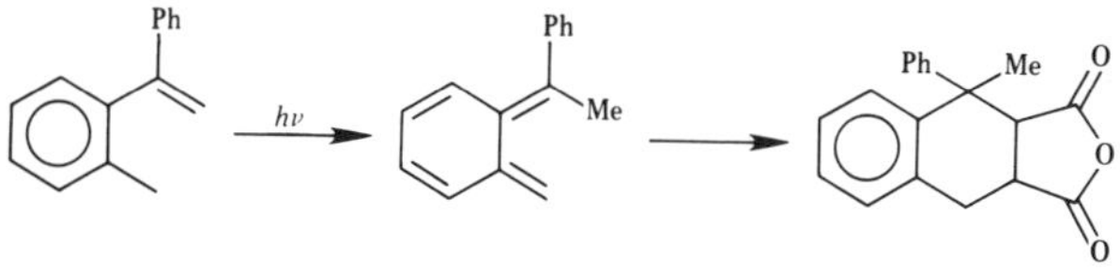

98

Numerous other examples of this type of process can be found else-where (72). However, the photoisomerization of perfluoroindene (**99**) is of particular interest because the isoindene product (**100**) can be isolated, and the process provides the first unambiguous example of a sigmatropic fluorine shift (97). The photoisomerization of indenes to isoindenes is in general a well-established process, but these products are normally unsta-ble and must be trapped (98).

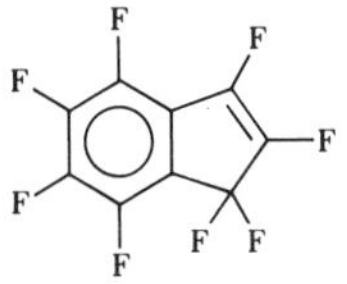

99 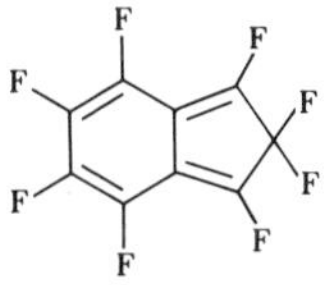   100

7. Photoisomerization of Stilbenes

The oxidative photocyclization of stilbenes to phenanthrenes is one of the classic reactions of organic photochemistry and has found numerous synthetic applications. The reaction undoubtedly proceeds by way of (a) initial trans–cis isomerization of the stilbene (discussed in detail in Essay 14) followed by (b) photoisomerization of the cis-stilbene to a trans-4a,4b-dihydrophenanthrene (**101**), as required by orbital symmetry con-siderations for a concerted process. Early work on the stilbene → phenan-threne isomerization has been reviewed (99), and there are numerous subsequent examples of the process (72). However, definitive proof of the proposed trans-dihydrophenanthrene intermediate has been provided only recently in the isolation (100) of the reasonably stable derivative **102** fol-lowing irradiation of diethylstilbestrol (**103**) at 254 nm. Irradiation of **102** at 366 nm reverses the process, but further irradiation or heat converts the diketone **102** to the dihydroxyphenanthrene derivative. The dimethyl ether of diethylstilbestrol yields the dihydrophenanthrene only as a tran-

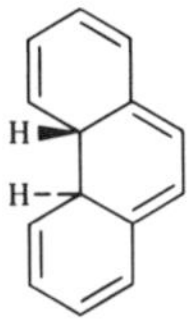

101 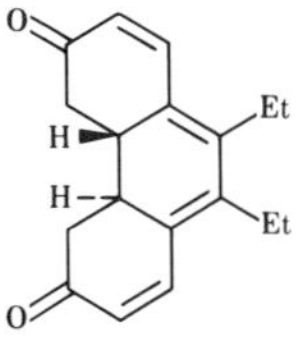   102 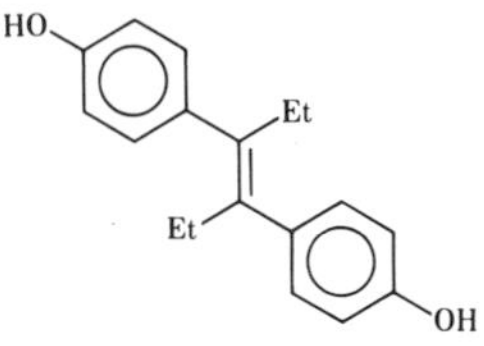   103

sient species, but the monomethyl ether gives a corresponding intermediate having a half-life of 18.2 min at 24°C.

8. Photoisomerization of Arylbutadienes

The 1,4-diphenylbuta-1,3-diene system in overcrowded molecules based on dibenzylidenesuccinic anhydrides and imides (104) is very photolabile and causes these compounds to exhibit photochromism. A typical example is provided by the yellow (E)-benzylidene-(E)-(α-phenylethylidene)succinic anhydride 104a, which on irradiation reversibly forms the red isomer 105 (101). Darcy et al. (102) can be consulted as a source of references to earlier work in this area.

104a R = H; R' = Me; X = O   105

9. Miscellaneous Photoisomerizations

A considerable number of photoreactions of benzene derivatives have been suggested to occur by way of nonaromatic intermediates, but in a great many cases the evidence for such intermediates is purely inferential. We shall therefore refer to only a few examples of such processes. The photolysis of N-benzoylenamines (106) and N-acylanilides (107) bearing substituents such as CO_2Me, $COMe$, CN, $CONH_2$, and OMe on the phenyl ring has been shown to give the respective products 108 and 109 (103). The zwitterionic intermediates 110 and 111 are commonly invoked. Related nonaromatic zwitterionic intermediates have also been proposed for photocyclizations of benzanilides (104) and diphenylamines (105); they are believed to be precursors of the carbazole products from diphenylamines.

106   107   108

109   110   111

Di- and tetraphenylcyclobutanes undergo an interesting photoisomerization to tetrahydroazulenes (106), as in the following example:

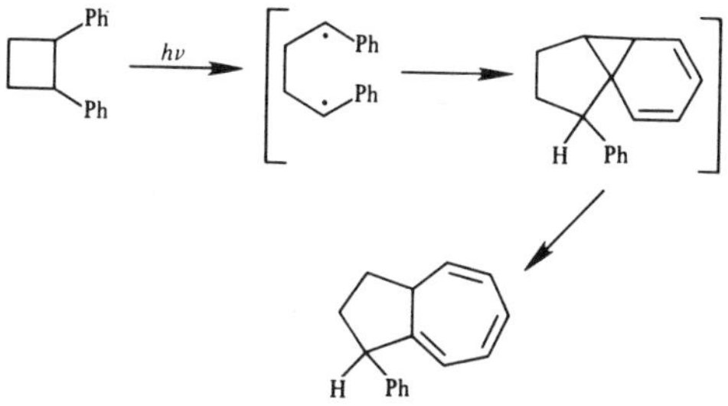

Although the photodimerization of diphenylacetylene to 1,2,3-triphenylnaphthalene (112) and 1,2,3-triphenylazulene (113) has been known for some time (*107*), it has only more recently been suggested that the primary photoprocess involves isomerization of the diphenylacetylene to the benzocyclobutadiene 114 (*108*); this is thought to dimerize to the products. The intermediate 114 has been isolated as green unstable crystals. It remains to be seen whether the known photodimerizations of phenylacetylene to 1-phenylazulene and 1-phenylnaphthalene likewise involve an initial photoisomerization of phenylacetylene to benzocyclobutadiene (*109*).

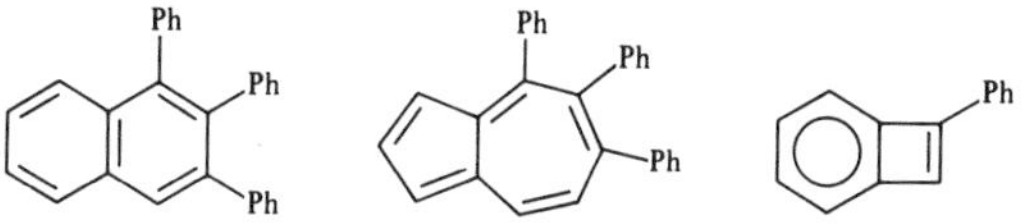

112   113   114

The interesting observation has been made (*110*) that the isocyanide 115 undergoes photoisomerization in cyclohexane or methanol to the azabenzazulene 116 and the phenanthridene 117; the latter is only a trace product in cyclohexane but a major product in methanol. The suggestion has been made that the initial stage of the process involves photoisomerization to the cyclopropanoneimine 118. As previously noted (*31*), related *thermal* processes occur in the naphthalene series, and the isocyanide 115

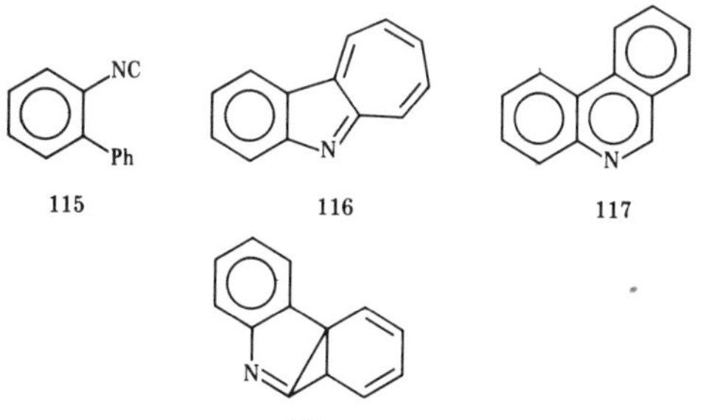

115   116   117

118

is indeed reported to isomerize to phenanthridine 117 in very low yield at 800°C (*111*).

REFERENCES

1. P. N. Rylander, S. Meyerson, and H. M. Grubb, *J. Am. Chem. Soc.* **79**, 842 (1957).
2. F. W. McLafferty and J. Winkler, *J. Am. Chem. Soc.* **96**, 5182 (1974).
2a. J. Shen and R. C. Dunbar, *J. Am. Chem. Soc.* **96**, 6227 (1974); R. C. Dunbar, *ibid.* **97**, 1382 (1975); D. A. McCrery and B. S. Freiser, *ibid.* **100**, 2902 (1978).
3. S. Takamuku, N. Sagi, K. Nagaoka, and H. Sakurai, *J. Am. Chem. Soc.* **94**, 6218 (1972).
4. O. S. Pascual and L. S. Bonoan, *Philipp. Nucl. J.* **1**, 53 (1966).
5. D. Bryce-Smith and N. A. Perkins, *J. Chem. Soc.* p. 5295 (1962).
5a. E. W. Garbisch, *J. Am. Chem. Soc.* **87**, 4971 (1965).
6. A. Baeyer, *Ber. Dtsch. Chem. Ges.* **19**, 159 (1886).
7. R. B. Thompson, *Org. Synth.* **27**, 21 (1947).
8. K. Auwers and G. Keil, *Ber. Dtsch. Chem. Ges.* **35**, 4207 (1902).
9. R. C. Cookson and N. S. Wariyar, *Chem. Ind.* (*London*) p. 915 (1955); *J. Chem. Soc.* p. 2302 (1956).
10. R. H. Thomson, *Q. Rev., Chem. Soc.* **10**, 27 (1956); see also Ershov *et al.* (*11*).
11. V. V. Ershov, A. A. Volod-Kin, and G. N. Bogdanov, *Russ. Chem. Rev.* (*Engl. Transl.*) **32**, 75 (1963).
12. G. M. Brooke, *Tetrahedron Lett.* p. 2377 (1971).
13. J. Green and D. McHale, *Chem. Ind.* (*London*) p. 1809 (1964).
14. E. D. Clifton, W. T. Flowers, and R. N. Haszeldine, *Chem. Commun.* p. 1216 (1969).
15. M. G. Barlow, R. N. Haszeldine, and M. J. Kershaw, *Tetrahedron* **31**, 1649 (1975).
16. V. Boekelheide and E. Sturm, *J. Am. Chem. Soc.* **91**, 902 (1969): cf. R. H. Mitchell and V. Boekelheide, *Tetrahedron Lett.* p. 1197 (1970).
17. R. H. Mitchell and V. Boekelheide, *J. Am. Chem. Soc.* **96**, 1547 (1974).
18. G. Quinkert, W. W. Wiersdorff, and M. Finke, *Justus Liebigs Ann. Chem.* **693**, 44 (1966).
19. G. Quinkert, W. W. Wiersdorff, M. Finke, and K. Opitz, *Tetrahedron Lett.* p. 2193 (1966).
20. R. Hug, H. J. Hansen, and H. Schmid, *Helv. Chim. Acta* **55**, 10 (1972); cf. W. Opolzer, *Angew. Chem., Int. Ed. Engl.* **11**, 1031 (1972).
21. M. R. Camp, R. H. Levin, and M. Jones, *Tetrahedron Lett.* p. 3575 (1974).
22. W. D. Crow and M. N. Paddon-Row, *J. Am. Chem. Soc.* **94**, 4746 (1972), and references therein.
23. B. Jaques and R. G. Wallace, *Chem. Commun.* p. 397 (1972).
24. W. D. Crow and C. Wentrup, *Tetrahedron Lett.* p. 4379 (1967); p. 5569 (1968); E. Hedaya, M. E. Kent, D. W. McNeil, F. P. Lossing, and T. McAllister, *ibid.* p. 3415.
25. R. A. Odum and M. Brenner, *J. Am. Chem. Soc.* **88**, 2074 (1966); W. von E. Doering and R. A. Odum, *Tetrahedron* **22**, 81 (1966); cf. R. J. Sundberg, *Tetrahedron Lett.* p. 477 (1966).
26. C. Wentrup, *Chem. Commun.* p. 1386 (1969).
27. P. G. Gassman and G. Greutzmacher, *J. Am. Chem. Soc.* **95**, 588 (1973).

28. W. von E. Doering and R. A. Bragole, *Tetrahedron* **22**, 385 (1966).
29. W. S. Trahanowsky and P. W. Mullen, *J. Am. Chem. Soc.* **94**, 5911 (1972); cf. J. Zsindely and H. Schmid, *Helv. Chim. Acta* **51**, 1510 (1968).
30. R. F. C. Brown, M. Butcher, and R. A. Fergie, *Chem. Commun.* p. 123 (1974).
31. J. H. Boyer and J. R. Patel, *Chem. Commun.* p. 855 (1977).
32. J. M. Blair and D. Bryce-Smith, *Proc. Chem. Soc., London* p. 287 (1957).
33. K. E. Wilzbach, J. S. Ritscher, and L. Kaplan, *J. Am. Chem. Soc.* **89**, 1031 (1967).
33a. L. Kaplan and K. E. Wilzbach, *J. Am. Chem. Soc.* **90**, 3291 (1968).
33b. L. Kaplan, D. J. Rausch, and K. E. Wilzbach, *J. Am. Chem. Soc.* **94**, 8638 (1972).
34. H. Lutz and G. Stein, *J. Phys. Chem.* **78**, 1909 (1974).
35. K. E. Wilzbach, private communication.
36. H. J. F. Angus and D. Bryce-Smith, *J. Chem. Soc.* p. 1409 (1960).
37. R. B. Cundall and D. A. Robinson, *J. Chem. Soc., Faraday Trans. 2* **68**, 1691 (1972).
38. Y. Izawa, H. Tomioka, T. Kagami, and T. Sato, *Chem. Commun.* p. 780 (1977).
39. K. E. Wilzbach, A. L. Harkness, and L. Kaplan, *J. Am. Chem. Soc.* **90**, 1116 (1968).
40. E. Farenhorst and A. F. Bickel, *Tetrahedron Lett.* p. 5911 (1966).
41. J. A. Berson and N. M. Hasty, *J. Am. Chem. Soc.* **93**, 1549 (1971).
42. D. Bryce-Smith, A. Gilbert, and H. C. Longuet-Higgins, *Chem. Commun.* p. 240 (1967).
43. T. J. Katz, E. J. Wang, and N. Acton, *J. Am. Chem. Soc.* **93**, 3782 (1971).
44. D. Bryce-Smith and A. Gilbert, *Tetrahedron* **32**, 1309 (1976).
45. S. A. Lee, J. M. White, and W. A. Noyes, *J. Chem. Phys.* **65**, 2805 (1976).
46. K. E. Wilzbach, personal communication.
47. D. Bryce-Smith, A. Gilbert, and D. A. Robinson, *Angew. Chem., Int. Ed. Engl.* **10**, 745 (1971).
48. H. R. Ward and J. S. Wishnok, *J. Am. Chem. Soc.* **90**, 1086 (1968).
49. E. Farenhorst, *Tetrahedron Lett.* p. 6465 (1966).
50. J. J. C. Mulder, *J. Am. Chem. Soc.* **99**, 5177 (1977).
51. L. Kaplan and K. E. Wilzbach, *J. Am. Chem. Soc.* **89**, 1030 (1967); L. Kaplan, H. R. Walsh, and K. E. Wilzbach, *ibid.* **90**, 5646 (1968); H. R. Ward and J. S. Wishnok, *ibid.* p. 5353.
52. I. Haller, *J. Chem. Phys.* **47**, 1117 (1967); F. Camaggi, F. Gozzo, and G. Cevidalli, *Chem. Commun.* p. 313 (1966); I. Haller, *J. Am. Chem. Soc.* **88**, 2070 (1966); A. Bergonin and F. Gozzo, *Chim. Ind. (Milan)* **50**, 745 (1968).
53. D. Bryce-Smith, B. E. Connett, A. Gilbert, and E. Kendrick, *Chem. Ind. (London)* p. 855 (1966).
54. E. Ratajczak, *Rocz. Chem.* **44**, 447 (1970).
55. G. P. Semeluk and R. D. S. Stevens, *Chem. Commun.* p. 1720 (1970).
56. M. E. McBeath, G. P. Semeluk, and I. Unger, *J. Phys. Chem.* **73**, 995 (1969).
57. M. G. Barlow, R. N. Haszeldine, and R. Hubbard, *J. Chem. Soc. C* p. 1232 (1970).
58. D. M. Lemal, J. V. Staros, and V. Austel, *J. Am. Chem. Soc.* **19**, 3373 (1965).
59. T. J. Katz and N. Acton, *J. Am. Chem. Soc.* **95**, 2738 (1973).
60. G. Porter, *Chem. Soc., Spec. Publ.* **9**, 139 (1958); B. A. Thrush, *Nature (London)* **178**, 155 (1955); L. Grajar and S. Leach, *J. Chim. Phys.* **61**, 1523 (1964); E. Migirdicyan, *Ber. Bunsenges. Phys. Chem.* **72**, 344 (1968); *C.R. Hebd. Seances Acad. Sci., Ser. C* **266**, 756 (1968); S. Leach, A. Lopez-Campillo, R. Lopez-Delgado, and M. C. Tomas-Magos, *J. Phys. (Paris)* **28**, C3-C147 (1967).
61. L. Kaplan, K. E. Wilzbach, W. G. Brown, and S. S. Yang, *J. Am. Chem. Soc.* **87**, 675 (1965).
62. J. A. Barltrop and A. C. Day, *Chem. Commun.* p. 177 (1975).

63. R. D. Chambers, R. Middleton, and R. Corbally, *Chem. Commun.* p. 731 (1975), and references therein.
64. K. E. Wilzbach and L. Kaplan, *J. Am. Chem. Soc.* **87**, 4004 (1965); I. E. Den Besten, L. Kaplan, and K. E. Wilzbach, *ibid.* **90**, 5868 (1968); see also reference 61.
65. H. G. Viehe, *Angew. Chem., Int. Ed. Engl.* **4**, 746 (1965).
66. C. A. Renner, T. J. Katz, J. Pouliquen, N. J. Turro, and W. H. Waddell, *J. Am. Chem. Soc.* **97**, 2568 (1975).
67. M. G. Barlow, R. N. Haszeldine, and M. J. Kershaw, *J. Chem. Soc., Perkin Trans.* I p. 1736 (1974).
68. K. E. Wilzbach and L. Kaplan, *J. Am. Chem. Soc.* **86**, 2307 (1964).
69. A. W. Burgstahler and P.-L. Chien, *J. Am. Chem. Soc.* **86**, 2940 (1964); A. W. Burgstahler, P.-L. Chien, and Abden-Rahman, *ibid.* p. 5281.
70. E. E. van Tamelen, S. P. Pappas, and K. L. Kirk, *J. Am. Chem. Soc.* **93**, 6092 (1971); E. E. van Tamelen and S. P. Pappas, *ibid.* **84**, 3789, (1962); **85**, 3297 (1963).
71. G. Porter and E. J. Wright, *Trans. Faraday Soc.* **51**, 1469 (1955).
72. D. Bryce-Smith, ed., "Photochemistry," Spec. Period. Rep., Vols. 1–10, Chem. Soc., London, 1970–1979.
73. E. M. Arnett and J. M. Bollinger, *Tetrahedron Lett.* p. 3803 (1964); C. Hoogzand and W. Hübel, *ibid.* p. 637 (1961).
74. R. West, M. Furue, and V. N. Mallikarjuna Rao, *Tetrahedron Lett.* p. 911 (1973).
75. G. Lodder, P. E. J. Du-Mee, and E. Havinga, *Tetrahedron Lett.* p. 5949 (1968).
76. V. Mende, J. L. Laseter, and G. W. Griffin, *Tetrahedron Lett.* p. 3747 (1970).
77. R. A. Abramovich and O. A. Koleoso, *J. Chem. Soc. B* p. 779 (1969); R. A. Abramovich and T. Takaya, *J. Chem. Soc., Perkin Trans.* I p. 1806 (1975).
78. K. Al-Ani, *J. Chem. Phys.* **58**, 5073 (1973).
79. T. Matsuura, Y. Hiromoto, A. Okada, and K. Ogura, *Tetrahedron* **29**, 2981 (1973).
80. H. E. Zimmerman and D. S. Crumrine, *J. Am. Chem. Soc.* **94**, 498 (1972).
81. J. J. Houser, M.-C. Chen, and S. S. Wang, *J. Org. Chem.* **39**, 1387 (1974).
82. P. G. Sammes, *Tetrahedron* **32**, 405 (1976).
83. G. Porter and M. F. Tchir, *J. Chem. Soc. A* p. 3772 (1971).
84. P. J. Wagner, *Pure Appl. Chem.* **49**, 259 (1977).
84a. P. G. Sammes and T. W. Wallace, *J. Chem. Soc., Perkin Trans.* I p. 1845 (1975).
85. N. C. Yang and C. Rivas, *J. Am. Chem. Soc.* **83**, 2213 (1961).
86. E. Block and R. Stevenson, *J. Chem. Soc., Perkin Trans.* I p. 308 (1973); M. Pfau, E. W. Sarver, and N. D. Heindel, *Bull. Chim. Soc. Fr.*, p. 183 (1973).
87. D. Creed, *Chem. Commun.* p. 121 (1976).
88. S. M. Mellows and P. G. Sammes, *Chem. Commun.* p. 21 (1971).
89. W. Oppolzer and K. Keller, *Angew. Chem., Int. Ed. Engl.* **11**, 728 (1972).
90. E. Rommel and J. Wirz, *Helv. Chim. Acta* **60**, 38 (1977).
91. G. Ciamician and P. Silber, *Ber. Dtsch. Chem. Ges.* **34**, 3040 (1901).
92. P. de Mayo and S. T. Reid, *Q. Rev., Chem. Soc.* **216**, 109 (1969).
93. R. Dessaker, and J. P. Paris, *Adv. Photochem.* **1**, 275 (1963); J. D. Margerum and L. J. Miller, *in* "Photochromism" (G. H. Brown, ed.), p. 580. Wiley (Interscience), New York, 1971.
94. R. C. Cookson, S. M. de B. Costa, and J. Hudec, *Chem. Commun.* p. 1272 (1969).
95. H. Kleinhuis, R. L. C. Wijting, and E. Havinga, *Tetrahedron Lett.* p. 255 (1971).
96. A. C. Pratt, *Chem. Commun.* p. 183 (1974).
97. W. J. Feat and W. E. Preston, *Chem. Commun.* p. 985 (1974).
98. W. R. Roth, *Tetrahedron Lett.* p. 1009 (1964); L. L. Miller and R. F. Boyer, *J. Am. Chem. Soc.* **93**, 650 (1971).

99. E. V. Blackburn and C. J. Timmons, *Q. Rev., Chem. Soc.* **23**, 482 (1969).
100. T. D. Doyle, W. R. Benson, and N. Filipescu, *J. Am. Chem. Soc.* **98**, 3262 (1976); M. Maienthal, W. R. Benson, E. B. Sheinin, T. D. Doyle, and N. Filipescu, *J. Org. Chem.* **43**, 972 (1978); T. J. H. M. Cuppen and W. H. Laarhoven, *J. Am. Chem. Soc.* **94**, 5914 (1972).
101. H. G. Heller and M. Szewczyk, *J. Chem. Soc., Perkin Trans.* I p. 1487 (1974).
102. P. J. Darcy, R. J. Hart, and H. G. Heller, *J. Chem. Soc., Perkin Trans.* I p. 571 (1978), and references therein.
103. I. Ninomiya, T. Kiguchi, and T. Naito, *Chem. Commun.* p. 81 (1974); also references in Bryce-Smith (*72*).
104. Y. Kanaoka and K. Itoh, *Chem. Commun.* p. 647 (1973).
105. E. W. Förster, K. H. Grellmann, and H. Linschitz, *J. Am. Chem. Soc.* **95**, 3108 (1973).
106. M. Sauerbier, *Chem.-Ztg.* **96**, 530 (1972); see also *Tetrahedron Lett.* p. 547 (1972).
107. G. Büchi, C. W. Perry, and E. W. Robb, *J. Org. Chem.* **27**, 4106 (1962).
108. K. Ota, K. Murofushi, T. Hoshi, and H. Inoue, *Tetrahedron Lett.* p. 1431 (1974).
109. D. Bryce-Smith and J. E. Lodge, *J. Chem. Soc.* p. 695 (1963).
110. J. de Jong and J. H. Boyer, *J. Org. Chem.* **37**, 3571 (1972); *Chem. Commun.* p. 961 (1971).
111. R. F. C. Brown, M. Butcher, and R. A. Fergie, *Aust. J. Chem.* **26**, 1319 (1973).

ESSAY 20 | # PHOTOREARRANGEMENTS VIA BIRADICALS OF SIMPLE CARBONYL COMPOUNDS

PETER J. WAGNER

I. INTRODUCTION

A. General Scope

This essay deals with a varied group of light-induced rearrangements that have but one feature in common: They all involve biradical or biradical-like intermediates. In all cases the rearrangements are actually coincidental, depending on the structure of the reactant, which may allow either formation of a biradical instead of a pair of radicals or internal rather than external trapping of some reactive intermediate. For example, 3-pentanone undergoes photocleavage to a propionyl–ethyl radical pair, the ensuing reactions of which yield no net rearrangement products. Cyclopentanone, in contrast, undergoes an identical cleavage to an acyl–alkyl biradical, the subsequent disproportionation of which yields net rearrangement products. Likewise, most bifunctional reactions can occur intramolecularly if the two functional groups are properly situated within a molecule. Thus, for example, internal photocycloaddition of various unsaturated ketones leads to bicyclic oxetanes.

REARRANGEMENTS IN GROUND AND EXCITED STATES, VOL. 3

In a mechanistic sense, none of the rearrangements to be discussed are actually intrinsic to the functional groups involved. In all cases, the mechanisms involve several steps. The actual formation of the rearrangement product is always but one of several competitive reactions of an intermediate.

The detailed presentation of these biradical-mediated rearrangements is organized according to the type of excited state process that produces the biradical.

B. Structure–Reactivity Correlations in Photochemistry

Since this essay deals exclusively with photoreactions, a brief reiteration of the factors that influence rates, efficiencies, and yields is necessary. Excited states are reactive intermediates that undergo many competitive reactions. Unlike ground state intermediates, such as carbonium ions, excited states can undergo various physical decay and quenching processes that lower the efficiency with which absorption of light may lead to a desired chemical change. As long as the competitive reactions of the excited state are only physical, the quantum efficiency of a photorearrangement may be lowered; the chemical yield is lowered only if other chemical changes compete. Excited states often undergo only one major chemical reaction. (Important competitive processes will be noted.) However, biradical intermediates always undergo several competitive reactions; these include coupling, disproportionation, rearrangement, and cleavage, any of which can lower the chemical yield of the desired overall rearrangement. The biradical also can return to ground state reactant, thus lowering the quantum efficiency of any rearrangement.

Equations (1) and (2) describe quantum yields and chemical yields, respectively, for triplet state photoreactions in terms of the rate constants for competing excited state and biradical reactions; all the k's are identified in Scheme 1. The k_d's refer to physical decay processes, and the k_c's to competitive chemical processes of excited states; k'_p includes all competitive chemical reactions of the biradical (BR).

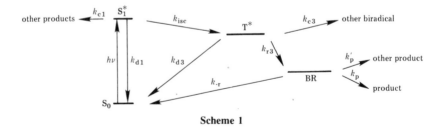

Scheme 1

$$\phi = \left(\frac{k_{isc}}{k_{isc} + k_{dl} + k_{cl}} \right) \left(\frac{k_{r3}}{k_{r3} + k_{d3} + k_{c3}} \right) \left(\frac{k_p}{k_p + k_p' + k_{-r}} \right) \quad (1)$$

$$Y = \left(\frac{k_{isc}}{k_{isc} + k_{cl}} \right) \left(\frac{k_{r3}}{k_{r3} + f k_{c3}} \right) \left(\frac{k_p}{k_p + k_p'} \right) \quad (2)$$

As the equations indicate, yields are the products of three independent probabilities: that each kinetically distinct intermediate will proceed toward product rather than do something else. As described above, the chemical yield Y is affected only by competing chemical reactions, whereas the quantum efficiency ϕ is also affected by competitive processes that return intermediates to ground state reactant.

One important point regarding how relative product yields relate to relative triplet state rate constants is not always recognized. Note that in Eq. (2) there is an f in the denominator of the second factor, whereas in Eq. (1) this is not the case. The f describes the fraction of the competitively formed biradicals that go on to stable by-products instead of returning to ground state reactant. Scheme 2 illustrates this problem for the case of two competitive triplet reactions. In terms of Scheme 2, the f in Eq. (2) equals $k_z(k_z + k_{-c})^{-1}$. The extent to which a competitive triplet reaction affects relative product yields depends on how efficiently the alternative biradical proceeds to a stable by-product. If the alternative biradical were to revert almost exclusively to reactant, the resulting very low Z/X product ratio would provide a very inaccurate estimate of k_{c3}/k_{r3}. Such situations are far from uncommon.

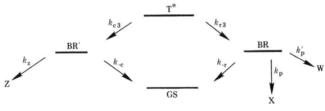

Scheme 2

$$\frac{Y_x}{Y_w} = \frac{k_p}{k_p'} \quad (3)$$

$$\frac{Y_x}{Y_z} = \frac{k_{r3}}{k_{c3}} \left(\frac{k_p}{k_p + k_p' + k_{-r}} \right) \left(\frac{k_z + k_{-c}}{k_z} \right) \quad (4)$$

Because the yields and efficiencies of these photoreactions are determined by the results of competitive processes of distinct intermediates, the detailed discussion below presents, as much as possible, two separate structure–reactivity profiles for each rearrangement—one for the excited state and one for the biradical.

II. CLEAVAGE REACTIONS

A. Cyclic Ketones

As mentioned briefly in Section I, ketones (and aldehydes) undergo facile photolysis to acyl–alkyl radical pairs (*1*). Cycloalkanones necessarily lead to acyl–alkyl biradicals, as exemplified below by cyclohexanone. The actual overall rearrangement results from disproportionation of the biradical to give unsaturated aldehyde and ketene. The competition between these two disproportionation modes and reclosure (which can result in epimerization of the α-carbon) varies markedly with structure.

General aspects of the reaction will be discussed before specific structure–reactivity patterns are presented.

The reaction proceeds most smoothly for cyclopentanones and α-substituted larger cycloalkanones. Cyclobutanones decarbonylate and rearrange to oxacarbenes (*2*); cyclohexanone and larger cycloalkanones undergo competitive photoreduction, both bimolecular and intramolecular. It is possible to utilize the rearrangement for syntheses, such as that of propylure (*3*).

The reaction has not been studied as thoroughly as other ketone photoreactions, possibly because both aldehyde and ketene products are unstable to light. The former undergo facile internal cycloadditions and hydrogen abstractions (*4*); they can also revert to cyclic ketones (*4,5*). The latter decompose to carbenes.

Ketenes are rarely if ever isolated. Their characteristic IR signals have been observed after low-temperature irradiation of cycloalkanones (*6*).

Most commonly they are trapped by nucleophilic solvents. In this regard, methanol and *t*-butyl alcohol are the best, since ketones are not as readily photoreduced in these solvents as they are in ethanol. Amines are not satisfactory, since they reduce excited ketones very rapidly. *t*-Butylamine has been employed successfully. Of course, water leads to acids. Methanol has been used to trap ketenes in most mechanistic studies.

The ketenes formed from suitable hydroxy ketones are trapped internally as lactones. Early examples were provided by the behavior of 5-hydroxy-6-cholestanone (7) and 4-hydroxydecalone (8).

Further photoreaction of unsaturated aldehydes sometimes can be controlled by conducting the initial reactions in methanol, possibly with a pinch of acid catalyst, in which case the aldehydes are largely converted to the nonabsorbing acetals (9).

Reclosure of biradical to ketone can cause epimerization of the α-carbon, as has been observed with several steroids (10), or can simply waste energy. Although this epimerization is a rearrangement, it will not

be discussed further. When the biradical undergoes some rearrangement, however, reclosure affords a skeletally rearranged ketone. Several interesting examples will be presented in Section II,A and III,C.

1. Excited State Considerations

The efficiency of excited state cleavage (biradical formation) depends on how well the rate constant for cleavage competes with other chemical reactions, since excited ketones undergo no rapid radiationless decay processes. The main possible competitive reactions are hydrogen abstraction, either internal or from solvent, and charge-transfer quenching by electron-rich solvents.

The rate constant for α-cleavage depends on the nature of the excited state, on the relative stability of the alkyl radical formed (C—C bond strength), probably on the degree of steric crowding in the reactant ketone, and perhaps on solvent polarity.

The reaction appears to demand n,π^* excitation, since several ketones with π,π^* lowest triplets cleave either slowly or not at all (*11*). As in hydrogen abstraction (*12*), the cleavage mimics an analogous reaction of alkoxy radicals, which n,π^* triplets resemble electronically (*13,14*).

Turro, Yang, and co-workers (*15,15a*) have shown that the n,π^* triplet of a given aliphatic ketone cleaves some 100 times faster than the first-formed n,π^* singlet, despite the greater exothermocity for the latter's cleavage. Several explanations have been advanced for the difference (*16,17*). For our purposes, it is sufficient to generalize that most rearrangements resulting from α cleavage occur from n,π^* triplets.

Phenyl ketone triplets cleave two to four orders of magnitude more slowly than the corresponding aliphatic ketone triplets, presumably because of unfavorable thermodynamics (*18,18a*). Since most ring substituents stabilize π,π^* triplets, very few phenones cleave efficiently, and the following discussion is directed entirely to aliphatic ketones.

With acyclic ketones, rate constants for triplet state cleavage range from $\sim 10^3$ sec^{-1} when R = CH$_3$ to $\sim 10^{10}$ sec^{-1} when R = benzyl, with a value of the order of 10^7 sec^{-1} for R = primary alkyl (*14*). The last value also applies to cyclohexanone (*16,19*). Cyclopentanone triplet cleaves ten times faster (*19–21*); cycloheptanone cleaves twice as fast (*19*). These increases presumably reflect release of ring strain; it is unfortunate that no rates have been measured for other ring sizes.

α-Alkyl substituents enhance cleavage rate constants by a factor of 20 for both cyclopentanone and cyclohexanone (*19,21*). Ring strain and α substitution combine to make the triplet cleavage of bicyclic ketones, such as norbornanone and camphor, extremely rapid, the latter reaction being unquenchable (*15*).

β-Alkyl substitution does not significantly change the cleavage rate of triplet cyclohexanone (*21*), whereas 4-alkyl substitution seems to slow cleavage considerably (*16*).

In cycloalkanones unsubstituted at either α-carbon, the major competing triplet reaction is photoreduction by solvent; this proceeds with a pseudounimolecular rate constant of $10^6 \, \text{sec}^{-1}$ in hexane (22) and $10^7 \, \text{sec}^{-1}$ in ethanol. The value is somewhere in between for methanol (23). In solvents such as acetonitrile, acetic acid, acetone, ethyl acetate, and t-butyl alcohol, photoreduction is very slow ($k < 10^4 \, \text{sec}^{-1}$).

As described in more detail later, (Section III,B) intramolecular hydrogen abstraction is extremely rapid whenever a γ-hydrogen is within bonding distance of the carbonyl oxygen. The triplet rate constant for a secondary γ C—H is $\sim 10^8 \, \text{sec}^{-1}$ (14). To make matters worse, singlet state γ-hydrogen abstraction is also rapid and thus can prevent formation of the triplet state required for cleavage.

The result of all these competitive rates is that cyclopentanones and most α-alkylcycloalkanones undergo efficient cleavage in many common organic solvents, provided that the α-alkyl substituent does not contain C—H bonds γ to the carbonyl (16,24). Six- to ten-carbon cycloalkanones without α substituents are primarily photoreduced in solvents such as alcohols, ethers, and alkanes. Larger cycloalkanones undergo internal hydrogen abstraction. The behavior of cyclododecanone (24) and that of its α-methyl homologue (25) demonstrate the efficiency of α substitution in promoting cleavage.

76%   10%   14%

The contrasting photochemistry of *cis*- and *trans*-2-n-propyl-4-t-butyl-cyclohexanone exemplifies the conformational requirements for competing internal hydrogen abstraction (26). The former has γ-hydrogens accessible to the carbonyl and undergoes very little α cleavage; the latter has no accessible γ-hydrogens and undergoes only α cleavage.

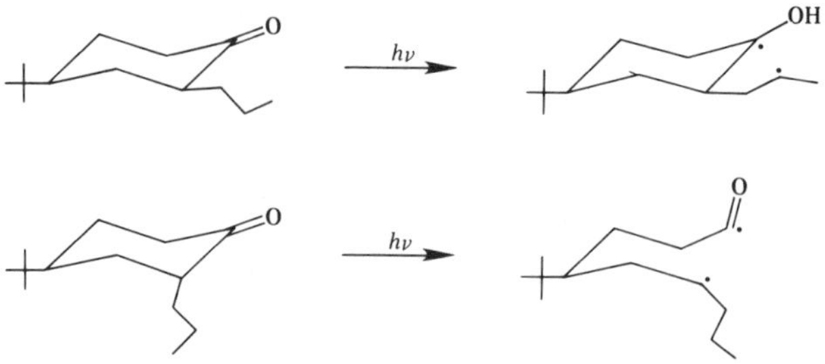

There is an unusual, poorly understood solvent effect on these α-cleavage reactions; quantum efficiencies and often chemical yields are very low in benzene, whereas they are respectable to good in alcohols. Many investigators have noted this effect; none have explained it. It is possible that, as in the β cleavage of alkoxy radicals (27), polar solvents enhance α-cleavage rates. However, what few kinetic data exist suggest only a twofold rate increase upon changing solvent from benzene (16) to methanol (19). It may also be that further decomposition of untrapped ketenes is responsible for low yields.

Unsubstituted cycloalkanones can cleave either of two equivalent C—C bonds. Substituents remove this symmetry such that one bond may cleave preferentially. With α substituents the more stable biradical is formed preferentially, as is obvious from the ability of α-alkylation to enhance cleavage rates. However, some α substitution forces cleavage of the other bond. The spiro ketone (29a) shown below not only forms a primary alkyl radical site preferentially over a tertiary cyclopropyl site, but also undergoes α cleavage preferentially over the well-known ring cleavage of acylcyclopropanes (30).

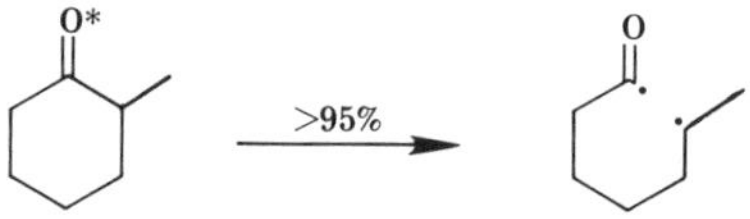

(28)

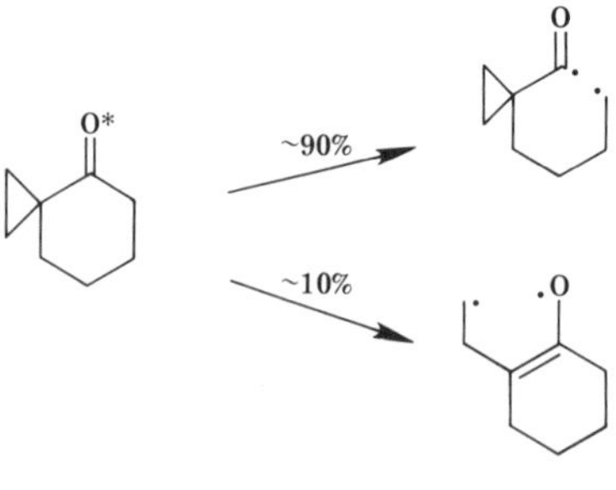

(29, 29a)

Biradical stabilization by cyclopropyl groups is also significant, so much so that 4-caranone opens in only one direction.

$(31, 31a)$

(32)

β-Alkyl substituents do not affect triplet state cleavage rates (21) but do markedly lower quantum efficiencies $(21,33)$. As described later, such substitution must influence primarily the behavior of the biradical. Thus, the $2:1$ product ratios from both 3-methylcyclopentanone (33) and 3-methylcyclohexanone (34), which may seem to suggest preferential opening of the bond away from the β substituent, probably reflect instead more favorable product formation from that biradical.

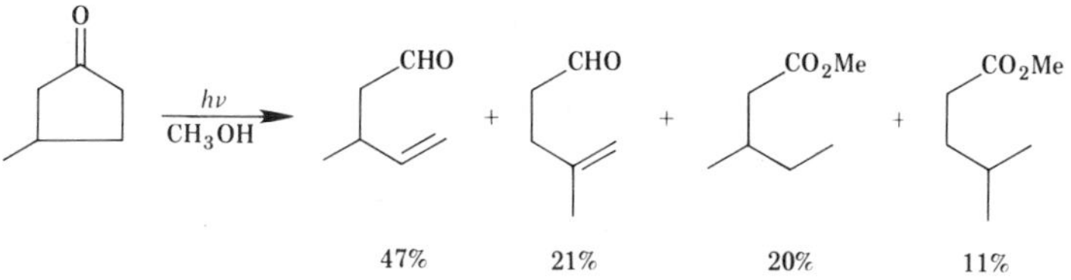

47%   21%   20%   11%

2. Biradical Partitioning

Even if a triplet ketone cleaves efficiently, the resulting biradical must disproportionate rather than merely recouple, or rearrange before recoupling, if any rearrangement is to be efficient. In the absence of competing triplet reactions, closure of the biradical lowers quantum efficiencies but not chemical yields.

Ring size, substituents, and solvent all perturb the partitioning of the biradical intermediates in ways that can usually be interpreted but are not always predictable. Each of the three competing reactions has a transition state of different geometry and thus proceeds best from different conformations of the biradical. Coyle has presented the most complete analysis of cyclohexanone rearrangements in terms of chairlike transition states (35). This sort of analysis is possible since the relatively long lifetimes of triplet-derived biradicals $(36–36b)$ indicate that conformational equilibrium is approached or attained before the biradicals form products. It must be remembered that all three competing reactions must have small activation energies so that substituent effects are often subtle rather than dramatic.

Substituents at various positions introduce gauche or 1,3-diaxial interactions that destabilize one or more of the reactive conformations relative to those leading to other processes. Specific examples follow.

Cyclopentanone reacts in 77% quantum efficiency in methanol and furnishes a 97% yield of 4-pentenal (33). In benzene the enal yield remains high but the quantum efficiency drops to only 28%. Cyclohexanone rearranges in lower quantum efficiency and furnishes comparable amounts of enal and ketene (1.6 : 1) (35). It seems clear that reclosure of the smaller biradical is retarded by the same ring strain that favored its formation. Quantum yields have not been reported for larger cycloalkanones.

2-Alkyl substitution results in product quantum yields and enal/ketene ratios that are higher than those observed for cyclohexanone (35). Presumably the more substituted the alkyl radical site, the more the biradical prefers disproportionation over recoupling, as in radical–radical reactions (37).

3-Methyl substitution on cyclopentanone (33) and 3- and 5-methyl substitution on cyclohexanone (21,35) lower rearrangement quantum efficiencies severely and favor ketene over enal formation.

3,3-Dimethylcyclopentanone gives products that appear to favor C-5—C-1 cleavage over C-1—C-2 cleavage by 9 : 1. The latter biradical cannot form enal and must recouple with high efficiency. If both biradicals form equally, the reported quantum yields (33) indicate the following competitions. The *gem*-dimethyl substitution apparently enhances ketene formation from the biradical which can form enal.

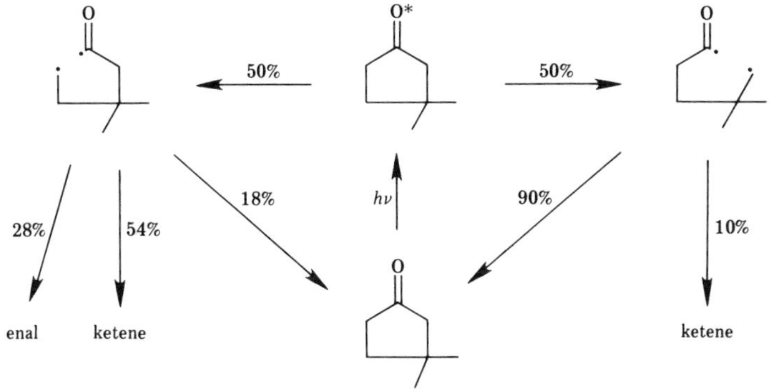

$$\text{biradical} \xleftarrow{50\%} \text{O*} \xrightarrow{50\%} \text{biradical}$$

28%   54%   18% $h\nu$ 90%   10%

enal   ketene   ketene

With 3,5-dimethylcyclohexanone, only one biradical can be formed. As shown in Coyle's scheme, a 3 substituent not only halves the number of hydrogens available for enal formation but also introduces 1,3-diaxial interactions into the transition state for enal formation. Since overall quantum efficiency is low *(21)*, both product-forming transition states must be destabilized.

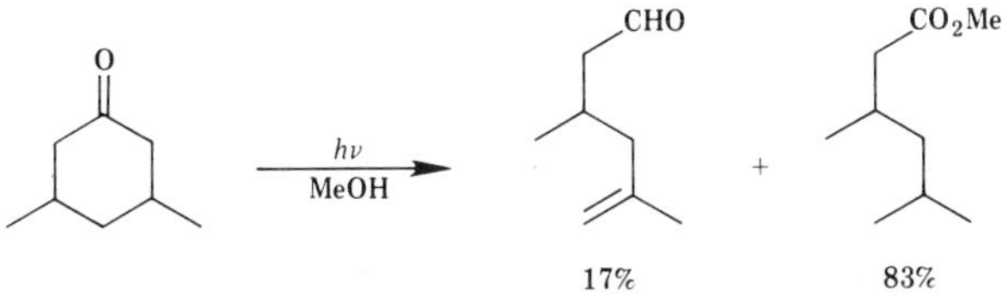

$$\xrightarrow[\text{MeOH}]{h\nu}$$

CHO CO_2Me

17%   83%

Even 5-alkyl substituents affect the partitioning of the biradical, apparently by introducing gauche interactions into the transition state for ketene formation *(38)*. 2-Methyl substitution has been used to force ring opening in one direction. Interestingly, the larger 5-alkyl groups depress ketene formation, in contrast to the effects noted for 3-methyl groups on cyclopentanone *(33)* just discussed.

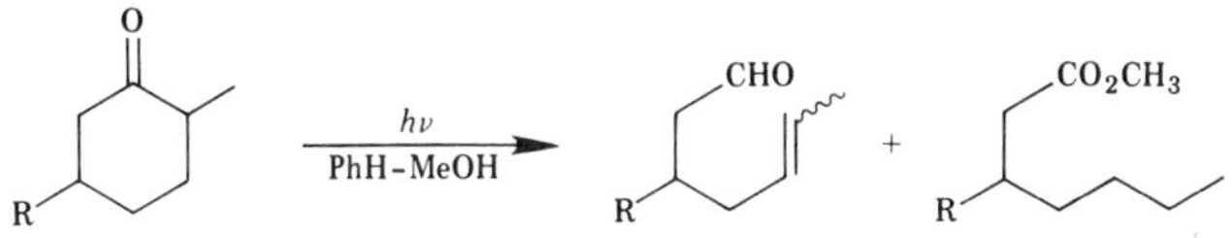

$$\xrightarrow[\text{PhH–MeOH}]{h\nu}$$

CHO CO_2CH_3

R = H	74%	26%
CH_3	69%	31%
i-Pr	84%	16%
t-Bu	90%	10%

The behavior of 3-methylcyclohexanone is puzzling. As indicated above, triplet cleavage apparently produces both possible biradicals about equally. It has been reported that both enal and ester products indicate a 2:1 cleavage preference away from the 3-methyl (*34*). Enal/ketene ratios have been reported that imply the opposite cleavage preference for ketene formation (*35*). Although the results already presented for 3-methylcyclopentanone (*33*) support the former product distribution, the latter is more consistent with other results. The branching ratio for the left biradical is identical to that observed in both cyclohexanone and 2,5-dimethylcyclohexanone. The preference for ketene formation from the right biradical agrees with the effects of 3-methyl groups on several other cyclohexanones (*37*).

4-Alkyl substituents also retard enal formation. 4-*t*-Butylcyclohexanone is photoreduced in cyclohexane (*18,18a*) and produces only 18% enal in benzene/methanol (*35*), presumably in very low quantum efficiency. It is probable that gauche interactions destabilize the transition state leading to enal. It is not clear how much the lack of cleavage in cyclohexane is due to a lowered rate of α cleavage as opposed to the very low efficiency of product formation from the biradical allowing a slower triplet reaction (H abstraction from solvent) to predominate.

The effects of a second methyl on the product distribution from 2-methylcyclohexanone (*35,38*) are summarized in Table 1.

Bicyclic ketones provide more rigid stereochemical and stereoelectronic limitations. The bicyclo[3.2.1]-6-octanone system presents a fine

TABLE 1

Effects of Substitution on the Product Distribution from 2-Methylcyclohexanone

	Enal (%)	Ketene (%)
	74	26
	43	57
	65	35
	69	31
	84	16

example (39). The larger R becomes, the more the acyl radical site is forced into an axial position, when only ketene formation is possible.

It has been found that, in simple cyclohexanones, the biradical attacks an originally axial β-hydrogen twice as fast as an originally equatorial β-hydrogen (34). Again, a pseudo-chair transition state would place the methylene group axial for transfer of H_e. It has not been pointed out before that stereoelectronic factors would force one hydrogen of the methylene very close to the axial hydrogen at C-5. That so much equatorial hydrogen transfer occurs anyway indicates that the transition state is a fairly spread-out chair.

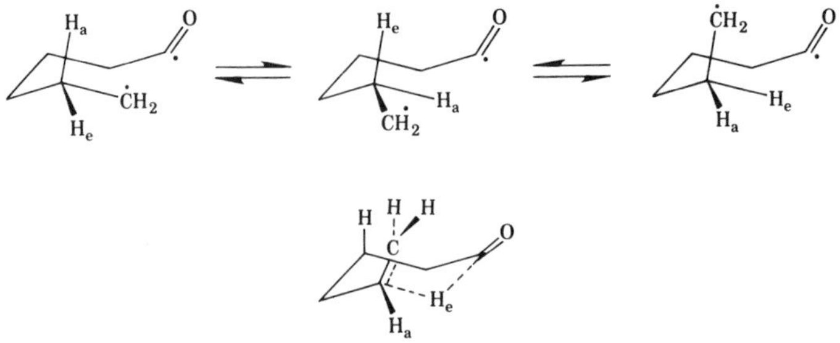

The bicyclononanone below provides an example of an unusually large remote substituent effect that is not easily rationalized (*31*).

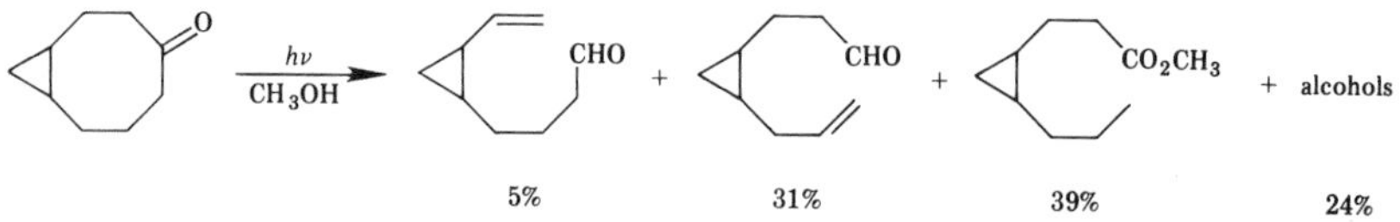

In 2-alkylcyclopentanones and 2-alkylcyclohexanones, a mixture of *cis*- and *trans*-enals is always formed (*28*). In fact, the common *cis*-enal/*trans*-enal ratio produced from both *cis*- and *trans*-2,3-dimethylcyclohexanone was early evidence for the intermediacy of a biradical (*40*).

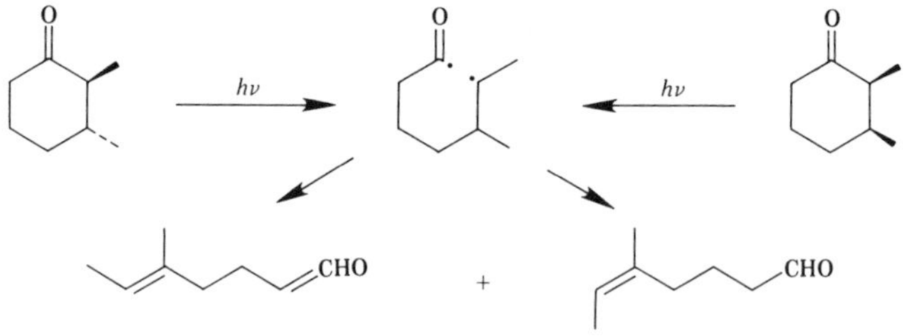

2-Methylcycloalkanones all cleave efficiently, even those with medium-sized rings (*41*). Although 2-methylcyclopentanone and 2-methylcyclohexanone produce no terminally unsaturated aldehydes, larger 2-methylcycloalkanones produce progressively larger percentages of terminal enal, as shown below. It had been reported earlier that 2,2,6,6-tetramethylcyclohexanone also furnishes a small amount of terminal enal (*42*). This competition again demonstrates the subtle conformational effects in those biradicals.

n	%	%
0	100	0
1	100	0
2	69	31
3	39	61
7	11	89

85%   11%

3. Biradical Rearrangements

The reasonably long lifetimes of these triplet-derived biradicals allow many monoradical rearrangements to occur. These rearrangements can be exploited synthetically.

α-Cyclopropyl ketones yield products in which the intermediate biradical has undergone the rapid rearrangement of cyclopropylcarbinyl to allylcarbinyl (43) (see Essay 21):

21%   29%   44%

A colorful example of this phenomenon is the rearrangement of α-dicyclopropyl ketones (42):

61%   20%

β,γ-Cyclopropyl ketones display the same rearrangements:

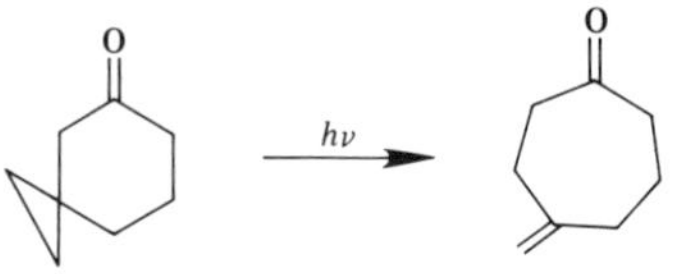

(29)

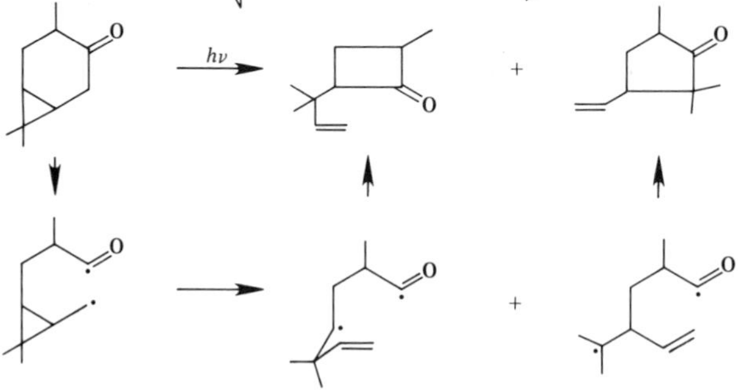

(32)

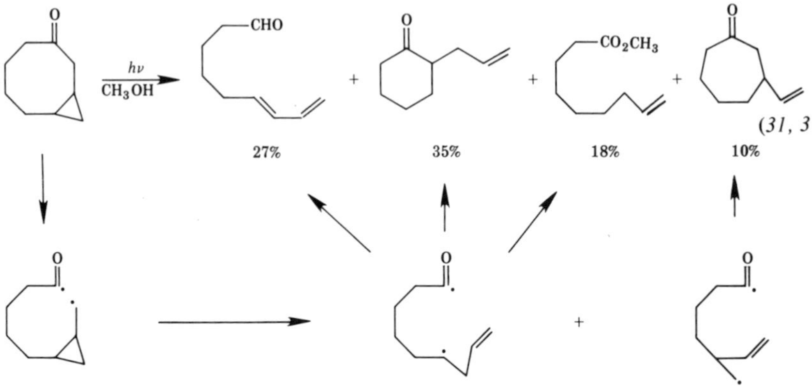

(31, 31a)

27%   35%   18%   10%

α-Oxiranyl substituents provide examples of similar rearrangements (45):

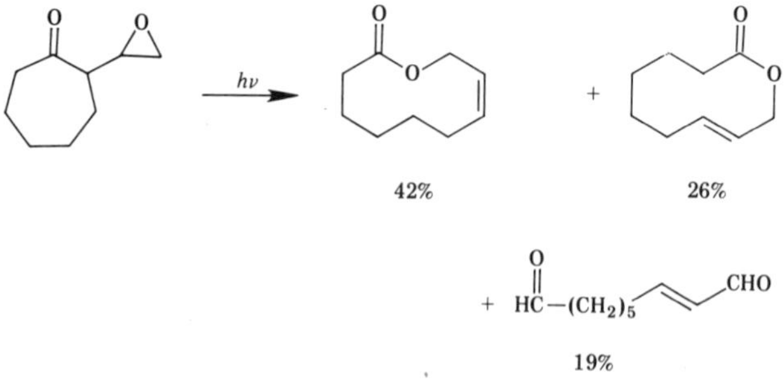

42%   26%

$$+ \quad \overset{O}{\overset{\|}{HC}}-(CH_2)_5 \diagup\diagdown CHO$$

19%

Two kinds of cyclopropyl ketones open to diradicals that possess cyclopropylacyl radical moieties (29,29a,46). These do not rearrange to ketenes, possibly because of the inherent relative stability of acyl radicals.

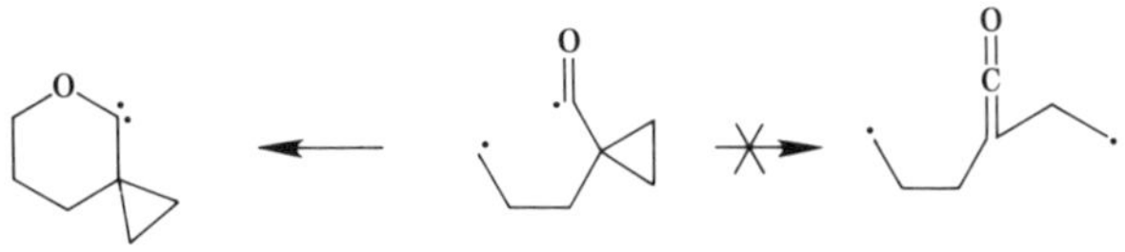

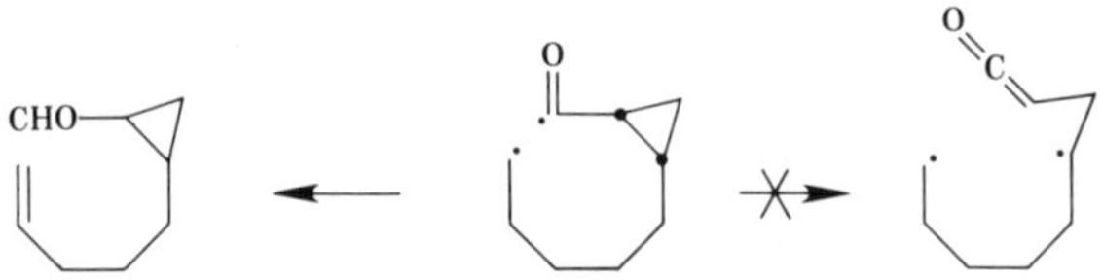

α-Vinylcycloalkanones, and β,γ-unsaturated ketones in general, undergo allylic rearrangements that can be interpreted most simply as reclosure of an allylic biradical. These reactions are complicated by other competing reactions and are treated in Essay 17 (*47*). Nonetheless, a few examples are presented here.

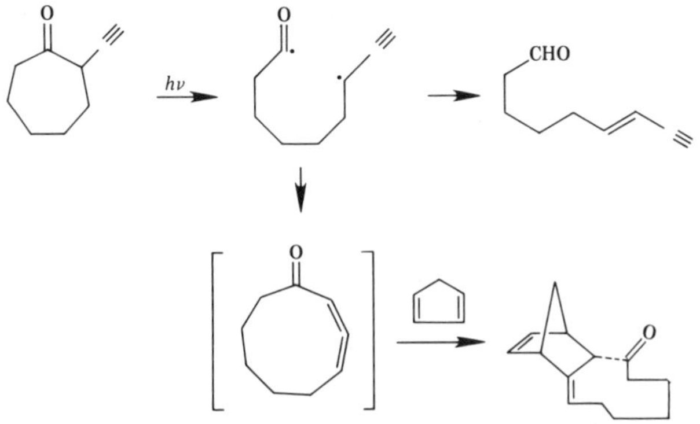

(*48*)

The last example is interesting in that the originally formed biradical is not allylic, since the acyl radical site is a σ radical, perpendicular to the α,β double bond.

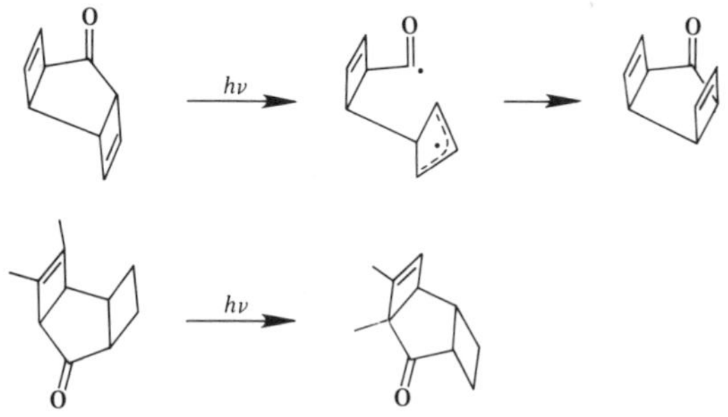

(*49*)

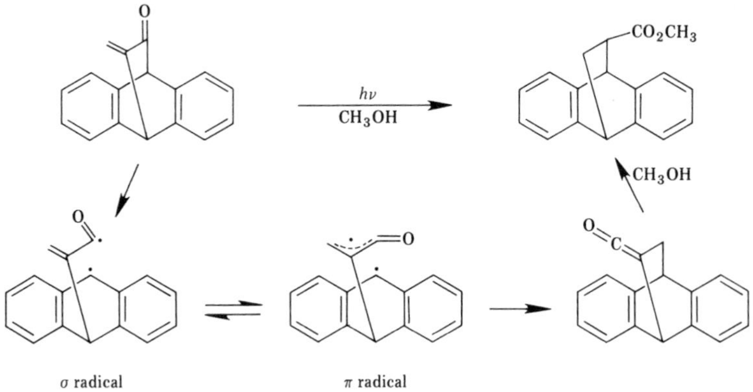

(50)

σ radical   π radical

Nonenolizable β-diketones rearrange to lactones via acyl enolate diradicals (51–52).

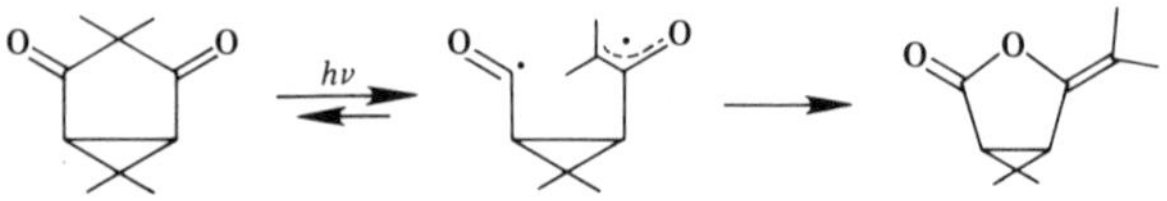

(51a)

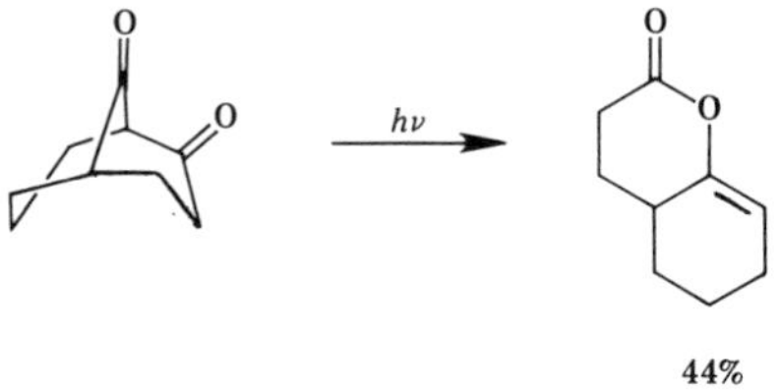

(52)

44%

The second example is interesting in that cleavage of the bridging carbonyl is less favored and leads to decarbonylation rather than to rearrangements (see below).

Finally, α-cyanocycloalkanones rearrange to ketenimides, which are captured by protic solvents (53).

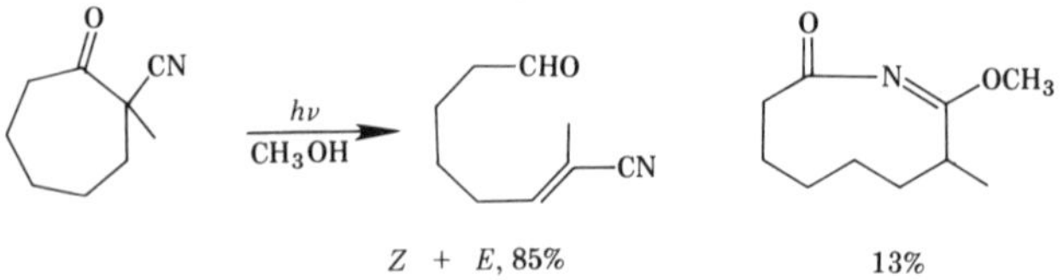

Z + E, 85%   13%

4. Competing Biradical Reactions

Decarbonylation occasionally competes with other biradical reactions if both α-carbons of the original ketone are substituted with strong radical-stabilizing groups or if serious ring strain can be relieved, especially in bicycloalkanones with bridging carbonyls.

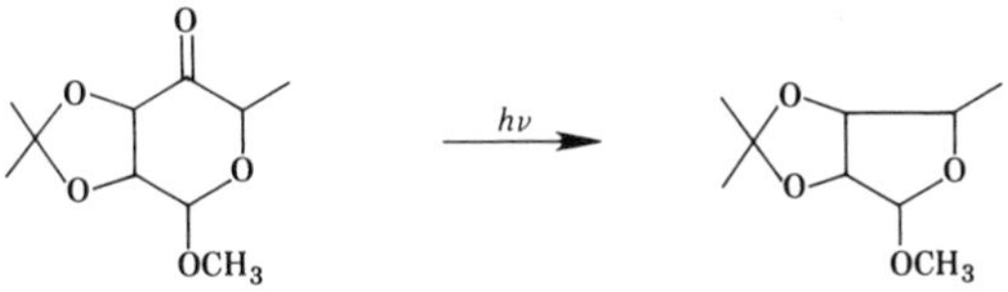

(54)

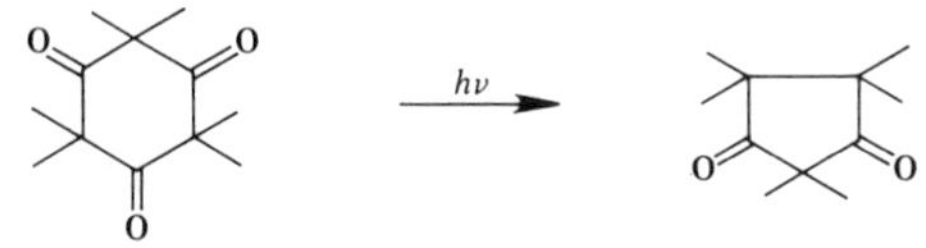

(51)

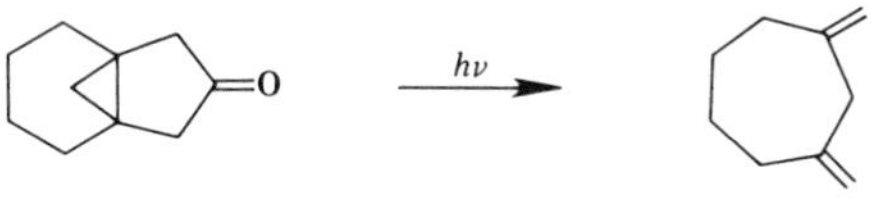

(55)

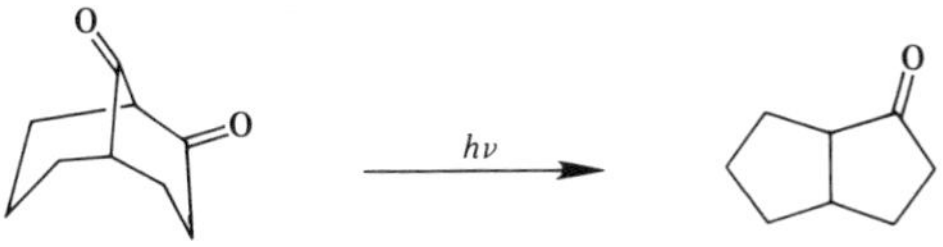

(52)

A case of stereospecific decarbonylation has been suggested to involve backside radical displacement (56). Stereochemistry is also retained during the competing ketene formation.

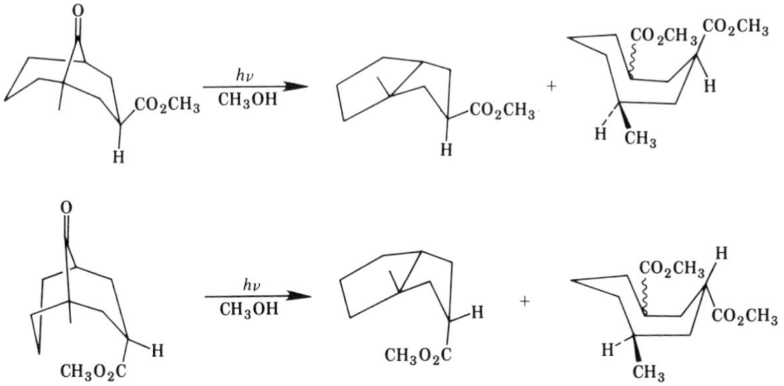

Cyclopentanones with unusual ring strain and most cyclobutanones undergo photorearrangement to oxacarbenes (57). In the case of cyclobutanones, it is not clear whether a biradical is involved (58). With the five-membered rings, however, carbene formation seems to be an alternative mode of biradical reclosure. When such ketones are irradiated in alcohol solvents, the carbenes are trapped as acetals. The overall reaction is a rearrangement plus addition, as shown for Yates' first reported example (*59*).

B. Lactones and Lactams

Very little attention has been devoted to the photochemistry of these acid derivatives, which do not absorb in the convenient near-UV region.

A study of δ-valerolactone showed that both C—C and C—O cleavage occur at 254 nm (*60*). The latter process is the minor one and leads to some loss of CO_2.

Aryl esters undergo the photo-Fries reaction, an overall rearrangement involving recoupling of radical pairs (*61*).

The analogous process in a cyclic system would yield spirocyclohexadienones, which apparently can rearrange right back to the ester (*62*). The expected phenolic ketene has been observed by low-temperature irradiation (63), but the absence of C—D bonds in the alcohol adduct prompted the suggestion that the alcohol adds to the spiro compound instead of to the ketene (64).

One example of a cyclic photo-Fries reaction resulting in a meta product has been reported (65).

Irradiation of pyrrolidones causes decomposition rather than rearrangement (66). However, larger-ring N-phenyllactams rearrange smoothly, presumably by N—C cleavage and recoupling (67).

III. HYDROGEN ABSTRACTION

A. General Considerations

Photoexcited ketones and aldehydes undergo characteristic internal hydrogen transfers to yield hydroxy biradicals. These biradicals cyclize to cycloalkanols and revert to starting materials. They can also undergo typical monoradical rearrangements before doing either. Acid derivatives also undergo excited state hydrogen transfers, but, perhaps because of the high energies involved, cyclizations are rare.

The most common mode of internal hydrogen transfer is 1,5 and is equivalent to a γ-hydrogen abstraction by the carbonyl oxygen. The resulting 1,4 biradical can cleave to olefin and enol—the famous Norrish type II reaction (68), discovered 20 years before the concomitant cyclization–rearrangement (69). The enol rapidly ketonizes, even in the gas phase (70). The cyclization of the biradical provides one of the best routes to cyclobutanols.

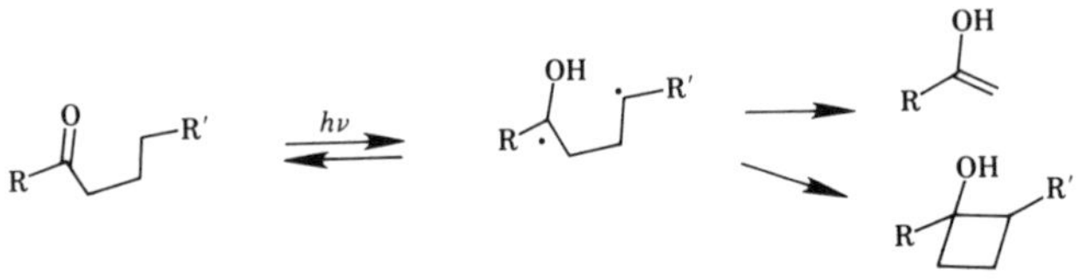

In acyclic ketones, cleavage is often dominant, although cyclization is always at least a minor contributor. In cyclic ketones, cyclization is often more competitive, and diradical cleavage becomes another form of rearrangement.

Hydrogen abstraction from positions other than a γ-carbon are less common, but examples of β, δ, ϵ, and even more remote abstractions are known. Below are some representative examples of cyclizations:

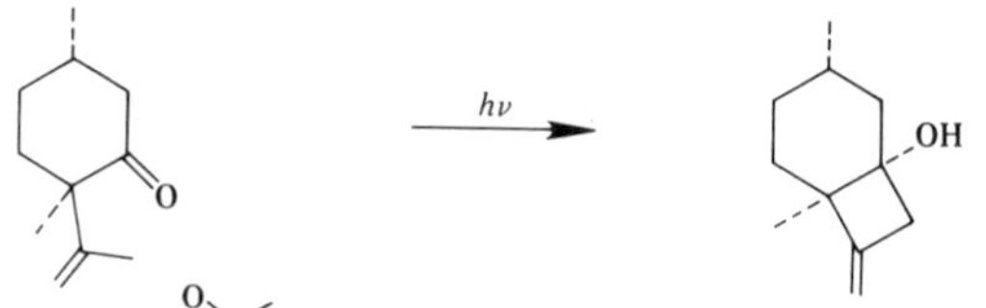

(71)

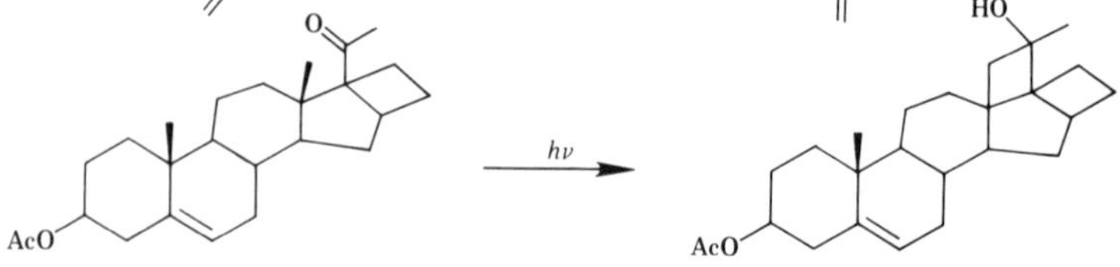

(72)

55%

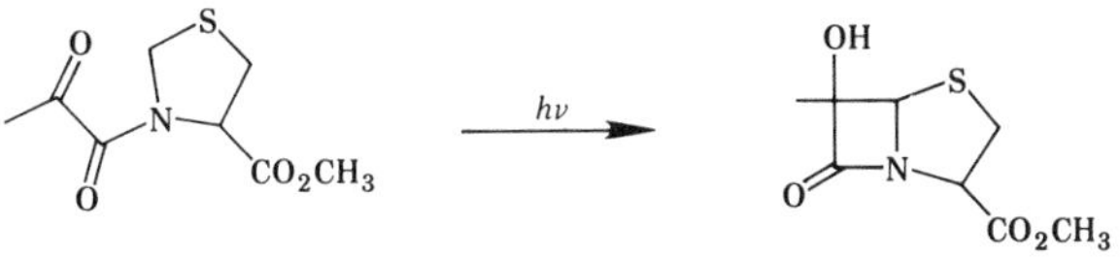

$$(73)$$

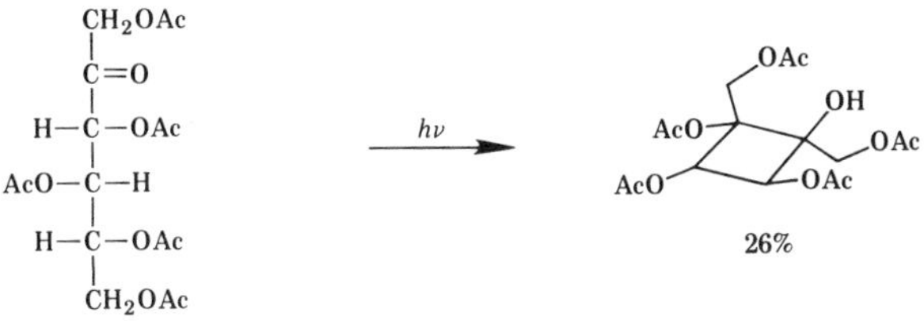

$$CH_2OAc$$
$$C=O$$
$$H-C-OAc$$
$$AcO-C-H$$
$$H-C-OAc$$
$$CH_2OAc$$

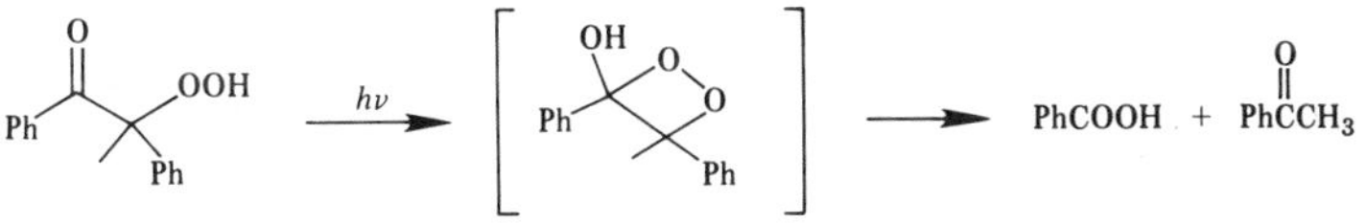

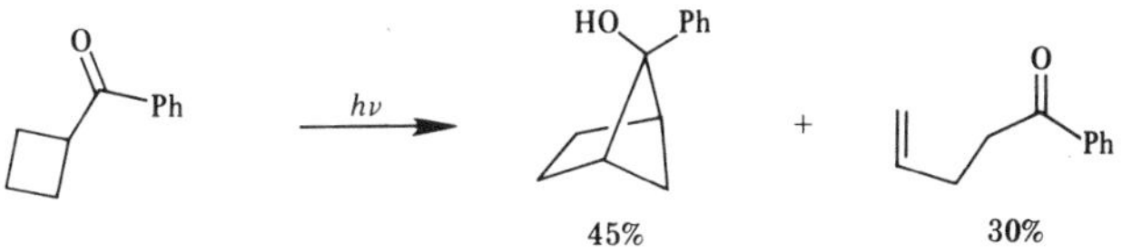

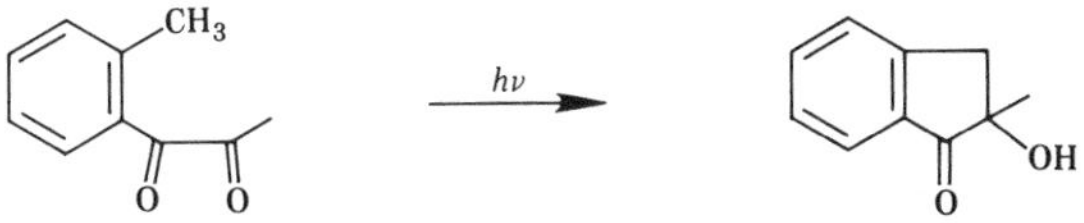

$$\xrightarrow{h\nu}$$

26% $$(74)$$

$$\xrightarrow{h\nu}$$ $$\longrightarrow$$ $$PhCOOH + PhCCH_3$$ $$(75)$$

$$\xrightarrow{h\nu}$$ 45% + 30% $$(76)$$

$$\xrightarrow{h\nu}$$ $$(77)$$

$$Ph-C-\underset{}{\bigcirc}-CO_2(CH_2)_9CH_3 \xrightarrow{h\nu}$$ $$(78)$$

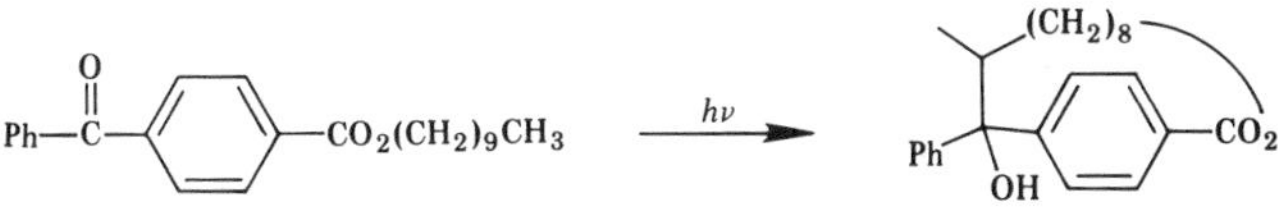

B. Excited State Considerations

As usual, the efficiency of biradical formation depends on how well hydrogen abstraction competes with other excited state reactions. It is important to note that excited ketones do not undergo any very rapid physical decay processes intrinsic to the carbonyl chromophore. Therefore, any competitive reaction is chemical, such as the α cleavage already discussed, or bifunctional, such as quenching by another functional group in the same molecule or by another molecule.

The rate constant for internal hydrogen abstraction depends on electronic configuration, on C—H bond strength or inductive substituent effects, and on conformational factors. There is no evidence that solvent effects are important, except to the extent that they may influence these other factors.

1. Singlet versus Triplet Reactivity

In aliphatic ketones, intersystem crossing is slow enough (k_{isc} = 1–5 × 10^8 sec^{-1}) that chemical reactions of n,π^* singlets can occur efficiently. In fact, the type II reaction was one of the first in which involvement of both triplets and singlets was demonstrated (79). However, it was soon noticed that the details of the singlet and triplet reactions differ substantially (80). It is now recognized that the two excited states follow different reaction pathways (14,17).

Several groups have pointed out that the electronic configuration of an n,π^* state allows hydrogen abstraction processes of low activation energy to take place and that triplet ketones can abstract a hydrogen atom directly to generate a triplet biradical with 100% efficiency. There is considerable evidence that n,π^* singlets interact with C—H bonds as rapidly as do triplets (80). How efficiently such bimolecular interactions produce radicals is uncertain (14). However, in the case of intramolecular interactions it is clear that radiationless decay back to ground state ketone is the primary result, with only a little biradical formation occurring. The singlet reaction apparently begins much like the triplet reaction but encounters the ground state surface before a true biradical state is reached (17,81). Further loss of vibrational energy can result in return to reactant as easily as formation of a metastable biradical.

MINDO calculations have been published recently which suggest that singlet state elimination may proceed by a concerted path in competition with the biradical path (82), a possibility for which there is considerable experimental evidence (80). The main evidence is that both cleavage (83) and radiationless decay (84) involve almost no loss of stereochemistry at the γ-carbon. Moreover, singlet states invariably show much higher cleavage/cyclization ratios than do triplets of the same ketones (84,85). Whereas the former observation can be, and has been, explained on the basis of a singlet biradical so short-lived as to border on semantics, the latter observation cannot be accommodated readily with only a stepwise mechanism, since the partitioning of the biradical would seem to have the wrong dependence on spin multiplicity (see below). The writer prefers a picture in which most of the decay and cleavage occur without biradical formation, with only a small fraction of the carbonyl singlet actually forming a biradical. That biradical is then free to disproportionate, cleave, and cyclize. It is currently impossible to predict how attack on the

γ C—H bond in a given singlet ketone will be partitioned among decay, biradical formation, and direct cleavage.

It has also been suggested that singlet state cyclization may proceed concertedly (82). There is no solid experimental evidence in support of this possibility. Ketones with asymmetric γ-carbons cyclize without complete loss of optical activity (86), but purely triplet cyclizations do likewise (87,88).

2. n,π* versus π,π* Reactivity

Aryl ketones generally undergo intersystem crossing so rapidly that most of their photoreactions are triplet-derived. However, they all possess π,π* triplet levels that lie either below or only slightly above their n,π triplets. Simple phenyl ketones undergo hydrogen abstraction reactions from their n,π* triplets at rates comparable to those displayed by analogous aliphatic ketone triplets. Ring substituents that lower the L_a π,π* level below the n,π* level decrease the observed rate constants for triplet state hydrogen abstraction, both inter- (89) and intramolecular (90). Systematic investigation has shown that the decreases in reactivity are proportional to the Boltzman factor which describes the equilibrium population of the n,π* triplet (90,91). In short, when the two triplet levels are energetically close enough to equilibrate thermally, reaction proceeds from the upper n,π* state.

Equilibration of the two states must involve small geometry changes along vibrational coordinates that are not necessarily related to any reaction coordinate. Although some photochemical reactions are best explained by invoking a state crossing along a reaction coordinate, such a suggestion here, however "modern" (92), is unnecessary. The low reactivity of π,π* triplets indicates that they must rise rapidly in energy when they begin to proceed along the reaction coordinate so that they become isoenergetic with the n,π* level (also rising, but more gradually) after very little motion. In a fuzzy first approximation the reaction coordinate is just another path by which the two triplets may equilibrate.

Naphthyl and biphenyl ketones have ^{3}π,π* levels so much below their ^{3}n,π* states that equilibration is not possible. Such ketones show triplet reactivity about 10^{-4} times as great as that displayed by ketones with n,π* lowest triplets (93). This reactivity is probably intrinsic to π,π* excitation, as is observed with C=C double bonds (94), and reflects the amount of unpaired spin density on oxygen in the π,π* triplet.

α,β-Unsaturated ketones, like phenyl ketones, have proximate n,π* and π,π* triplet levels. β,γ-Unsaturated ketones show complicated mixing of n,π* and π,π* excitation. In neither case has there been any systematic study of hydrogen abstraction rates (see Essay 17).

3. Inductive Effects and Bond Strength

Inasmuch as n,π^* excitation of a carbonyl involves some loss of electron density from the oxygen n orbital, n,π^* triplets respond to the inductive effects of substituents near the C—H bond being attacked, as do typical electron-deficient radicals. In fact, there is an almost exact parallel in relative C—H reactivities toward alkoxy radicals and toward triplet ketones (80,95). The rate constant for γ-hydrogen abstraction in a series of δ-substituted valerophenones varies over two orders of magnitude; a Hammett plot versus σ_1 values indicates a ρ value of -1.85 (96). This effect falls off in the usual fashion with additional insulating methylene groups.

Typical rate constants for γ-hydrogen abstraction by n,π^* triplets of acyclic ketones are 1×10^7, 1×10^8, and 5×10^8 sec^{-1} for primary, secondary, and tertiary C—H bonds, respectively (80). Substituents other than alkyl groups on the γ-carbon stabilize the incipient γ-radical site but usually have deactivating inductive effects. Table 2 contains representative rate constants for γ-hydrogen abstraction by n,π^* triplet phenones.

4. Conformational Limitations and Regioselectivity

In acyclic ketones, hydrogen abstraction from the γ-carbon is far faster than that from any other position. The preference for such a 1,5-hydrogen shift is common in free-radical chemistry (97) and presumably reflects a strain-free, chairlike, cyclic six-atom transition state (98).

The rate of δ-hydrogen abstraction is only about 1/20 that of γ-hydrogen abstraction for equivalent C—H bonds (98). The behavior of triplet δ-methoxyvalerophenone best defines the difference: The methoxy group sufficiently activates the δ C—H bonds and deactivates the γ C—H bonds that the two positions become equally reactive (99).

In acyclic systems, 1,6-hydrogen transfers are intrinsically slower than 1,5 transfers because the seven-atom transition state involves a greater entropy loss and more torsional strain. No activation parameters have been measured for δ-hydrogen abstraction to separate the relative importance of the two causes. The entropy effect can be viewed as the probability that a molecule will attain the correct geometry (conformation) for reaction. In the usual simple transition state picture, the reaction coordi-

TABLE 2

Rates of γ-Hydrogen Abstraction in
Triplet Phenyl Ketones,
$PhCOCH_2XCHR_1R_2$

R_1	R_2	k_H, 10^7 sec^{-1}
	$X = CH_2$	
H	H	0.8
CH_3	H	12.5
CH_3	CH_3	50
C_6H_5	H	39
OCH_3	H	62
$N(Me)_2$	H	80
Cl	H	3.0
OAc	H	1.2
$COOCH_3$	H	1.0
CN	H	0.4
CH_2CN	H	1.0
CH_2CH_2CN	H	4.5
	$X = O$	
H	H$'$	300
	$X = S$	
H	H	75

nate for hydrogen abstraction involves primarily a C—H—O stretch and
not more complex conformational motions such as cyclization; the reactant is one of the small fraction of molecules already in the proper cyclic
conformation. This viewpoint introduces the interesting question of how
excited state decay and conformational changes compete.

All of these intramolecular bifunctional interactions are subject to the
same conformational limitations: The interacting groups must be able to
rotate within a minimal distance of each other for proper orbital overlap
and reaction. The following scheme incorporates the minimal number of
competing processes to summarize the general problem:

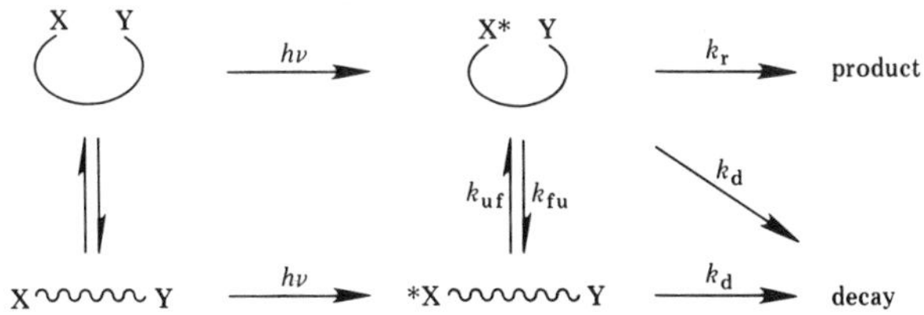

The ground state is composed of an equilibrium mixture of conformations with generally only a small fraction favorable for reaction between

excited X and Y. Excitation instantaneously (on the time scale of bond rotations) produces the same distribution of excited conformers modified only by any slight difference in extinction coefficients between different conformers. The competition among conformational change, reaction, and decay (all other excited state processes that do not lead to the product in question) provides three boundary conditions:

1. Conformational equilibrium $k_{uf}, k_{fu} \gg k_r, k_d$
2. Ground state control $k_{uf}, k_{fu} \ll k_r, k_d$
3. Rotational control $k_{uf} \sim k_d; k_{fu} \sim k_r$

Examples of all three boundary conditions are provided by different ketones. In general, conformational equilibrium is established in the excited state before reaction because hydrogen abstraction is an activated process and intrinsically somewhat inefficient. The larger the fraction of excited molecules in favorable cyclic conformations, the larger the observed rate constant for reaction. At equilibrium (which may or may not equal the ground state conformational equilibrium) k_r (observed) = $k_r k_{uf}/(k_{uf} + k_{fu})$. For example, it was found that γ-hydrogen abstraction is more rapid in cyclic ketones than in acyclic ketones (100). Representative rates are shown below. It was concluded that the rate enhancements reflect the increased number of "frozen" C—C bonds in the reactant, i.e., a decreased probability that the molecule can exist in a conformation unsuitable for reaction. In support of this interpretation, 2-benzoylnorbornane shows the same triplet state activation energy (3.6 ± 0.2 kcal/mol) as valerophenone but an activation entropy that is 8 e.u. less negative.

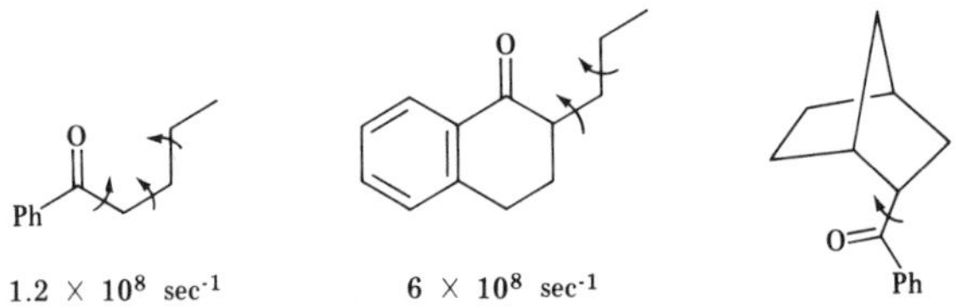

$k_{\gamma \cdot H}$ 1.2×10^8 sec⁻¹ 6×10^8 sec⁻¹

7×10^9 sec⁻¹

The opposite extreme is exemplified by the very inefficient triplet state hydrogen abstraction in benzoylcyclobutanes, which occurs from the mere 0.001% of triplets in a pseudoaxial conformation (101). In fact, this work represents an elegant example of the use of photochemistry to measure conformational equilibria. Whereas the observed value of k_H is 10^4 sec⁻¹, the value for triplet benzoylbicyclohexane is $>10^9$ sec⁻¹ (102).

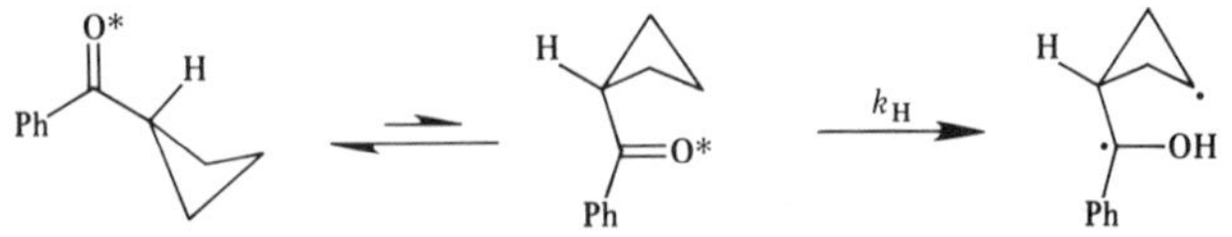

The competing cleavage and cyclization of 1-benzoyl-1-methylcyclo-pentane occur from kinetically indistinguishable triplets, whereas the corresponding competing reactions of 1-benzoyl-1-methylcyclohexane occur from kinetically distinct triplets (*103*). Both excited state reactions are faster than cyclohexane ring flips but slower than cyclopentane ring undulations. The former condition represents ground state control of photochemistry.

Viewed in terms of conformational limitations, intramolecular hydrogen abstraction from any positions more remote than γ becomes increasingly slower as more otherwise freely rotating bonds must become fixed in strained transition states. With ketones that do not possess γ C—H bonds, δ-hydrogen abstraction may still occur efficiently if there are no other rapid triplet decay processes.

(*104*)

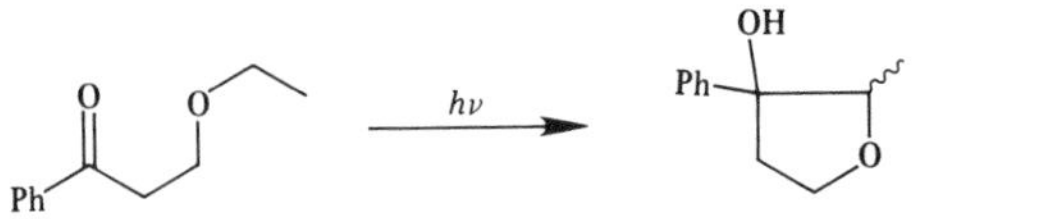

(98, 105)

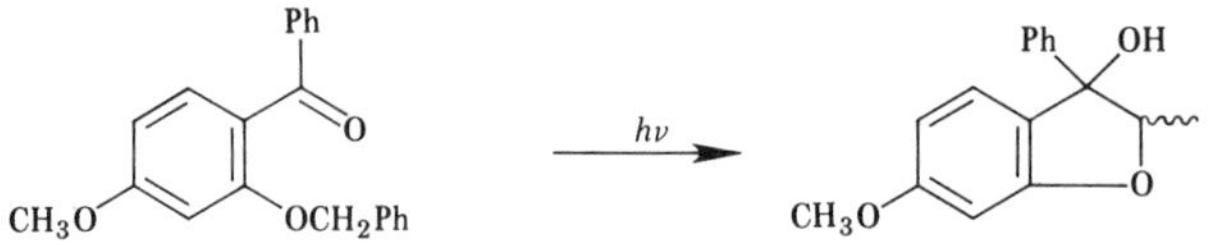

(106)

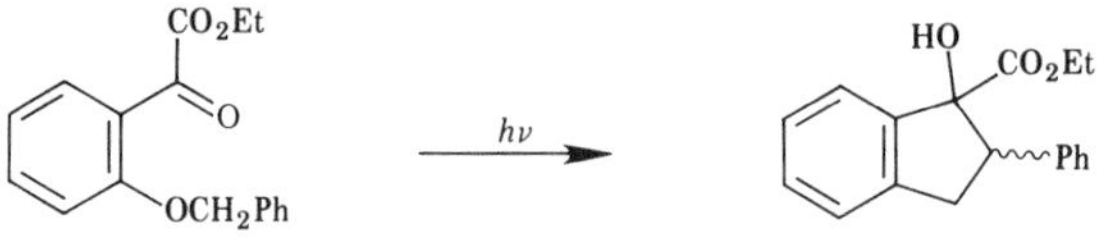

(107)

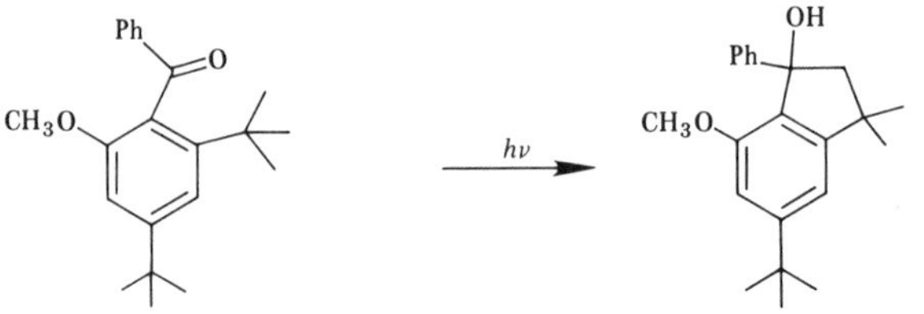

(108)

The last three examples all involve δ-hydrogen abstraction from ortho substituents. One would expect such reactions to be considerably faster than in acyclic ketones because the reactants are nearly frozen in the conformation required for hydrogen transfer. However, triplet decay rates for both o-benzyloxy systems are the same as in β-ethoxypropiophenone (98,105): 1–2 × 10^7 sec^{-1}. At the time these examples were reported it was not recognized that such reactions may be rotationally controlled; only one of the two rotamers about the phenyl–acyl bond can react. We have suggested that the rate of anti → syn rotation in triplet o-alkyl ketones is 2 × 10^7 sec^{-1} and that hydrogen abstraction in the syn rotamer is much faster (109). There are several indications that δ-hydrogen abstraction may indeed be quite rapid in the above molecules. For example, the π,π^* naphthyl ketone triplet reacts with a rate constant of 10^4 sec^{-1} (104); extrapolation to an n,π^* triplet suggests a rate constant > 10^8 sec^{-1}. Also, 2,4-di-t-butylvalerophenone undergoes no type II elimination (110).

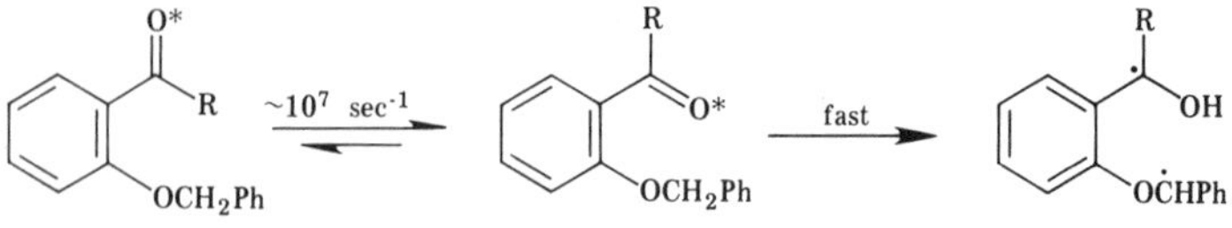

The di-*t*-butylbenzophenone derivative is remarkable in that it cyclizes in isopropyl alcohol, in which the rate constant for reduction of triplet benzophenone itself is $10^6 M^{-1}$ sec^{-1}. Moreover, δ-hydrogen abstraction occurs specifically at the *t*-butyl methyls instead of at the intrinsically more labile methoxy methyl (see Table 2). It is probable that the predominant conformation is the one drawn above, another example of ground state control of excited state reactions.

β-Hydrogen abstraction is very rare. Two examples that probably involve charge-transfer interactions are discussed below. Some α-methylene ketones form acylcyclopropanes, presumably via trimethylene-methane biradicals (*111*), and several benzoquinone-diene Diels–Alder

adducts undergo photoinduced β-hydrogen transfer and subsequent cyclization both in solution (*112*) and in the solid state (*113*).

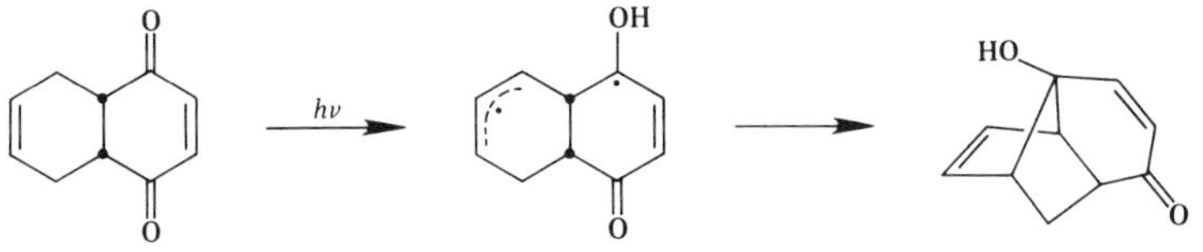

It is interesting that both types of β-hydrogen abstraction share three uncommon features: (a) The β-hydrogen is allylic; (b) the β-hydrogen is held by enone conjugation or by a preferred ring shape in an ideal position for abstraction; and (c) the reactive excited state is an n,π* singlet. The first two features help to form and stabilize a biradical. Scheffer has clearly pointed out the unusually long initial O—H distance (~2.5 Å) over which the singlets react. This aspect of the reaction identifies another way in which singlet and triplet reactions differ.

It has been suggested (*26*) that internal hydrogen abstractions are subject to the stereoelectronic requirement that the C—H bond being attacked lie in the nodal plan of the carbonyl π system, along the axis of the oxygen n orbital. Unfortunately, there are no unequivocal experimental tests of this hypothesis. In fact, efficient γ-hydrogen abstraction occurs in several relatively rigid polycyclic systems in which the hydrogen being attacked lies at least 45° above the plane. It is entirely possible that reactivity is proportional to a cosine function, in which case reactivity would remain measurable as long as the hydrogen does not lie in the nodal plane of the oxygen n orbital. The observed photostability of the rigid ketone shown below has been interpreted as evidence for such a stereoelectronic effect (*113*). Unfortunately, a low quantum yield could just as well reflect the (expected) almost exclusive singlet reaction.

5. Role of Charge Transfer

It is well known that good electron donors interact with excited ketones in charge-transfer processes to form exciplexes in which the donor has radical cation character (*114*). In the case of amines, subsequent proton transfer from amine generates a pair of radicals with about 50% efficiency. With sulfides, the efficiency is quite low. An obvious question is whether a comparable two-step process can work intramolecularly to produce biradicals.

Several aroylaziridines undergo rearrangements that seem to involve abstraction of a β-hydrogen (*115*). Both major products can arise from internal cleavage of a 1,4 biradical species.

Aroylazetidines photorearrange to pyrroles (*116*). The suggested mechanism again involves a β-hydrogen transfer which does not occur in benzoylcyclobutane and therefore probably is assisted by charge transfer.

There is an intriguing report that some β-aminopropiophenones, but not others, photorearrange to β-aminocyclopropanols (*117*). The mechanism of this reaction deserves closer scrutiny.

α-Alkylamino ketones might be expected to yield azetidinols yet do not unless the nitrogen is acylated so as to inhibit charge transfer (*118*). Although these ketones do not undergo significant intersystem crossing, not even triplet sensitization of α-dimethylaminoacetophenone produces any azetidinol (*119*). It is possible that the exciplex assumes a fairly rigid geometry in which the γ-hydrogens are held away from the carbonyl oxygen. Biradical formation and subsequent cyclization can then arise only from the direct triplet state hydrogen abstraction which competes with charge transfer.

The above explanation does seem to describe the behavior of γ-amino ketones. For example, γ-dimethylamino-β-butyronaphthone has an unreactive triplet in aprotic solvents but forms products in alcohol solvents (120). The π,π^* triplet does not abstract a γ-hydrogen directly but does undergo efficient exciplex formation. Rearrangement of this exciplex to a 1,4 biradical requires an external proton source.

On the other hand, as discussed in more detail below, Kanaoka has studied several N-substituted phthalimide systems in which long-range hydrogen transfer is promoted by intramolecular charge-transfer interactions (121). It does not appear to be possible to generalize about the role of charge transfer in these rearrangements. (See Section III,D.)

6. Competing Reactions

Internal hydrogen abstraction must compete with α cleavage, as discussed above, and with all bimolecular quenching processes such as photoreduction and electron transfer. Since phenyl ketones are very reactive in hydrogen abstraction processes, but not in α cleavages, a form of decay not shared by aliphatic ketones can be competitive. Triplet aryl ketones are quenched by their own ground states, sometimes with quite large bimolecular rate constants, in a "self-quenching" process that is not yet well defined (122,123). Photoreduction by solvent usually is not a serious problem unless only methyl hydrogens are available internally. Energy, electron, and charge-transfer processes can be diffusion-controlled and thus must be avoided.

C. Biradical Behavior

1. Biradical Lifetimes

It has been demonstrated by flash spectroscopic methods that the biradicals formed from triplet phenyl ketones such as valerophenone have lifetimes of the order of 10^{-7} sec (36b). These lifetimes depend very little on solvent or on substitution (124). Triplet aliphatic ketones produce longer-lived biradicals (36,125).

It is not clear which rate processes determine these biradical lifetimes. There is general agreement that the triplet biradicals must undergo intersystem crossing to singlet biradicals, which then can proceed over low activation energy barriers to ground state products. Two kinetic extremes are as follows. (a) The decay rate of 10^7 sec^{-1} represents rate-determining intersystem crossing, with reactions of the singlet biradical being very rapid; and (b) intersystem crossing is rapid and equilibrates the nearly isoenergetic singlet and triplet biradicals, so that the 10^7 sec^{-1} represents the combined rate constants for all chemical reactions of the biradical.

There are various experimental results that are difficult to reconcile with one or the other of the two extremes, and it is possible that in many cases intersystem crossing and chemical reaction have competitive rates. This topic is of considerable fundamental importance and is currently being studied by diverse techniques in several laboratories. For the purposes of this essay, it is not necessary to define the lifetime more fully. It is important to realize that other reactions of the triplet-derived biradicals, such as bimolecular trapping, rearrangements, and conformational changes, have only 10^{-7} sec in which to occur.

2. Cyclization versus Cleavage

Several factors control the cyclization/cleavage ratio of 1,4 biradicals. In *n*-alkyl ketones, 80–90% of the biradicals cleave, and only 10–20% cyclize. These proportions vary with temperature and solvent. Substitution at the γ- or δ-carbon, or on the phenyl ring of phenones, can influence the quantum efficiency of product formation substantially but does not affect product ratios significantly (*126*). In contrast, β,β-dimethylbutyrophenone barely cyclizes at all (*126*), whereas α-substituted phenones preferentially cyclize (*127*).

It is widely accepted that rapid cleavage of a 1,4 biradical requires that it be able to achieve a conformation in which both singly occupied p orbitals can overlap significantly with the C-2—C-3 σ bond. The geometry shown below is ideal in that the middle C—C bond is parallel to both p orbitals and in a staggered conformation. Such a stereoelectronic requirement is obvious but not easy to quantify. If structural features prevent the biradical from assuming an "ideal" geometry with 100% overlap, the decreased overlap should increase the barrier to cleavage—but how much? Since cyclization is always competitive, a small relative increase in the barrier to cleavage is sufficient to markedly enhance cyclization yields. For example, a change from 15% cyclization to 90% cyclization requires a relative increase in the barrier to cleavage of 2.5 kcal/mol.

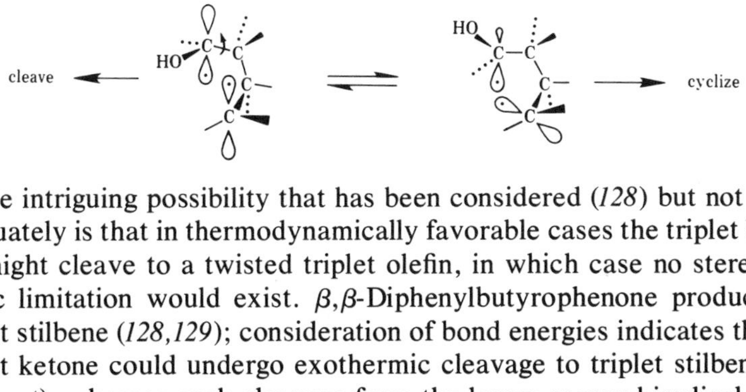

One intriguing possibility that has been considered (*128*) but not tested adequately is that in thermodynamically favorable cases the triplet biradical might cleave to a twisted triplet olefin, in which case no stereoelectronic limitation would exist. β,β-Diphenylbutyrophenone produces no triplet stilbene (*128,129*); consideration of bond energies indicates that the triplet ketone could undergo exothermic cleavage to triplet stilbene (but does not), whereas such cleavage from the lower-energy biradical would be endothermic (*87*).

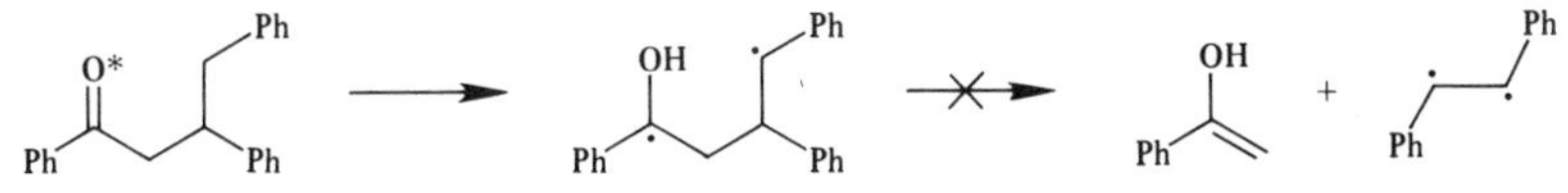

It has been pointed out that the puckered shape and strained bonding of cyclobutanes allow cyclization of 1,4 biradicals from conformations with poor overlap for cleavage (*18a*). It is not easy to predict the effects of structural variations on relative cyclization rates. For example, the case of benzoylcyclobutane (*76*) cited above was probably the first in which it was noted (*130*) that the large bicyclobutanol yield certainly would not have been predicted on the basis of product stabilities. Cleavage releases significant amounts of ring strain; cyclization creates much more. The biradical possesses very poor overlap for cleavage, yet it does cleave. It is possible that both reactions are slowed significantly (quantum yields are very low), but clarification requires more extensive measurements and better understanding of biradical lifetimes.

The only general conclusion with which the present writer feels comfortable is that the competition between the highly exothermic reactions of these biradicals is affected only slightly by relative product stabilities. Thus, the exclusive cyclization of 4-methyl-4-penten-2-one (*131*) is readily explained by the occurrence of zero overlap in the biradical.

There are several distinct classes of ketones that undergo primarily cyclobutanol formation: cycloalkanones, α-cycloalkyl ketones, and α-diketones. Three types of α-substitution affect the cyclization/cleavage competition substantially. *t*-Alkyl ketones, such as α,α-dimethylvalerophenone (*18,18a*), undergo ~70% cyclization. It has been suggested that this α-alkyl effect is a specific example of the stereoelectronic requirement for cleavage: Rotation of the biradical into a conformation suitable for cleavage introduces eclipsing interactions between the α-alkyl groups and the benzene ring (especially its ortho hydrogens) (*18a,126*).

α-Fluorination of phenyl ketones also promotes cyclization at the expense of cleavage, α,α-difluorophenones producing *only* cyclobutanols (*132*). It is possible that fluorine hyperconjugation stabilizes biradical conformations unsuitable for cleavage. The fluorine atoms would also certainly destabilize the enol produced during cleavage; it is not known how important this added impediment toward cleavage is, given the normal insensitivity to product stability.

Heteroatoms at the α-carbon produce dramatic effects on product ratios: α-Alkoxy ketones often yield over 50% cyclobutanols (*133*), whereas α-thioalkoxy (*134*) and α-dialkylamino ketones (*135*) produce none. Although the latter two undergo significant competitive charge-transfer quenching of their excited states, careful kinetic analysis reveals that they do undergo some triplet state γ-hydrogen abstraction, and this leads entirely to cleavage. In all cases heteroatom conjugation with both radical sites of the biradical may produce a coulombic repulsion against cyclization as well as a conformational bias against cleavage. With sulfur and nitrogen, perhaps internal hydrogen bonding holds the biradicals in conformations unable to cyclize.

As discussed above, acyclic ketones undergo very little cyclization from their n,π^* singlets. Naphthyl ketones undergo inefficient cleavage but no cyclization from their singlets (*136*).

3. Stereochemistry, Revertibility, and Solvent Effects

With both S-5-methyl-2-heptanone (*84*) and S-γ-methylhexanophenone (*87*), reverse hydrogen transfer (disproportionation) in the triplet-derived biradical regenerates racemic ground state ketone. It was established independently that the major reaction of such triplet 1,4 biradicals is reversion to ground state ketone (*137*). Since it is now known that the triplet biradicals live for at least 10^{-7} sec, stereorandomization of the γ-radical site is to be expected.

Nonetheless, cyclobutanols formed from several chiral ketones with asymmetric γ-carbons show some optical activity (*86–88*). With phenyl ketones, it may be assumed that such activity represents a few percent retention, 10^{-7} sec not being quite enough time for complete randomization. With aliphatic ketones, it was originally suggested that retention during cyclization indicated a concerted reaction. Unfortunately, this early example was not separated into its singlet and triplet components. S-5-Methyl-2-heptanone undergoes almost no measurable racemization from its singlet (*84*); concerted cyclization or a short-lived biradical are both possible.

Solvents that are reasonable Lewis bases prevent reversion of triplet-

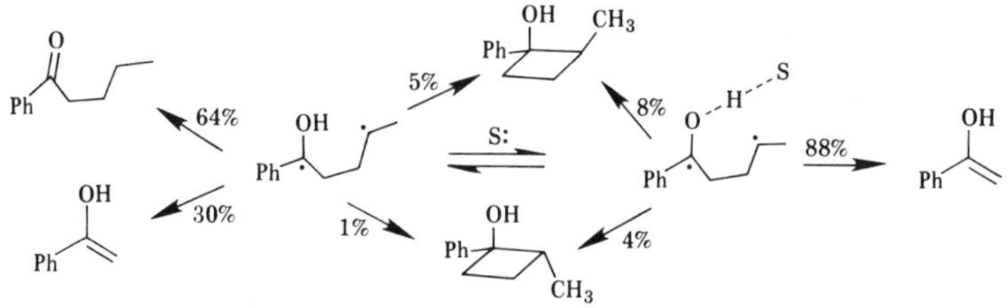

Scheme 3

generated 1,4-biradicals to ground state ketone (*138*). In the process, they slightly raise the cleavage/cyclization ratio and change the stereochemistry of cyclization. All these effects are explicable by a mechanism whereby hydrogen bonding of the hydroxybiradical to solvent suppresses disproportionation and slows that mode of cyclization in which a single substituent originally on the γ-carbon ends up cis to the hydroxy group. The original observation on valerophenone (*137*) has proven to be completely general.

The above scheme assumes equilibrium solvation of the biradicals because their lifetimes seem too long for kinetically controlled hydrogen bonding.

An important stereochemical refinement was added by the observation that α-methylbutyrophenone forms only one 2-methylcyclobutanol (*127*), whereas valerophenone forms both stereoisomers, although favoring Z.

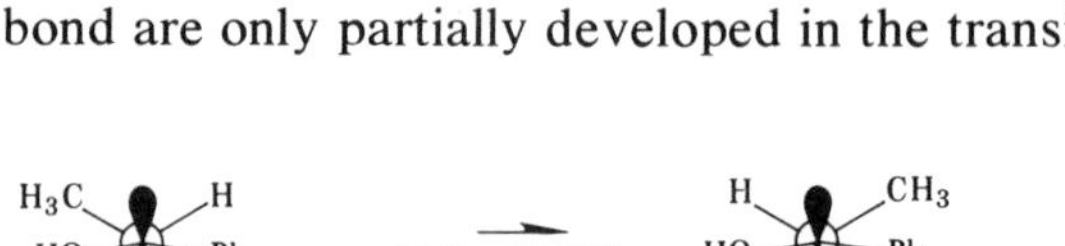

The explanation provided is that gauche interactions across the C-1—C-2 bond persist throughout the biradical's reactions, whereas those across the C-1—C-4 bond are only partially developed in the transition state for cyclization.

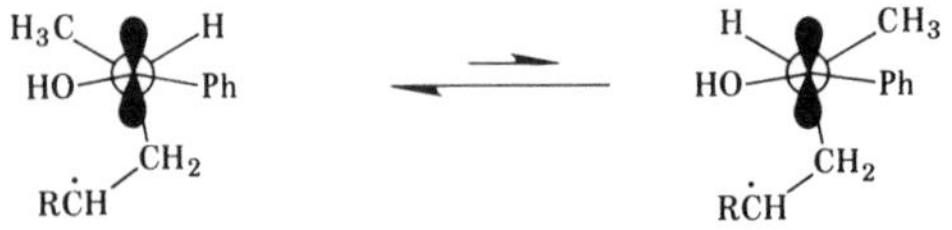

One remarkable stereochemical feature of the cyclization is the observation that the larger the alkyl group in γ-alkylbutyrophenone, the less the Z-cyclobutanol is favored relative to the E isomer (*126*), until the preference vanishes for *t*-butyl.

The only other intermediates from internal hydrogen abstraction for which solvent-dependent behavior has been observed are 1,5 biradicals. Unlike 1,4 biradicals, 1,5-biradicals cyclize in lower quantum yields in t-butyl alcohol or acetonitrile than in hydrocarbon solvents. It might have been expected that hydrogen bonding would be effective at preventing reversion to ketone independently of biradical size. Recently, it has been found that the main path for reversion in the 1,5 biradicals formed from β-ethoxypropiophenone involves transfer of an α C—H bond to form the enol (105). It is remarkable that hydrogen abstraction by triplet ketone is faster for 1,6 than for 1,4 biradicals, whereas the opposite order seems to hold for biradical disproportionation.

	Benzene		t-BuOH	
	X = H	X = D	X = H	X = D
k_{-r} (rel)	15	15	0	0
k_e (rel)	36	13	36	13
k_c (rel)	49	49	15	15

Lewis bases affect the stereochemistry of cyclopentanol formation from δ-hydrogen abstraction in the same manner as that just discussed for cyclobutanol formation from γ-hydrogen abstraction. Analysis indicates that biradical solvation slows both disproportionation and cyclization. This point is important because cyclization of the o-alkoxy ketones discussed in Section III,B,4 also displays lower quantum efficiencies in polar solvents than in hydrocarbons. None of these ketones is enolizable, so it must be concluded that solvation does not suppress biradical disproportionation.

4. Competing Biradical Reactions

The relatively long lifetimes of triplet-derived biradicals allow them to undergo typical monoradical reactions. Not very many bimolecular reactions are fast enough for this purpose, but hydrogen abstraction from HBr *(36)* and from thiols *(36a)* does occur. The result is primarily quenching, although some of the semi-pinacol radicals so generated dimerize.

Various δ-substituted ketones undergo photoinduced elimination to yield 4-benzoyl-1-butene *(139)*. The mechanism seems to involve initial γ-hydrogen abstraction followed by radical cleavage of the δ substituent. This process is competitive only when a δ substituent is a good radical leaving group.

There is a single example of cleavage of a β substituent from a 1,4 biradical: the photoelimination of alcohol from some β-alkoxy ketones *(140)*. This process occurs in competition with oxacyclopentanol formation, but only when γ-hydrogen abstraction occurs *(141)*. Alkoxy radicals are very poor leaving groups, so the mechanism may be concerted.

One form of biradical cyclization is surprisingly rare; the biradicals from phenyl ketones might be expected to furnish tetralones. Although various investigators have reported trace quantities of products that might arise from cyclization through the benzene ring, there is only one clean example of this process *(142)*.

5. Biradical Rearrangements

When ketones possess C=C double bonds such that one or the other radical site of the photoproduced biradical is allylic, cyclization products and regenerated ketone show the results of double-bond participation or allylic rearrangements.

(143)

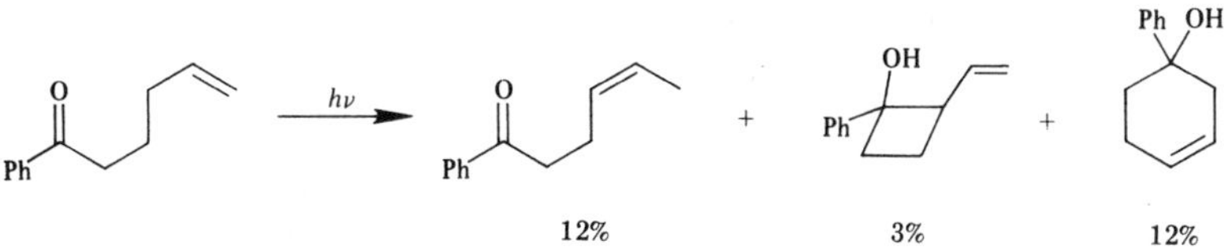

(144)

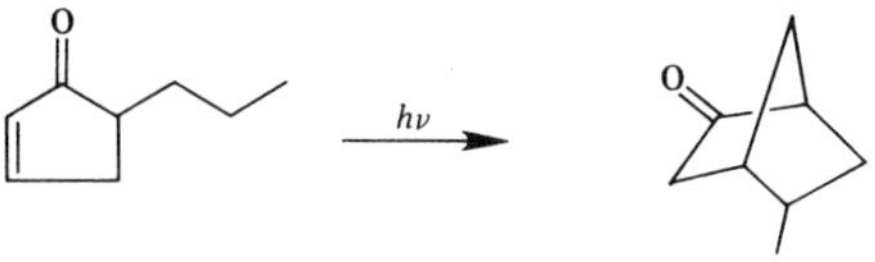

12%   3%   12%

(145)

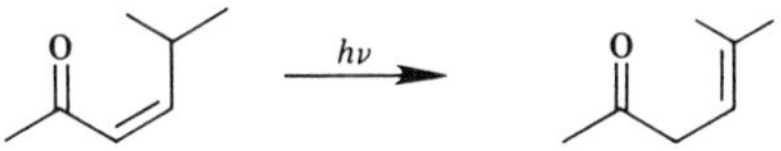

(146)

The 10^{-7} sec lifetime of triplet-derived 1,4 biradicals allows them to undergo some radical rearrangements. Two forms of cyclopropyl ketones show cyclopropylcarbinyl to allylcarbinyl rearrangement.

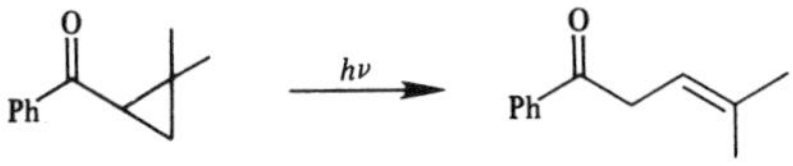

(147)

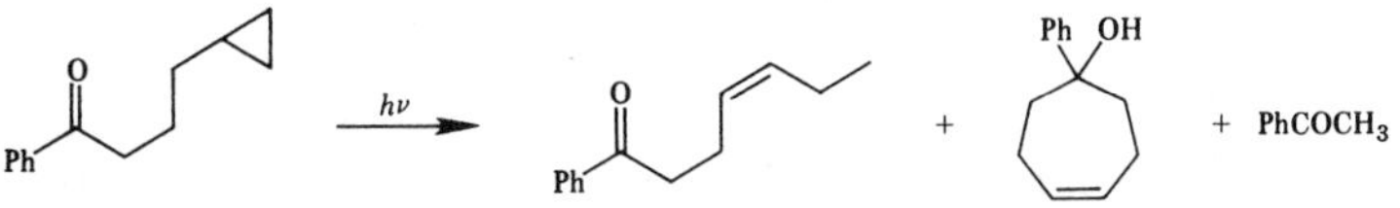

+ PhCOCH$_3$ (148)

Interestingly, the epoxide corresponding to γ-cyclopropylbutyrophenone does not undergo any photoinduced ring opening (148). However, the epoxy ketone below does rearrange (149).

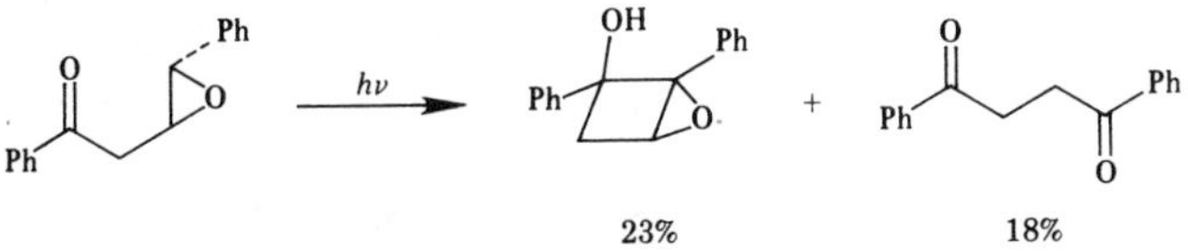

23%   18%

Finally, α-allylbutyrophenone furnishes a very small amount of 2-phenyl-2-norbornanol (150). The 5-hexenyl to cyclopentylcarbinyl rearrangement is too slow to be very competitive with other biradical reactions.

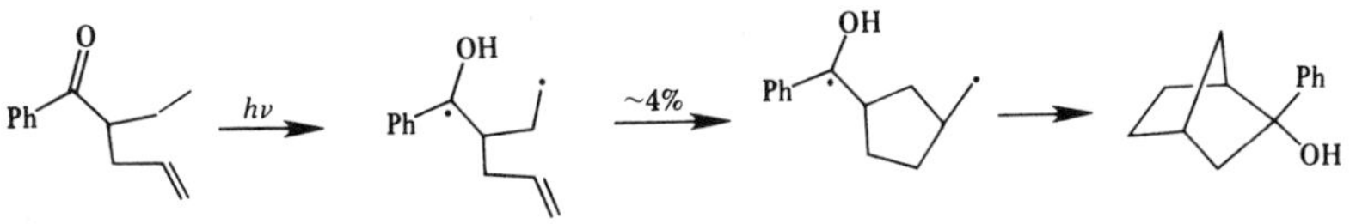

D. Specific Classes of Compounds

Several classes of carbonyl compounds show unique or characteristic behavior which combines excited state and biradical reactions; it is thus easier to discuss them separately.

1. Cycloalkanones

Cycloalkanones with no α substituents undergo efficient type II cyclization provided that they are large enough to assume conformations with the carbonyl pointing inside the ring. Cyclononanone and the smaller ketones undergo either α cleavage or photoreduction. Cyclodecanone is unique in forming only decalols; apparently, ϵ-hydrogens are the only ones readily accessible (151).

75%   25%

In the larger homologues, γ-hydrogen abstraction provides the predominant cyclization route. When these ketones are irradiated in cyclohexane, the amount of photoreduction is 12 and 1% for C_{11} and C_{12}, respectively; it is undetectable for C_{14} (152,152a). Increasing ring size undoubtedly increases the fraction of conformations with the carbonyl inside the ring. This effect certainly enhances the effective rate of γ-hydrogen abstraction and may also hinder bimolecular reactions involving the carbonyl oxygen (153). A careful study of cyclododecanone indicates a triplet decay rate of only $6 \times 10^6 \, sec^{-1}$ (154). The corresponding rate of γ-hydrogen abstraction in triplet 2-hexanone is $10^8 \, sec^{-1}$ (85). Therefore, even though hydrogen abstraction by triplet cyclododecanone is efficient (ϕ products = 0.5), the carbonyl oxygen apparently spends very little time close enough to a C—H to react.

With the C_{11}–C_{13} cycloalkanones, the majority of reaction arises from the triplet (152,152a). The cis-cyclobutanol/trans-cyclobutanol ratio is ~5 for these ketones but falls to 1.5 for C_{15} and C_{16}. Interestingly, the small fraction of singlet reaction for C_{12} and C_{13} is reported to give only cis cyclization.

64%   11%   8%

The competition between cyclization and ring cleavage is also dependent on ring size. The ratio is $7:1$ and $9:1$ for the C_{11} and C_{12} ketones, respectively, $1.6:1$ for C_{14}, and $1:3$ for C_{16}. Presumably the biradicals formed from the smaller rings have some difficulty in achieving the best overlap for cleavage.

A unique example of biradical disproportionation that yields an unsaturated alcohol has been reported; cycloundecanone furnishes a small percentage of 4-cycloundecenol (*152a*).

5%

α-Alkylcyclohexanones often cyclize in much higher yields than do acyclic ketones. The α substituent prefers to be equatorial to the cyclohexane ring, even in the biradical, thus impeding the overlap required for cleavage. Fleming studied a group of such ketones and questioned the importance of stereoelectronic factors, especially in singlet reactions, which may produce a "hotter" biradical (*155*). In all cases studied, the triplet state preferentially cyclizes, whereas the singlet state produces more, often predominant cleavage. Of course, if the majority of singlet reaction is a concerted cleavage, the consequent low biradical yields would ensure low cyclization yields. Fleming concluded that unsuitably oriented α,β C—C bonds depress both cyclization and cleavage efficiencies. Below are shown two ketones the singlet and triplet contributions of which could be separated cleanly. In the α-cyclohexylcyclohexanone, the α,β C—C bond must be axial to both rings for easy cleavage; it shows

	Cleavage (%)	Cyclization (%)
hv		
65% singlet	87	13
35% triplet	27	73
hv		
50% singlet	36	64
50% triplet	20	80

enhanced cyclization/cleavage ratios in both states. The efficient singlet state cleavage of the 4-*t*-butyl ketone is remarkable in that the α-propyl group cannot become properly axial.

2. Acylcycloalkanes

These deserve separate mention because of the huge effect of α-alkylation. Whereas several benzoylcycloalkanes (except benzoyl-cyclobutane) undergo only cleavage, 1-methyl-1-benzoylcycloalkanes and 1-methyl-1-benzoylbicycloalkanes undergo exclusively cyclization (*103,156*).

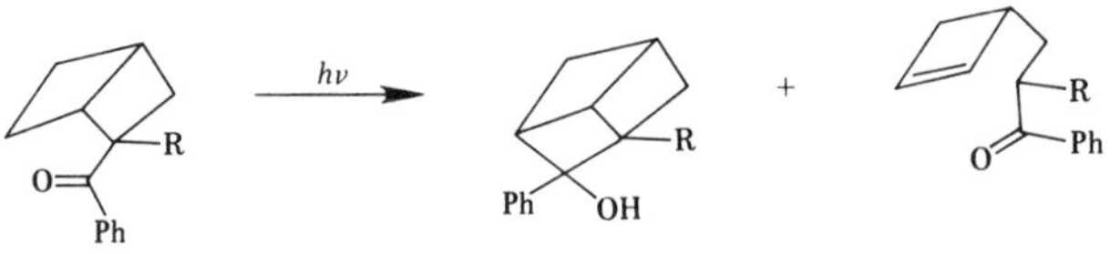

(*157*)

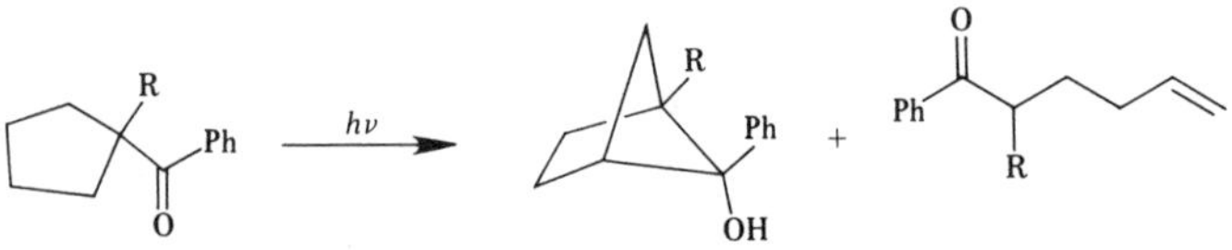

(*103*)

3. α-Cycloalkyl Ketones

Cycloalkylacetones undergo primarily cyclization. The first report concerned adamantylacetone and was one of the first papers to recognize the stereoelectronic requirement for cleavage (*158*). The α,β C—C bond is held nearly perpendicular to the p orbital on the γ-carbon of the biradical. Overall quantum efficiency for cleavage is only 3.9% in methanol, with 25% of the cyclization occurring from the singlet.

Simple acyclic ketones cyclize primarily from their triplets; for 2-hexanone the cyclization/cleavage ratio is 0.44 from the triplet and 0.07 from the singlet (*85*). Nonetheless, adamantylacetone undergoes no cleavage from its singlet.

Cyclohexenylacetones undergo only singlet state cyclization, with no triplet reaction at all (*159*). Dalton reported the following clever demonstration of the likelihood of a true singlet biradical common to two starting ketones. Cleavage is impossible in these biradicals both because allylic resonance prevents proper overlap and because cleavage would produce a twisted cyclic allene.

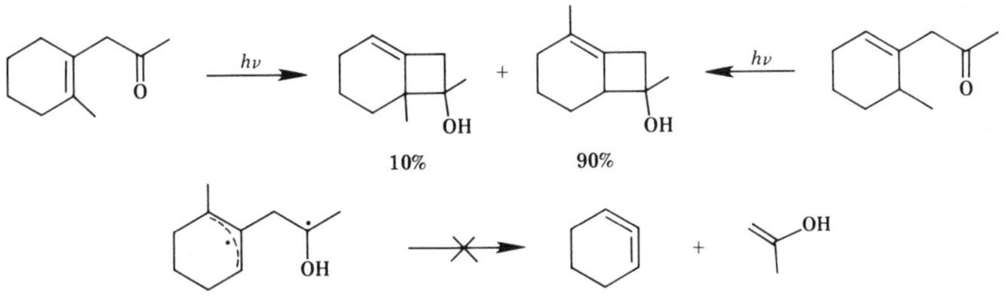

10%   90%

4. α-Diketones

α-Diketones undergo intramolecular photoreactions unique in three respects: (a) Hydroxycyclobutanones are the only products of γ-hydrogen abstraction; (b) γ-hydrogen abstraction is regiospecific to the C—H bonds β to the second carbonyl; and (c) photoenolization is sometimes competitive. All reactions are exclusively triplet-derived (88,160).

The exclusive cyclization of the biradicals is connected with the regiospecificity of hydrogen abstraction. The keto group in the biradical allows allylic and donor–acceptor conjugation across one radical site and holds the α,β C—C bond perpendicular to that π system.

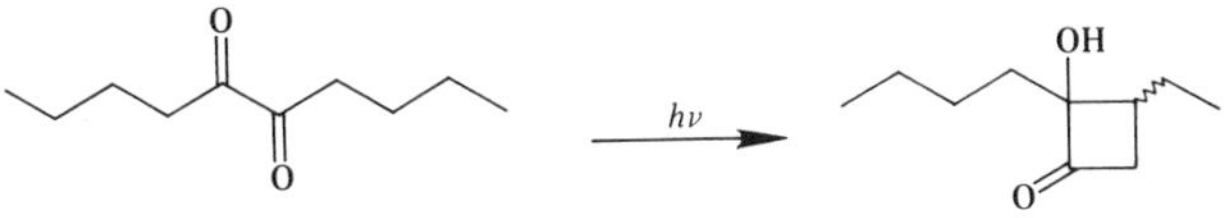

(160)

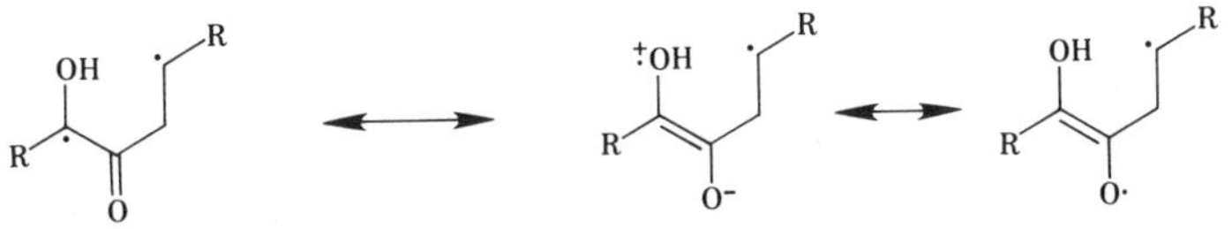

No satisfactory explanation has been presented for the regiospecificity of hydrogen abstraction. An entropy effect was once suggested, but careful consideration of kinetic and thermodynamic data provides no evidence for such an effect (88). The original idea was that the trans coplanarity of the triplet dicarbonyl would essentially freeze one C—C bond into the conformation necessary for hydrogen abstraction. However, monoketones themselves apparently exist preferentially in a similar conformation about the carbonyl–α-carbon bond (161).

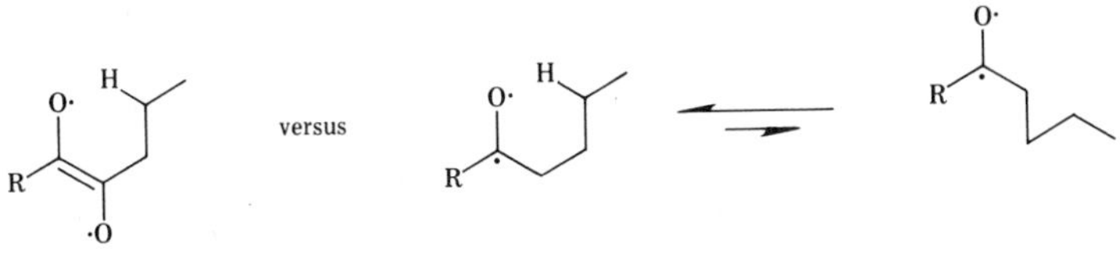

versus

It was a decade after the initial report of photocyclization of diketones before an example was found of γ-hydrogen abstraction from a carbon δ to the second carbonyl (*162*). In the compound studied the presence of the *gem*-dimethyl group prevents both the usual γ-hydrogen abstraction and cyclization.

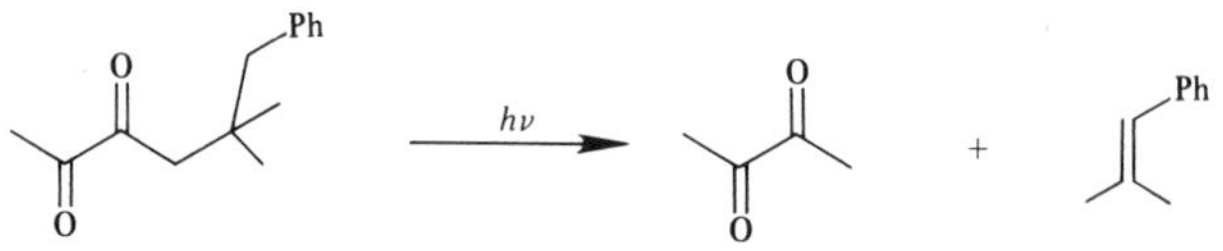

A diphenyldione that provides both cyclobutanol and cyclopentanol products had been studied earlier (*163*). The simplest explanation for this is a 9:1 preference for γ- rather than δ-hydrogen abstraction by the outside carbonyl. However, it was suggested that the rapid tautomerization of the biradicals indicated below may confuse interpretation. It is conceivable that the same problem afflicts the interpretation of all diketone behavior.

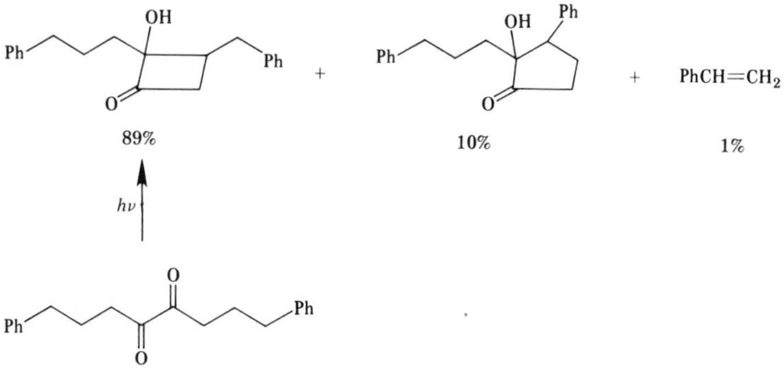

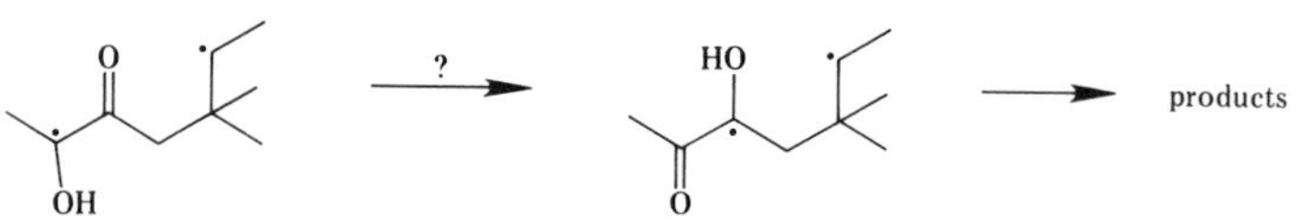

Although hydrogen atom abstraction by triplet α-diketones is considerably slower than that by triplet monoketones (*164*), γ-hydrogen abstraction shows comparable dependence on C—H bond strength (*88*). The competing enolization process involves attack on a β-hydrogen and is far more sensitive to bond strength, as demonstrated by the three diketones shown below.

α-Diketones with no γ-hydrogens undergo efficient enolization (*88*). It has been suggested that the process may be partially ionic, since an oxyallyl intermediate seems to be involved (*88*). The enols are quite stable

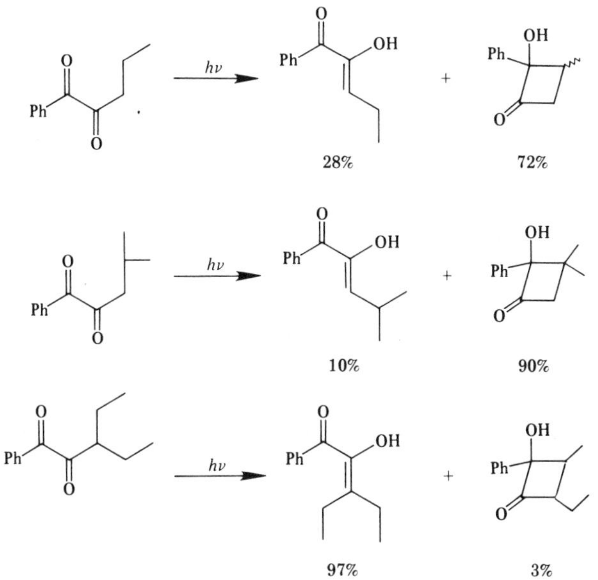

28% 72%

10% 90%

97% 3%

thermally but revert to diketone instantaneously when treated with acid or base.

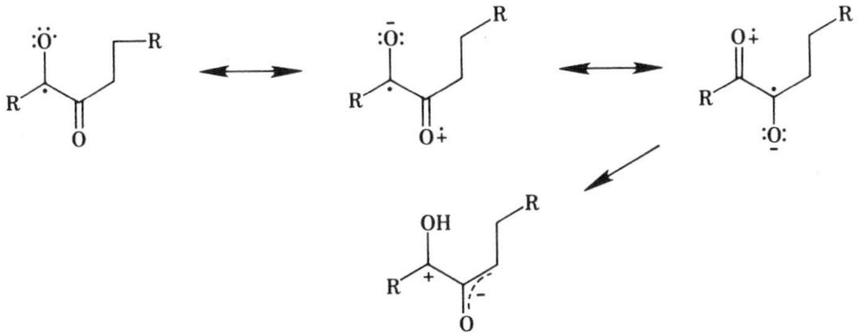

5. *o*-Alkyl Ketones: Enolization and Cyclization

The photoenolization of *o*-alkylphenyl ketones has been known for some time (*165,165a*) and represents a major type of photochromism. The enols are not stable but can be trapped with dienophiles (*165,165a*) and oxygen (*166*); this process has synthetic potential.

The actual mechanism of enolization is fairly complex and has been fully appreciated only recently (*169*). Rotation about the phenyl–carbonyl bond is somewhat restricted in the excited state, so ground state conformational preferences are important. Some of the enolization arises from the singlet state, some from a very short-lived triplet, and some from a

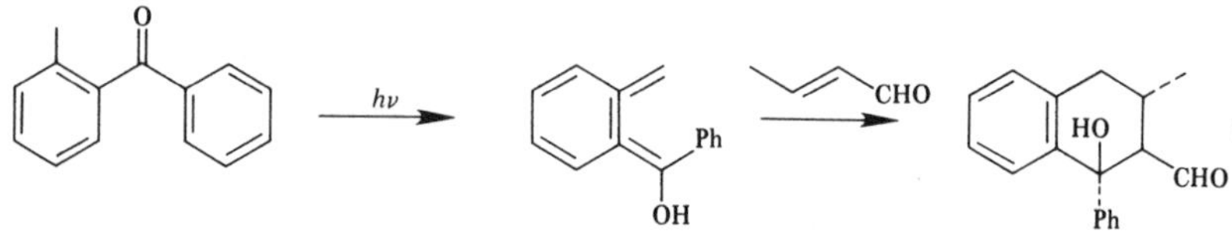

(167)

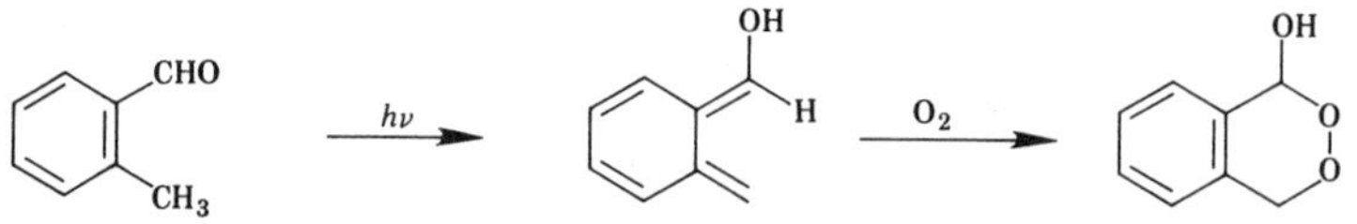

(168)

readily quenched long-lived triplet. The scheme below has been proposed to explain the excited state dynamics (109). A key point is that the syn and anti conformers represent kinetically distinct triplets; the former is perfectly disposed geometrically to rapidly abstract a γ-hydrogen from the o-alkyl group; the latter undergoes fairly slow, rate-determining rotation to the former in competition with other typical triplet reactions such as reaction with solvent or with γ C—H bonds.

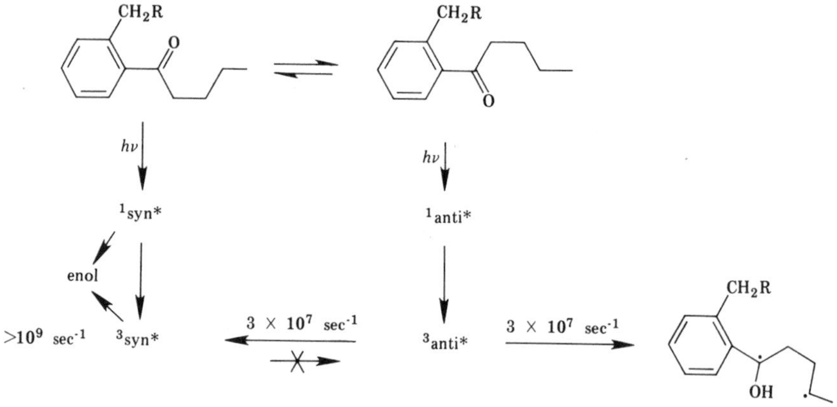

The extent of normal type II reaction of o-alkyl ketones thus is determined by the ground state fraction of anti conformers; this fraction is 20% for o-methylvalerophenone and decreases as the o-alkyl group gets larger and as α substitution increases (170). The evidence for the above scheme is twofold: Acyclic ketones display two kinetically independent triplets, whereas cyclic ketones, such as 8-methyl-1-tetralone (which is fixed in a "syn" conformation), display only one short-lived triplet; the observed rate constant for enolization of the long-lived triplet is independent of C—H bond strength and electronic configuration. This rate constant does decrease as solvent polarity increases for reasons not yet understood.

Inasmuch as the triplet benzoyl group is planar, hydrogen abstraction generates a twisted triplet enol (the benzylic radical site is twisted out of conjugation, so the rapid rate is probably due entirely to the favorable conformation). This possibility was recognized with the observation that *E*-enol is formed directly from excited ketone (*165a*). Original flash-spectroscopic studies of photoenolization interpreted transients with lifetimes of 10^{-7} sec as triplet ketones (*166,171*). These have now been identified as the triplet enols (*169*). Independent evidence has been provided that the triplet enols correspond to twisted biradicals in the following photocyclization (enolization would violate Bredt's rule) (*172*):

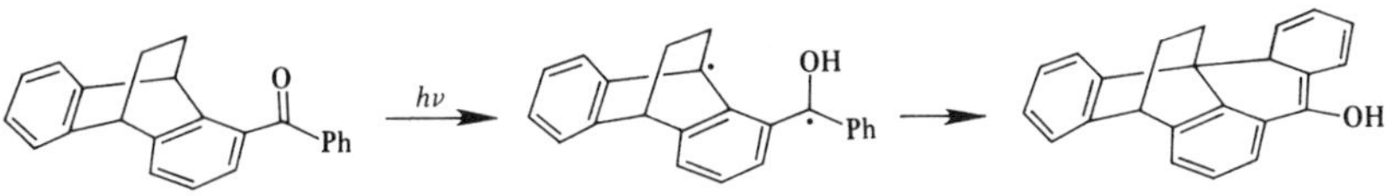

The next problem concerns the stereochemistry of the enols. Until recently, all trapping experiments indicated the presence of only the *E*-enol; it could be questioned whether any *Z*-enol is formed (*173*). This question was answered by flashing an 8-methyl-1-tetralone and observing no long-lived enol but only a short-lived enol, the lifetime of which was increased dramatically by Lewis base solvents (*169*). The *Z*-enol can undergo an allowed [1,5] sigmatropic rearrangement to regenerate ground state ketone and does so rapidly ($k \sim 10^7$ sec^{-1}) unless the hydroxylic proton is tied up by hydrogen bonding. Acyclic ketones also produce the longer-lived enol ($\tau \sim 1$ sec) observed in all earlier flash studies. Trapping of a *Z*-enol thus may be possible if a super dienophile is employed in solvents such as HMPA.

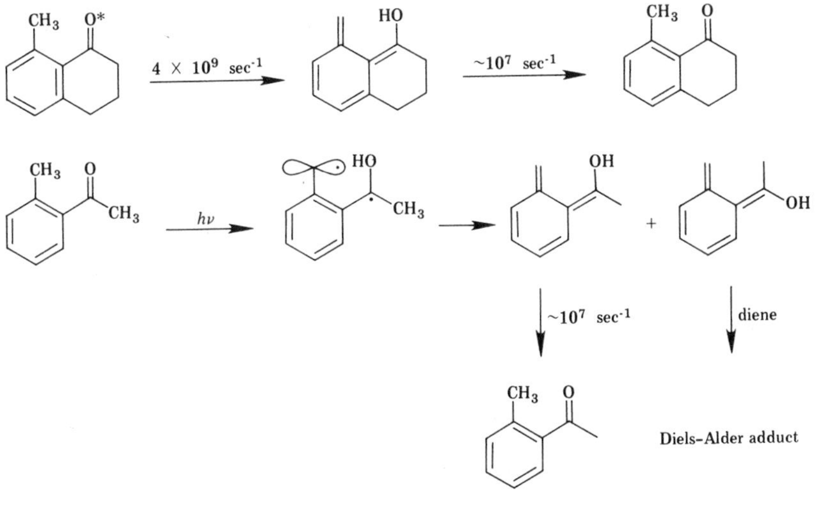

If the photochemistry of o-alkyl ketones seems fairly well understood, that of 2,6-dialkylphenyl ketones remains so confusing as to cause valid concern that our understanding of o-alkyl ketones may not be as complete as is thought. First, 2,6-dialkyl ketones do not form stable enols but rather yield benzocyclobutenols (*174*). Second, although distinct syn and anti conformations are not possible, the ketones form two kinetically distinct triplets. Only the short-lived one cyclizes (*170*); the long-lived triplet can undergo normal competitive reactions and also decays unusually rapidly ($k = 6 \times 10^7$ sec^{-1}). The kinetics defy present understanding. Cyclization rather than enolization is usually blamed on steric problems in the first-formed enol; these are presumed to be relieved by cyclization (*174*). Some prefer to postulate that in 2,6-dimethyl ketones the first-formed cyclo-butenols cannot open to sterically uncrowded enol (*173*). Given the flash evidence for triplet enols, the former explanation seems preferable, al-though the unusual kinetics suggest that the real explanation awaits fur-ther study.

Benzocycloalkenones with large enough rings also cyclize (*175*). The formation of a cyclic peroxide implicates the presence of an enol. The presence of an extra o-methyl group allows an interesting competition that is dependent on ring size.

$n = 1-3$	0	55–78%
$n = 4$	55%	12%
$n = 6, 8$	33–49%	0

Finally, o-alkylphenyl α-diketones undergo a unique photocyclization (*77*). A considerable amount of work has been carried out to show that the reaction proceeds by initial enolization followed by nucleophilic attack on carbonyl rather than by a direct δ-hydrogen abstraction (*176*). Given a transoid triplet dicarbonyl, δ-hydrogen abstraction is impossible in the conformation that can enolize. However, it is certainly possible in the other conformation, the presence of which has not been considered.

6. α,β-Unsaturated Ketones

Several unsaturated ketones have been examined in which the C=C double bond abstracts a hydrogen atom from elsewhere in the molecule (*177*). Conjugated enones have n,π^* and π,π^* triplets of comparable energies; this reaction presumably originates from the π,π^* level and involves an initial 1,5-hydrogen transfer.

The ability of alkene triplets to abstract hydrogen atoms from solvent (*94*) and from elsewhere in the same molecule is well known. In fact, the reaction of α-alkylstyrenes is analogous to the Norrish type II reaction (*178*).

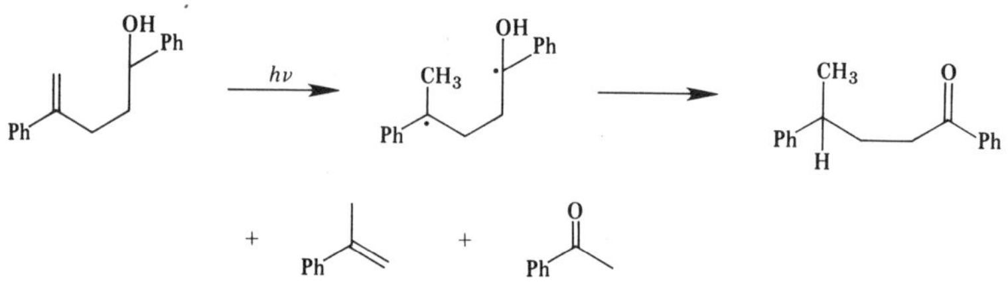

Below are presented a few examples of internal hydrogen abstraction by enones that have been recorded since the first reported example (*179*). Note that the third example indicates that the order of hydrogen transfer is 1,5 > 1,6 > 1,4.

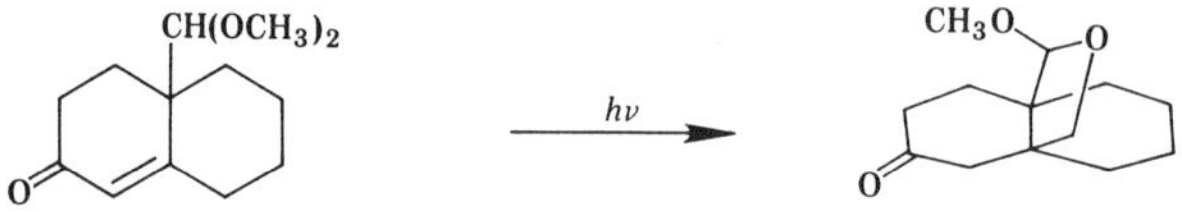

(*180*)

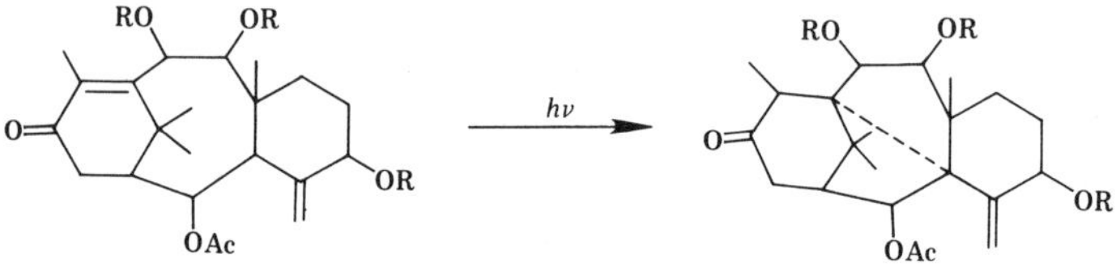

(*181*)

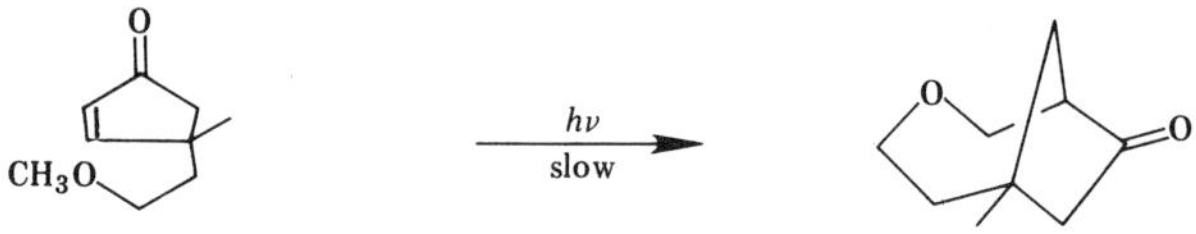

(*182*)

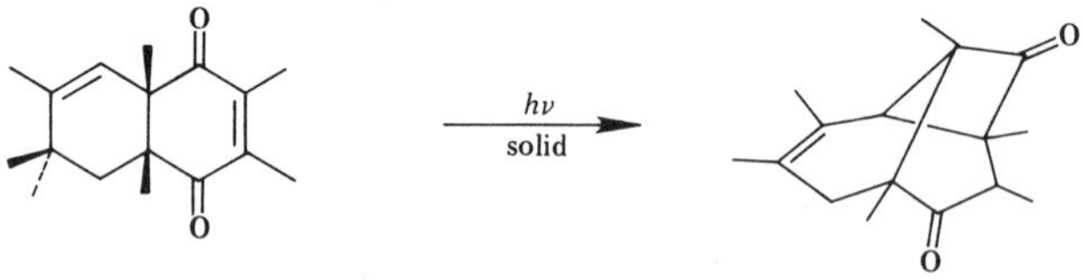

(*183*)

7. *o*-Pyridyl Ketones

2-Pyridyl ketones undergo photocyclization to cyclopropanols in competition with normal type II processes (*184*). The reaction was proposed to involve the n,π* triplet level of the pyridine, which is nearly isoenergetic with the carbonyl triplet. Internal hydrogen abstraction by excited azaaromatics had been reported earlier (*185*). So far this process has been demonstrated only for acylpyridines and pyrimidines. The excited pyridine level appears to be much less selective toward C—H bond strength than are carbonyl triplets, but both excited states share a preference for hydrogen abstraction through six-atom transition states.

R = H	0	100%
R = CH$_3$	40%	50%
R = CH$_2$CH$_3$	85%	0

8. p-Benzoylbenzoate Esters

p-Benzoylbenzoate esters can undergo remote triplet state hydrogen atom abstraction if the alkyl group of the ester is long enough (78). The selectivity of this and analogous internal hydrogen atom abstractions has been exploited to functionalize steroids (186). Systematic studies of the original n-alkyl esters have demonstrated that the rate constants for remote hydrogen abstraction parallel the calculated equilibrium fraction of molecules in which the alkyl tail has coiled around the benzene ring close enough to the carbonyl for reaction (187). There is no reaction for esters shorter than n-decyl, for which the rate constant for remote abstraction is only 10^4 sec^{-1}. The rate constant rises to 4–10×10^4 sec^{-1} for n-octadecyl, the exact value depending on solvent. The cycloalkanols so produced are stable but can be oxidized quantitatively to keto alcohols (188).

9. Thio Ketones

There has been an extensive study of the fascinating photochemistry of thiones (*189*). These compounds undergo photoreactions from two distinct excited states. *t*-Alkylphenylthiones undergo intramolecular hydrogen abstractions following excitation. Irradiation in the visible region produces the lowest, n,π^* triplet, which reacts only with activated C—H bonds (*190*). In particular, γ-hydrogen abstraction leads to cyclobutane-thiols.

When the same alkoxythione is irradiated in the ultraviolet region into its second excited singlet, an additional product corresponds to ϵ-hydrogen abstraction; both products apparently are formed from the same long-lived, high-energy π,π^* singlet. Aralkylthio ketones without heteroatoms in their alkyl chain undergo primarily δ-hydrogen abstraction when irradiated into their second singlets (*190*) and provide useful syntheses of cyclopentanethiols (*191*). δ-Hydrogen abstraction is preferred over γ-hydrogen abstraction, even when the γ C—H bonds are far weaker. It has been proposed that conformational preferences vary from that displayed by n,π^* states because the unpaired-electron density is entirely in the π system above the carbonyl (*190*).

Cyclizations from excited thiocarbonyl groups are known which may give three-, four-, five-, or six-membered rings. The cyclization of thiofenchone illustrated here is duplicated by selenofenchone (189).

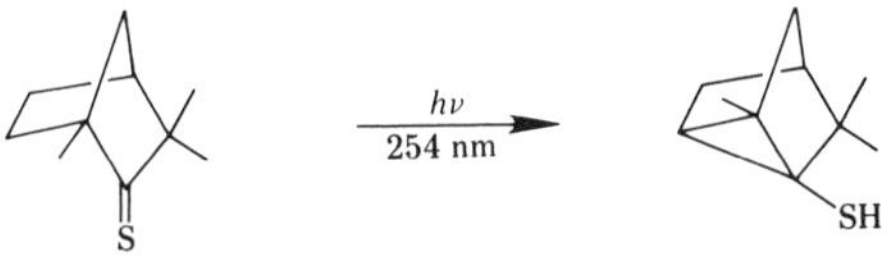

Thio ketones also undergo a photodimerization that can compete with internal hydrogen abstraction. Self-quenching rate constants for all thio ketones are very rapid; some of this quenching leads to stable products.

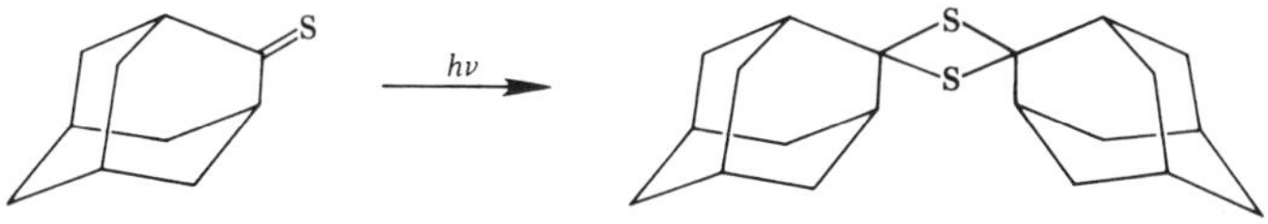

10. Imides

Most acid derivatives do not photocyclize. Several studies on the photochemistry of esters have indicated that type II cleavage occurs, usually from excited singlets (192). In fact, this reaction has been exploited to prepare adamantene as a transient (193).

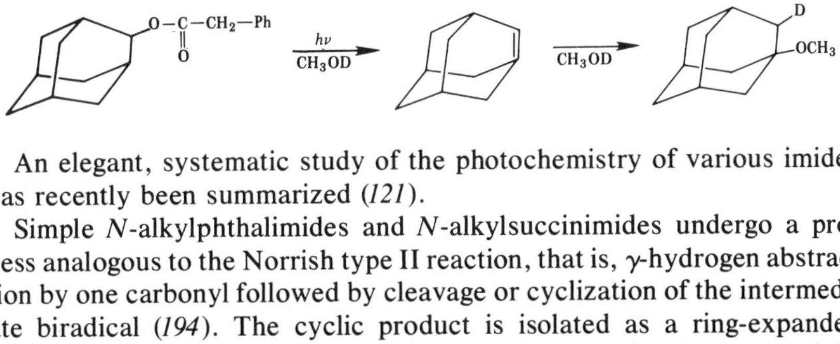

An elegant, systematic study of the photochemistry of various imides has recently been summarized (121).

Simple N-alkylphthalimides and N-alkylsuccinimides undergo a process analogous to the Norrish type II reaction, that is, γ-hydrogen abstraction by one carbonyl followed by cleavage or cyclization of the intermediate biradical (194). The cyclic product is isolated as a ring-expanded ketolactam, which can undergo further photoreaction because of its ketone unit. In this simple hydrogen abstraction the imides behave much as ketones, although cyclization yields are quite high and the radical can disproportionate to an unsaturated alcohol. Moreover, δ-hydrogen abstraction is highly competitive.

The ease of δ-hydrogen abstraction and the relative stability of the azacyclopentanols so produced is exemplified by the behavior of N-(o-alkyl)phenylimides. Just as with phenyl ketones, electron-donating substituents on the phthalimide ring retard the photocyclization, probably by stabilizing a π,π^* lowest triplet (195).

Alkoxymethyl- and 3-alkoxypropylphthalimides also react exclusively by δ-hydrogen abstraction (196). The absence of product from γ-hydrogen abstraction in the latter indicates that δ-hydrogen abstraction by these imides competes much better than in the case of excited ketones.

Phthalimides have relatively low reduction potentials, so it is not surprising that two classes of N-substituted phthalimides show signs of strong charge-transfer character in their photochemistry. Several ω-arylalkylphthalimides undergo hydrogen abstraction exclusively from the benzylic position, however far it is from the carbonyl (197). Quantum efficiency is maximal when $n = 4$ and is enhanced by electron-donating substituents on the remote benzene ring. It has been suggested that a ground state charge-transfer complex brings the benzylic carbon close to the imide carbonyl. Such complexing would be even better in the excited state; the quantum efficiencies are a composite of ring size effects on complexation and on cyclization/reversal in the biradical.

Finally, ω-thiomethoxyalkylphthalimides display remote hydrogen abstraction from carbons as far as 15 atoms away from the carbonyl (198). Interestingly, the major product shows a 6- to 12-fold preference for attack on the S-methyl rather than on the closer S-methylene. Such preferences have previously been observed in bimolecular ketone–amine exciplex reactions (199). Keto sulfides show efficient intramolecular triplet state charge-transfer quenching but no remote hydrogen transfers (134). When $n = 2$, a thiaazacyclohexanol is produced even from thioethoxy- and thioisopropoxyimides. As in γ-amino ketones (119,120) the geometry of the exciplex apparently is rigid enough to prevent transfer of a γ proton.

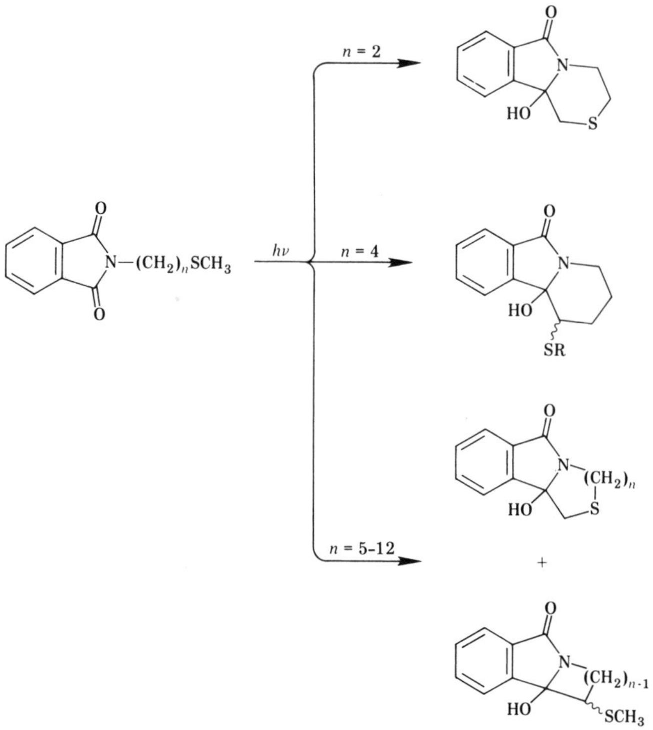
n = 2
hν
n = 4
n = 5-12
HO
S
N
SR
(CH2)n
+
(CH2)n-1
SCH3
N—(CH2)nSCH3

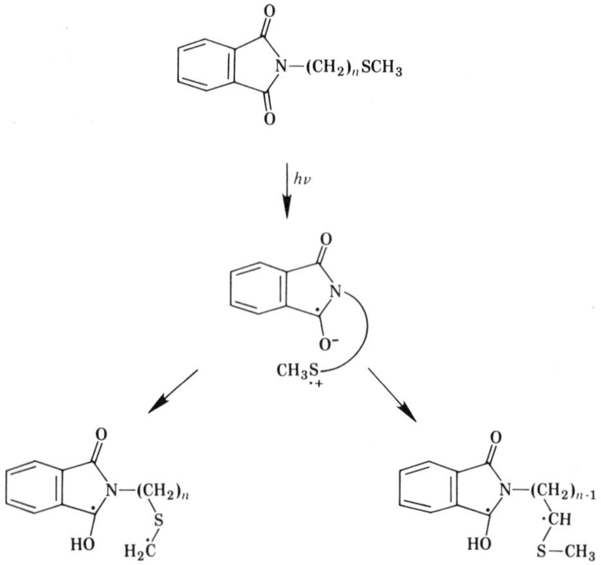
N—(CH2)nSCH3
hν
O⁻
CH3S
HO
(CH2)n
H2C
(CH2)n-1
CH
S—CH3

With longer chains there is apparently enough flexibility for the negative carbonyl to attack a proton on either side of the positive sulfur.

IV. CYCLOADDITIONS

A good number of nonconjugated unsaturated carbonyl compounds undergo internal photocycloadditions that are exactly analogous to the bimolecular cycloadditions except for conformational limitations. Such reactions technically are molecular rearrangements. De Schryver has recently reviewed this entire field (200).

REFERENCES

1. The most recent review: O. L. Chapman and D. S. Weiss, in "Organic Photochemistry" (O. L. Chapman, ed.), Vol. 3, p. 197. Dekker, New York, 1973.
2. W. D. Stohrer, P. Jacobs, K. H. Kaiser, G. Weich, and G. Quinkert, Top. Curr. Chem. 46, 181 (1974).
3. J. Kossanyi, B. Furth, and J.-P. Morizur, Tetrahedron Lett. p. 3459 (1973).
4. J. Kossanyi, B. Guiard, and B. Furth, Bull. Soc. Chim. Fr. p. 305 (1974).
5. W. C. Agosta, D. K. Herron, and W. W. Lowrance, Jr., Tetrahedron Lett. p. 4521 (1969).
6. G. Quinkert, E. Blanke, and F. Homburg, Chem. Ber. 97, 1799 (1964).
7. T. Tsuyuki, S. Yamada, and T. Takahashi, Bull. Chem. Soc. Jpn. 41, 511 (1968).
8. N. Sugiyama, K. Yamada, and H. Aoyama, J. Chem. Soc. C p. 830 (1971).
9. P. Yates, Pure Appl. Chem. 16, 93 (1968).
10. A. Butenandt and L. Paschmann, Chem. Ber. 77, 394 (1944); H. Wehrli and K. Schaffner, Helv. Chim. Acta 45, 385 (1962).
11. A. A. Baum, J. Am. Chem. Soc. 94, 6866 (1972); F. D. Lewis and J. G. Magyar, J. Org. Chem. 37, 2102 (1972).
12. C. Walling and M. J. Gibian, J. Am. Chem. Soc. 87, 3361 (1965).
13. P. J. Wagner and G. S. Hammond, Adv. Photochem. 5, 21 (1968); N. J. Turro, J. C. Dalton, K. Dawes, G. Farrington, R. Hautala, D. Morton, M. Niemczyk, and N. Schore, Acc. Chem. Res. 5, 92 (1972).
14. P. J. Wagner, Top. Curr. Chem. 66, 1 (1976).
15. J. C. Dalton, D. M. Pond, D. S. Weiss, F. D. Lewis, and N. J. Turro, J. Am. Chem. Soc. 92, 2564 (1970).
15a. N. C. Yang, E. D. Feit, M. H. Hui, N. J. Turro, and J. C. Dalton, J. Am. Chem. Soc. 92, 6974 (1970).
16. J. C. Dalton, K. Dawes, N. J. Turro, D. S. Weiss, J. A. Barltrop, and J. D. Coyle, J. Am. Chem. Soc. 93, 7213 (1971).
17. L. Salem, J. Am. Chem. Soc. 96, 3486 (1974).
18. P. J. Wagner and J. M. McGrath, J. Am. Chem. Soc. 94, 3849 (1972); F. D. Lewis and J. G. Magyar, ibid. 95, 5973 (1973).
18a. F. D. Lewis and T. A. Hilliard, J. Am. Chem. Soc. 94, 3852 (1972).
19. J. D. Coyle, Ph.D. Thesis, Oxford University (1969), quoted in J. C. Dalton and N. J. Turro, Annu. Rev. Phys. Chem. 21, 499 (1970).

20. R. Simonaitis, G. W. Cowell, and J. N. Pitts, Jr., *Tetrahedron Lett.* p. 3751 (1967).
21. P. J. Wagner and R. W. Spoerke, *J. Am. Chem. Soc.* **91**, 4437 (1969).
22. P. J. Wagner, *J. Am. Chem. Soc.* **88**, 5672 (1966).
23. D. R. Charney, J. C. Dalton, R. R. Hautala, J. J. Snyder, and N. J. Turro, *J. Am. Chem. Soc.* **96**, 1407 (1974); R. W. Yip and W. Siebrand, *Chem. Phys. Lett.* **13**, 209 (1972).
24. B. Guiard, B. Furth, and J. Kossanyi, *Bull. Soc. Chim. Fr.* p. 3021 (1974); J. P. Morizur, B. Furth, and J. Kossanyi, *ibid.* p. 1959 (1970).
25. D. S. Weiss and P. M. Kochanek, *Tetrahedron Lett.* p. 763 (1977); T. Mori, K. Matsui, and H. Nozaki, *ibid.* p. 1175 (1970).
26. N. J. Turro and D. S. Weiss, *J. Am. Chem. Soc.* **90**, 2185 (1968); K. Dawes, J. C. Dalton, and N. J. Turro, *Mol. Photochem.* **3**, 71 (1971); I. Fleming, A. V. Kemp-Jones, and E. J. Thomas, *Chem. Commun.* p. 1158 (1971).
27. C. Walling and P. J. Wagner, *J. Am. Chem. Soc.* **86**, 3368 (1964).
28. C. C. Badcock, M. J. Perona, G. O. Pritchard, and B. Rickborn, *J. Am. Chem. Soc.* **91**, 543 (1969).
29. A. Sonoda, I. Moritani, J. Miki, and T. Tsuji, *Tetrahedron Lett.* p. 3187 (1969).
29a. J. K. Crandall and R. J. Seidewand, *J. Org. Chem.* **35**, 697 (1970).
30. W. G. Dauben, G. W. Shaffer, and E. J. Delviny, *J. Am. Chem. Soc.* **92**, 6273 (1970).
31. J. K. Crandall, J. P. Arrington, and C. F. Mayer, *J. Org. Chem.* **36**, 1428 (1971).
31a. S. Moon and H. Bohm, *J. Org. Chem.* **36**, 1434 (1971).
32. D. C. Heckert and P. J. Kropp, *J. Am. Chem. Soc.* **90**, 4911 (1968).
33. C. D. Badcock, B. Rickborn, and G. O. Pritchard, *Chem. Ind. (London)* p. 1053 (1970).
34. W. C. Agosta and W. L. Schreiber, *J. Am. Chem. Soc.* **93**, 3947 (1971).
35. J. D. Coyle, *J. Chem. Soc. B* p. 1736 (1971).
36. H. E. O'Neal, R. G. Miller, and E. Gunderson, *J. Am. Chem. Soc.* **96**, 3351 (1974).
36a. P. J. Wagner and K. C. Liu, *J. Am. Chem. Soc.* **96**, 5952 (1974).
36b. R. O. Small, Jr. and J. C. Scaiano, *Chem. Phys. Lett.* **50**, 431 (1977).
37. J. Grotewold and J. A. Kerr, *J. Chem. Soc.* pp. 4337 and 4342 (1963).
38. W. B. Hammond and T. S. Yeung, *Tetrahedron Lett.* p. 1169 (1975).
39. W. C. Agosta and S. Wolff, *J. Am. Chem. Soc.* **97**, 456 (1975).
40. J. A. Barltrop and J. D. Coyle, *Chem. Commun.* p. 1081 (1969).
41. D. S. Weiss, P. M. Kochanek, and J. J. Lipka, *Tetrahedron Lett.* p. 1261 (1977).
42. J. M. Beard and R. H. Eastman, *Tetrahedron Lett.* p. 3029 (1970).
43. R. S. Carlson and E. L. Biersmith, *Chem. Commun.* p. 1049 (1969).
44. R. G. Carlson and W. S. Mardis, *J. Org. Chem.* **40**, 817 (1975).
45. R. G. Carlson, J. H.-A. Huber, and D. E. Henton, *J. Chem. Soc., Chem. Commun.* p. 223 (1973).
46. L. Paquette and R. F. Eizember, *J. Am. Chem. Soc.* **91**, 7108 (1969).
47. D. I. Schuster, "Photorearrangements of Unsaturated Ketones," this book.
48. R. G. Carlson and D. E. Henton, *Chem. Commun.* p. 674 (1969).
49. M. R. Willcott, R. L. Cargill, T. Y. King, and A. B. Sears, *J. Org. Chem.* **36**, 1423 (1971).
50. D. L. Dean and H. Hart, *J. Am. Chem. Soc.* **94**, 687 (1972).
51. R. C. Cookson, A. G. Edwards, J. Hudec, and M. Kingsland, *Chem. Commun.* p. 98 (1965).
51b. T. Okada, K. Kamogawa, M. Kawanisi, and H. Nozaki, *Bull. Chem. Soc. Jpn.* **43**, 2908 (1970).
52. H. Kato, M. Miyamoto, M. Kawanisi, and H. Nozaki, *Tetrahedron* **26**, 2975 (1970).

53. C. K. Chip and T. R. Lynch, *Can. J. Chem.* **52**, 2249 (1974).
54. P. M. Collins, *Chem. Commun.* p. 403 (1968).
55. J. F. Stan and R. H. Eastman, *J. Org. Chem.* **31**, 1393 (1966).
56. D. S. Weiss, M. Haslanger, and R. G. Lawton, *J. Am. Chem. Soc.* **98**, 1050 (1976).
57. P. Yates and R. O. Loutfy, *Acc. Chem. Res.* **8**, 209 (1975).
58. G. Quinkert and P. Jacobs, *Chem. Ber.* **107**, 2473 (1974).
59. P. Yates and L. Kilmurry, *Tetrahedron Lett.* p. 1739 (1964).
60. R. Simonaitis and J. N. Pitts, *J. Am. Chem. Soc.* **91**, 108 (1969).
61. J. W. Meyer and G. S. Hammond, *J. Am. Chem. Soc.* **94**, 2219 (1972).
62. P. O. L. Mack and J. T. Pinhey, *J. Chem. Soc., Chem. Commun.* p. 451 (1972).
63. O. L. Chapman and C. L. McIntosh, *J. Am. Chem. Soc.* **91**, 4309 (1969).
64. C. D. Gutsche and B. A. M. Oude-Alink, *J. Am. Chem. Soc.* **90**, 5855 (1968).
65. G. J. Sinta, R. W. Franck, and A. A. Ozorio, *J. Chem. Soc., Chem. Commun.* p. 910 (1974).
66. P. H. Mazzocchi and J. J. Thomas, *J. Am. Chem. Soc.* **94**, 8281 (1972).
67. M. Fischer, *Chem. Ber.* **102**, 342 (1969).
68. R. G. W. Norrish, *Trans. Faraday Soc.* **33**, 1521 (1937).
69. N. C. Yang and D.-H. Yang, *J. Am. Chem. Soc.* **80**, 2913 (1958).
70. G. R. McMillan, J. G. Calvert, and J. N. Pitts, Jr., *J. Am. Chem. Soc.* **86**, 3602 (1964).
71. R. C. Cookson, J. Hudec, A. Szabo, and S. E. Usher, *Tetrahedron* **24**, 4353 (1968).
72. P. Sunder-Plassman, P. H. Nelson, P. H. Boyle, A. Cruz, J. Iriarte, P. Crabbé, J. A. Zderic, J. A. Edwards, and J. H. Fried, *J. Org. Chem.* **34**, 3779 (1969).
73. K. R. Henery-Logan and C. S. Chen, *Tetrahedron Lett.* p. 1103 (1973).
74. R. L. Whistler and L. W. Doner, *J. Org. Chem.* **38**, 2900 (1973).
75. W. H. Richardson, G. Ranney, and F. C. Montgomery, *J. Am. Chem. Soc.* **96**, 4688 (1974).
76. A. Padwa, E. Alexander, and M. Niemcyzk, *J. Am. Chem. Soc.* **91**, 456 (1969).
77. R. Bishop and N. K. Hamer, *J. Chem. Soc. C* p. 1193 (1970).
78. R. Breslow and M. A. Winnik, *J. Am. Chem. Soc.* **91**, 3083 (1969).
79. P. J. Wagner and G. S. Hammond, *J. Am. Chem. Soc.* **87**, 4009 (1965); T. J. Dougherty, *ibid.* p. 4011.
80. P. J. Wagner, *Acc. Chem. Res.* **4**, 168 (1971).
81. J. Michl, *Top. Curr. Chem.* **46**, 1 (1974).
82. M. J. S. Dewar and C. Doubleday, *J. Am. Chem. Soc.* **100**, 4935 (1978).
83. L. M. Stephenson, P. R. Cavigli, and J. L. Parlett, *J. Am. Chem. Soc.* **93**, 1984 (1971); C. P. Casey and R. A. Boggs, *ibid.* **94**, 6457 (1972).
84. N. C. Yang and S. P. Elliot, *J. Am. Chem. Soc.* **91**, 7550 (1969).
85. D. R. Coulson and N. C. Yang, *J. Am. Chem. Soc.* **88**, 4511 (1966).
86. I. Orban, K. Schaffner, and O. Jeger, *J. Am. Chem. Soc.* **85**, 3033 (1963); K. H. Schulte-Elte and G. Ohloff, *Tetrahedron Lett.* p. 1143 (1964).
87. P. J. Wagner, P. A. Kelso, and R. G. Zepp, *J. Am. Chem. Soc.* **94**, 7480 (1972).
88. P. J. Wagner, R. G. Zepp, K. C. Liu, M. Thomas, T.-J. Lee, and N. J. Turro, *J. Am. Chem. Soc.* **98**, 8125 (1976).
89. N. C. Yang and R. Dusenbery, *J. Am. Chem. Soc.* **90**, 5899 (1968).
90. P. J. Wagner, A. E. Kemppainen, and H. N. Schott, *J. Am. Chem. Soc.* **95**, 5604 (1968); P. J. Wagner, M. J. Thomas, and E. Harris, *ibid.* **98**, 7675 (1976).
91. M. Berger, E. McAlpine, and C. Steel, *J. Am. Chem. Soc.* **100**, 5147 (1978).
92. N. J. Turro, "Modern Molecular Photochemistry," pp. 382 and 389. Benjamin/Cummings, Menlo Park, California, 1978.

93. G. S. Hammond and P. A. Leermakers, *J. Am. Chem. Soc.* **84**, 207 (1962); P. J. Wagner and G. S. Hammond, *Adv. Photochem.* **5**, 21 (1968); N. J. Turro and C. G. Lee, *Mol. Photochem.* **4**, 427 (1972).

94. P. J. Kropp, *J. Am. Chem. Soc.* **91**, 5783 (1969).

95. C. Walling and M. J. Gibian, *J. Am. Chem. Soc.* **87**, 3361 (1965).

96. P. J. Wagner and A. E. Kemppainen, *J. Am. Chem. Soc.* **94**, 7495 (1972).

97. C. Walling, *in* "Molecular Rearrangements" (P. de Mayo, ed.), p. 448. Wiley (Interscience), New York, 1963; R. H. Hesse, *Adv. Free-Radical Chem.* **1**, 83 (1969).

98. P. J. Wagner, P. A. Kelso, A. E. Kemppainen, and R. G. Zepp, *J. Am. Chem. Soc.* **94**, 7500 (1972).

99. R. G. Zepp and P. J. Wagner, *J. Am. Chem. Soc.* **93**, 4958 (1971).

100. F. D. Lewis, R. W. Johnson, and D. R. Kory, *J. Am. Chem. Soc.* **96**, 6100 (1974).

101. E. C. Alexander and J. A. Uliana, *J. Am. Chem. Soc.* **96**, 5644 (1974).

102. A. Padwa and W. Eisenberg, *J. Am. Chem. Soc.* **94**, 5859 (1972).

103. F. D. Lewis, R. W. Johnson, and D. E. Johnson, *J. Am. Chem. Soc.* **96**, 6090 (1974).

104. C. D. DeBoer, W. G. Herkstroeter, A. P. Marchetti, A. G. Schultz, and R. H. Schlessinger, *J. Am. Chem. Soc.* **95**, 3963 (1973).

105. P. J. Wagner and C. Chiu, *J. Am. Chem. Soc.* **101**, 7134 (1979).

106. G. R. Leppin and S. Zannucci, *J. Org. Chem.* **36**, 1808 (1971).

107. S. P. Pappas and R. D. Zehr, *J. Am. Chem. Soc.* **93**, 7112 (1971).

108. E. J. O'Connell, *J. Am. Chem. Soc.* **90**, 6550 (1968).

109. P. J. Wagner and C. P. Chen, *J. Am. Chem. Soc.* **98**, 239 (1976).

110. W. Bergmark, private communication.

111. J. R. Scheffer, B. M. Jennings, and J. P. Louwerens, *J. Am. Chem. Soc.* **98**, 7040 (1976).

112. J. R. Scheffer and A. A. Dzakpasu, *J. Am. Chem. Soc.* **100**, 2163 (1978).

113. N. Sugiyama, T. Nishio, K. Yamada, and H. Aoyama, *Bull. Chem. Soc. Jpn.* **43**, 1879 (1970).

114. S. G. Cohen, A. Parola, and G. H. Parsons, *Chem. Rev.* **73**, 141 (1973).

115. A. Padwa and R. Gruber, *J. Am. Chem. Soc.* **92**, 100 and 107 (1970).

116. A. Padwa and W. Eisenhardt, *J. Am. Chem. Soc.* **93**, 1400 (1971).

117. H. J. Roth and M. H. El Raie, *Arch. Pharm. (Weinheim, Ger.)* **305**, 213 and 219 (1972).

118. E. H. Gold, *J. Am. Chem. Soc.* **93**, 2793 (1971).

119. P. J. Wagner, T. Jellinek, and A. E. Kemppainen, *J. Am. Chem. Soc.* **94**, 7512 (1972).

120. P. J. Wagner and D. A. Ersfeld, *J. Am. Chem. Soc.* **98**, 4515 (1976).

121. Y. Kanaoka, *Acc. Chem. Res.* **11**, 407 (1978).

122. D. I. Schuster, *Pure Appl. Chem.* **41**, 601 (1975).

123. M. W. Wolf, K. D. Legg, R. E. Brown, L. A. Singer, and J. H. Parks, *J. Am. Chem. Soc.* **97**, 4490 (1975).

124. R. D. Small, Jr. and J. C. Scaiano, *J. Phys. Chem.* **81**, 828 and 2126 (1977).

125. M. V. Encinas and J. C. Scaiano, *J. Am. Chem. Soc.* **100**, 7108 (1978).

126. P. J. Wagner *et al., J. Am. Chem. Soc.* **94**, 7506 (1972).

127. F. D. Lewis and T. A. Hilliard, *J. Am. Chem. Soc.* **92**, 6670 (1970).

128. R. A. Caldwell and P. Fink, *Tetrahedron Lett.* p. 2987 (1969).

129. P. J. Wagner and P. A. Kelso, *Tetrahedron Lett.* p. 4152 (1969).

130. P. J. Wagner and A. E. Kemppainen, *J. Am. Chem. Soc.* **90**, 5896 (1968).

131. N. C. Yang and D. M. Thap, *Tetrahedron Lett.* p. 3671 (1966).

132. P. J. Wagner and M. J. Thomas, *J. Am. Chem. Soc.* **98**, 241 (1976).

133. F. D. Lewis and N. J. Turro, *J. Am. Chem. Soc.* **92**, 311 (1970).

134. M. C. Caserio, W. Lauer, and T. Novinson, *J. Am. Chem. Soc.* **92**, 6082 (1970); M. J. Lindstrom, Ph.D. Thesis, Michigan State University, East Lansing, (1978).
135. A. Padwa, W. Eisenhardt, R. Gruber, and D. Pashayan, *J. Am. Chem. Soc.* **93**, 6998 (1971).
136. J. C. Coyle, *J. Chem. Soc., Perkin Trans. 2* p. 233 (1973).
137. P. J. Wagner, *J. Am. Chem. Soc.* **89**, 5898 (1967).
138. P. J. Wagner, I. Kochever, and A. E. Kemppainen, *J. Am. Chem. Soc.* **94**, 7489 (1972).
139. P. J. Wagner, J. H. Sedon, and M. J. Lindstrom, *J. Am. Chem. Soc.* **100**, 2579 (1978).
140. D. J. Coyle, R. V. Peterson, and J. Heicklen, *J. Am. Chem. Soc.* **86**, 3850 (1964); P. Yates and J. M. Pal, *Chem. Commun.* p. 553 (1970).
141. P. J. Wagner and R. G. Zepp, *J. Am. Chem. Soc.* **93**, 4958 (1971).
142. M. J. Perkin, N. B. Peynircioglu, and B. V. Smith, *J. Chem. Soc., Chem. Commun.* p. 222 (1976).
143. W. L. Schreiber and W. C. Agosta, *J. Am. Chem. Soc.* **93**, 6292 (1971).
144. A. Padwa and D. Eastman, *J. Am. Chem. Soc.* **91**, 462 (1969).
145. W. C. Agosta and A. B. Smith, *J. Am. Chem. Soc.* **93**, 5513 (1971).
146. M. J. Jorgensen and N. C. Yang, *J. Am. Chem. Soc.* **85**, 1698 (1963).
147. W. G. Brown, *U.S. Govt. Res. Rep.* **38**, 25 (1963).
148. P. J. Wagner and T. Noguchi, unpublished work.
149. A. Padwa, *J. Am. Chem. Soc.* **87**, 4205 (1965).
150. P. J. Wagner and K. C. Liu, *J. Am. Chem. Soc.* **96**, 5952 (1974).
151. M. Barnard and N. C. Yang, *Proc. Chem. Soc., London* p. 302 (1958).
152. K. H. Schulte-Elte, B. Willhalm, A. F. Thomas, M. Stoll, and G. Ohloff, *Helv. Chim. Acta* **54**, 1759 (1971).
152a. K. Matsui, T. Mori, and H. Nozaki, *Bull. Chem. Soc. Jpn.* **44**, 3440 (1971).
153. N. J. Turro, M. Niemczyk, and D. M. Pond, *Mol. Photochem.* **2**, 345 (1970).
154. P. J. Burchill, A. G. Kelso, and A. J. Power, *Aust. J. Chem.* **29**, 2477 (1976).
155. I. Fleming, A. V. Kemp-Jones, W. E. Long, and E. J. Thomas, *J. Chem. Soc., Perkin Trans. 2* p. 7 (1976).
156. F. D. Lewis, R. W. Johnson, and R. A. Ruden, *J. Am. Chem. Soc.* **94**, 4292 (1972).
157. J. Meinweld and J. Mioduski, *Tetrahedron Lett.* p. 4137 (1974).
158. R. B. Gagosian, J. C. Dalton, and N. J. Turro, *J. Am. Chem. Soc.* **92**, 4752 (1970); **97**, 5189 (1975).
159. J. C. Dalton and H. F. Chan, *J. Am. Chem. Soc.* **95**, 4085 (1973).
160. W. H. Urry and D. J. Trecker, *J. Am. Chem. Soc.* **84**, 713 (1962).
161. G. J. Karabatsos and D. J. Fenoglio, *Top. Stereochem.* **5**, 167 (1970).
162. R. Bishop, *J. Chem. Soc., Chem. Commun.* p. 1288 (1972).
163. T. L. Burkoth and E. F. Ullman, *Tetrahedron Lett.* p. 145 (1970).
164. N. J. Turro and R. Engel, *J. Am. Chem. Soc.* **91**, 7113 (1969); N. J. Turro and T. Lee, *ibid.* p. 5651.
165. E. F. Zwicker, L. J. Grossweiner, and N. C. Yang, *J. Am. Chem. Soc.* **85**, 2671 (1963).
165a. K. R. Huffman, M. Loy, and E. F. Ullman, *J. Am. Chem. Soc.* **87**, 5417 (1965).
166. G. Porter and M. F. Tchir, *J. Chem. Soc. A* p. 3772 (1971).
167. M. Pfau, E. W. Sarver, and N. D. Heindel, *Bull. Soc. Chim. Fr.* p. 183 (1973).
168. D. M. Findley and M. F. Tchir, *J. Chem. Soc., Chem. Commun.* p. 514 (1974).
169. R. Haag, J. Wirz, and P. J. Wagner, *Helv. Chim. Acta* **60**, 2595 (1977).
170. P. J. Wagner, *Pure Appl. Chem.* **49**, 259 (1977).
171. H. Lutz, E. Breheret, and L. Lindqvist, *J. Chem. Soc., Faraday Trans. 1* p. 2096 (1973).

172. M. F. Tchir, private communication.
173. P. G. Sammes, *Tetrahedron* **32**, 405 (1976).
174. T. Matsuura and T. Kitaura, *Tetrahedron* **25**, 4487 (1969).
175. M. L. Viriot-Villaume, C. Carré, and P. Caubere, *Tetrahedron Lett.* p. 3301 (1974).
176. N. K. Hamer and C. J. Samuel, *J. Chem. Soc., Perkin Trans. 2* p. 1316 (1973); Y. Ogata and K. Takagi, *J. Org. Chem.* **39**, 1385 (1974); N. K. Hamer, *J. Chem. Soc., Chem. Commun.* p. 557 (1975).
177. S. Wolff, W. L. Schreiber, A. B. Smith, and W. C. Agosta, *J. Am. Chem. Soc.* **94**, 7797 (1972).
178. J. M. Hornback, *J. Am. Chem. Soc.* **96**, 6773 (1974).
179. W. Herz and M. G. Nair, *J. Am. Chem. Soc.* **89**, 5475 (1967).
180. J. Gloor, K. Schaffner, and O. Jeger, *Helv. Chim. Acta* **54**, 1864 (1971).
181. T. Kobayashi, M. Kurono, H. Sato, and K. Nakanishi, *J. Am. Chem. Soc.* **94**, 2863 (1972).
182. S. Ayral-Kaloustian, S. Wolff, and W. C. Agosta, *J. Am. Chem. Soc.* **99**, 5984 (1977).
183. W. K. Appel, T. J. Greenhough, J. R. Scheffer, and J. Trotter, *J. Am. Chem. Soc.* **101**, 213 (1979).
184. E. C. Alexander and R. J. Jackson, *J. Am. Chem. Soc.* **96**, 5663 (1974); **98**, 1609 (1976); unpublished results.
185. F. R. Stermitz and C. C. Wei, *J. Am. Chem. Soc.* **91**, 3103 (1969).
186. R. Breslow, S. Baldwin, T. Fletchner, P. Kalicky, S. Liu, and W. Washburn, *J. Am. Chem. Soc.* **95**, 3251 (1973).
187. M. A. Winnick, *Acc. Chem. Res.* **10**, 173 (1977).
188. R. Breslow, J. Rothbard, F. Herman, and M. L. Rodriguez, *J. Am. Chem. Soc.* **100**, 1213 (1978).
189. P. de Mayo, *Acc. Chem. Res.* **9**, 52 (1976).
190. P. de Mayo and R. Suau, *J. Am. Chem. Soc.* **96**, 6807 (1974); Y. Ohnishi and A. Ohno, *Bull. Chem. Soc. Jpn.* **46**, 3868 (1973).
191. P. de Mayo and R. Suau, *J. Chem. Soc., Trans. Perkin 2* p. 2559 (1974).
192. J. A. Barltrop and J. D. Coyle, *J. Chem. Soc. B* p. 251 (1971); A. A. Scala and G. E. Hussey, *J. Org. Chem.* **36**, 598 (1971).
193. J. E. Gano and L. Eizenberg, *J. Am. Chem. Soc.* **95**, 972 (1973).
194. Y. Kanaoka, Y. Mitiga, K. Koyama, Y. Sato, H. Nakai, and T. Mizoguchi, *Tetrahedron Lett.* p. 1193 (1973).
195. Y. Kanaoka and K. Koyama, *Tetrahedron Lett.* p. 4517 (1972).
196. Y. Kanaoka, Y. Mitiga, Y. Sato, and H. Nakai, *Tetrahedron Lett.* p. 51 (1973).
197. Y. Kanaoka and Y. Mitiga, *Tetrahedron Lett.* p. 3693 (1974).
198. Y. Sato, H. Nakai, T. Mizoguchi, Y. Hatanaka, and Y. Kanaoka, *J. Am. Chem. Soc.* **98**, 2349 (1976).
199. S. G. Cohen and N. M. Stein, *J. Am. Chem. Soc.* **93**, 6542 (1971).
200. F. C. DeSchryver, N. Boens, and J. Put, *Adv. Photochem.* **10**, 359 (1977).

ESSAY **21** | # PHOTOCHEMICAL REARRANGEMENTS INVOLVING THREE-MEMBERED RINGS

MICHEL NASTASI and JACQUES STREITH

I. INTRODUCTION

The study of syntheses and chemical reactivity patterns of hetero-atomic three-membered rings has gained momentum during the last decade. This appears to be expecially true of photoinduced rearrange-ments of, and toward, such strained three-membered heterocycles as those of type A [X, Y, Z = C, N, O, Si, S], yet in only a few instances could both the three-membered heterocycles A and the corresponding open-chain isomers B be isolated; in most cases only one of the two isomeric partners is a stable species. In fact, the transient existence of three-membered heterocycles has often been postulated only as the most reasonable mechanistic pathway.

The purpose of this essay is to provide insight into a wide variety of

445

REARRANGEMENTS IN GROUND AND EXCITED STATES, VOL. 3
Copyright © 1980 by Academic Press, Inc.

sometimes puzzling interconversions that three-membered heterocycles undergo, together with their open-chain isomers, upon electronic excitation.

In general, photoinduced interconversions of three-membered heterocycles with their open-chain isomers seem to proceed with heterolytic bond cleavage and bond formation. In a few cases, however, photoinduced homolysis and ring closure from a nondipolar precursor may also occur. The fact is, quite regrettably, that there is no such thing as a simple unifying mechanistic scheme underlying the photochemical interconversions to be described.

II. THREE-MEMBERED HETEROCYCLES WITH ONE HETEROATOM

A. Saturated Rings

1. Oxiranes

a. Photochemical Ring Opening. The two main types of rearrangements that occur upon UV irradiation of oxiranes are (a) homolytic cleavage of one of the C—O bonds and subsequent 1,2 migration of a ring substituent, resulting in the formation of the corresponding carbonyl compound, and (b) heterolysis of the ring C—C bond, leading to a colored and short-lived carbonyl ylide (Scheme 1).

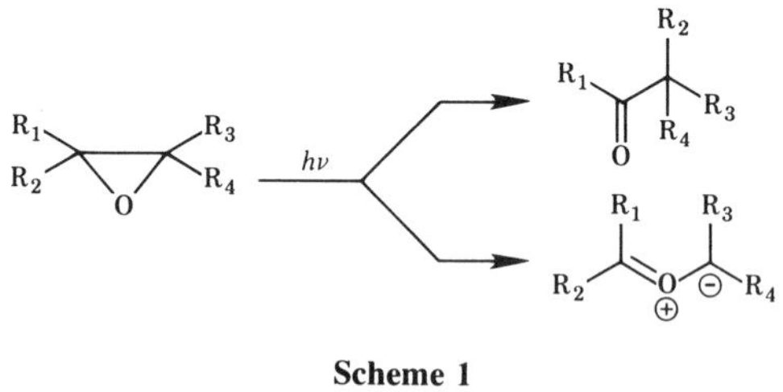

Scheme 1

The first process has been observed in a large number of cases, including simple saturated epoxides (*1*), α,β-epoxy ketones (*2–8*), α,β-epoxy esters (*9,10*), α,β-epoxy olefins (*11,12*), aryloxiranes (*1,13,14*), and α-nitro epoxides (*15*). Homolysis of the C—O bond is always proposed to be the most likely primary photochemical step. Unsymmetric alkyloxiranes, which are not conjugated with any other functional group, lead to photolytic cleavage of both C—O bonds. For example, methyloxirane leads to acetone and to propionaldehyde (*1*). In contrast, all oxiranes that bear in the α position a second functional group undergo photolytic cleavage of the C—O bond β to that group: α,β-Epoxy ketones lead to β-diketones, α,β-epoxy esters to β-keto esters, α,β-epoxy olefins to β,γ-unsaturated ketones, and aryloxiranes to β-aryl ketones. In all cases migrational aptitudes are as follows: $H > RCH_2 > CH_3 > C_6H_5$. Sensitizing and quenching experiments suggest triplet state reactivity for α- and β-epoxy esters and for α,β-epoxy olefins but singlet state (5,7) or short-lived triplet state reactivity (7) for α,β-epoxy ketones. Besides this general C—O bond cleavage process, competitive ring C—C bond homolysis is observed with indene oxide (1), leading to isochromene (3) (14) (Scheme 2).

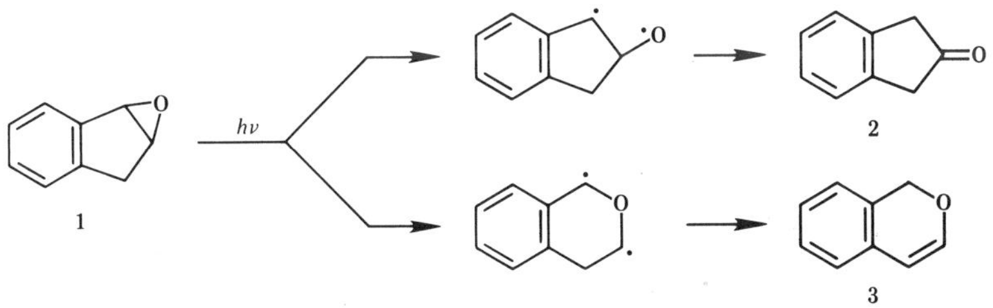

Scheme 2

The second type of rearrangement, yielding carbonyl ylide intermediates, occurs solely with aryloxiranes. The zwitterionic primary photoproduct has been detected by trapping experiments with dipolarophiles. Monocyclic oxiranes exhibit photochromic behavior at very low temperature (77 K) only (16–18). Further irradiation of this colored zwitterionic species leads to cleavage into a carbene and a carbonyl compound (Scheme 3). It has been shown by means of low-temperature flash photol-

Scheme 3

ysis and by trapping experiments that α-cyanostilbene oxides undergo photoinduced cis–trans isomerization via carbonyl ylide intermediates (18a). In contrast, when the oxirane ring is incorporated into a cyclic system, the colored zwitterionic intermediate is more stable and can be observed at room temperature (19,20).

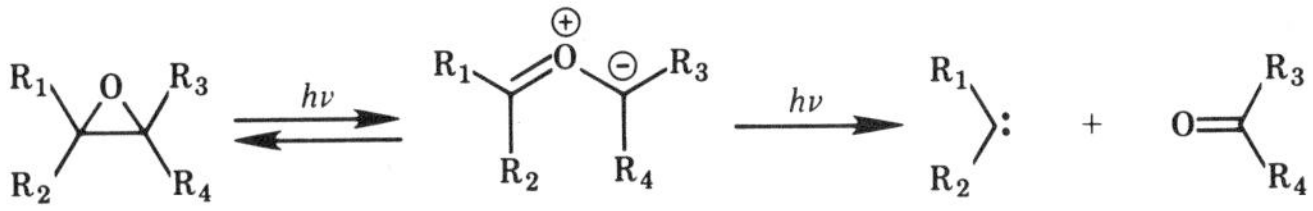

The fate of the carbonyl ylide depends on the ring size. Cyclobutene oxide 4, although exhibiting photochromic behavior, is remarkably photostable (16,19). In contrast, cyclopentene 5 and cyclohexene oxide 6 ring-open upon further irradiation of the ylid to give ketones **9** and **10**, respectively (*16*) (Scheme 4).

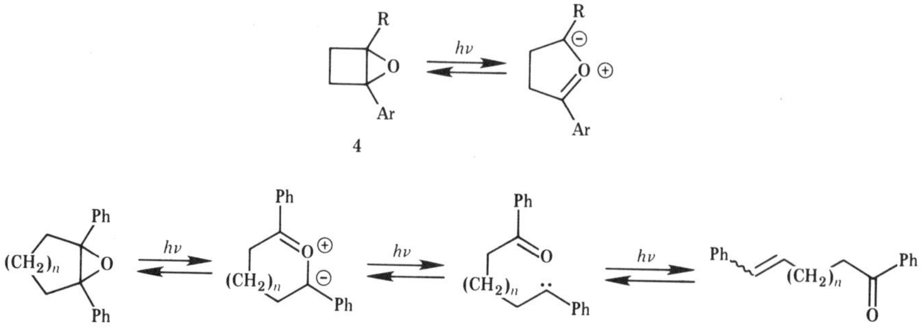

4

5 $n = 1$
6 $n = 2$

7 $n = 1$
8 $n = 2$

9 $n = 1$
10 $n = 2$

Scheme 4

The occurrence of carbonyl ylides **7** and **8** as intermediates in these reactions has been demonstrated by trapping experiments and by showing that double irradiation, both in the UV (epoxide absorption) and in the visible (ylide absorption) regions, increases the conversion of the starting material (*16*).

Photolysis of the azoepoxide **11** in the presence or in the absence of benzophenone leads to the azine **12** in high yield (*21*). Nitrogen extrusion from **11** does not occur; this is probably due to the strengthening of the C—N bonds caused by the conjugation between the epoxide ring and the azo moiety.

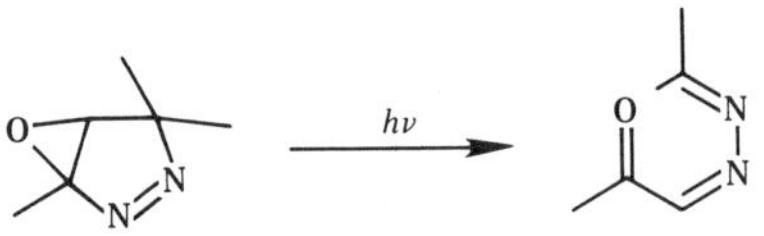

11 12

Photoisomerization of 9,10-phenanthrene oxide (**13**) to dibenzoxepine (**15**) is best explained by assuming a "walk rearrangement" to epoxide **14** (*22*), followed by valence tautomerism (Scheme 5).

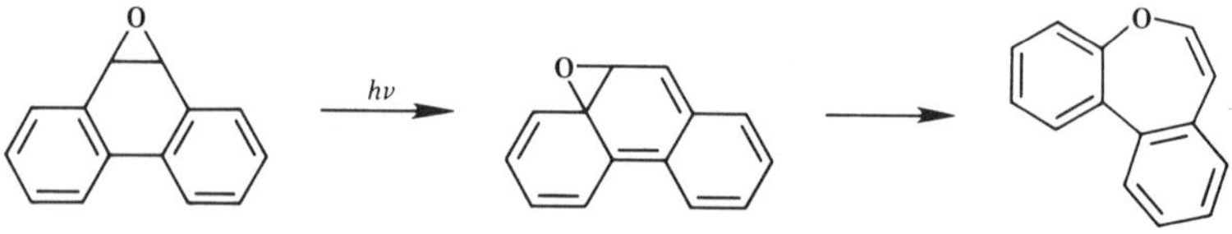

13 14 15

Scheme 5

Two competing primary photoprocesses occur upon irradiation of 2,4-cyclohexadienone 4,5-epoxides (**16**) (Scheme 6). The minor pathway is α cleavage and leads to the butenolide **17**. The major pathway is cleavage of the C-4—O epoxide bond, yielding the diradical **18**. Further rearrangement of **18** yields compounds **19–22** depending on the substitution pattern (*23,24*).

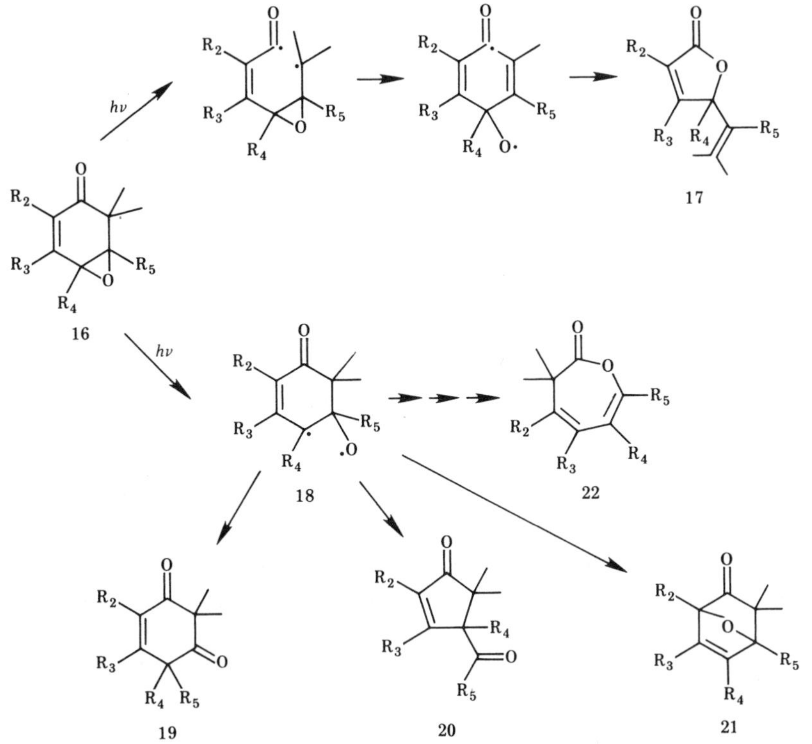

Scheme 6

Valence isomerization to oxonin **24** occurs by direct (*25*) or by benzophenone-sensitized (*26*) irradiation of cyclooctatetraene oxide (**23**).

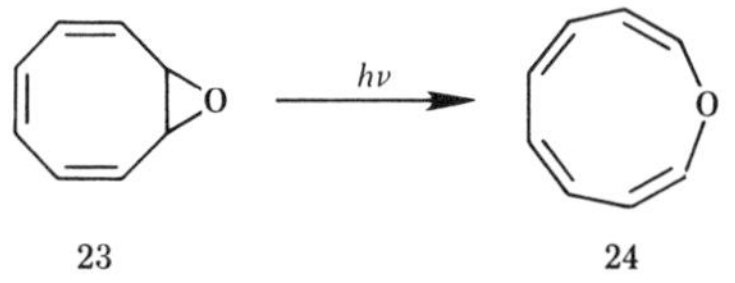

Room-temperature irradiation of bicyclo[2.2.0]hexa-2,5-diene oxide (**25**) yields the oxepin–benzene oxide system **26** (*27*). Low-temperature irradiation of **26** leads to benzene, phenol, and 2-oxabicyclo[3.2.0]hepta-3,6-diene. In the presence of a sensitizer, phenol is the sole product, suggesting that benzene is derived from the singlet state of benzene oxide (**28**) (Scheme 7).

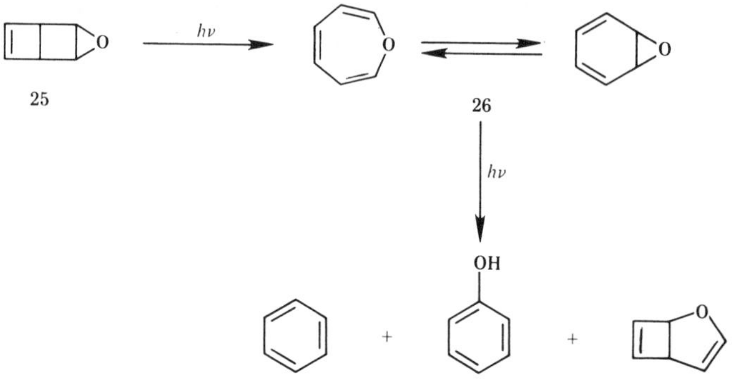

Scheme 7

b. Photochemical Ring Formation. The photoinduced rearrangement of hindered γ-pyrones (**27**) to α-pyrones (**29**) has been reported to involve two consecutive photoreaction processes (*29,30*). The first step is a ring closure to the 4,5-epoxycyclopentanone **28**, the second an isomerization of the latter, leading to **29** (Scheme 8). Except in the case of β-hydroxy-γ-pyrone (**30**), for which the two major photoproducts are the α-diketone **31** and the epoxyhemiketal **32** (*31*), the type **28** oxirane intermediates cannot be isolated or trapped in these reactions. Their occurrence as true intermediates in the γ-pyrone to α-pyrone rearrangement is strongly supported by the fact that the tetraphenylcyclopentadienone

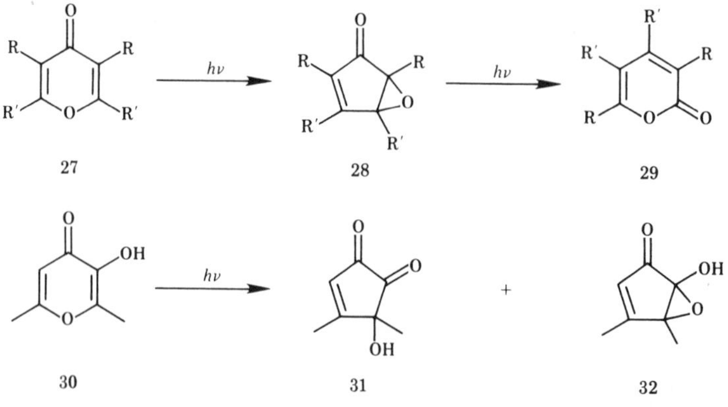

Scheme 8

oxide **28** (R = R′ = Ph) leads to α-pyrone **29** (R = R′ = Ph) when excited by UV light *(32)*.

Cleavage of the C—C bond α to the carbonyl occurs upon irradiation of the 2-phenyl-2-oxazolin-4-one **33**. Rearrangement to a 1,3 diradical followed by ring closure leads to the oxirane **34** *(33)* (Scheme 9).

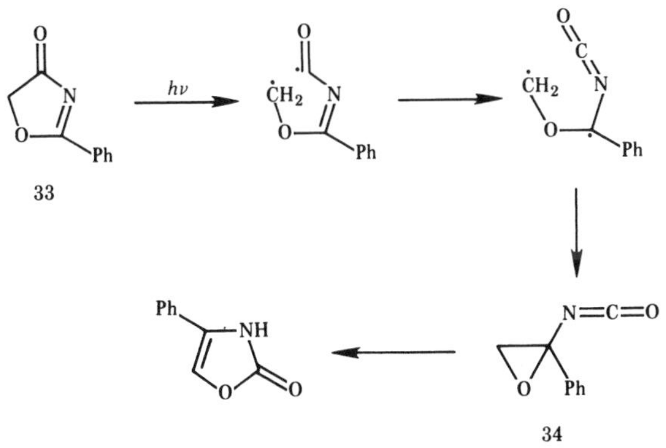

Scheme 9

Irradiation of the γ-oxo α,β-unsaturated ester **35** leads to the γ-lactone **37** *(34)*. Initial ring closure to the oxirane **36** is postulated for this peculiar rearrangement (Scheme 10).

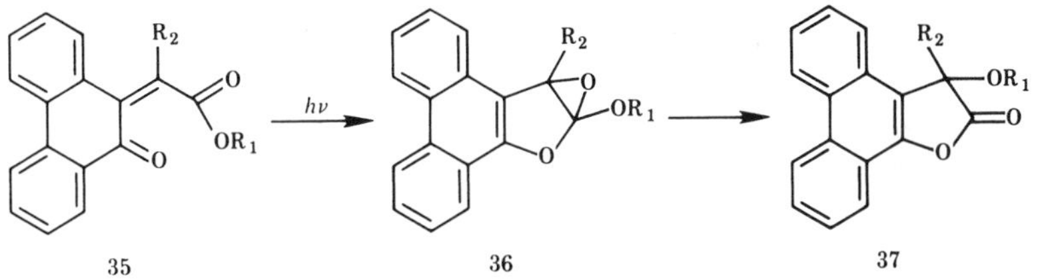

Scheme 10

2. Aziridines

Photochemical Ring Opening. The photoinduced ring opening of aziridines has been extensively studied. The most general primary photochemical process is the heterolytic C—C bond cleavage leading to an azomethine ylide intermediate, the further transformation of which depends on the ring substitution pattern. It was shown that cis–trans isomerization of the dimethyl 1-arylaziridine-2,3-dicarboxylate **38** involves, in the first step, a symmetry-allowed disrotatory ring opening to the 1,3 dipolar species **39** (Scheme 11) *(35,36)*. By means of trapping experiments and of flash photolysis measurements, the total energy profile of these interconversions could be drawn (36). The stereospecificity of these photoinduced ring-opening processes is fully consistent with orbital symmetry conservation rules (37).

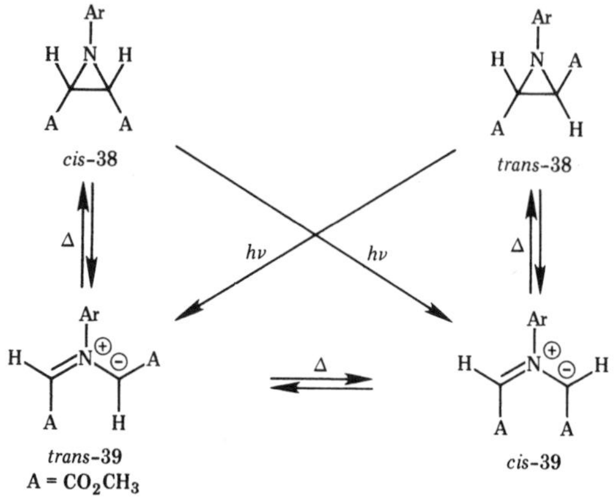

Scheme 11

Irradiation of the 2,4,6-triphenyl-1,3-diazabicyclo[3.1.0]hex-3-ene **40** results in the formation of enediimine **42**, which leads, by way of thermal electrocyclic ring closure, to the dihydropyrazine **43** (38–40). The azomethine ylide intermediate could be trapped with a dipolarophile before the formation of **42** (41–43) (Scheme 12).

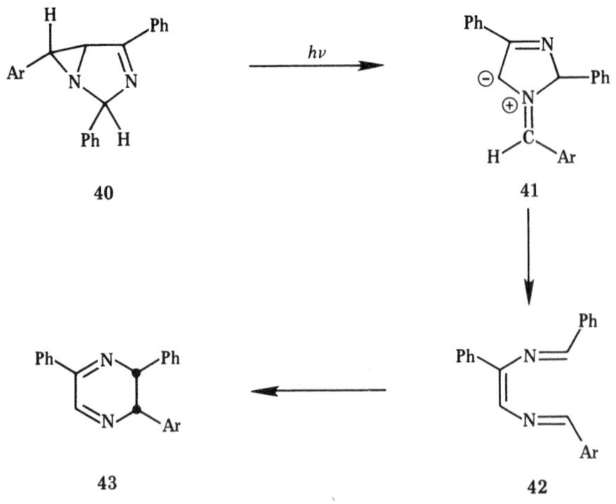

Scheme 12

Aziridines **40** display photochromic behavior: Upon irradiation of aziridine **40** (Ar = Ph) at 77 K a bright red color appears (*41*), indicative of the formation of zwitterion **41** (Ar = Ph). The same phenomenon occurs even at room temperature with **40** when Ar = *p*-NO$_2$—C$_6$H$_4$ (*42,43*). The coloration disappears as soon as a dipolarophile is added, which clearly shows that the photochromic behavior of compounds **40** is due to their interconversion with the azomethine ylides **41**. The stereochemistry of this reaction suggests a conrotatory ring opening, in contrast to the disrotatory process reported by Huisgen (*35,36*). To account for these observations it has been postulated that a "hot" ground state reaction is operating, i.e., that electron demotion occurs before bond cleavage (*41–43*).

The photochemistry of the related aziridine **44** has also been investigated (*44*). Once again, the first step is heterolytic ring opening to an azomethine ylide, which subsequently ring-opens to the diazaoctatetraene **45**. Further rearrangement of **45** affords compounds **46–48** (Scheme 13).

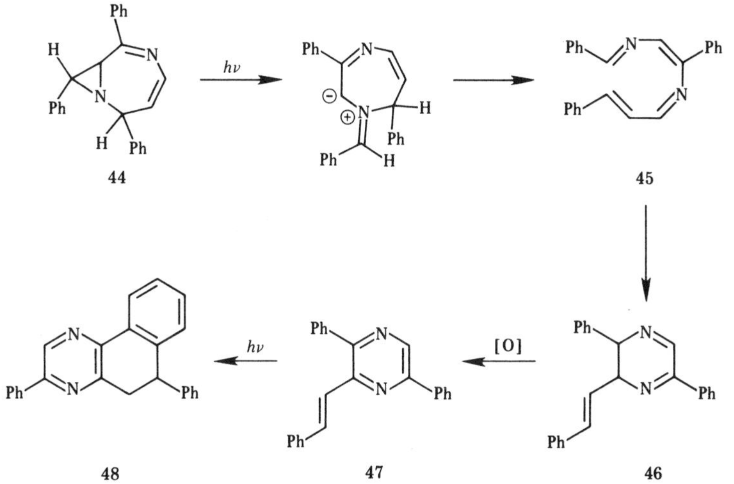

Scheme 13

A similar electrocyclic ring opening was reported in the case of the aziridinoimide **49** (*45*). The resulting open-chain 1,3 dipole **50** could be trapped by dimethyl acetylenedicarboxylate, leading to the bicyclic adduct **51** (Scheme 14).

A rather different photochemical rearrangement was reported for the *trans*-2-aroyl-3-arylaziridine **52**. In this case the primary photoprocess is not heterolytic C—C bond cleavage; instead, a 1,5-hydrogen shift occurs, leading to the aminoenone **53** (*46,47*) (Scheme 15). That a hydrogen shift

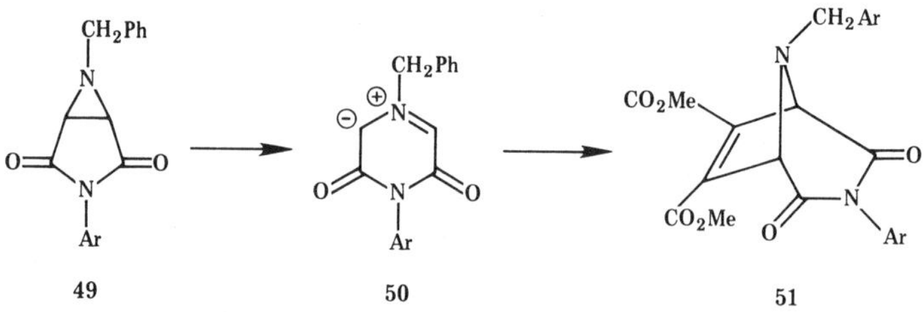

Scheme 14

takes place has been firmly established by deuterium labeling experiments and by the fact that *cis*-**52** does not rearrange to **53**. Sensitization studies suggest that this reaction derives from the n–π* triplet state.

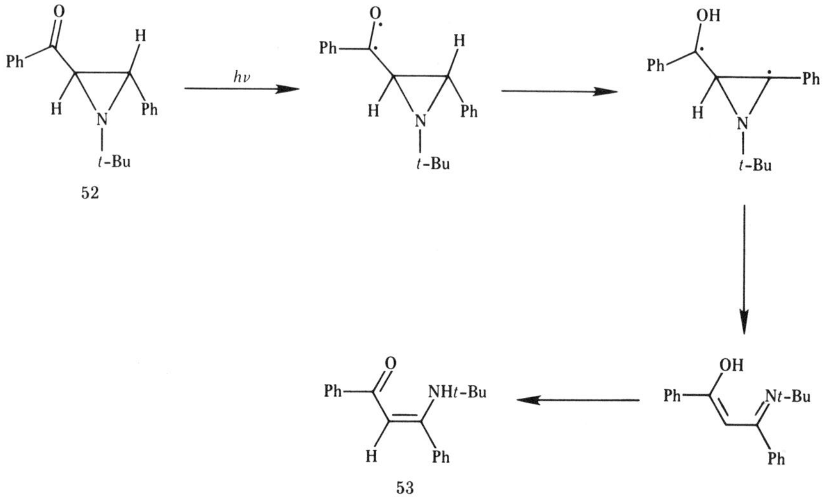

Scheme 15

A similar C—N bond cleavage was reported for the N-cyano-2,3-diphenylaziridine **54** (*48*). When *trans*-aziridine **54** is irradiated, both isomerization to *cis*-**54** and rearrangement to imine **55** are observed; under the same conditions *cis*-**54** yields solely the rearrangement product **55**. The failure to observe the C—N bond cleavage when the N-cyano group of the aziridine ring is replaced by a less electron-withdrawing substituent suggests a high dependence of the reactivity on the substitution at N; i.e., scission takes place only when the C—N linkage is polarized by a strongly attractive group. 1,2,3-Triphenylaziridine (**56**) undergoes photoinduced fragmentation to benzalaniline (**57**) and phenyl-carbene (*49*). A stepwise mechanism initiated by the cleavage of the C—C

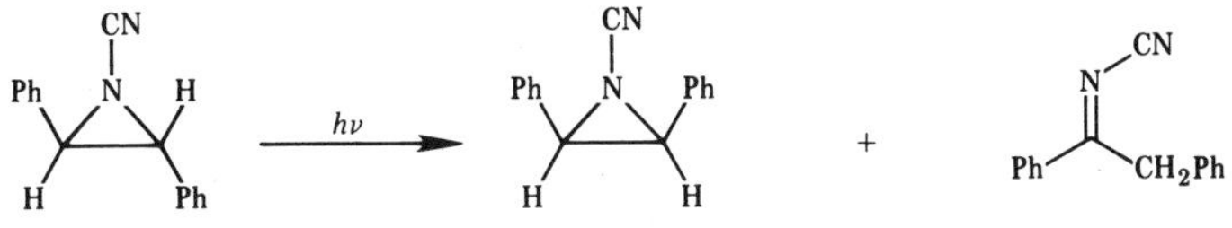

trans-54 *cis*-54 55

bond appears to be involved since an intermediate can be intercepted by cyclohexene (Scheme 16).

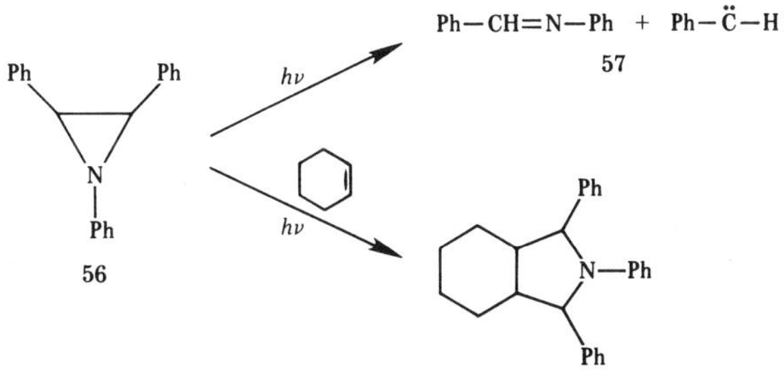

56

57

Scheme 16

In contrast to the photochemical behavior observed for **56**, irradiation of 1,(2,4,6-trinitrophenyl)-2,3-diphenylaziridine (**58**) yields the benzimidazole **59** (*50*). A mechanism involving interaction between the aziridine ring and a nitro group and implicating a seven-membered intermediate is postulated (Scheme 17).

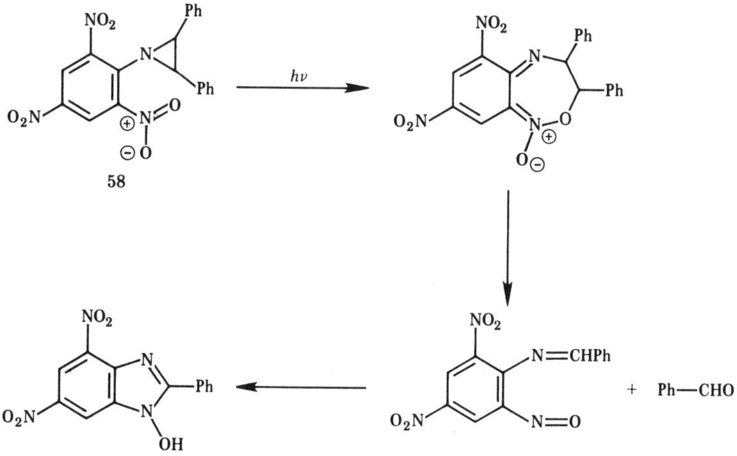

58

59

Scheme 17

Finally, it is of interest that the synthesis of the aza[17]annulene **61** was achieved by low-temperature photolysis of the polycyclic aziridine **60** (*50a*).

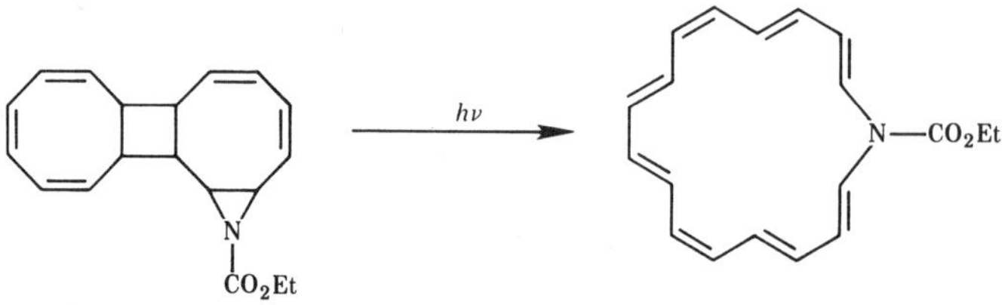

b. *Photochemical Ring Formation.* Photoinduced ring closure to the aziridine skeleton can be achieved either from an open-chain precursor or from a higher-membered heterocycle. Representative of the first type of reactions are the photocyclizations of imines, allylamines, and azomethine ylides. Photochemical ring contraction of five-, six-, eight-, and nine-membered heterocycles to an aziridine ring, which may be either a short-lived intermediate or a stable photoproduct, is illustrative of the second type of rearrangements.

Irradiation of the benzophenone *N*-benzhydrylimine **62** was reported to yield the tetraphenylethylamine **64** (*51*). A two-step mechanism initiated by ring closure to the aziridine **63** followed by photoreduction to **64** was proposed by analogy with the known photocyclization of phenylpropenes to phenylcyclopropanes (*52,53*) (Scheme 18). One may assume for the first step a photoinduced prototropy, leading to the corresponding azomethine ylide, which, by way of thermal or photochemical electrocyclic ring closure, would lead to the aziridine **63**.

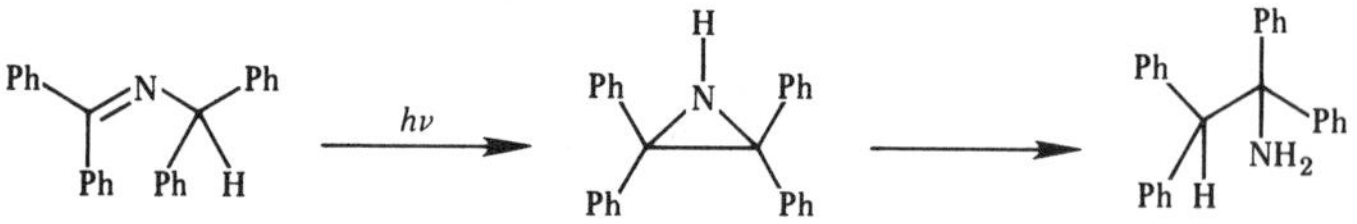

Scheme 18

The photorearrangement of the aliphatic allylamines **65** to the stable aziridines **66** has been reported (*54*). Details of this reaction have not been studied, but an intramolecular charge-transfer process between the amine and the olefin moieties has been proposed.

Interconversion between azomethine ylides and the corresponding aziridines is an allowed process, both thermally and photochemically. In most cases the aziridines are thermodynamically the more stable entities,

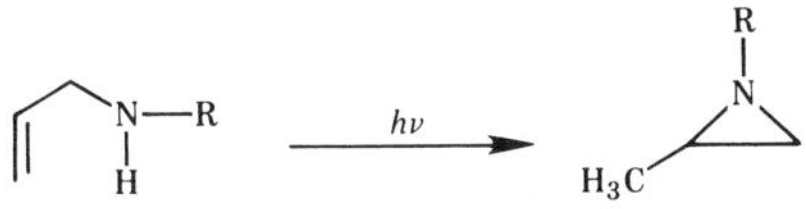

R = H, n-Bu, cyclo-C_6H_{11}, t-Bu

so that their isomeric azomethine ylide partners can usually be trapped only with a dipolarophile (35,36). The photochemical conversion of 3-oxido-1-phenylpyridinium betaine **67** to the aziridinic isomer **68** constitutes a notable exception (55). It should be noted that betaines of type **67** behave as typical ground state 1,3 dipoles (56).

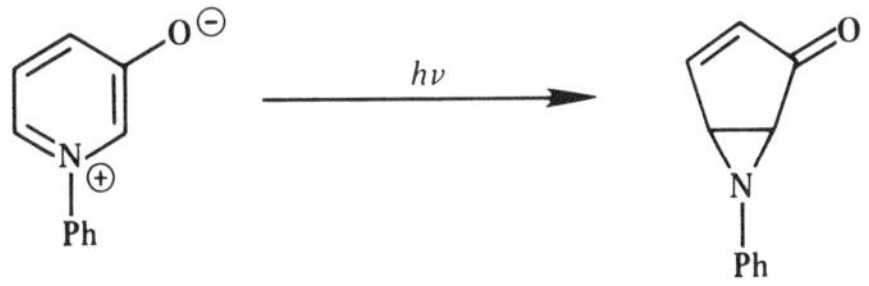

Formation of aziridines as transient intermediates has also been postulated in the photoisomerization of some aromatic N-methylides. Pyridinium dicyanomethylide (**69**), when irradiated by UV light in benzene, leads to the isomeric 2-(2′,2′-dicyanovinyl)pyrrole **71** (57) (Scheme 19). It is believed that the reaction pathway leading from **69** to **71** goes via the 1-azanorcaradiene **70** as the primary photoproduct (57).

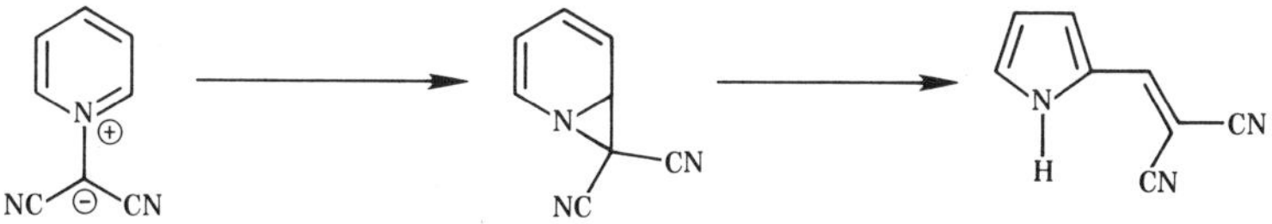

Scheme 19

Similarly, the pyridazinium dicyanomethylides **72** gave, among other products, the isomeric pyrazoles **76** (58). Here, too, aziridine intermediates of type **73** have been postulated as transient intermediates leading to the open-chain diazo isomers **74** and then to pyrazolenines **75**, none of which, however, have been isolated (Scheme 20).

Isoquinolinium diethoxycarbonyl-N-methylide (**77**), when irradiated, leads in low yield to the isomeric benzazepine **78** (59), the formation of which can best be accounted for by postulating the pathway depicted in Scheme 21.

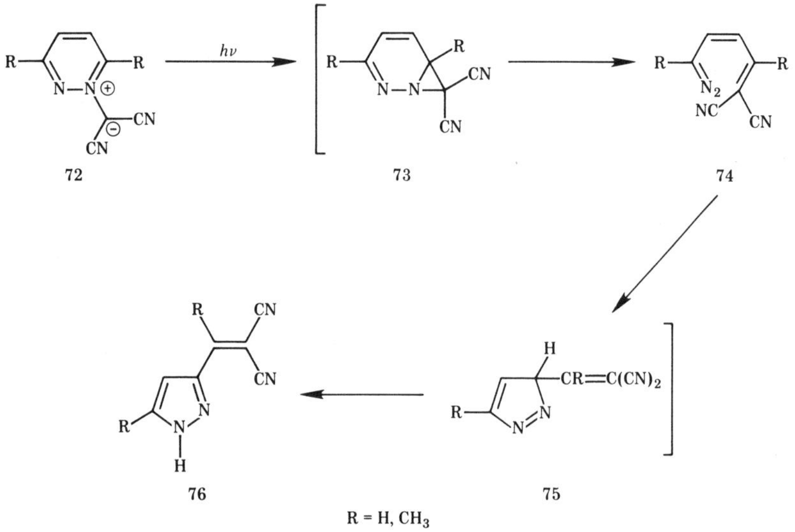

72   **73**   **74**

76   **75**

R = H, CH$_3$

Scheme 20

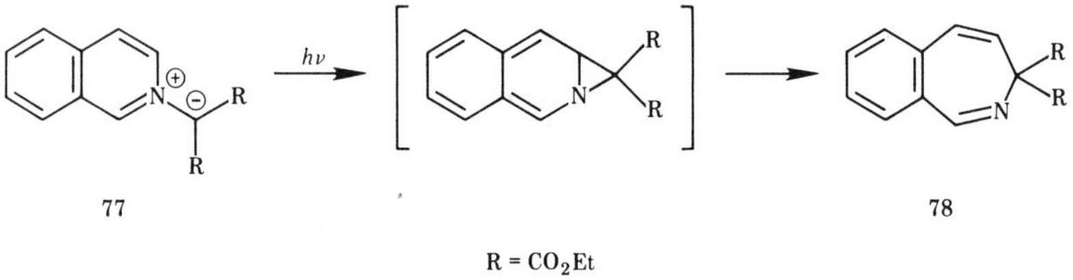

77   **78**

R = CO$_2$Et

Scheme 21

The photoinduced ring contraction of five-membered heterocycles to the corresponding unstable aziridines is discussed in detail in Essay 22. We shall therefore restrict ourselves to some typical examples. N-Methyl-2-cyanopyrrole (**79**) photoisomerizes to the 3-cyano derivative **82**; bicyclic compounds **80** and **81** have been shown to occur as intermediates by means of Diels–Alder cycloaddition reactions (*60,61*) (Scheme 22).

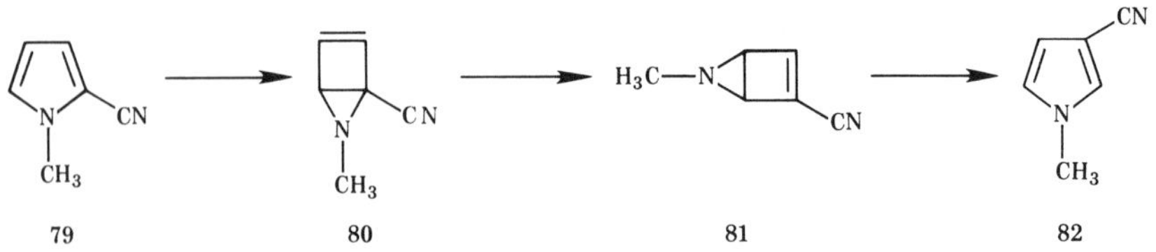

79   **80**   **81**   **82**

Scheme 22

The same process has been observed in the pyrazole (62), imidazole (62), and oxazole series (63). The oxadiazoline **83** rearranges to the unstable aziridinone **84**, which subsequently fragments into diphenyl ketene and diphenyldiazomethane (Scheme 23). The formation of compound **84** has been ascertained by trapping experiments (64).

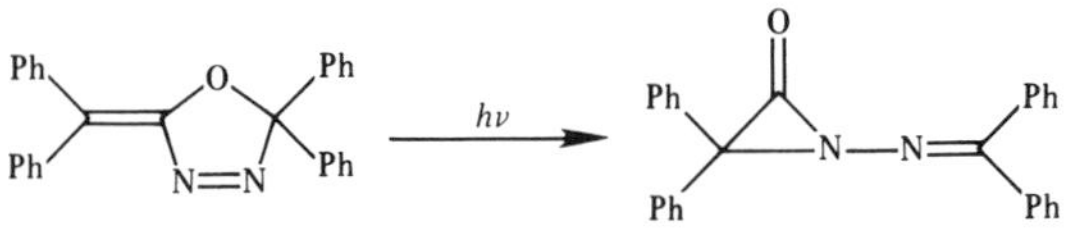

Scheme 23

Through methyl labeling experiments it has been shown that the photoinduced rearrangement of 2-thiazolines **85** to the N-alkenylthioamides **87** proceeds via the initial formation of the thioacylaziridines **86** (65) (Scheme 24).

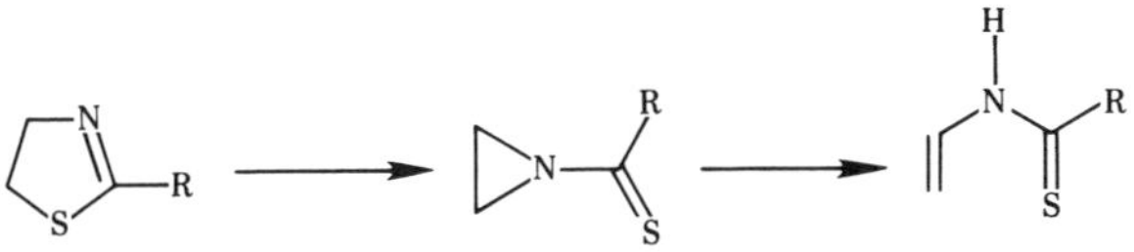

Scheme 24

Photoinduced contraction of six-membered heterocycles to the aziridine ring has also been described. The rearrangement of the hindered 4-pyridones **88** to the corresponding 2-pyridones **90** has been reported to proceed via the bicyclic aziridine intermediate **89** (30a,30b,66,67) (Scheme 25). However, attempts to trap a transient azomethine ylide derived from **89** were unsuccessful. This photoreaction involves the $\pi-\pi^*$ singlet state of **88,** as shown by quenching experiments and by heavy-atom pertubation (30a).

Irradiation of the benzazocine **91** yields the tricyclic aziridine **92** as the

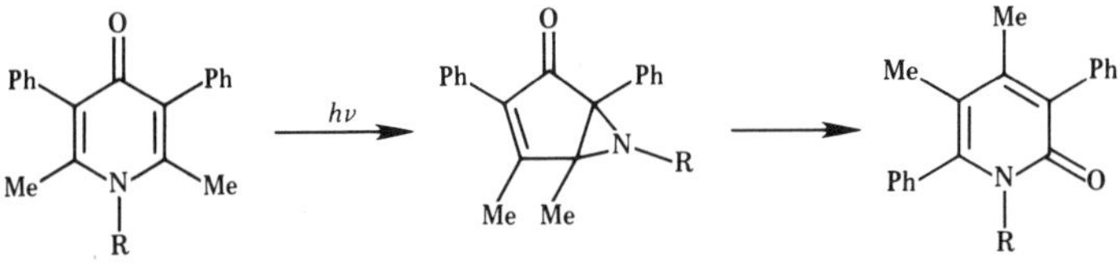

Scheme 25

major photoproduct, probably via a [1,2]-acyl shift comparable to the formation of cyclopropanes from β,γ-unsaturated ketones (68).

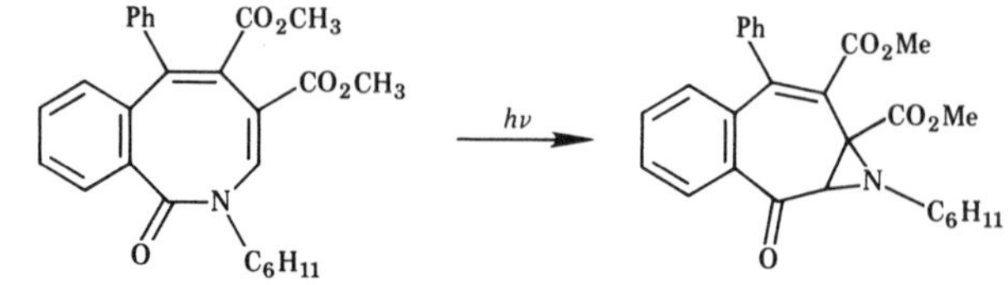

Finally, it should be mentioned that photoinduced valence-bond isomerization of 1*H*-azonine (**93**) leads to the stable aziridine **94** (69).

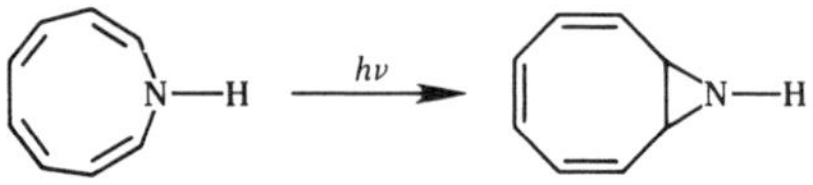

3. Thiiranes

a. Ring Formation from Higher-Membered Heterocycles. The photoreactive mesoionic compound **95** has been reported to yield, upon irradiation, the 1,4-dithiane **99**. A complex mechanism involving initial ring contraction to the bicyclic thiirane **96,** loss of COS and formation of the antiaromatic thiirene intermediate **97**, cycloaddition of **97** to **95** leading to adduct **98**, and, finally, fragmentation of the latter to compound **99** has been proposed (70) (Scheme 26). Although this mechanistic scheme seems reasonable, it lacks experimental support.

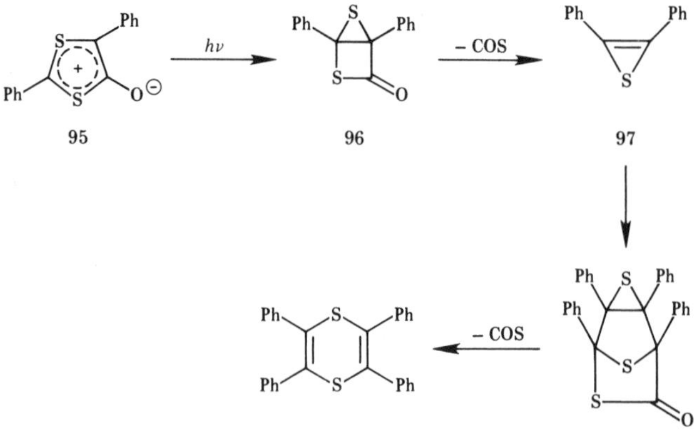

Scheme 26

Stereoselective ring contraction to the unstable vinyl episulfides **102** and **103** occurs upon irradiation of the dihydrothiophenes **100**. Photoproducts **102** and **103** undergo facile stereospecific desulfurization but have been identified unambiguously by spectroscopic methods; in one case (R = *t*-Bu) they were isolated. The biradical **101**, which results from C—S bond cleavage and participation of the carbomethoxy group, has been proposed as the key intermediate in this rearrangement (*71,72*) (Scheme 27).

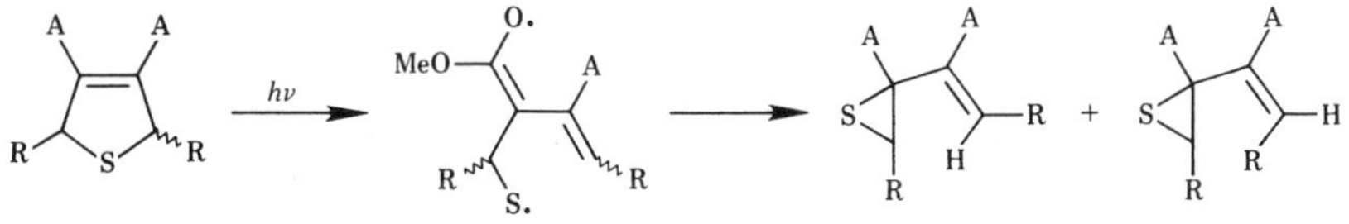

100   101   102   103

A = CO₂Me

Scheme 27

The Dewar thiophene structure **105**, which was proposed to be the photoproduct of tetrakis(trifluoromethyl)thiophene **104** on the basis of its ¹⁹F NMR spectrum (*73*), was confirmed by X-ray analysis of its furan cycloadduct (*74*).

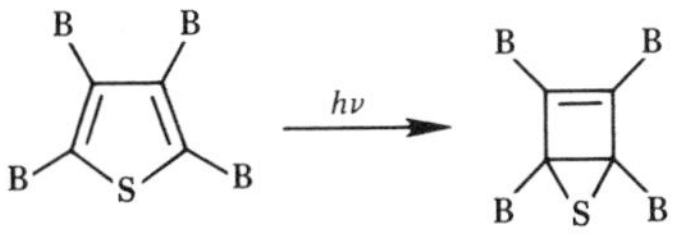

104   105

B = CF₃

It was reported that *cis*- and *trans*-dibenzoylstilbenes were the desulfurization photoproducts of a compound to which thiirane structure **107** had first been ascribed (*75*). Subsequent work established that the material was, in fact, the 1,3-oxathiole **106**, the decomposition of which to the dibenzoylstilbenes proceeds via a thermally reversible photorearrangement to **107** (*76*) (Scheme 28).

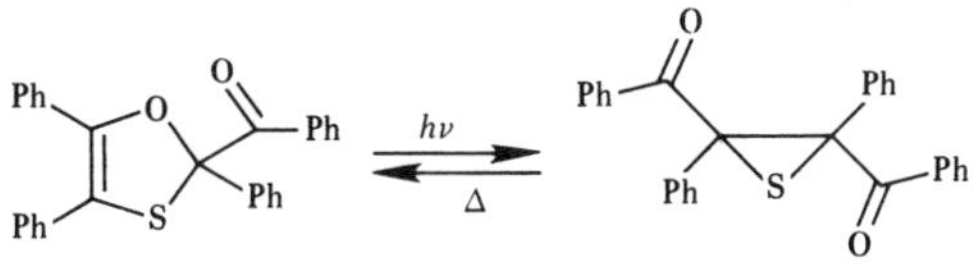

106   107

Scheme 28

Irradiation of the hindered thiopyranones **108** leads in nearly quantitative yields to the cyclopentadienones **111**. Quenching and sensitizing experiments clearly indicate that a triplet state of **108** is operating; that the n–π* transition is responsible for that rearrangement was shown by heavy-atom perturbation experiments (77). By analogy with the photorearrangement of 4,4-diphenylcyclohexa-2,5-dienone (77a), a mechanistic pathway involving the thiirane intermediates **109** and **110** was proposed (Scheme 29). Attempts to detect these transients, however, proved unsuccessful (77,78).

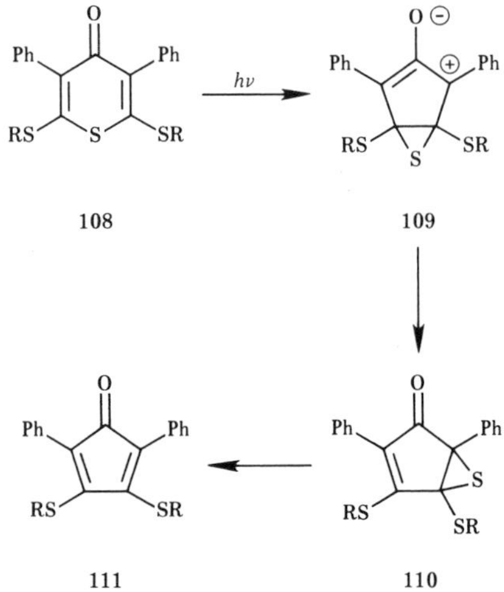

Scheme 29

The structurally related 4H-thiopyrane **112** rearranges to the 2H-thiopyrane **114** on excitation to the π–π* triplet state, probably through intermediate formation of the bicyclic thiirane **113** (79) (Scheme 30).

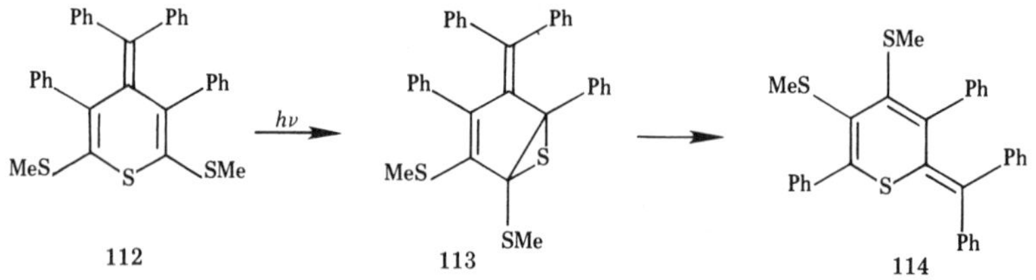

Scheme 30

The photochemistry of the 9-thiabicyclo[3.3.1]nonenone **115** displays a remarkable dependence on wavelength. Whereas irradiation of **115** at 313 nm yields the 2-thiabicyclo[6.1.0]nonenone **116**, irradiation at 254 nm results in the formation of the tricyclic thiirane **117** and the bicyclo[5.1.0]-octenone **118**. It was found that compound **118** is not a primary photoproduct of **115**, but is formed by photochemical sulfur extrusion from **117**. A mechanism involving initial homolytic cleavage of the C—S bond and subsequent addition of the diradical to the adjacent double bond is postulated (*80*) (Scheme 31).

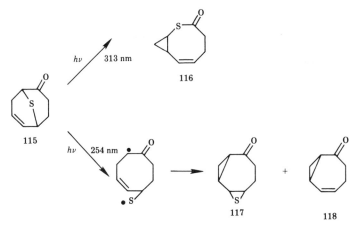

Scheme 31

b. Photochemical Ring Opening. The principal primary process that occurs in the photochemistry of the thiirane ring is extrusion of the sulfur atom, leading to the corresponding olefinic compound (*81*). This process has been reported for, *inter alia,* episulfide (*82*), *cis*-stilbene episulfide (*83*), and tetraphenyl episulfide (*17*). However, it has been shown by means of low-temperature irradiation of tetraphenyl episulfide (**119**) that the primary photoprocess is, in fact, ring opening, leading to a colored intermediate which undergoes subsequent photolytic cleavage to tetraphenyl-ethylene (*17*) (Scheme 32).

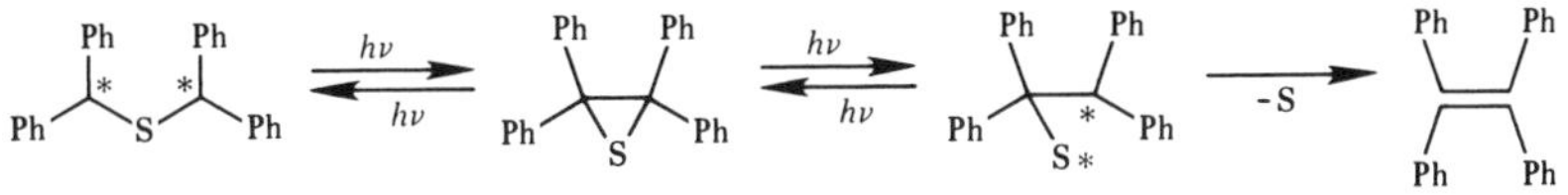

Scheme 32

On the other hand, homolytic cleavage of the C—S bond has been proposed to be the primary photoprocess occurring in propylene episulfide (**120**); it leads to allyl disulfide (*1*) (Scheme 33).

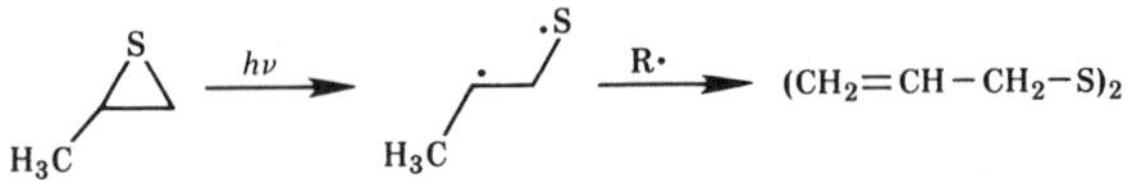

120

Scheme 33

In contrast to the above-mentioned photofragmentation of the thiirane ring, rearrangement to the 2-thiabicyclo[3.2.1]octadiene **122** has been reported to occur upon irradiation of norbornadiene episulfide (**121**) (*84*).

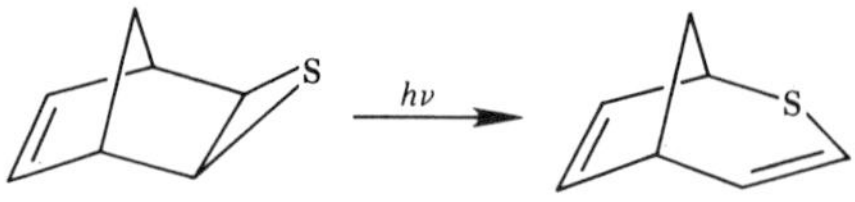

121   122

Rearrangement to the oxathietane intermediate **124** has been reported as a possible primary process in the photolysis of dibenzoylstilbene episulfoxide (**123**) (*85,86*). Subsequent fragmentation of **124** affords monothiobenzil (**125**) and benzil (**126**) in a manner that is analogous to the thermal decomposition of 1,2-dioxetanes (Scheme 34).

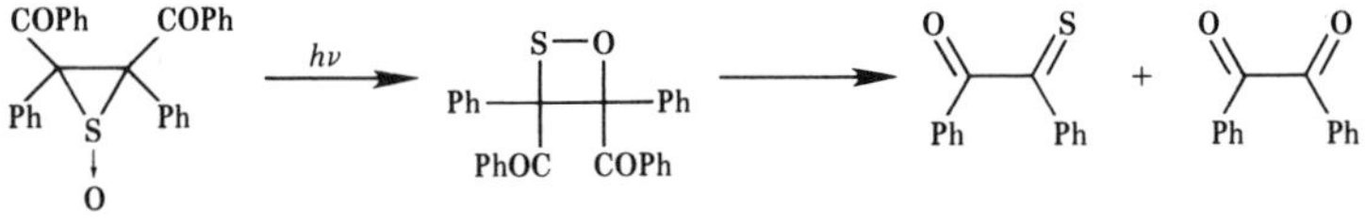

123   124   125   126

Scheme 34

4. Silacyclopropanes

a. Ring Formation. The transient zwitterionic silacyclopropane **128** has been proposed as a possible intermediate in the photoinduced conversion of the 4-sila-2,5-cyclohexadienone **127** to the cyclopentenone **129** in *t*-butanol (*87*). In sharp contrast to the photochemistry of the carbocyclic analogue 2,5-cyclohexadienone (*77a*), no intermediate of type **130** was formed, as evidenced by the absence of the positionally isomeric 5-silylcyclopent-2-enone among the photoproducts. Furthermore, attempts to detect a product of type **130** at low temperature in nonnucleophilic solvents were unsuccessful (Scheme 35).

The silacyclopropane ring system **132** was detected by NMR spectroscopy during irradiation of the 1,2-disila-3,5-cyclohexadienes **131** (*88*).

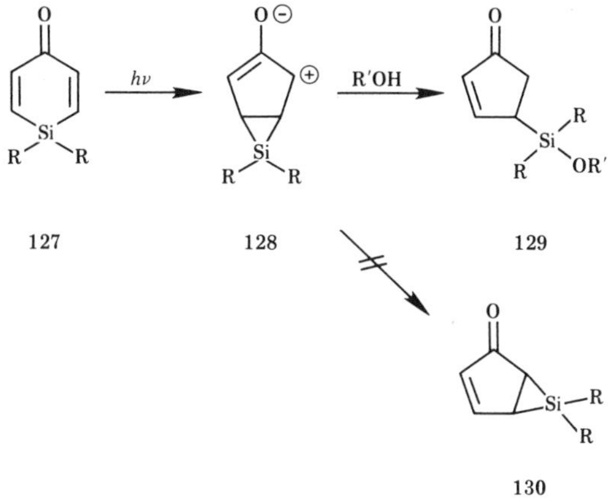

Scheme 35

Compound **132** then undergoes either photochemical (R = H) or thermal (R = Ph) rearrangement to the 5,6-disilabicyclo[2.1.1]hexene **133** (Scheme 36). The relative thermal stabilities of the two valence-bond isomers **132** and **133** depend on substitution: The silacyclopropane **132** is more stable when R = H, whereas the silacyclopentene **133** is the more stable isomer when R = Ph.

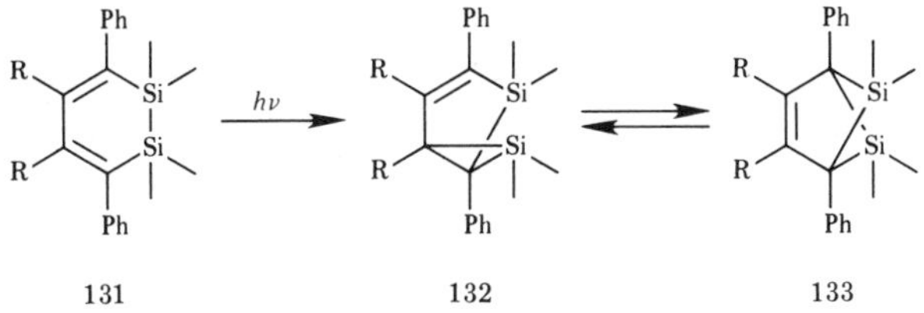

Scheme 36

The vinyldisilane **134** photorearranges to the silacyclopropane **135** (89) by a [1,2] shift of the trimethylsilyl group, which is reminiscent of the propene–cyclopropane (52,53) and the imine–aziridine (51) rearrangements. Addition of methanol to the transient **135** yields adduct **136**, as

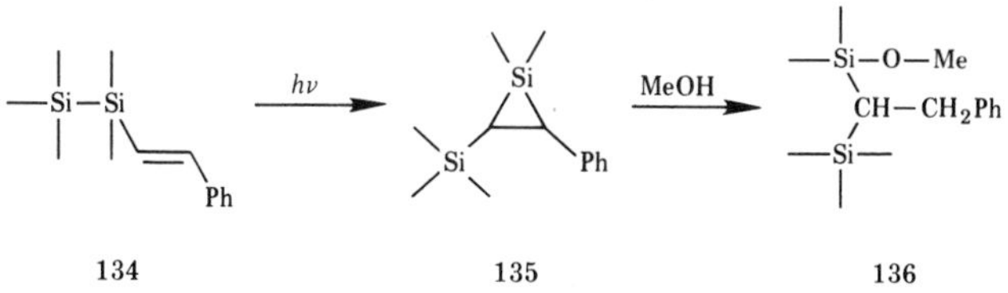

Scheme 37

expected from what is known of the reaction of silacyclopropanes and alcohols (*90*) (Scheme 37).

b. Ring Opening. A 1,3-hydrogen shift was observed when the silacyclopropane **137** was irradiated in cyclohexane solution (*91*).

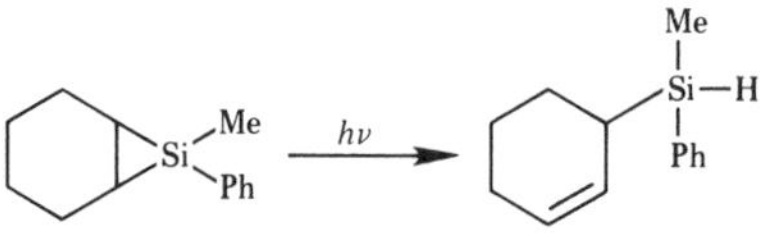

137   138

B. Unsaturated Rings

1. Oxirenes

So far, the oxirene ring system has been neither isolated nor detected by spectroscopic means. However, there is good evidence in favor of its occurrence as an intermediate in the photofragmentation of ketones (*92,93*) and in the photodecomposition of unsymmetrically substituted α-diazo ketones (*93a*). For instance, photolysis of α-diazo ketone ^{13}C-labeled in the carbonyl moiety yields the corresponding ketenes, in which the ^{13}C label is scrambled (*92*). Photolysis of ketene ^{14}C-labeled at the C-2 position yields appreciable amounts of ^{14}CO (*93*). Dimethyl ketene and diphenyl ketene ^{13}C-labeled at C-1 yield a mixture of both labeled and unlabeled carbene and carbon oxide (*92*). All these results are consistent with an oxirene intermediate in these reactions and hence with the occurrence of a photoinduced ketene to oxirene ring closure (Scheme 38).

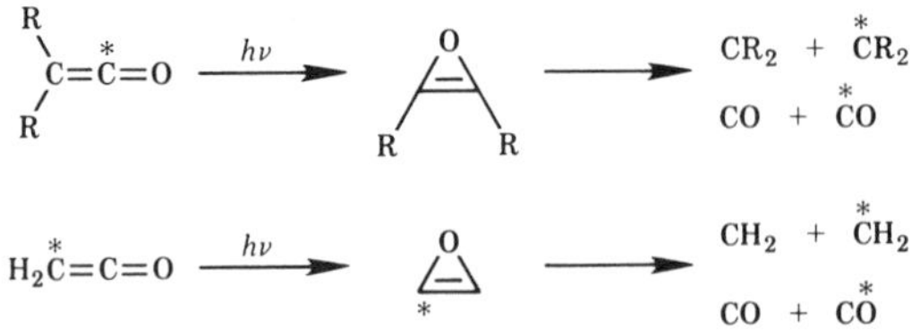

Scheme 38

2. Azirines

Despite several synthetic attempts, neither oxirenes (*vide supra*) nor 1*H*-azirines (**139**) have been isolated so far, presumably because of the intrinsic instability that arises from their antiaromatic character. However, the matrix isolation of the related thiirene and selenirene during the irradiation of thiadiazole and selenadiazole, respectively, has been reported (*93b*). In contrast, the isomeric 2*H*-azirine system **140** displays a remarkable stability, and its thermal as well as photochemical reactivities have been studied extensively. A great number of publications have appeared in the field of 2*H*-azirine photochemistry, as have several review articles (*94–96*).

139   140

a.   Ring Opening to Nitrile Ylides. Swiss (*94*) and American chemists (*95*) showed independently that 2*H*-arylazirines **141** undergo irreversible photoinduced ring opening, leading to the reactive nitrilium methylides **142**, which can be intercepted with a variety of dipolarophiles (Scheme 39). Low-temperature irradiation of arylazirines in a rigid matrix gives rise to a new maximum in the UV spectrum (*97*), which vanishes in the presence of dipolarophiles when the temperature is raised. This experiment clearly demonstrates the intermediacy of short-lived 1,3 dipoles in the cycloaddition reaction. It was also shown that the nitrilium ylide undergoes photochemical, but not thermal, cyclization to the azirine (*97*). The photocycloaddition of arylazirines with dipolarophiles was shown to be a stereo- and regiospecific process; it was carried out with electron-deficient olefins (*98*), aldehydes (*99*), ketones (*100*), esters (*101*), dialkyl azodicarboxylates (*102*), acid chlorides (*103*) and vinylphosphonium salts (*104*). In the absence of dipolarophile, irradiation of arylazirines led to dimeric cycloaddition products (**144**) between the ground state azirine molecule and the nitrile ylide (*105*) (Scheme 39).

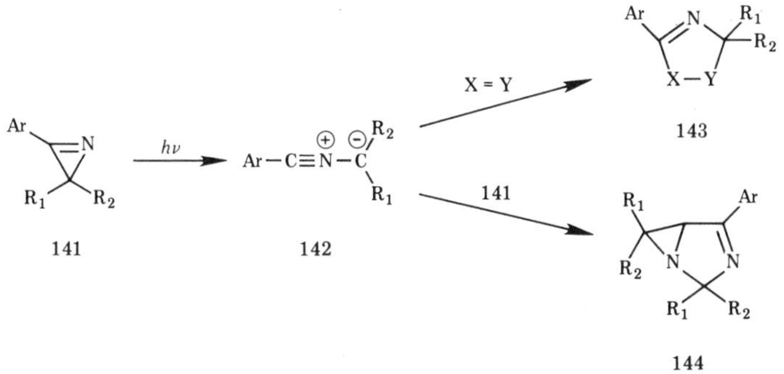

Scheme 39

b.   Ring Formation from Five-Membered heterocycles. The ring contraction of isoxazoles to azirines is a well-known photorearrangement and represents an example of a type I mechanism, which is discussed in Essay 22. It was first demonstrated to occur along the reaction pathway leading from isoxazole **145** to oxazole **147**, the intermediate azirine **146** having been isolated (*106–108*) (Scheme 40).

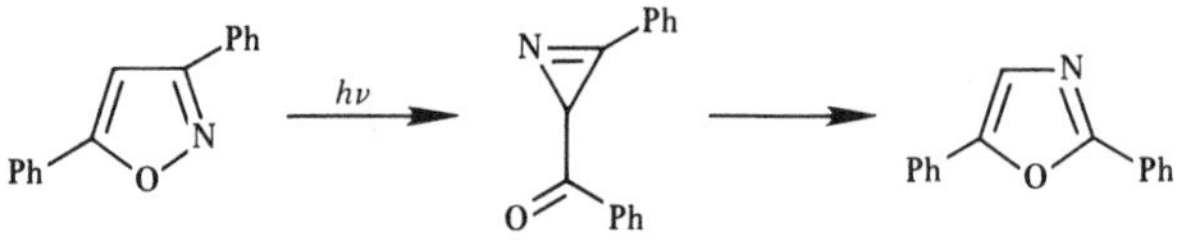

145　　　　　　146　　　　　　147

Scheme 40

3. Silacyclopropenes

The remarkable photorearrangement of alkynyldisilane (**148**) to silacyclopropene (**149**) was described independently by two Japanese groups (*109,110*). Photoproduct **149** could be trapped with ketones and with alcohols; it proved sufficiently stable in solution to permit identification by NMR spectroscopy.

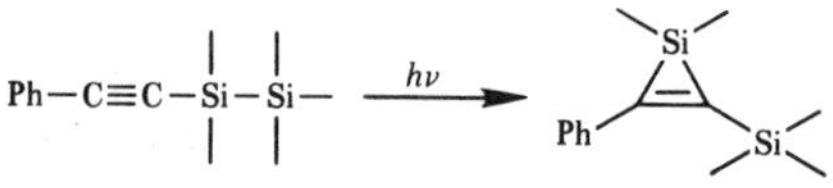

148　　　　　　　149

III. THREE-MEMBERED HETEROCYCLES WITH TWO HETEROATOMS

A. *Saturated Rings*

1. Oxaziridines

a. From Nitrones. Nitrones, being 4π-electron 1,3-dipolar species, can undergo both thermal and photoinduced electrocyclic ring closure to the corresponding oxaziridines according to orbital symmetry conservation rules (*37*). Nevertheless, oxaziridines are usually unstable species when heated; most oxaziridines are not even stable enough to be isolated at room temperature. It is rather unlikely, therefore, that oxaziridines could be isolated from the corresponding nitrones by thermal activation, and no such electrocyclic ground state ring closure has yet been described. On the contrary, photoinduced ring closure is well known; a well-documented review on the photochemistry of nitrones appeared in 1970 (*111*).

Since the beginning of this century it has been known that nitrones **150** change color when exposed to light (*111*). In most instances they isomerize to amides. Not until 1957 was a mechanism put forward which postulated that oxaziridines **151** occur on the reaction pathway leading from the nitrones to the amides (*112*). That this is indeed the case was proved unambiguously in 1958, the oxaziridines having been isolated as stable entities (*113*). The same oxaziridines were also obtained via peracid epoxidation of the corresponding imines (*114*). Rearrangement of these oxaziridines to amides **152** and **153** then occurs thermally (*115,116*) (Scheme 41).

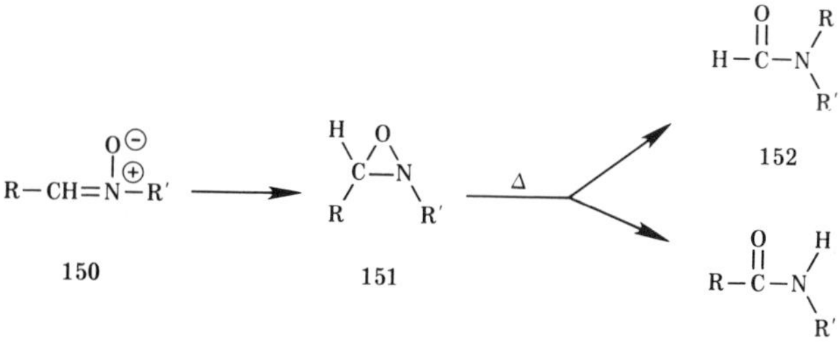

Scheme 41

Oxaziridine formation from nitrones has been shown to be a $\pi-\pi^*$ singlet state reaction (*117,118*), whereas a triplet state induces deoxygenation to the corresponding imines (*119*).

Many acyclic and cyclic nitrones have been photoisomerized into oxaziridines of varying stability. Irradiation of *N*-phenyldibenzoylnitrone (**154**) has been reported to lead quantitatively to *N*-phenyl-dibenzoyloxaziridine (**155**) (*120*) (Scheme 42). Similar results have

Scheme 42

been described with other acyclic nitrones, although the corresponding oxaziridines proved to be generally of low thermal stability (*121–124*). Ultraviolet irradiation of a series of variously substituted Δ^1-pyrroline 1-oxides (**156**) leads, in fair to good yields, to the corresponding oxaziridino[2,3-*a*]pyrrolidines **157,** which rearrange upon further irradiation or by thermal activation to the 2-pyrrolidones **158** (*115,125,126*)

(Scheme 43). In some cases azetidines **159** have also been isolated (*126–127a*). The pattern of results seems to indicate that when R = H the predominant rearrangement product is the pyrrolidone **158**, whereas when R = alkyl or nitrile the azetidine **159** is formed preferentially. Results of the photorearrangement of piperidine-derived oxaziridines are also consistent with this pattern (*128*).

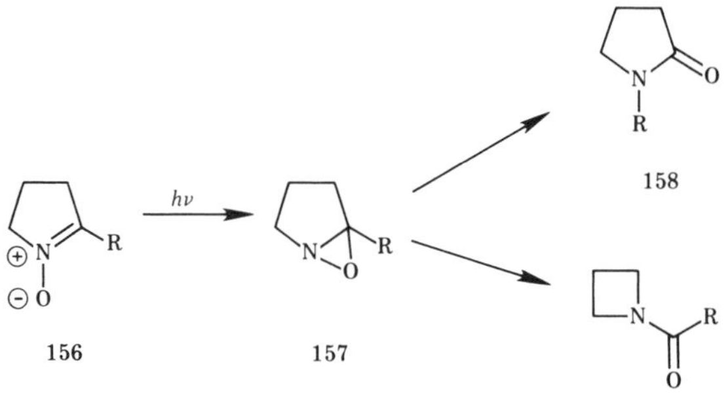

Scheme 43

According to orbital symmetry conservation rules, the photoinduced electrocyclic ring closure of nitrones to oxaziridines should follow a disrotatory mode (*37*). In contrast to the azomethine ylide–aziridine system (see Section II,A,2,a) the stereochemistry of the nitrone photocyclization can be observed only at the carbon and nitrogen atoms. Irradiation of some *trans*-nitrones (**160**, R = Ph or *p*-NMe$_2$C$_6$H$_4$) at −60°C yielded exclusively *trans*-oxaziridines, proving the stereospecific nature of this ring closure (*129*) (Scheme 44).

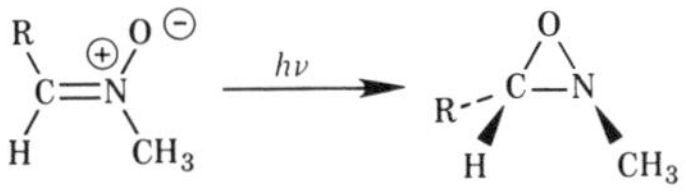

Scheme 44

Nevertheless, care must be taken to check the stereochemical fate of this ring closure since (a) nitrones may undergo either thermal or photochemical cis–trans isomerization (*129*); (b) *cis*-oxaziridines may undergo rapid pyramidal inversion to their trans stereoisomers at room temperature (*130*); (c) in a few cases oxaziridines may photoisomerize reversibly to the nitrones (*131*). In the last instance it is interesting that optically active oxaziridines (**162**), which have a stable pyramidal nitrogen configuration, may photoracemize via a mechanism involving C—O bond cleavage and a nitrone intermediate (163) (Scheme 45).

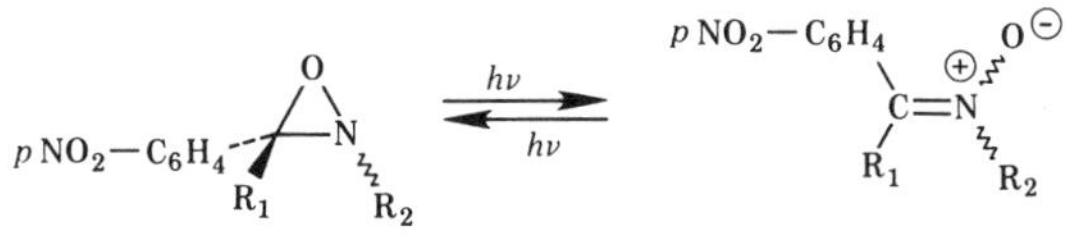

Scheme 45

Nonbonding interactions may lead to asymmetrically induced ring closure for cyclic nitrones. For example, irradiation of Δ^1-pyrroline 1-oxide 164 leads stereospecifically to oxaziridine 165, whereas peracid oxidation of the corresponding Δ^1-pyrroline gives specifically the other stereoisomer, 166 (132) (Scheme 46).

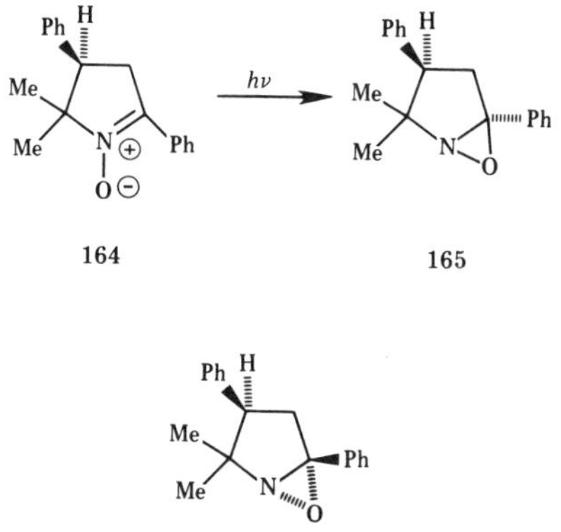

Scheme 46

Finally, irradiation of some nitrones in chiral solvents leads to optically active oxaziridines, with a maximal enantioselectivity of about 30% (133).

Oxaziridines could be isolated upon irradiation of various polycyclic nitrones, such as 2H-1,4-benzodiazepin-2-one 4-oxides (134). Semicyclic nitrones 167 and 169 lead photochemically to the corresponding oxaziridines 168 (135) and 170 (136), respectively (Scheme 47).

Oxaziridines have been postulated as intermediates upon UV irradiation of a large number of nitrones. For example, the photoinduced rearrangement of 2,3-polymethylenebenzimidazole 1-oxides 171 (n = 5, 6, 7) to the corresponding 1,3-polymethylenebenzimidazolones 173 can be rationalized in terms of an intermediate oxaziridine (172) (137) (Scheme 48).

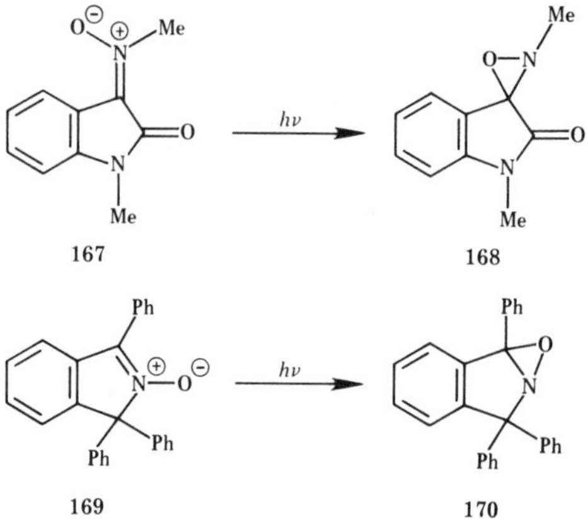

Scheme 47

Likewise, the photorearrangement of indole oxide **174** to the oxindole **176** is postulated to proceed via the oxaziridine **175** (*138*) (Scheme 48).

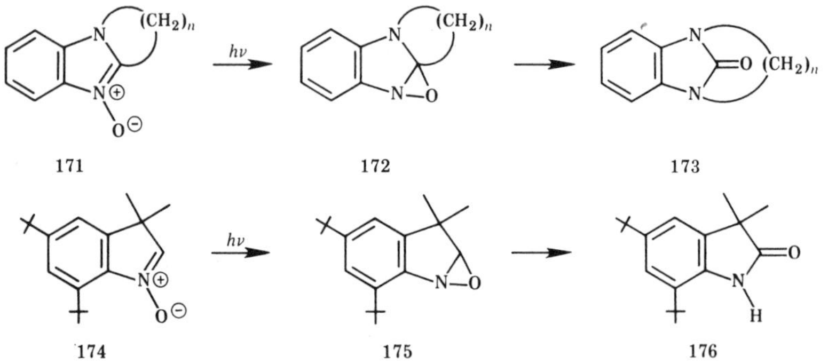

Scheme 48

Ultraviolet excitation of fluorenone-anil *N*-oxide (**177**) leads to *N*-phenylphenanthridone (**179**), a rearrangement that is best explained by

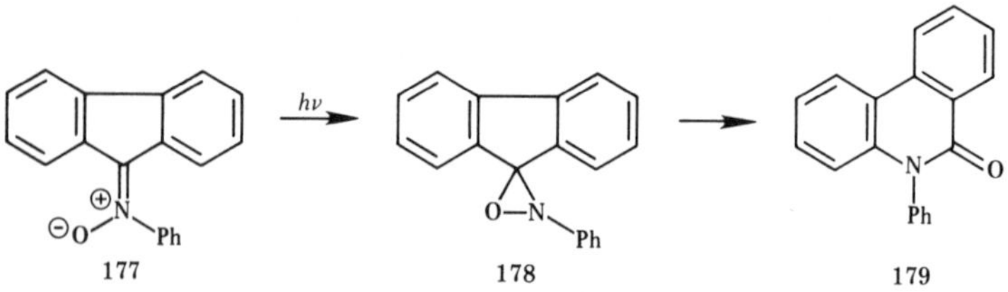

Scheme 49

assuming the occurrence of oxaziridine **178** as an intermediate (*139*) (Scheme 49).

The formation of oxaziridine **181** as a transient species has been proposed to account for the photoinduced rearrangement of the nitronyl nitroxide **180** to compounds **182** and **183** (*140*) (Scheme 50).

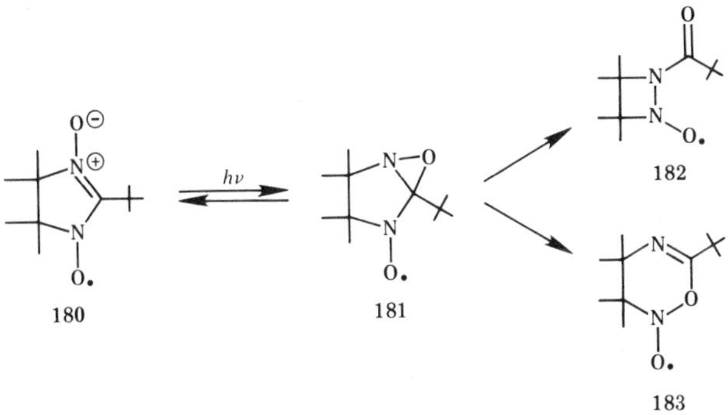

Scheme 50

Photolysis of the quinone-imine di-*N*-oxides **184** (R = Ph, *p*-MeOC$_6$H$_4$) leads to the carbonyl compound **186** and to arylnitrene. Again, the transient oxaziridine **185** seems to be the obvious precursor for these cleavage products (*141*) (Scheme 51).

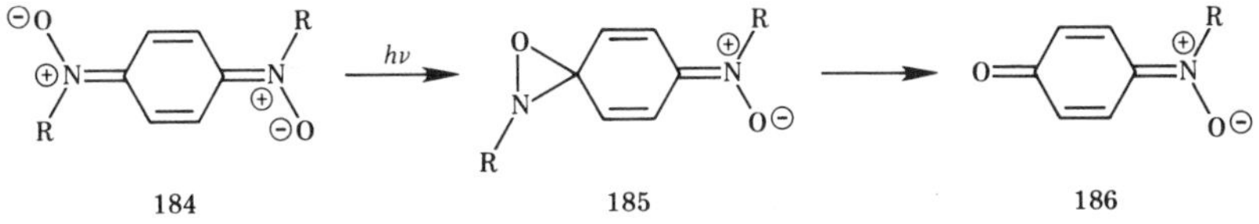

Scheme 51

b. From Aromatic Amine N-*Oxides.* The photochemistry of a large variety of aromatic amine *N*-oxides has been thoroughly investigated. The literature until 1976 has been covered in two review articles (*111,142*). We shall therefore restrict ourselves to the description of a few typical examples as well as to mechanistic aspects of some *N*-oxide photorearrangements.

Aromatic amine *N*-oxides can be formally regarded as 1,3-dipolar nitrones that have been incorporated into aromatic nuclei. Experimentally some similarities have indeed been found in the chemical behavior of aromatic amine *N*-oxides and of nitrones: (a) Both types of compounds lead to 1,3-dipolar cycloaddition reactions in the ground state (*143*); (b) both lead to atomic oxygen abstraction reactions; (c) both undergo photoinduced isomerization reactions, nitrones leading to oxaziridines and thence to amides, whereas aromatic N-oxides yield photoisomers of various structural types, all of which may be formally derived from transient oxaziridines. Actually, oxaziridine formation is almost always considered to be the primary photochemical step, although oxaziridines have never been isolated.

The photoactive absorption bands of pyridine N-oxide are of the $\pi-\pi^*$ type (144). Excited singlet states are believed to trigger the photoisomerization processes (145,146), whereas triplet states are clearly responsible for deoxygenation of aromatic amine N-oxides (147–150).

In order to explain the formation of all the isomers obtained photochemically from a large variety of aromatic amine N-oxides, it seemed straightforward to postulate oxaziridines as the first-formed intermediates. Thus, irradiation of 2-cyano-4-methylquinoline N-oxide (187) in the presence of secondary amines leads to the corresponding N-aminocarbostyrils 189. By analogy with aliphatic oxaziridines, which react with secondary amines to yield hydrazine derivatives, it is assumed that the secondary amines react with the oxaziridine intermediates 188 (Scheme 52) (151).

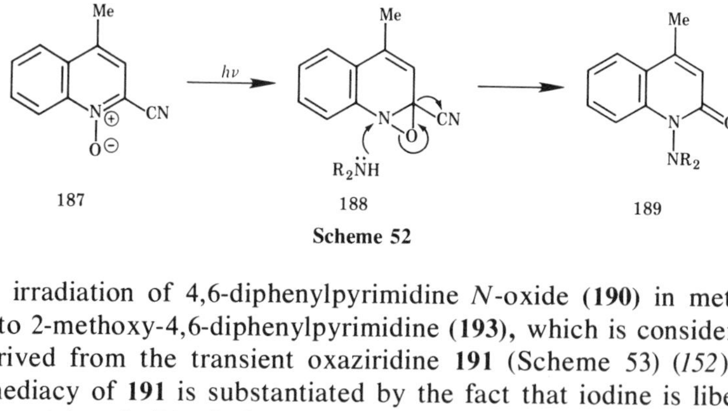

Scheme 52

The irradiation of 4,6-diphenylpyrimidine N-oxide (190) in methanol leads to 2-methoxy-4,6-diphenylpyrimidine (193), which is considered to be derived from the transient oxaziridine 191 (Scheme 53) (152). The intermediacy of 191 is substantiated by the fact that iodine is liberated from potassium iodide during photolysis of 190 (152).

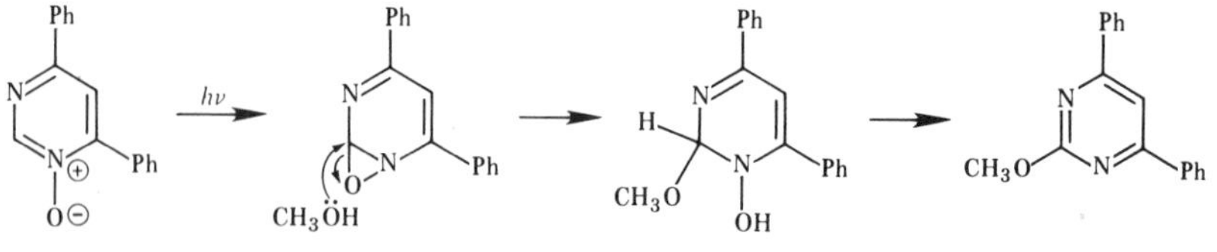

Scheme 53

Ultraviolet irradiation of some acridine N-oxides (194, R = CN, Cl) leads to the corresponding dibenzoxazepines **196** (*153*). The latter revert to the corresponding *N*-oxides thermally. Both processes can be explained by assuming the intermediate formation of **195** (Scheme 54).

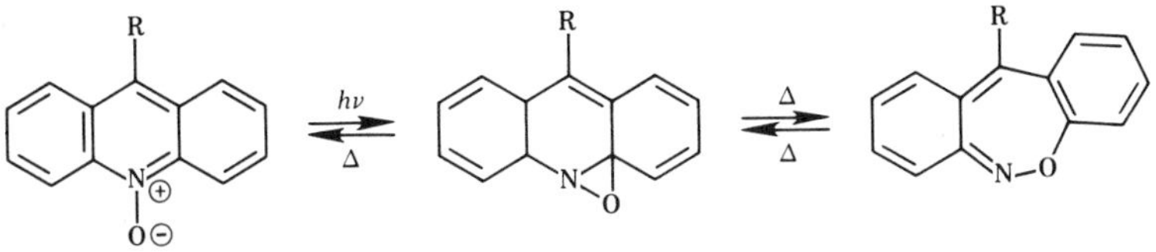

Scheme 54

Independent support for the intermediacy of oxaziridines comes from a study of the thermal addition of nitrile oxides to 2-phenylbenzazete (**197**). The adducts **198** are obtained at low temperature. Upon warming, 1,3,5-oxadiazepine derivatives **202** are obtained, most likely via a multistep mechanism (Scheme 55) (*154*).

The same oxadiazepines (**202**) are also obtained by UV irradiation of the

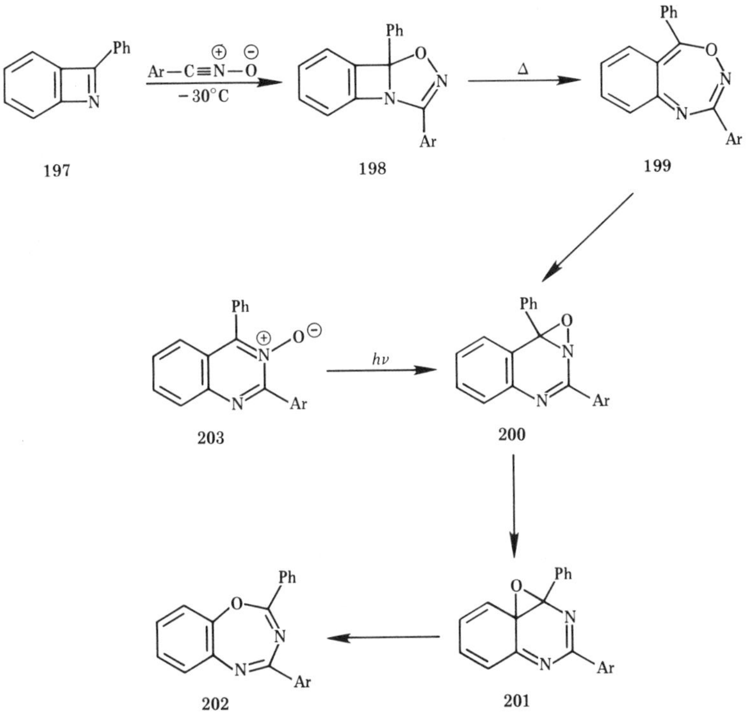

Scheme 55

corresponding quinazoline 3-N-oxides (**203**) (*154*). The formation of a transient oxaziridine has nevertheless been ruled out in the photolysis of 3,6-diphenylpyridazine N-oxide (**204**), a reaction that leads to a mixture of 2,5-diphenylfuran (**206**) and 3-benzoyl-5-phenylpyrrazole (**207**) (*150*). Here it could be shown, by nanosecond flash photolysis, that the diazoketone **205** is probably the primary photoproduct (Scheme 56).

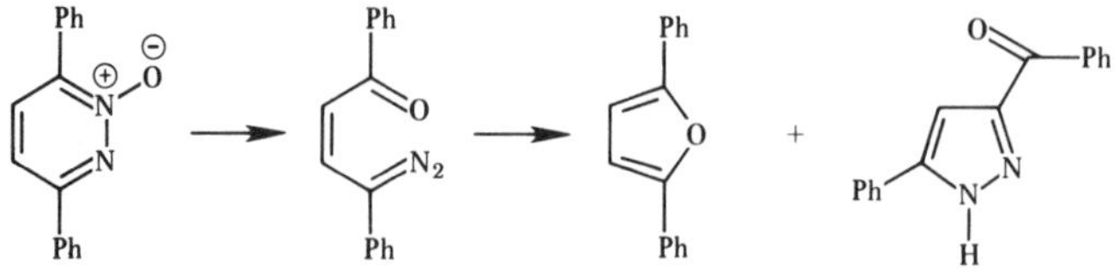

Scheme 56

Of the typical photoproducts obtained from aromatic amine N-oxides, one may cite the following. In all cases oxaziridines are the most probable primary photoproducts. (a) 2-Pyridones are obtained photochemically from pyridine N-oxides (*155,156*), and carbostyrils (*145,157*) and isocarbostyrils (*148,158*) are obtained from quinoline N-oxides and isoquinoline N-oxides, respectively; (b) 3-hydroxypyridines (*147,156*) and 3-hydroxyquinolines (*159*) from the corresponding pyridine N-oxides and quinoline N-oxides (Scheme 57); (c) 1,3-oxazepines from substituted pyridine N-oxides (*147,160,161*) and from quinoline N-oxides (*162–164*) (Scheme 57); and (d) 2-acylpyrroles (*155,156,161*) from pyridine N-oxides and 2-acylindoles from quinoline N-oxides (*165*) (Scheme 58). In Scheme 57 compounds **209** and **210,** and in Scheme 58 compounds **214, 215, 216,** and **217,** are merely postulated intermediates.

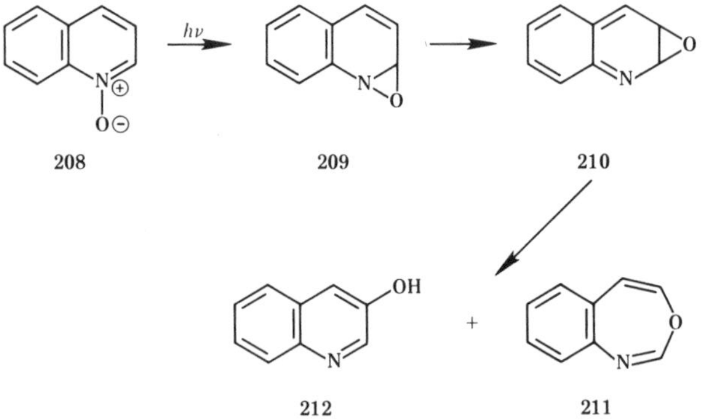

Scheme 57

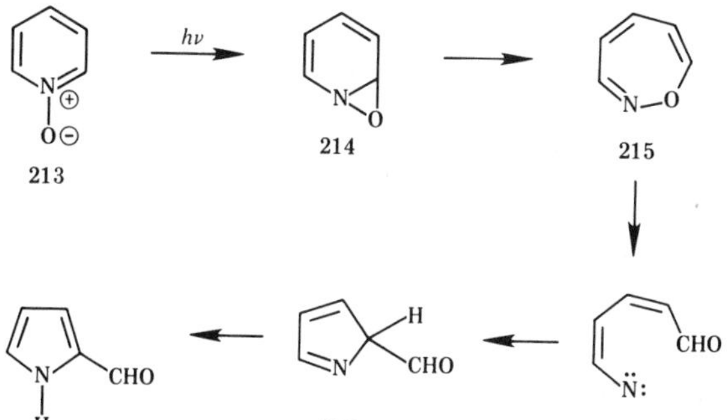

213 214 215 216 217 218

Scheme 58

c. Ring Formation from Oximes. The photo-Beckman rearrangement, i.e., the photoinduced ring conversion of oximes to lactams and amides, originally reported in 1963 (*166*), has been extensively studied in recent years. Intermediate oxaziridines (Scheme 59) have been postulated in many reports (*166–176*), but little consistent evidence has been given.

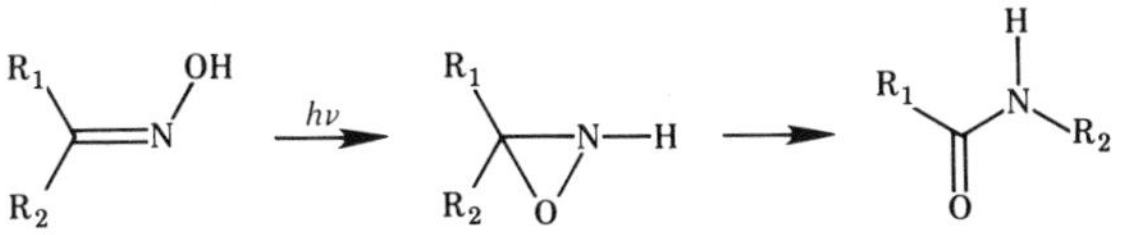

Scheme 59

The absorption band of a transient was detected during the photolysis of 1,1-dimethyl-2-naphthalenone oxime (**219**); the absorption was tentatively

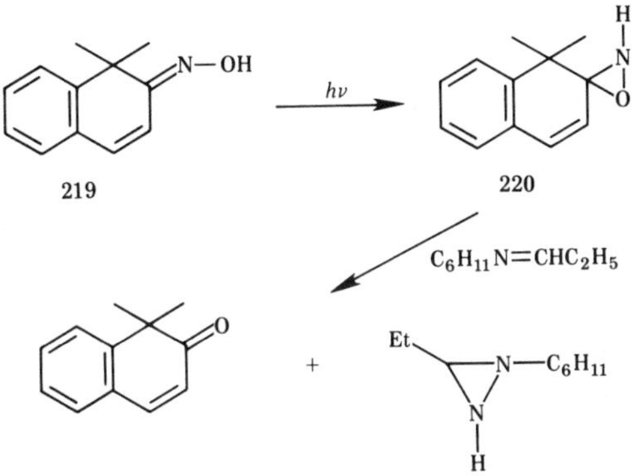

219 220 221 222

Scheme 60

attributed to the (not isolated) oxaziridine **220**. The chemical behavior of the transient is characteristic of an oxaziridine ring, and, in particular, the formation of diaziridine **222** and of naphthalenone **221** in the presence of an imine is *prima facie* evidence in favor of **220** (*170*) (Scheme 60). Irradiation of oxaziridine **223** or of cyclohexanone oxime **224** leads to the same two compounds (**225** and **226**), although the product distribution is different (*169*) (Scheme 61).

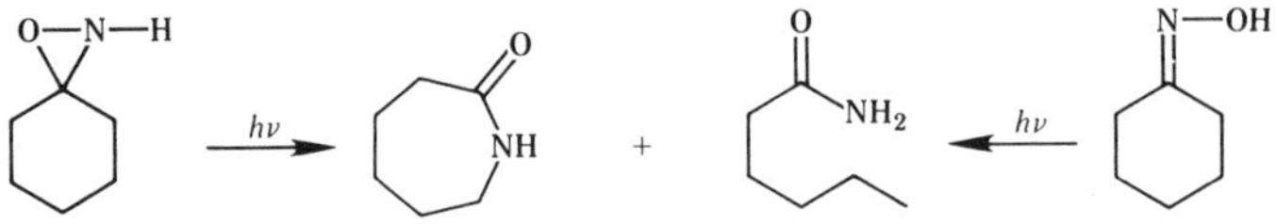

Scheme 61

Photoinduced rearrangement of cholestan-6-one oxime (**227**) leads to the two lactams **228** and **229**, in which the original β configuration at C-5 is retained, a result that may suggest a concerted pathway from an excited singlet state of the hypothetical oxaziridine intermediate (*173*) (Scheme 62).

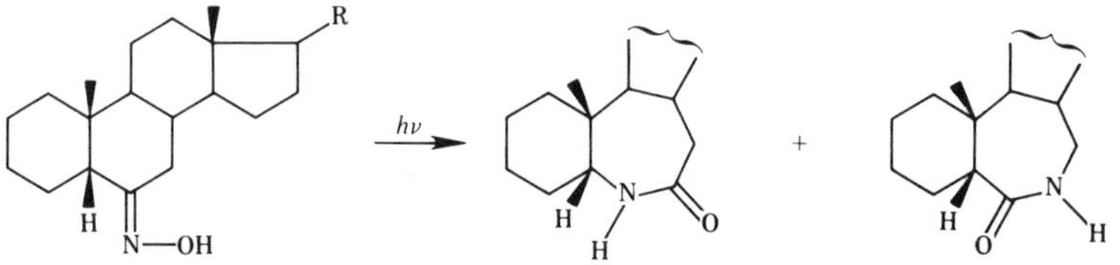

Scheme 62

All the data published so far are consistent with the formation of an oxaziridine in the photo-Beckman rearrangement, but they do not permit one to rule out other, perhaps more direct pathways.

d. Photochemical Ring Opening. Closely related to the photo-Beckman rearrangement is the photoinduced ring opening of the oxaziridine ring. Irradiation of oxaziridine **230** leads to the ring contraction product **231** exclusively (*128*), whereas Δ^1-pyrroline oxide (**156**) gives 2-pyrrolidinone (**158**) and N-acylazetidine (**159**) (*125*) (Schemes 63 and 64, respectively). However, in the case of oxaziridine **232**, C-4—C-5 bond cleavage is preferred to C-5—H bond cleavage, a result that is interpreted in terms of the preferential formation of the tertiary alkyl radical, thus supporting the general free-radical mechanism that has been postulated for these reactions (*127*) (Scheme 63).

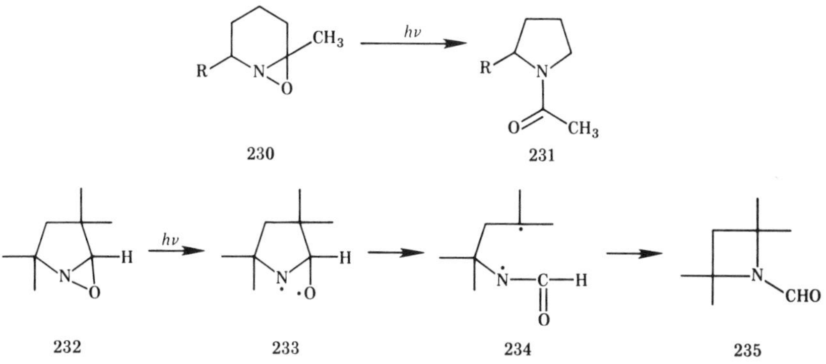

230   231

232   233   234   235

Scheme 63

Free-radical mechanisms do not seem, however, to be involved in all photochemical oxaziridine ring openings. For example 2-substituted spirooxaziridines **236** photorearrange preferentially to lactams **239**, a result that, within the free-radical hypothesis, would imply preferential formation of a primary alkyl radical (*177,178*) (Scheme 64). Finally, it should be noted that the regioselectivity observed in the photorearrangement of oxaziridines **236** is not consistent with the generally proposed mechanism for photo-Beckman rearrangements (see Section III,A,1,c). For example, oxime **242** is photochemically converted to a 1 : 1 mixture of the isomeric lactams **243** and **244** (*168*) (Scheme 65). Hence, formation of an oxaziridine intermediate is somewhat doubtful.

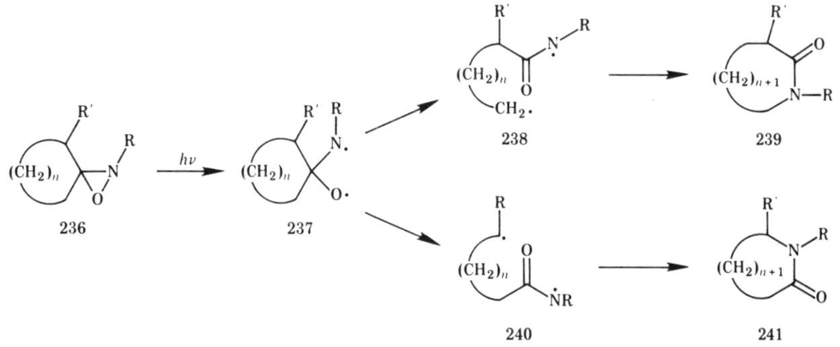

236   237   238   239

240   241

Scheme 64

The photochemistry of the monocyclic *N*-arylsulfonyloxaziridine **245** results in the formation of the isomeric amide **246** (*179*) (Scheme 66) in agreement with some theoretical calculations (*180*). A similar rearrangement to amide **248** has been observed upon irradiation of **247** (*181*)

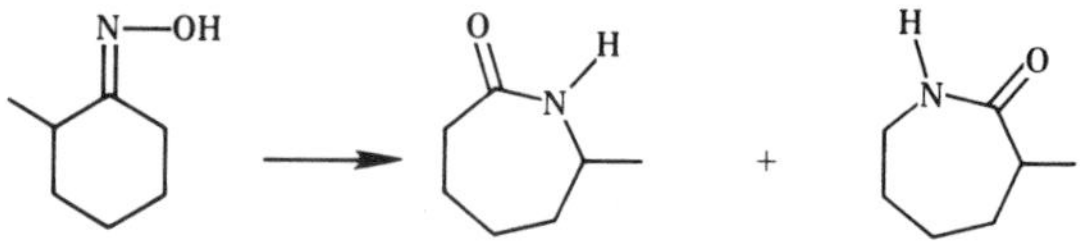

242   243   244

Scheme 65

(Scheme 66). These two rearrangements are reminiscent of the well-known oxirane to ketone photoisomerization (Section II,A,1,a).

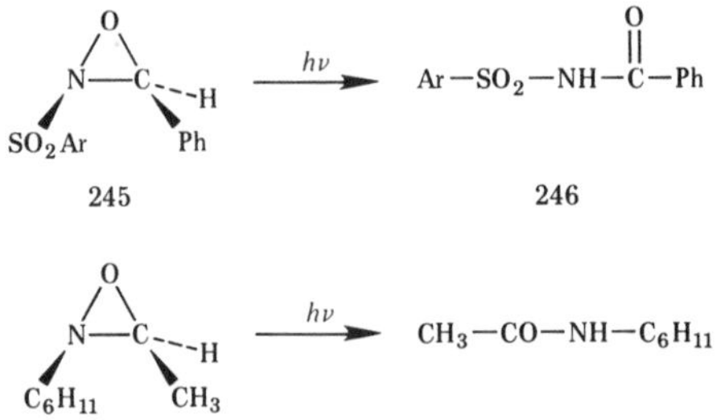

245   246

247   248

Scheme 66

2. Diaziridines

a. From Azomethine Imines. Azomethine imines are 1,3-dipolar species that are usually generated *in situ* and reacted immediately with dipolarophiles (*143*). Only rarely are they encountered as stable entities. Being 4π 1,3-dipolar compounds, azomethine imines could in principle undergo photoinduced electrocyclic ring closure to the corresponding diaziridines (*37*). This has indeed been observed in a few instances.

The azomethine imine **249** undergoes photochemical ring closure to the isomeric diaziridine **250** (*182*) (Scheme 67). A suspension of the conjugated azomethine imine **251** in dioxane, when irradiated, leads to only one of the two possible diastereoisomeric 6-phenyl-1,5-diaza-bicyclo[3.1.0]2-hexanones **252** (*183*). This crystalline diaziridine is labile when heated and reacts with methanol to give **253** (*183*). That only one diaziridine (**252**) is obtained undoubtedly is due to the fact that the starting azomethine imine molecules (**251**) are stacked in the microcrystalline suspension in only one of the two possible configurations. Irradiation of **251** in methanol leads directly to **253** (*183*) (Scheme 67).

Similar reactions have been observed with azomethine imines **254** ($R_1 =$ CH$_3$, H; $R_2 = C_6H_5$, *p*-CH$_3$—C$_6$H$_4$, *p*-Cl—C$_6$H$_4$, CH$_3$); these lead, in high yield, either to the bicyclic diaziridines **255** (dioxane suspensions) or to

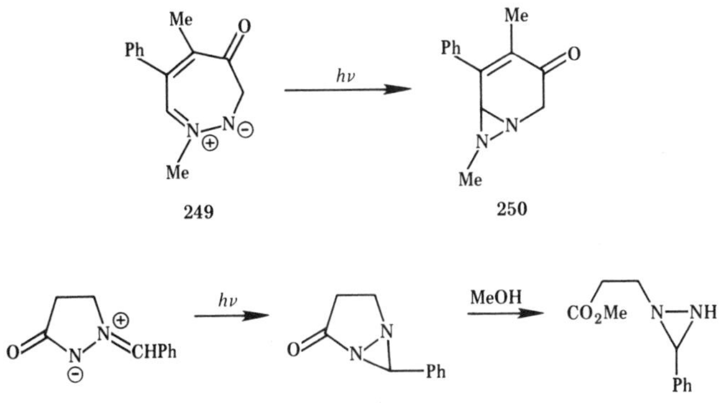

249 250

251 252 253

Scheme 67

the monocyclic diaziridines **256** (methanol solution (*184,185*) (Scheme 68). When $R_2 = CH_3$ the corresponding azomethine imines **254** do not lead to diaziridines, perhaps because of the very low thermal stability of the expected diaziridine.

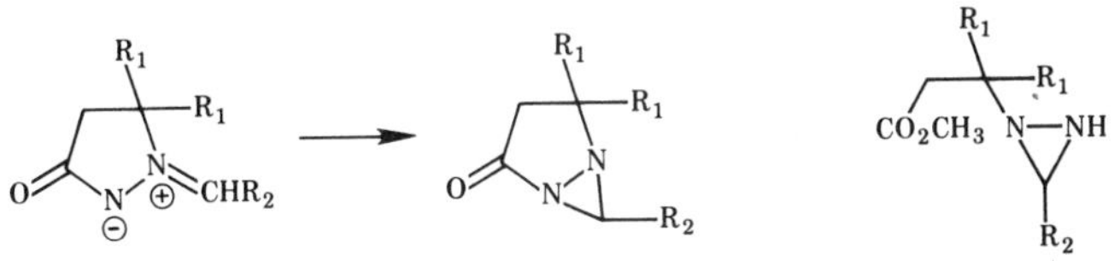

254 255 256

Scheme 68

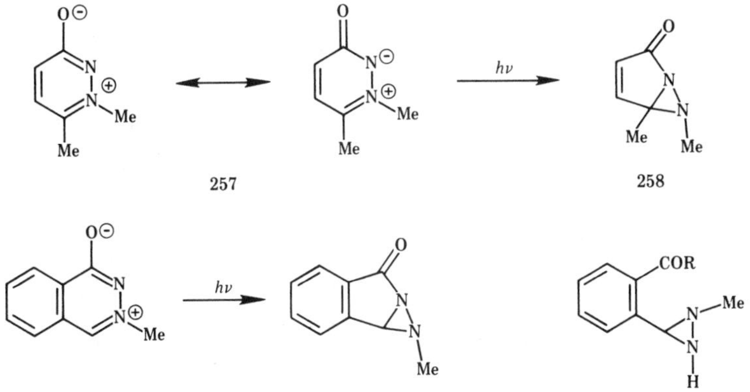

257 258

259 260 261

Scheme 69

Ultraviolet irradiation of the aromatic betaines **257** and **259** leads to the corresponding bicyclic (**258**) and tricyclic diaziridines (**260**) (*186*), respectively (Scheme 69). The latter, when treated with nucleophiles (methanol or ethylamine) leads to diaziridines **261** (R = OCH$_3$, NHEt) (*186*).

The cyclic conjugated azomethine imine **262** when irradiated leads to the tricyclic pyrimidone **265**, presumably via diaziridine **263** and ketene **264** (*187*) (Scheme 70).

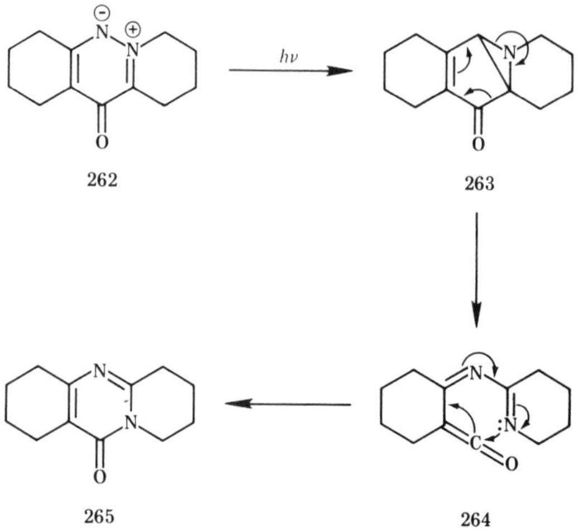

Scheme 70

b. From Aromatic Amine N-Imines. *N*-Iminopyridinium ylides (**266**) are aromatic analogues of azomethine imines. Indeed, they behave as such since they undergo typical 1,3-dipolar cycloaddition reactions in the ground state (*188*). The same type of 1,3-dipolar reactivity is shown by isoquinoline *N*-imines (*189*). When irradiated, pyridine *N*-imines (**266**, Y = CO$_2$Et, COPh, SO$_2$Ar) undergo a ring enlargement to the isomeric 1,2-diazepines **268**, presumably via the 1,7-diazanorcaradiene intermediates **267** (*190*) (Scheme 71).

Photolytic N—N bond cleavage also occurs as a minor reaction pathway leading to pyridine and to the corresponding nitrenes Y—N, which can be trapped by solvent molecules (*191*). It was shown that, when triplet sensitizers are irradiated in the presence of ylide **266** (Y = CO$_2$Et), only N—N bond cleavage occurred, ring expansion to the corresponding diazepine **268** (Y = CO$_2$Et) being entirely suppressed (*192*). Furthermore, determination of the spin multiplicity of the nitrene, which is obtained by direct irradiation of ylide **266** (Y = CO$_2$Et), showed it to be entirely in its triplet state (*193*). From these two experiments it can be inferred that the ring expansion process of ylides **266** derives from an excited singlet state, whereas the photolytic N—N bond cleavage is triggered by an excited triplet state (*193*).

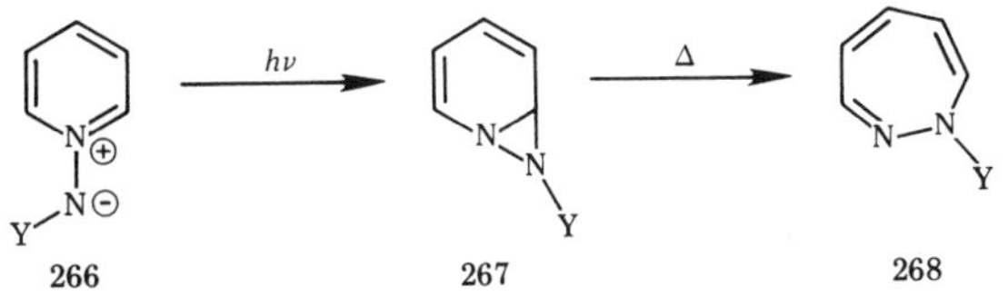

Scheme 71

The nature of the "chromophoric handle" N—Y has a crucial effect on the photochemical behavior of pyridinium ylides **266**. Amide-sulfonamide–, and urethane–N anion groups initiate the photochemical ring expansion; on the other hand, anilino– (*194*) and thioureido–N (*195*) anion groups lead only to N—N photolytic bond cleavage. Although 1,7-norcaradienes (**267**) have been postulated by all authors as the most likely intermediates, such hypothetical transients have not been detected as yet by any spectroscopic method. Some 1,2-diazepines (**268**) were shown to ring-contract thermally back to the corresponding iminopyridinium ylides (**266**) (*196*). Again, **267** can be postulated to be the most likely intermediates for this ground state rearrangement. This experiment demonstrates that the elusive 1,7-diazanorcaradienes (**267**) cannot be in equilibrium with their tautomeric 1,2-diazepine isomers (**268**) at room temperature.

The photoinduced rearrangement of *N*-iminopyridinium ylides, which are substituted in the C-2 or the C-3 position, might in principle lead to two different 1,2-diazepines. It was found that 2-methyl- and 2-cyano-1-iminopyridinium ylides (**269**) rearrange in a regiospecific way to the corresponding 3-substituted diazepines (**271**, R = CH₃, CN) (Scheme 72); this means that electrocyclic ring closure occurs in the direction of the least substituted site of the pyridinium ring (*197–199*).

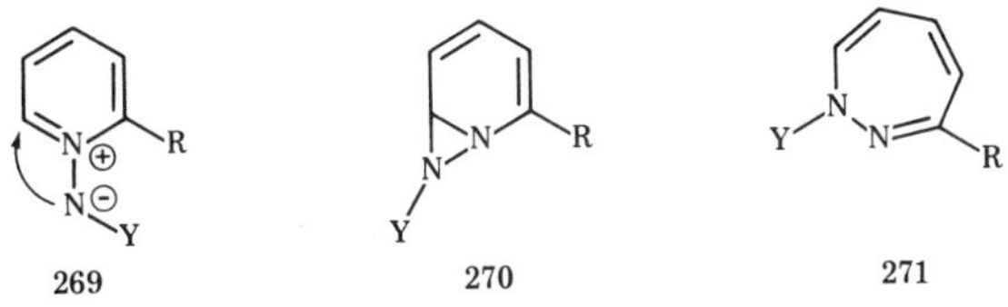

Scheme 72

The 5,6,7,8-tetrahydroiminoquinolinium ylides **272** (Y = COCH₃, CO₂CH₃) also undergo regiospecific photorearrangements to the corresponding 3,4-disubstituted 1,2-diazepines **273** (*200*), as does the steroidal pyridinium ylide **274** to **275** (*200*) (Scheme 73).

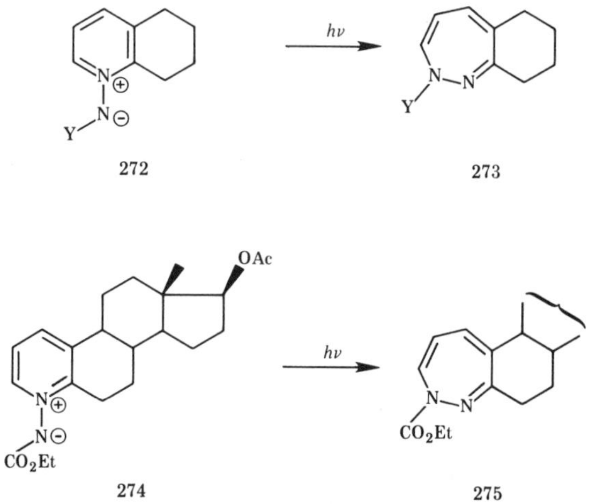

Scheme 73

It would seem that substituents in the 2 position undergo steric interaction with the exocyclic nitrogen chromophore in the photoactivated ylides **269, 272,** and **274,** so that ring closure occurs toward the unsubstituted C-6 carbon atom only, i.e., that steric factors play a dominant role.

3-Substituted 1-iminopyridinium ylides are devoid of any such steric interaction. Electron-attracting substituents (ethoxycarbonyl, cyano, and amido groups) induce a photoregiospecific ring enlargement process since only the corresponding 4-substituted 1,2-diazepines (**278**) are formed (Y = CO_2Et, COPh; A = CO_2Et, CN, $CONH_2$) (*197,201*) (Scheme 74).

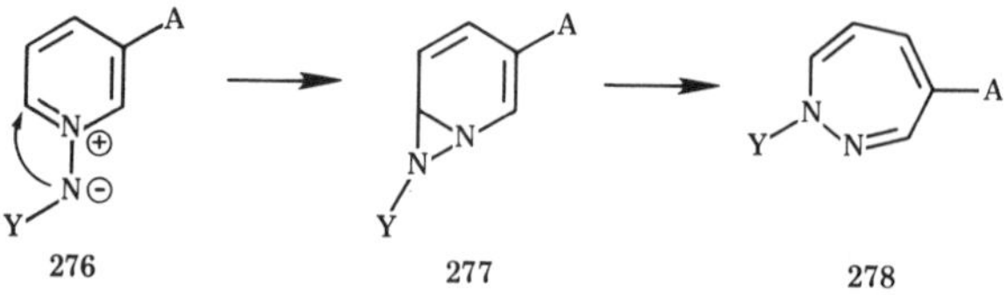

Scheme 74

Electron-donating groups attached at C-3 do not exert any directing effect (Scheme 75); irradiation of ylides **279** (Y = CO_2Et, COPh; B = CH_3, OCOPh, F, Cl, Br, I) leads to mixtures of both 4- (**280**) and 6-substituted 1,2-diazepines (**281**) (*201*) (Scheme 75).

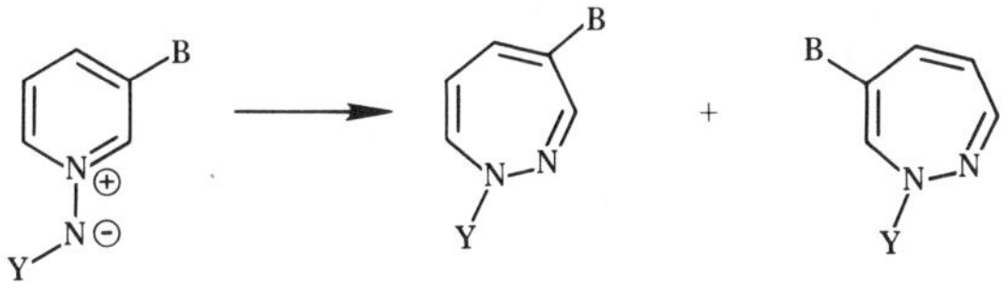

279 280 281

Scheme 75

Formation of 2-aminopyridine isomers from the corresponding *N*-iminopyridinium ylides has also been reported, diaziridines being postulated as intermediates (*198*). Some quinoline (**282**) and isoquinoline *N*-iminopyridinium ylides (**285**) have been irradiated. Cleavage of the N—N bond may occur, but mostly isomerization to the corresponding α-aminoquinolines (**284**) and to α-aminoisoquinolines (**287**) takes place, presumably via diaziridine intermediates **283** and **286** (R = Ph, OEt, Me) (*202–204*) (Scheme 76).

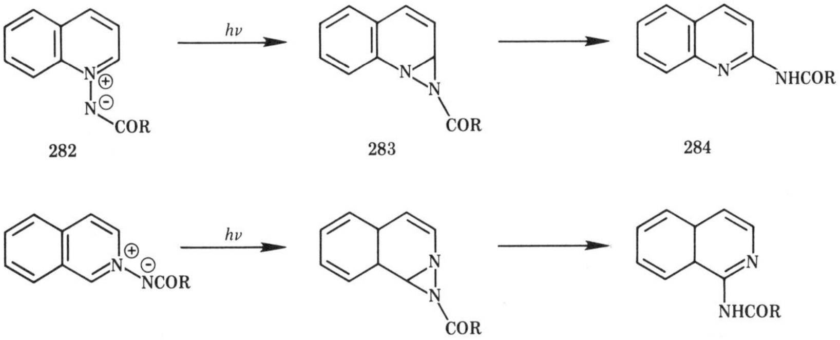

282 283 284

285 286 287

Scheme 76

Irradiation of fused polycyclic aromatic *N*-imines leads only rarely to ring expansion to diazepine derivatives. An exception is the irradiation of quinoline *N*-imines **288** (R′ = CH_3, OEt) in alcohol media, which leads to benzodiazepines **290**, possibly via **289** (*203,205*) (Scheme 77).

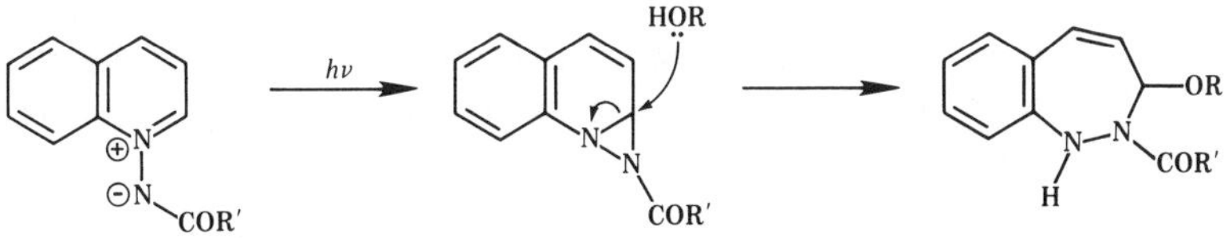

288 289 290

Scheme 77

A general photochemical synthesis of 1*H*-1,2-benzodiazepines (**293**) from *N*-iminoquinolinium ylide dimers (**292**) has been described (*206*). It is believed that a small amount of the dimer is dissociated and that the monomeric *N*-iminoquinolinium ylide **291** undergoes the photoinduced rearrangement (Scheme 78).

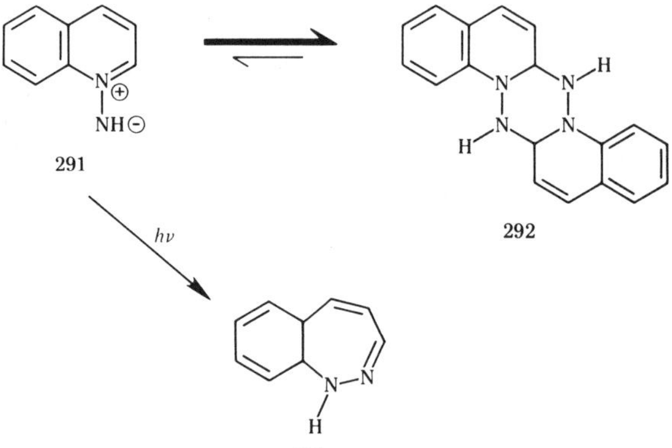

Scheme 78

3-Iminoquinazolinium ylides **294** undergo photolytic N—N bond cleavage to the parent quinazolines **295** as well as ring expansion, perhaps via a diaziridine, to benzotriazepines **296** (R = OEt, OCH$_2$Ph, Ph; R$_2$ and R$_4$ = H and/or CH$_3$) (*207*) (Scheme 79).

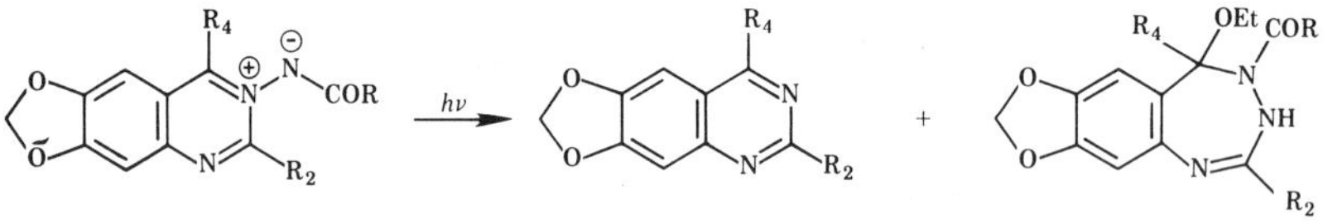

Scheme 79

The formation of pyrazoles **301** by irradiation of *N*-ethoxycarbonyliminopyrazinium ylides **297** has been described. A mechanism involving the 1,2,5-triazepine intermediate **299** has been proposed. This should then undergo disrotatory photoinduced ring closure to the bicyclic **300,** from which expulsion of nitriles R$_1$CN gives the pyrazoles **301** (*208*) (Scheme 80).

c. From Hydrazones. In order to explain the photoinduced conversion of the androsterone acylhydrazone **302** to lactams **305** and **306** a mechanism involving initial ring closure to the spirodiaziridine **303** has been

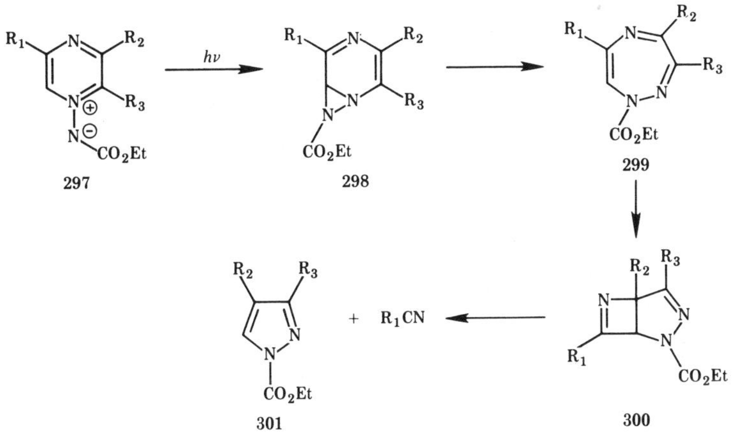

Scheme 80

invoked (*209*). No direct evidence in favor of this pathway has been given, although it has close similarities with the photo-Beckman rearrangement (Scheme 81). One may assume that the corresponding azomethine imine, which is directly derived from **302** by prototropy, is the primary photo-product. Such a prototropy has been shown to occur in the ground state (*210*). In a second step this hypothetical 1,3-dipolar species could then close, either thermally or photochemically, to the postulated diaziridine **303**.

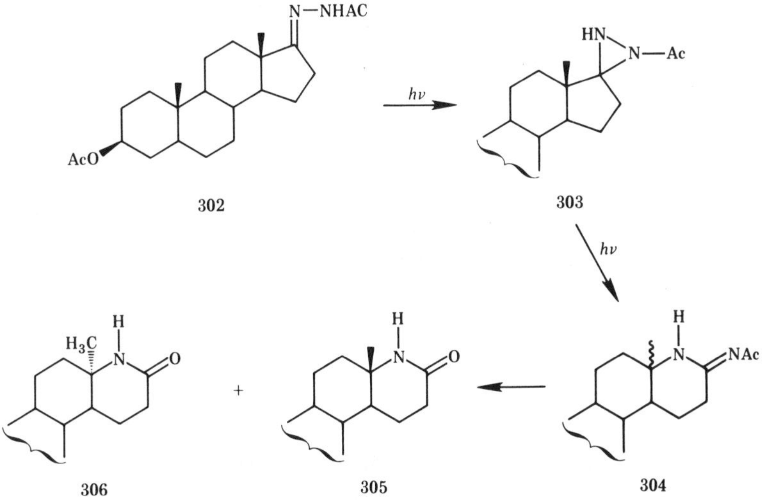

Scheme 81

d. From Sydnones. The primary photoprocess generally proposed to account for the photoreactivity of arylsydnones of type **307** (Ar = Ph, *p*-CH$_3$C$_6$H$_4$; R = H, CH$_3$, Ph), is a symmetry-allowed ring closure to the bicyclic diaziridines **308** *(211–213)*. Decarboxylation then leads to the antiaromatic 1*H*-diazirine **309**, which rearranges to nitrile imines **310**. The latter may then dimerize *(214)* or add to various dipolarophiles *(211–213)* (Scheme 82).

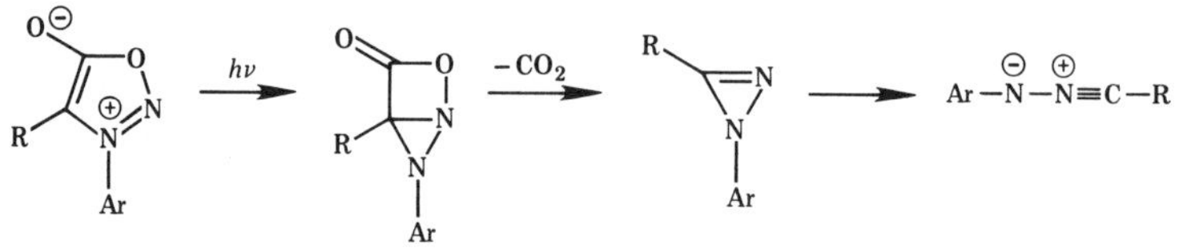

Scheme 82

It has been shown that irradiation of [2-^{15}N]-3,4-diphenylsydnone **(311)** leads to the formation of [1,3-^{15}N]-2,4,5-triphenyl-1,2,3-triazole **(315),** thus proving that the nitrile imine formation is necessarily induced by a bond formation between N-2 and C-4 in sydnone **311** *(215)* (Scheme 83). This labeling experiment represents the only good evidence, so far, in favor of the generally accepted mechanism depicted in Scheme 82.

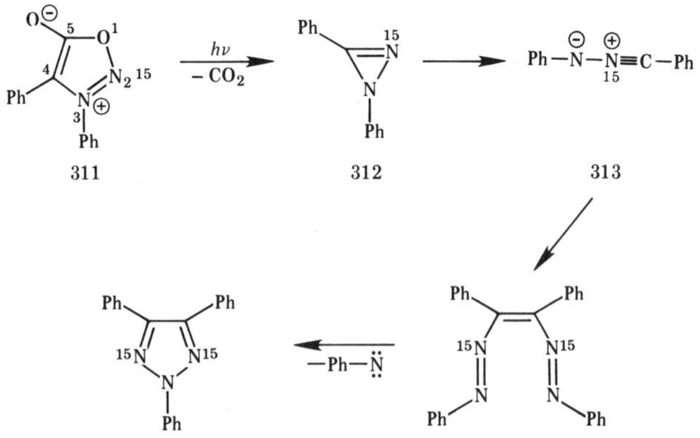

Scheme 83

A similar mechanistic scheme has been put forward for the photochemical conversion of **316** to **320** *(216)*; no evidence for **317** and **318** has been given (Scheme 84).

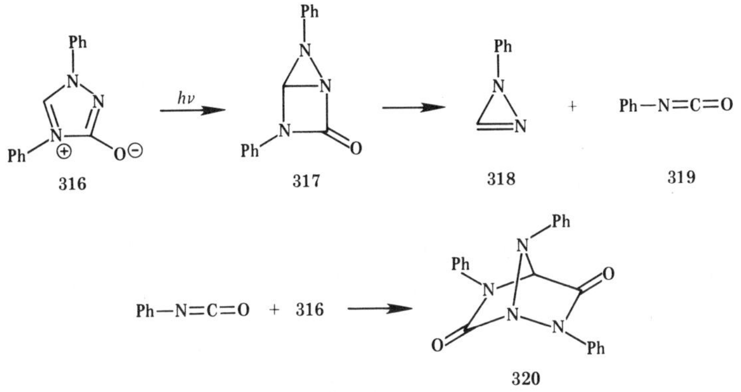

Scheme 84

3. Thiaziridines

Irradiation of sydnones usually leads to their cleavage into two fragments, one of which undergoes a deep-seated rearrangement (Section III,A,2,d). Irradiation of 4-phenyl-1,3,2-oxathiazolylio 5-oxide (**321**) leads to the formation of benzonitrile **326**, carbon dioxide, and sulfur (*217–220*). It is assumed that photoinduced valence isomerization gives first the bicyclic thiaziridine **322**, which then expels carbon dioxide, leading to phenylthiazirine **323**. Ring opening of the latter gives phenylnitrile *N*-sulfide (**324**), which can be trapped with dimethyl acetylenedicarboxylate to give the stable isothiazole **325** (Scheme 85).

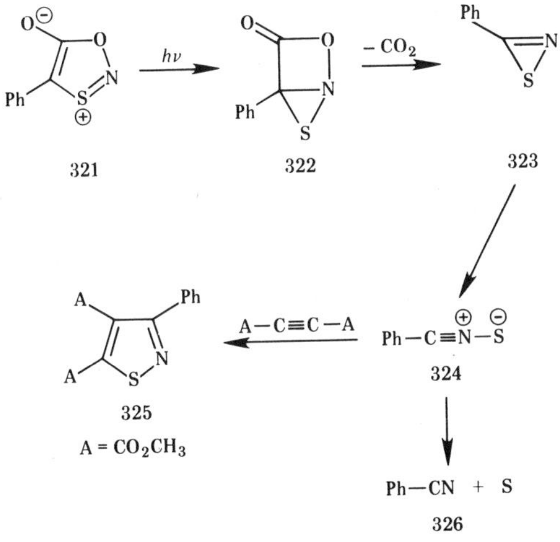

A = CO$_2$CH$_3$

Scheme 85

B. Unsaturated Rings: Diazirines

Ring opening of the hypothetical thiazirines to the corresponding nitrile sulfides has been discussed in Section III,A,3. We shall therefore restrict ourselves to the photoinduced ring closure of some diazoalkanes to the corresponding diazirines.

Although diazoalkanes usually undergo photolytic expulsion of a nitrogen molecule, leading to highly reactive carbenes (*221*), some diazoalkanes bearing particular structural features undergo photoinduced electrocyclic ring closure to the corresponding diazirines. For example, α-diazoamides **327** when exposed to visible light lead in moderate yields to diazirines **328** (R = NHMe, NEt$_2$, NMePh, NPh$_2$) (*222*). Analogously, 3-diazo-2-oxoindolines **329** (R = H, CH$_3$) undergo photoinduced and thermally reversible conversion to diazirines **330** and constitute the first example of photochromic valence isomerizations in these series (*223*) (Scheme 86).

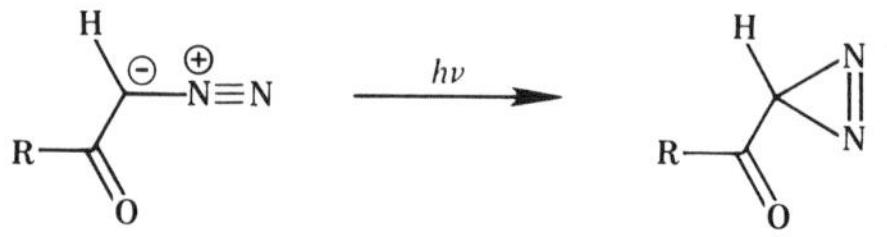

327   328

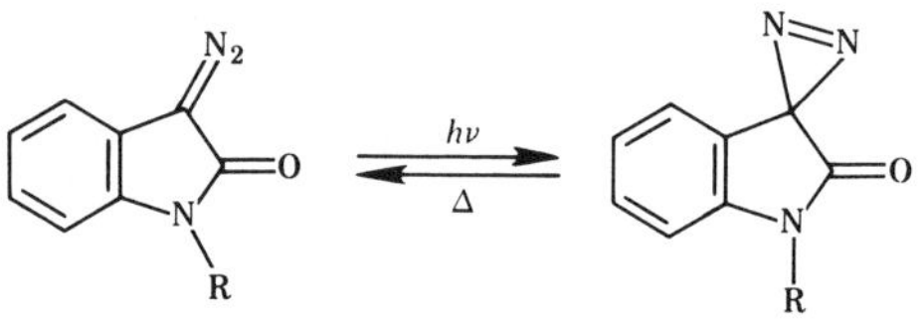

329   330

Scheme 86

Although the photoisomerization of diazo compounds to diazirines appeared at first to be restricted to α-diazoamides (*222*), this type of electrocyclic ring closure has been encountered with various diazoalkanes. For example, the polycyclic diazoketones **331** and **333** undergo photoisomerization to the stable diazirines **332** and **334**, respectively (*224*) (Scheme 87).

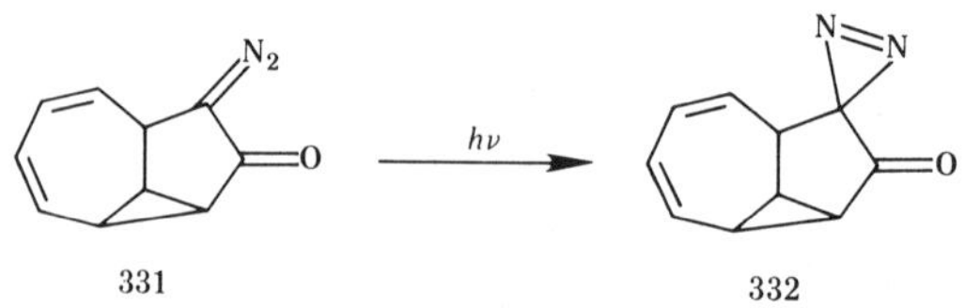

331   332

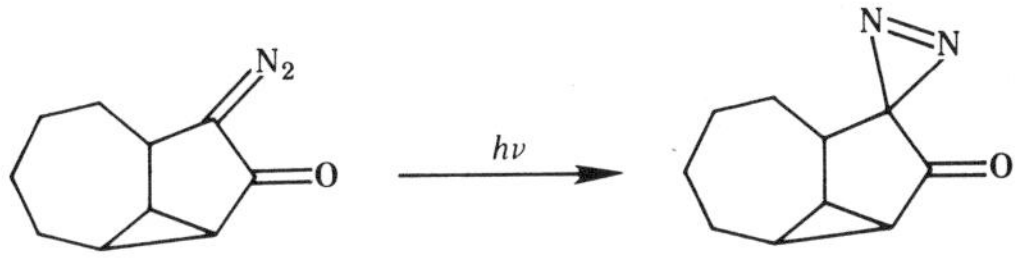

Scheme 87

Finally, it is of interest that irradiation of trimethylsilyldiazomethane (335) isolated in an argon matrix at 8 K produces a photostationary state involving trimethylsilyldiazirine (336) (225,226) (Scheme 88). The latter is also formed upon irradiation of 335 in a variety of solvents at room temperature and can be isolated as a relatively stable species.

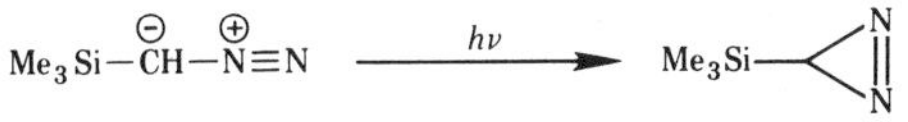

Scheme 88

IV. THREE-MEMBERED HETEROCYCLES WITH THREE HETEROATOMS

A. Oxadiaziridines

Azoxybenzene has been known for a long time to undergo photochemical rearrangement to o-hydroxyazobenzene (111,227). The corresponding oxadiaziridine isomer, the formation of which would be expected, has never been isolated, although it has been claimed that its occurrence as a transient species was ascertained polarographically (228).

Irradiation of azoxy-t-butane (337, R = t-Bu) leads to di-t-butyloxadiaziridine (338), a labile compound that reverts quantitatively to 1,3 dipole 337 at 20°C (229). Similar results have been obtained with various dialkylazoxy compounds (337, $R_1 = R_2 = t$-Bu, i-Pr, n-Bu; $R_1 = CH_3$; $R_2 = t$-Bu; $R_1 = CH_3$, $R_2 = C_6H_{11}$). All oxadiaziridines 338 seem to occur in their trans configuration (230–232) (Scheme 89).

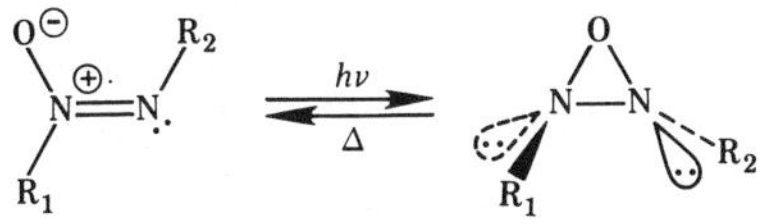

Scheme 89

Irradiation of some other acyclic and cyclic azoxy compounds leads to photoproducts the formation of which can be explained by assuming the occurrence of transient oxadiaziridines. For example, irradiation of *trans*-phenylalkylazoxy compounds **339** leads to a mixture of all four possible *cis*- and *trans*-azoxy compounds (**339** and **341**), presumably via oxadiaziridine **340** (*233*) (Scheme 90).

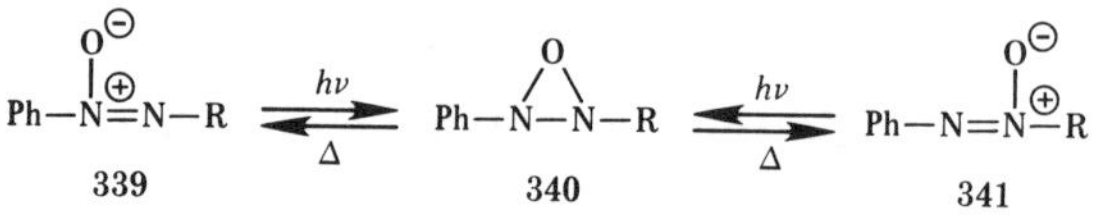

Scheme 90

Photoisomerizations of 1-methyl-1,2,3-benzotriazole 3-oxide (**342**) to the isomeric 2-oxide **344** (*234*) and of 1,2,3-thiadiazole 2-oxides (**345**) to the isomeric 3-oxides **347** [R_1 = H, Ph; R_2 = Ph, H; R_1, R_2 = $(CH_2)_3$, $(CH_2)_4$, $(CH_2)_5$, $(CH_2)_6$] (*235*) are likely to occur via the transient oxadiaziridines **343** and **346**, respectively (Scheme 91).

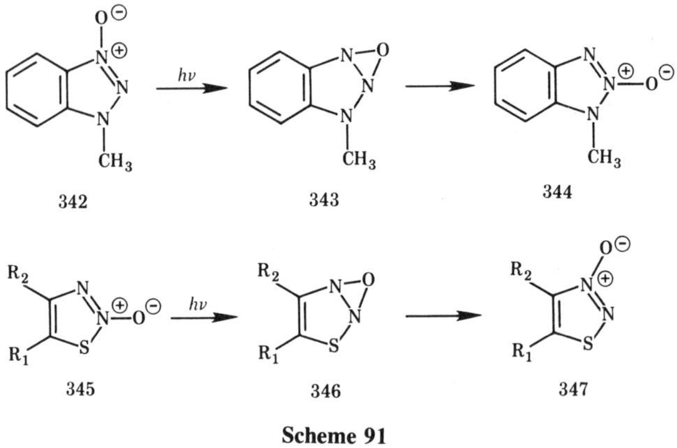

Scheme 91

B. Triaziridines

Ultraviolet irradiation of *N*-cyclohexyloxatriazolone sydnone (**348**) has been reported to afford cyclohexanone in low yield (*216*). The elusive triaziridine **349** has been proposed merely as a working hypothesis; **349** is said to expel carbon dioxide, leading to cyclohexyltriazirine **350** and then to azidocyclohexane **351**. Photolysis of the latter would then give the corresponding cyclohexylnitrene, which, by isomerization to the corresponding imine followed by hydrolysis, leads to cyclohexanone (Scheme

92). Unfortunately, the azidocyclohexane has not been trapped, and the formation of triazirine **350** is therefore doubtful.

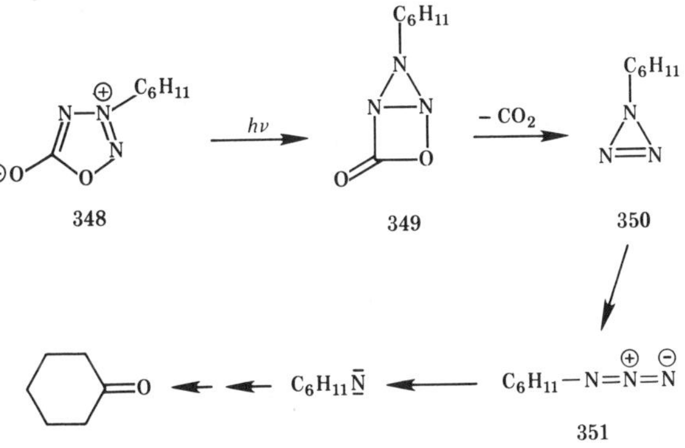

Scheme 92

V. CONCLUSION

The photochemical interconversion processes of three-membered heterocycles with their isomeric open-chain partners represent some important rearrangement patterns in modern organic chemistry. No unifying scheme underlying all the mechanistic pathways that have been proved or proposed as working hypotheses has been found. Nevertheless, photoinduced electrocyclic interconversion of 4π 1,3-dipolar species with their three-membered heterocyclic isomers has been described several times in this essay and may well be a general feature (*236*).

REFERENCES

1. R. J. Gritter and E. C. Sabatino, *J. Org. Chem.* **29**, 1965 (1964).
2. S. Bodforss, *Ber. Dtsch. Chem. Ges.* **51**, 214 (1918).
3. C. K. Johnson, B. Dominy, and W. Reusch, *J. Am. Chem. Soc.* **85**, 3894 (1963).
4. H. E. Zimmermann, B. R. Cowley, C. Y. Tseng, and J. W. Wilson, *J. Am. Chem. Soc.* **86**, 947 (1964).
5. C. S. Markos and W. Reusch, *J. Am. Chem. Soc.* **89**, 3363 (1967).
6. J. P. Pete and M. L. Villaume, *Tetrahedron Lett.* p. 3753 (1969).
7. J. P. Pete and M. L. Viriot-Villaume, *Bull. Soc. Chim. Fr.* p. 3699 (1971).
8. J. P. Pete and M. L. Viriot-Villaume, *Bull. Soc. Chim. Fr.* p. 3709 (1971).
9. M. Tokuda, M. Hataya, J. Imai, M. Itoh, and A. Suzuki, *Tetrahedron Lett.* p. 3133 (1971).
10. V. V. Chung, M. Tokuda, A. Suzuki, and M. Itoh, *Bull. Chem. Soc. Jpn.* **49**, 341 (1976).

11. D. R. Paulson, G. Korngold, and G. Jones, *Tetrahedron Lett.* p. 1723 (1972).
12. D. R. Paulson, F. Y. N. Tang, and R. B. Sloan, *J. Org. Chem.* **38**, 3967 (1973).
13. H. Kristinsson and G. W. Griffin, *J. Am. Chem. Soc.* **88**, 1579 (1966).
14. H. Kristinsson, R. A. Mateer, and G. W. Griffin, *Chem. Commun.* p. 415 (1966).
15. I. Saito, M. Takami, T. Konoike, and T. Matsuura, *Bull. Chem. Soc. Jpn.* **46**, 3198 (1973).
16. K. Nishiyama, K. Ishikawa, I. Sarkar, D. C. Lankin, and G. W. Griffin, *Heterocycles* **6**, 1337 (1977).
17. R. S. Becker, R. O. Bost, J. Kolc, N. R. Bertoniere, R. L. Smith, and G. W. Griffin, *J. Am. Chem. Soc.* **92**, 1302 (1970).
18. G. W. Griffin, D. M. Gibson, and K. Ishikawa, *Chem. Commun.* p. 595 (1975); G. W. Griffin, K. Ishikawa, and I. J. Lev, *J. Am. Chem. Soc.* **98**, 5697 (1976).
18a. R. Huisgen, V. Markowski, and H. Herman, *Heterocycles* **7**, 61 (1977); V. Markowski and R. Huisgen, *Tetrahedron Lett.* p. 4643 (1976).
19. D. R. Arnold and L. A. Karnischky, *J. Am. Chem. Soc.* **92**, 1404 (1970).
20. D. R. Arnold, A. B. Evnin, and L. A. Karnischky, *Pure Appl. Chem.* **24**, 523 (1970).
21. L. E. Friedrich, N. L. de Vera, W. P. Hoss, and J. T. Warren, *Tetrahedron Lett.* p. 3139 (1974).
22. N. E. Brightwell and G. W. Griffin, *Chem. Commun.* p. 37 (1973).
23. H. Hart and E. Shih, *J. Org. Chem.* **41**, 3377 (1976).
24. H. Hart, C. Peng, and E. Shih, *J. Org. Chem.* **42**, 3635 (1977).
25. S. Masamune, S. Takada, and R. T. Seidner, *J. Am. Chem. Soc.* **91**, 7769 (1969).
26. A. G. Anastassiou and R. P. Cellura, *Chem. Commun.* p. 903 (1969).
27. E. E. van Tamelen and D. Carty, *J. Am. Chem. Soc.* **89**, 3922 (1967).
28. J. M. Ilolovka and P. D. Gardner, *J. Am. Chem. Soc.* **89**, 6390 (1967).
29. N. Ishibe, M. Odani, and M. Sunami, *Chem. Commun.* p. 1034 (1971).
30. N. Ishibe, M. Sunami, and M. Odani, *J. Am. Chem. Soc.* **95**, 463 (1973).
30a. N. Ishibe and S. Yutaka, *J. Org. Chem.* **43**, 2138 (1978).
30b. N. Ishibe, S. Yutaka, J. Masui, and N. Ihda, *J. Org. Chem.* **43**, 2144 (1978).
31. M. Shiozaki and T. Hiraoka, *Tetrahedron Lett.* p. 4655 (1972).
32. J. M. Dunston and P. Yates, *Tetrahedron Lett.* p. 505 (1964).
33. T. H. Koch and R. M. Rodehorst, *Tetrahedron Lett.* p. 4039 (1972).
34. A. Mosterd, L. J. de Noten, and H. J. T. Bos, *Recl. Trav. Chim. Pays-Bas* **96**, 16 (1977).
35. R. Huisgen, W. Scheer, and H. Huber, *J. Am. Chem. Soc.* **89**, 1753 (1967).
36. H. Hermann, R. Huisgen, and H. Mäder, *J. Am. Chem. Soc.* **93**, 1779 (1971).
37. R. B. Woodward and R. Hoffmann, "Conservation of Orbital Symmetry." Academic Press, New York, 1969.
38. A. Padwa, S. Clough, and E. Glazer, *J. Am. Chem. Soc.* **92**, 1778 (1970).
39. A. Padwa and E. Glazer, *Chem. Commun.* p. 838 (1971).
40. A. Padwa and E. Glazer, *J. Am. Chem. Soc.* **94**, 7788 (1972).
41. A. Padwa and E. Glazer, *J. Org. Chem.* **38**, 284 (1973).
42. T. Do Minh and A. M. Trozzolo, *J. Am. Chem. Soc.* **92**, 6997 (1970).
43. T. Do Minh and A. M. Trozzolo, *J. Am. Chem. Soc.* **94**, 4046 (1972).
44. A. Padwa and L. Gehrlein, *J. Am. Chem. Soc.* **94**, 4933 (1972).
45. S. Oida and E. Ohki, *Chem. Pharm. Bull.* **17**, 2461 (1969).
46. A. Padwa and W. Eisenhardt, *J. Am. Chem. Soc.* **90**, 2442 (1968).
47. A. Padwa and W. Eisenhardt, *J. Am. Chem. Soc.* **93**, 1400 (1971); A. Padwa, D. Dean, and T. Oine, *ibid.* **97**, 2822 (1975).
48. A. G. Anastassiou and R. B. Hammer, *J. Am. Chem. Soc.* **94**, 303 (1972).

49. H. Nozaki, S. Fujita, and R. Noyori, *Tetrahedron* **24**, 2193 (1968).
50. H. W. Heine, G. J. Blosick, and G. B. Lowrie, *Tetrahedron Lett.* p. 4801 (1968), H. Roettele, G. Heil, and G. Schroeder, *Chem. Ber.* **111**, 84 (1978).
51. K. N. Mehrotra and T. V. Singh, *Tetrahedron Lett.* p. 4949 (1972).
52. G. W. Griffin, J. Covell, R. C. Petterson, R. M. Dodson, and G. Klose, *J. Am. Chem. Soc.* **87**, 1410 (1965).
53. S. S. Hixson, *Tetrahedron Lett.* p. 1155 (1972).
54. S. J. Cristol, T. D. Ziebarth, and G. A. Lee, *J. Am. Chem. Soc.* **96**, 7844 (1974).
55. A. R. Katritzky and H. Wilde, *Chem. Commun.* p. 770 (1975).
56. A. R. Katritzky and Y. Takeuchi, *J. Am. Chem. Soc.* **92**, 4134 (1970); Y. Tamura, M. Akita, H. Kiyokawa, L. C. Chen, and H. Ishibashi, *Tetrahedron Lett.* p. 1751 (1978).
57. J. Streith and J. M. Cassal, *C. R. Hebd. Seances Acad. Sci., Ser. C* **264**, 1307 (1967).
58. H. Arai, H. Igeta, and T. Tsuchiya, *Chem. Commun.* p. 521 (1973).
59. A. Lablache-Combier and G. Surpateanu, *Tetrahedron Lett.* p. 3081 (1976).
60. H. Hiraoka, *Chem. Commun.* p. 1306 (1970).
61. J. Barltrop, A. C. Day, P. D. Moxon, and R. R. Ward, *Chem. Commun.* p. 786 (1975).
62. P. Beak and W. Messer, *Tetrahedron* **25**, 3287 (1969).
63. J. Grimshaw and D. Mannus, *J. Chem. Soc., Perkin Trans. 1* p. 2096 (1977).
64. C. J. Michejda, *Tetrahedron Lett.* p. 2281 (1968).
65. T. Matsuura and Y. Ito, *Tetrahedron* **31**, 1245 (1975).
66. N. Ishibe and J. Masui, *J. Am. Chem. Soc.* **95**, 3396 (1973).
67. N. Ishibe and J. Masui, *J. Am. Chem. Soc.* **96**, 1152 (1974).
68. A. Padwa, P. Sackman, E. Shefter, and E. Vega, *Chem. Commun.* p. 680 (1972).
69. A. G. Anastassiou, S. W. Eachus, R. L. Elliott, and E. Yakali, *Chem. Commun.* p. 531 (1972).
70. H. Kato, M. Kawamura, and T. Shiba, *Chem. Commun.* p. 959 (1970).
71. R. M. Kellogg, *J. Am. Chem. Soc.* **93**, 2344 (1971).
72. R. M. Kellogg and W. L. Prins, *J. Org. Chem.* **39**, 2366 (1974).
73. H. A. Wiebe, S. Braslavsky, and J. Heicklen, *Can. J. Chem.* **50**, 2721 (1972).
74. Y. Kobayashi, I. Kumadaki, A. Ohsawa, and Y. Sekine, *Tetrahedron Lett.* p. 2841 (1974).
75. A. Padwa, D. Crumrine, and A. Shubber, *J. Am. Chem. Soc.* **88**, 3064 (1966).
76. U. Jacobsson, T. Kempe, and T. Norin, *J. Org. Chem.* **39**, 2722 (1974).
77. N. Ishibe and M. Odani, *Chem. Commun.* p. 702 (1971).
77a. P. J. Kropp, *Org. Photochem.* **1**, 1 (1967).
78. N. Ishibe, M. Odani, and R. Tanuma, *J. Chem. Soc., Perkin Trans. 1* p. 1203 (1972).
79. N. Ishibe and M. Tamura, *Chem. Commun.* p. 48 (1974).
80. A. Padwa and A. Battisti, *J. Am. Chem. Soc.* **94**, 521 (1972).
81. A. Padwa, *Int. J. Sulfur Chem., Part B* **7**, 331 (1972).
82. P. Fowles, M. de Sorgo, A. J. Yarwood, O. P. Strausz, and H. E. Gunning, *J. Am. Chem. Soc.* **89**, 1352 (1967).
83. T. Sato, Y. Goto, T. Tohyama, S. Hayashi, and K. Hata, *Bull. Chem. Soc. Jpn.* **40**, 2975 (1967).
84. T. Fujisawa and T. Kobori, *Japan Kokai* 74/42677; *Chem. Abst.* **81**, 135999 (1974).
85. D. C. Dittmer, G. C. Levy, and G. E. Kuhlmann, *J. Am. Chem. Soc.* **89**, 2793 (1967).
86. D. C. Dittmer, G. E. Kuhlmann, and G. C. Levy, *J. Org. Chem.* **35**, 3676 (1970).
87. T. H. Koch, J. A. Soderquist, and T. H. Kinstle, *J. Am. Chem. Soc.* **96**, 5576 (1974).
88. Y. Nakadaira, S. Kanouchi, and H. Sakurai, *J. Am. Chem. Soc.* **96**, 5623 (1974).
89. H. Sakurai, Y. Kamiyama, and Y. Nakadaira, *J. Am. Chem. Soc.* **98**, 7424 (1976).
90. R. L. Lambert, Jr. and D. Seyferth, *J. Am. Chem. Soc.* **94**, 9246 (1972).

91. M. Ishikawa and M. Kumada, *J. Organomet. Chem.* **81**, C3 (1974).
92. J. Fenwick, G. Frater, K. Ogi, and O. P. Strausz, *J. Am. Chem. Soc.* **95**, 124 (1973), and references cited therein.
93. R. L. Russell and F. S. Rowland, *J. Am. Chem. Soc.* **92**, 7508 (1970).
93a. R. A. Cormier, K. M. Freeman, and D. M. Schnur, *Tetrahedron Lett.* p. 2231 (1977).
93b. A. Krantz and J. Laureni, *J. Am. Chem. Soc.* **99**, 4842 (1977).
94. P. Gilgen, H. Heimgartner, and H. Schmid, *Heterocycles* **6**, 143 (1977).
95. A. Padwa, *Acc. Chem. Res.* **9**, 371 (1976).
96. V. Nair and Ki Hyup Kim, *Heterocycles* **7**, 353 (1977).
97. W. Sieber, P. Gilgen, S. Chaloupka, H. J. Hansen, and H. Schmid, *Helv. Chim. Acta* **56**, 1679 (1973).
98. A. Padwa and S. I. Wetmore, Jr., *J. Org. Chem.* **39**, 1396 (1974).
99. H. Giezendanner, H. Heimgartner, B. Jackson, T. Winkler, H. J. Hansen, and H. Schmid, *Helv. Chim. Acta* **56**, 2611 (1973).
100. A. Orahovats, H. Heimgartner, and H. Schmid, *Helv. Chim. Acta* **57**, 2626 (1974).
101. P. Gilgen, H. J. Hansen, H. Heimgartner, W. Sieber, P. Uebelhart, and H. Schmid, *Helv. Chim. Acta* **58**, 1739 (1975).
102. P. Gilgen, H. Heimgartner, and H. Schmid, *Helv. Chim. Acta* **57**, 1382 (1974).
103. U. Schmid, P. Gilgen, H. Heimgartner, H. J. Hansen, and H. Schmid, *Helv. Chim. Acta* **57**, 1393 (1974).
104. N. Gakis, H. Heimgartner, and H. Schmid, *Helv. Chim. Acta* **57**, 1403 (1974).
105. A. Padwa, M. Dharan, J. Smolanoff, and S. I. Wetmore, *J. Am. Chem. Soc.* **95**, 1945 (1973).
106. E. F. Ullman and B. Singh, *J. Am. Chem. Soc.* **88**, 1844 (1966).
107. B. Singh and E. F. Ullman, *J. Am. Chem. Soc.* **89**, 6911 (1967).
108. B. Singh, A. Zweig, and J. B. Gallivan, *J. Am. Chem. Soc.* **94**, 1199 (1972).
109. M. Ishikawa, T. Fuchikami, and M. Kumada, *J. Am. Chem. Soc.* **99**, 245 (1977).
110. H. Sakurai, Y. Kamiyama, and Y. Nakadaira, *J. Am. Chem. Soc.* **99**, 3879 (1977).
111. G. G. Spence, E. C. Taylor, and O. Buchardt, *Chem. Rev.* **70**, 231 (1970).
112. F. Kröhnke, *Justus Liebigs Ann. Chem.* **604**, 203 (1957).
113. J. S. Splitter and M. Calvin, *J. Org. Chem.* **23**, 651 (1958).
114. W. D. Emmons, *J. Am. Chem. Soc.* **78**, 6208 (1956); **79**, 5739 (1957).
115. R. Bonnett, V. M. Clark, and A. Todd, *J. Chem. Soc.* p. 2102 (1959).
116. J. S. Splitter and M. Calvin, *J. Org. Chem.* **30**, 3427 (1965).
117. K. Shinzawa and I. Tanaka, *J. Phys. Chem.* **68**, 1205 (1964).
118. L. S. Kaminsky and M. Lamchen, *J. Chem. Soc. B* p. 1085 (1968).
119. J. S. Splitter and M. Calvin, *Tetrahedron Lett.* p. 3995 (1970).
120. M. L. Scheinbaum, *Tetrahedron Lett.* p. 4221 (1969).
121. H. Mauser and H. Bokranz, *Z. Naturforsch., Teil B* p. 477 (1969).
122. K. Koyano, H. Suzuki, J. Mori, and I. Tanaka, *Bull. Chem. Soc. Jpn.* **43**, 3582 (1970).
123. M. L. Drullinger, R. W. Shelton, and S. R. Lammert, *J. Heterocycl. Chem.* **13**, 1001 (1976).
124. G. J. Smets and S. C. Matsumoto, *J. Polym. Sci., Polym. Chem. Ed.* **14**, 2983 (1976).
125. L. S. Kaminsky and M. Lamchen, *J. Chem. Soc. C* p. 2295 (1966).
126. L. S. Kaminsky and M. Lamchen, *J. Chem. Soc. C* p. 2128 (1967).
127. D. St. C. Black and K. G. Watson, *Aust. J. Chem.* **26**, 2505 (1973).
127a. D. St. C. Black and A. B. Boscacci, *Chem. Commun.* p. 129 (1974); D. St. C. Black, N. A. Blackman, and A. B. Boscacci, *Tetrahedron Lett.* p. 175 (1978).
128. J. Parello, M. Rivière, E. Desherces, and A. Lattes, *C. R. Hebd. Seances Acad. Sci., Ser. C* p. 1097 (1971).

129. J. S. Splitter, Tah-Mun Su, H. Ono, and M. Calvin, *J. Am. Chem. Soc.* **93**, 4076 (1971).
130. H. Ono, J. S. Splitter, and M. Calvin, *Tetrahedron Lett.* p. 4107 (1973).
131. J. Bjørgo, D. R. Boyd, R. M. Campbell, and D. C. Neill, *Chem. Commun.* p. 162 (1976).
132. J. B. Bapat and D. St. C. Black, *Chem. Commun.* p. 73 (1967).
133. D. R. Boyd and D. C. Neill, *Chem. Commun.* p. 51 (1977).
134. R. Y. Ning, G. F. Field, and L. H. Sternbach, *J. Heterocycl. Chem.* **7**, 475 (1970).
135. H. G. Aurich and U. Grigo, *Chem. Ber.* **109**, 200 (1976).
136. B. Singh, *J. Am. Chem. Soc.* **90**, 3893 (1968).
137. R. Fielden, O. Meth-Cohn, and H. Suschitzky, *J. Chem. Soc., Perkin Trans. 1* p. 702 (1973).
138. D. Döpp, *Tetrahedron Lett.* p. 3215 (1972).
139. D. R. Eckroth, T. H. Kinstle, D. O. De La Cruz, and J. K. Sparacino, *J. Org. Chem.* **36**, 3619 (1971).
140. E. F. Ullman, L. Call, and S. S. Tseng, *J. Am. Chem. Soc.* **95**, 1677 (1973).
141. A. R. Forrester, M. M. Ogilvy, and R. H. Thomson, *Chem. Commun.* p. 483 (1972).
142. F. Bellamy and J. Streith, *Heterocycles* **4**, 1391 (1976).
143. R. Huisgen, R. Grashey, and J. Sauer, *in* "The Chemistry of Alkenes" (S. Patai, ed.), p. 806. Wiley (Interscience), New York, 1964.
144. K. Seibold, G. Wagnière, and H. Labhart, *Helv. Chim. Acta* **52**, 789 (1969).
145. O. Buchardt, P. L. Kumler, and C. Lohse, *Acta Chem. Scand.* **23**, 159 (1969).
146. O. Buchardt, *Tetrahedron Lett.* p. 1911 (1968).
147. P. L. Kumler and O. Buchardt, *Chem. Commun.* p. 1321 (1968).
148. C. Lohse, *J. Chem. Soc., Perkin Trans. 2* p. 229 (1972).
149. I. Ono and N. Hata, *Bull. Chem. Soc. Jpn.* **46**, 3658 (1973).
150. K. B. Tomer, N. Harrit, I. Rosenthal, O. Buchardt, P. L. Kumler, and D. Creed, *J. Am. Chem. Soc.* **95**, 7402 (1973).
151. C. Kaneko, I. Yokoe, and M. Ishikawa, *Tetrahedron Lett.* p. 5237 (1967).
152. F. Roeterdink and H. C. Van der Plas, *J. Chem. Soc., Perkin Trans. 1* p. 1202 (1976).
153. S. Yamada, M. Ishikawa, and C. Kaneko, *Chem. Commun.* p. 1093 (1972).
154. C. W. Rees, R. Somanathan, R. C. Storr, and A. D. Woolhouse, *Chem. Commun.* p. 740 (1975).
155. J. Streith and C. Sigwalt, *Tetrahedron Lett.* p. 1347 (1966).
156. J. Streith and C. Sigwalt, *Bull. Soc. Chim. Fr.* p. 2180 (1969).
157. O. Buchardt, *Acta Chem. Scand.* **17**, 1461 (1963).
158. M. Ishikawa, S. Yamada, H. Hotta, and C. Kaneko, *Chem. Pharm. Bull.* **14**, 1102 (1966).
159. C. Kaneko and S. Yamada, *Chem. Pharm. Bull.* **15**, 663 (1967).
160. O. Buchardt, C. L. Pedersen, and N. Harrit, *J. Org. Chem.* **37**, 3592 (1972).
161. M. Ishikawa, C. Kaneko, I. Yokoe, and S. Yamada, *Tetrahedron* **25**, 295 (1969).
162. O. Buchardt, C. Lohse, A. M. Duffield, and C. Djerassi, *Tetrahedron Lett.* p. 2741 (1967).
163. C. Kaneko, S. Yamada, and M. Ishikawa, *Tetrahedron Lett.* p. 2145 (1966).
164. O. Simonsen, C. Lohse, and O. Buchardt, *Acta Chem. Scand.* **24**, 268 (1970).
165. O. Buchardt, P. L. Kumler, and C. Lohse, *Acta Chem. Scand.* **23**, 2149 (1969).
166. J. H. Amin and P. de Mayo, *Tetrahedron Lett.* p. 1585 (1963); cf. H. Izawa, P. de Mayo, and T. Tabata, *Can. J. Chem.* **47**, 51 (1969).
167. G. Just and L. S. Ng Lim, *Can. J. Chem.* **46**, 3381 (1968).
168. M. Cunningham, L. S. Ng Lim, and G. Just, *Can. J. Chem.* **49**, 2891 (1971).
169. G. Just and M. Cunningham, *Tetrahedron Lett.* p. 1151 (1972).

170. T. Oine and T. Mukai, *Tetrahedron Lett.* p. 157 (1969).
171. H. Suginome, H. Takahashi, and T. Masamune, *Bull. Chem. Soc. Jpn.* **45**, 1836 (1972).
172. H. Suginome and T. Uchida, *Tetrahedron Lett.* p. 2293 (1973).
173. H. Suginome and H. Takahashi, *Bull. Chem. Soc. Jpn.* **48**, 576 (1975); H. Suginome and F. Yagihashi, *J. Chem. Soc., Perkin Trans. 1* p. 2488 (1977).
174. Y. Kobayashi, *Bull. Chem. Soc. Jpn.* **46**, 3467 (1973).
175. A. C. Ghosh and W. Korytnyk, *Tetrahedron Lett.* p. 4049 (1974).
176. P. Margaretha, *Tetrahedron Lett.* p. 4205 (1974); R. Okazaki, M. Watanabe, and N. Inamoto, *Tetrahedron Lett.* p. 4515 (1977).
177. E. Desherces, M. Rivière, J. Parello, and A. Lattes, *C. R. Hebd. Seances Acad. Sci., Ser. C* p. 581 (1972).
178. E. Oliveros-Desherces, M. Rivière, J. Parello, and A. Lattes, *Tetrahedron Lett.* p. 851 (1975).
179. F. A. Davis and U. K. Nadir, *Tetrahedron Lett.* p. 1721 (1977).
180. B. Schilling and J. P. Snyder, *J. Am. Chem. Soc.* **97**, 4422 (1975).
181. S. T. Reid and J. N. Tucker, *Chem. Commun.* p. 1286 (1970).
182. M. G. Pleiss and J. A. Moore, *J. Am. Chem. Soc.* **90**, 4738 (1968).
183. M. Schultz and G. West, *J. Prakt. Chem.* **312**, 161 (1970).
184. M. Schultz and G. West, *J. Prakt. Chem.* **315**, 711 (1973).
185. M. Schultz, G. West, U. Mueller, and D. Henke, *J. Prakt. Chem.* **318**, 946 (1976).
186. Y. Maki, M. Kawamura, H. Okamoto, M. Suzuki, and K. Kaji, *Chem. Lett.* p. 1005 (1977).
187. R. Y. Ning, J. F. Blount, W. Y. Chen, and P. B. Madan, *J. Org. Chem.* **40**, 2201 (1975).
188. H. J. Timpe, *Adv. Heterocycl. Chem.* **17**, 213 (1974).
189. R. Huisgen, R. Grashey, and R. Krischke, *Justus Liebigs Ann. Chem.* **3**, 506 (1977).
190. M. Nastasi, *Heterocycles* **4**, 1509 (1976), and references cited therein.
191. J. Streith and J. M. Cassal, *Bull. Soc. Chim. Fr.* p. 2175 (1969).
192. J. Streith, J. P. Luttringer, and M. Nastasi, *J. Org. Chem.* **36**, 2962 (1971).
193. M. Nastasi, H. Strub, and J. Streith, *Tetrahedron Lett.* p. 4719 (1976).
194. V. Snieckus and G. Kan, *Chem. Commun.* p. 172 (1970).
195. K. T. Potts and R. Dugas, *Chem. Commun.* p. 732 (1970).
196. G. Kan, M. T. Thomas, and V. Snieckus, *Chem. Commun.* p. 1022 (1971).
197. M. Nastasi and J. Streith, *Bull. Soc. Chim. Fr.* p. 630 (1973).
198. A. Balasubramanian, J. M. McIntosh, and V. Snieckus, *J. Org. Chem.* **35**, 433 (1970).
199. R. A. Abramovitch and T. Takaya, *J. Org. Chem.* **38**, 3311 (1973).
200. A. Frankowski and J. Streith, *Tetrahedron* **33**, 427 (1977).
201. J. Streith and J. L. Schuppiser, *Tetrahedron Lett.* p. 4859 (1976).
202. Y. Tamura, H. Ishibashi, N. Tsujimoto, and M. Ikeda, *Chem. Pharm. Bull.* **19**, 1285 (1971).
203. Y. Tamura, S. Matsugashita, H. Ishibashi, and M. Ikeda, *Tetrahedron* **29**, 2359 (1973).
204. J. Becher and C. Lohse, *Acta Chem. Scand.* **26**, 4041 (1972).
205. T. Shiba, K. Yamana, and H. Kato, *Chem. Commun.* p. 1592 (1970).
206. T. Tsuchiya, J. Kurita, and V. Snieckus, *J. Org. Chem.* **42**, 1856 (1977).
207. J. Fetter, K. Lempert, J. Møller, and G. Szalai, *Tetrahedron Lett.* p. 2775 (1975).
208. T. Tsuchiya, J. Kurita, and K. Ogawa, *Chem. Commun.* p. 250 (1976).
209. H. Suginome and T. Uchida, *Tetrahedron Lett.* p. 2289 (1973).
210. R. Grigg, J. Kemp, and N. Thompson, *Tetrahedron Lett.* p. 2827 (1978).
211. C. H. Krauch, J. Kuhls, and H. J. Piek, *Tetrahedron Lett.* p. 4043 (1966).
212. C. S. Angadiyavar and M. V. George, *J. Org. Chem.* **36**, 1589 (1971).
213. H. Gotthardt and F. Reiter, *Tetrahedron Lett.* p. 2749 (1971).

214. M. Märky, H. J. Hansen, and H. Schmid, *Helv. Chim. Acta* **54**, 1275 (1971).
215. M. Märky, H. Meier, A. Wunderli, H. Heimgartner, and H. Schmid, *Helv. Chim. Acta* **61**, 1477 (1978).
216. H. Kato, T. Shiba, H. Yoshida, and S. Fujimori, *Chem. Commun.* p. 1591 (1970).
217. H. Gotthardt, *Chem. Ber.* **105**, 188 (1972).
218. H. Gotthardt, *Tetrahedron Lett.* p. 1277 (1971).
219. A. Holm, N. Harrit, K. Bechgaard, O. Buchardt, and S. E. Harnung, *Chem. Commun.* p. 1125 (1972).
220. I. R. Dunkin, M. Poliakoff, J. J. Turner, N. Harrit, and A. Holm, *Tetrahedron Lett.* p. 873 (1976).
221. W. Kirmse, "Carbene, Carbenoide und Carbenanaloge," Chemische Taschenbücher 7. Verlag Chemie, Weinheim, 1969.
222. R. A. Franich, G. Lowe, and J. Parker, *J. Chem. Soc., Perkin Trans. 1* p. 2034 (1972).
223. E. Voigt and H. Meier, *Chem. Ber.* **108**, 3326 (1975).
224. T. Miyashi, T. Nakajo, and T. Mukai, *Chem. Commun.* p. 442 (1978).
225. O. L. Chapman, C. C. Chang, J. Kolc, M. E. Jung, J. A. Lowe, T. J. Barton, and M. L. Tumey, *J. Am. Chem. Soc.* **98**, 7844 (1976).
226. M. R. Chedekel, M. Skoglund, R. L. Kreeger, and H. Shechter, *J. Am. Chem. Soc.* **98**, 7846 (1976).
227. N. J. Bunce, J. P. Schoch, and M. C. Zerner, *J. Am. Chem. Soc.* **99**, 7986 (1977).
228. H. Mauser, G. Gauglitz, and F. Stier, *Justus Liebigs Ann. Chem.* **739**, 84 (1970).
229. S. S. Hecht and F. D. Greene, *J. Am. Chem. Soc.* **89**, 6761 (1967).
230. F. D. Greene and S. S. Hecht, *J. Org. Chem.* **35**, 2482 (1970).
231. J. Swigert and K. G. Taylor, *J. Am. Chem. Soc.* **93**, 7337 (1971).
232. K. G. Taylor, S. R. Isaac, and J. L. Swigert, *J. Org. Chem.* **41**, 1146 (1976).
233. K. G. Taylor and T. Riehl, *J. Am. Chem. Soc.* **94**, 250 (1972).
234. M. P. Servé, W. A. Feld, P. G. Seybold, and R. N. Steppel, *J. Heterocycl. Chem.* **12**, 811 (1975).
235. H. P. Braun, K. P. Zeller, and H. Meier, *Justus Liebigs Ann. Chem.* p. 1257 (1975).
236. The support of the Centre National de la Recherche Scientifique is gratefully acknowledged.

ESSAY **22** | # PHOTOCHEMICAL REARRANGEMENTS OF FIVE-MEMBERED RING HETEROCYCLES

ALBERT PADWA

I. INTRODUCTION

Considerable attention has been focused in recent years on the photochemistry of five-membered heterocyclic ring systems. By far the greatest area of activity in this field has been a study of photoisomerizations that result in a change of the heterocyclic nucleus. Indeed, this aspect has

REARRANGEMENTS IN GROUND AND EXCITED STATES, VOL. 3

been the subject of earlier reviews, to which the reader is referred for additional references and background (1–3). The purpose of this essay is to provide an indication of the wide diversity of transformations that five-membered heterocycles undergo upon electronic excitation. The literature coverage is not exhaustive, and in many cases arbitrary decisions on the degree of coverage have been made. Examples that illustrate specific problems or provide special insight concerning mechanism have been selected.

Since there have been numerous investigations of the mechanism of these photorearrangements, we begin the discussion with an outline of the routes that have been observed or proposed. Five major mechanisms have been suggested to rationalize many of the photorearrangements that are discussed in the subsequent sections.

II. MECHANISTIC POSSIBILITIES FOR PHOTOISOMERIZATION OF FIVE-MEMBERED HETEROCYCLES

A. *Mechanism I: Ring Contraction–Ring Expansion Route*

Mechanism I is an attractive route to explain the interchange of the positions of two ring atoms of a number of heterocycles. Absorption of light leads to cleavage of the weakest of the single bonds in the ring. The intermediate so formed closes to a three-membered ring, which, on further excitation, affords the rearranged product.*

As will be noted in the sections dealing with specific reactions, mechanism I is well established as one of the chief routes by which five-

---

* For a discussion of three-membered heterocycles, see Essay 21.

membered ring heterocycles undergo valence rearrangement. The process was first demonstrated for the photorearrangement of 3,5-diarylisoxazoles to 2,5-diaryloxazoles (4).

B. Mechanism II: Internal Cyclization–Isomerization Route

The photoisomerization of a number of five-membered ring heterocycles does not appear to follow the ring contraction–ring expansion sequence. An alternative pathway for rearrangement was initially proposed (5) to account for the formal interchange of the 2 and 4 positions of N-methyldiazoles. This mechanism involves an initial disrotatory formation of a bicyclic isomer, followed by a [1,3] sigmatropic shift to a second bicyclic isomer, which then undergoes a subsequent disrotatory ring opening to the rearranged product.

These transformations are allowed as concerted photochemical processes in systems having appropriate symmetry according to the Woodward–Hoffmann rules (6). Analogies for this sequence can be found in the photochemistry of benzene (7), pyrazolenines (8), cyclopentadiene (9), and other carbocycles (10). The [1,3] sigmatropic shift may terminate at either position 3 (Z atom) or 4 (C atom) to give either bicyclic isomer 6 or 5. Termination at both positions is possible to give rearranged heterocycles 7 and/or 8. The observed regioselectivity can be attributed to the preferred formation of the more stable bicyclic isomer. This mechanism has been suggested to occur in a variety of five-membered ring heterocyclic systems.

C. Mechanism III: Van Tamelen–Whitesides General Mechanism

A general mechanistic proposal to account for the photorearrangement of all five-membered heteroaromatic compounds has been made by van Tamelen and Whitesides (11). This involves initial cleavage of the weakest single bond to form a cyclopropene or its heterocyclic analogue (2) in equilibrium with a bicyclic isomer (9), as shown below, thus accounting for the interchange of the 2 and 4 positions of the ring. In several of the heteroaromatic systems examined (12,13) the formation of cumulenes suggests the development of considerable free valence during the reaction. This competing process can be attributed to migration of a substituent at the diradical stage to afford a cumulene or triple bond.

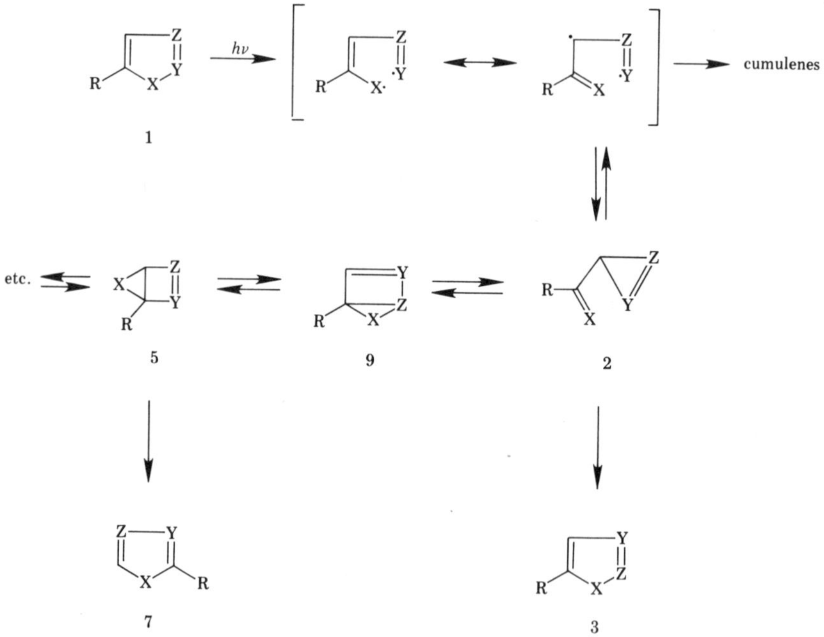

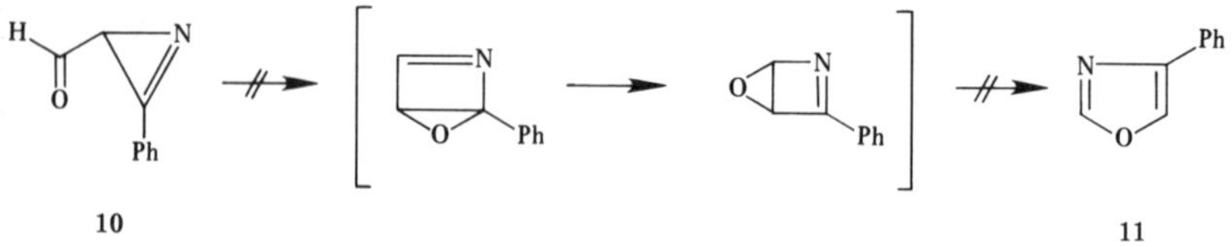

This scheme, which is a composite of the two previously outlined mechanisms, does not operate with all the five-membered ring systems studied. For example, azirine 10 cannot be in equilibrium with the bicyclic isomer because this azirine is characterized by its complete resistance to conversion to oxazole **11** (*14,15*). The only product obtained on irradiation of **10** was oxazole **12**, derived by cyclization of a transient nitrile ylide. (*14*).

D. Mechanism IV: Zwitterion–Tricyclic Route

Another mechanism, initially proposed (*16*) to rationalize the very complex rearrangements of the thiophene ring system, involves valence shell expansion of a sulfur atom. According to this mechanism the sulfur 3d orbitals are allowed to interact with the neighboring double bond to give a tricyclic zwitterion, which subsequently collapses to the rearranged product. A related tricyclic sulfonium cation intermediate has also been suggested to account for the products formed on irradiation of phenyltriazoles (17).

The observation that the rate of rearrangement of these sulfur heterocycles increases in polar media has been used in support of this hypothesis (16). A more recent version of this mechanism suggests that excitation of the five-membered ring sulfur heterocycle results in a drastic geometric distortion of the ring (18). It was proposed that the molecule in the excited state adopts a conformation in which three atoms remain in the same plane while the remaining two atoms are wrenched 90° out of the plane. It was suggested that the resulting geometry provides a significant degree of stabilization in the excited state. There is still much controversy regarding this mechanism.

E. Mechanism V: Fragmentation–Readdition Route

The photochemical rearrangement of oxadiazoles (19) as well as a number of dihydro aromatic compounds (20,21) can best be rationalized in terms of a fragmentation–readdition. A major characteristic of this route is that the yield of product is significantly enhanced when the irradiation of

starting material is carried out in the presence of excess nitrile. Further evidence for the existence of this pathway is provided by the trapping of the initially produced 1,3 dipole with an added dipolarophile.

It should be noted that the phototranspositions encountered with any given heterocyclic ring system can occur by more than one pathway. Other mechanisms have also been proposed to account for particular transformations and not as general processes.

III. FIVE-MEMBERED RING SYSTEMS WITH ONE HETEROATOM

A. Furans

The phototransformations of furans have been independently studied by Srinivasan (22) and by van Tamelen (11,23) and shown to proceed via a ring contraction–ring expansion route (mechanism I). 2-Methyl- (20) and 2,5-dimethylfuran (21) photoisomerize to 3-methyl- (22) and 2,4-dimethylfuran (23), respectively (22). The photorearrangement proceeds via an initial valence tautomerization to a cyclopropene ring followed by ring expansion. Support for a ring-contracted species was obtained by the

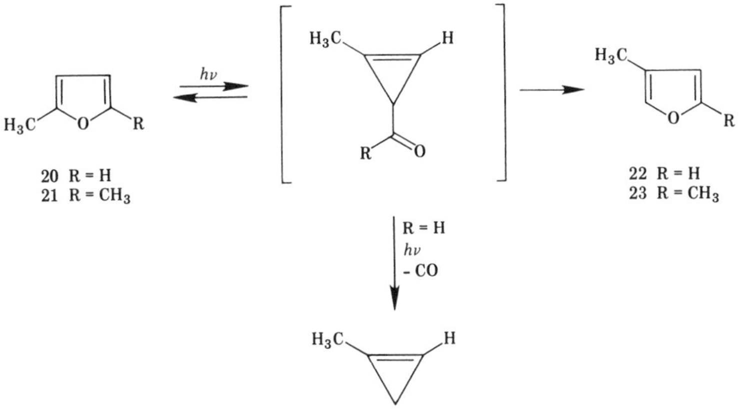

20 R = H
21 R = CH₃

22 R = H
23 R = CH₃

R = H
hν
- CO

24

isolation of cyclopropene 24, which was suggested to be derived by loss of carbon monoxide from a transient cyclopropenecarboxyaldehyde. In fact, when the 2 and 5 positions of the furan ring were substituted with alkyl groups, the ring-contracted product was sufficiently stable to be isolated.

The photolysis of a series of *t*-butyl-substituted furans was studied in detail by van Tamelen and Whitesides (11,23). The results were also rationalized in terms of a mechanism involving C—O cleavage in the excited state to give a diradical intermediate that closed to give either a cyclopropene or the starting furan.

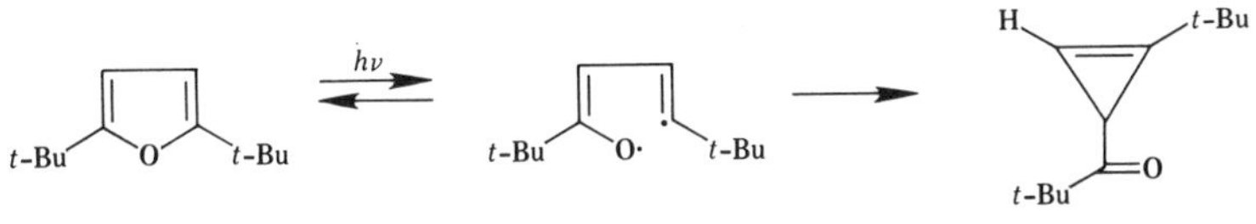

25

26

The absorption of a second photon of light by the cyclopropene could lead to a number of different intermediates, depending on which bond in the three-membered ring broke (24) and which conformation the oxygen atom assumed in the intermediate. If the oxygen atom were trans to the vinyl radical center, closure to a furan would be unlikely for steric reasons. For example, in structure 28, stabilization of the diradical can be achieved only by migration of a hydrogen atom to give the allenyl ketone 29.

The results obtained on photolysis of 2,4-di-t-butylfuran (27) reveal that the reaction is highly selective. Cleavage of the cyclopropene ring occurs on the side of the ring with the greater substitution at the α position.

The photochemistry of 2,3,5-tri-*t*-butylfuran (**32**) was also explained in terms of the ring contraction–ring expansion mechanism. The two cleavage reactions afforded intermediates **33** and **34**, which closed to cyclopropenes **35** and **36**, respectively.

Further excitation of cyclopropene **36** results in an intramolecular hydrogen abstraction to give diradical **37**, which subsequently cyclizes to give bicyclic ketone **38**. This type of intramolecular hydrogen abstraction has been noted with related systems that possess substituents bearing γ-hydrogens in the 3 position of the cyclopropene ring (*25*). The unusual

photochemical behavior encountered with cyclopropene **36** is probably related to the fact that this compound has the *t*-butyl group on the carbonyl group in close proximity to the excited double bond. This is undoubtedly due to the strain that would result in eclipsing two *t*-butyl groups in conformation **36a**. Since cyclopropene **36** does not exist in the proper cisoid conformation required for furan formation, intramolecular hydrogen abstraction becomes the dominant reaction.

The mercury-sensitized photolysis of 2,5-dimethylfuran was studied (22) and found to be a rather complex process leading to a number of products, among which was 4-methylcyclopent-2-enone (41). With this system, opening of the furan ring leads to a vinyl carbene, which can insert into a C—H bond of the neighboring methyl group. This result tends to suggest that vinylcarbenes are transient intermediates in the formation of cyclopropenes.

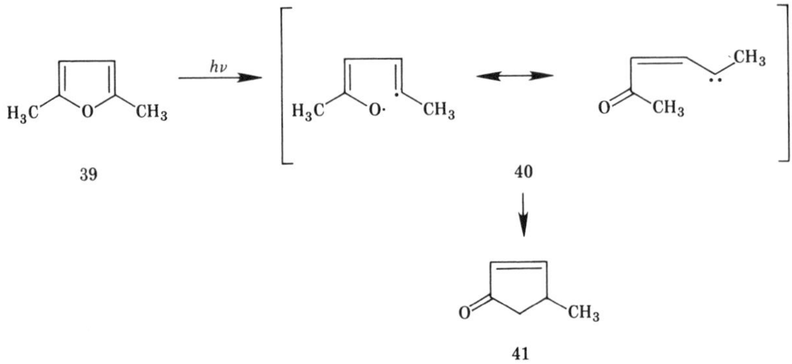

Hiraoka (26) predicted the most probable cyclopropenes to be formed from substituted furans, and Couture and Lablache-Combier (27,28) succeeded in trapping the intermediate cyclopropenes with propylamine, as shown below. The results obtained are compatible with calculations (26),

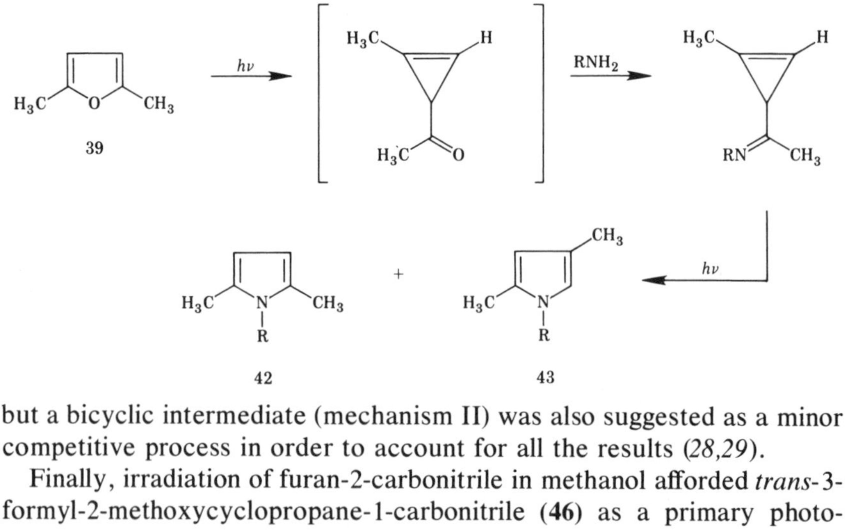

but a bicyclic intermediate (mechanism II) was also suggested as a minor competitive process in order to account for all the results (28,29).

Finally, irradiation of furan-2-carbonitrile in methanol afforded *trans*-3-formyl-2-methoxycyclopropane-1-carbonitrile (46) as a primary photoproduct, thereby establishing that a photochemical ring contraction route operates with this system (30).

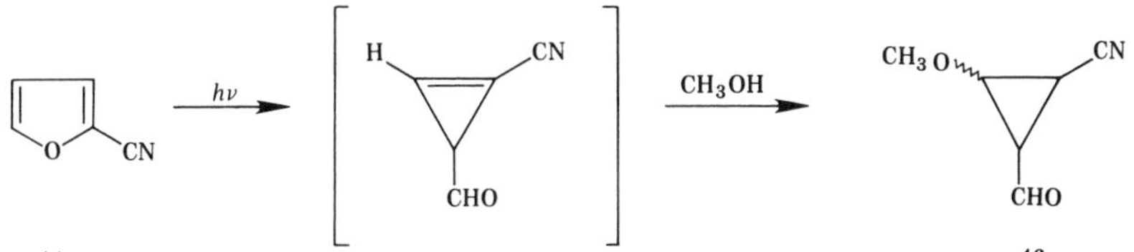

B. Pyrroles

Photoisomerizations involving transfer of a substituent from the 2 position to the 3 position have also been observed in the pyrrole series (31,32). Hiroaka was the first to show that 2-cyanopyrrole and its N-methyl analogue (47) rearrange, on UV excitation, to the corresponding 3-cyano isomer (48).

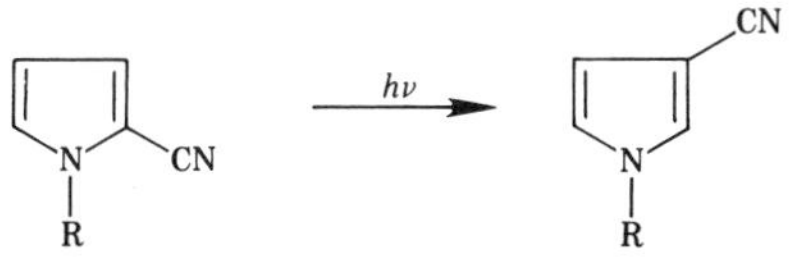

Similar results were reported (32) for pyrroles 49–51. The mechanism suggested to account for these results involves 2,5 bonding to give 56 as a

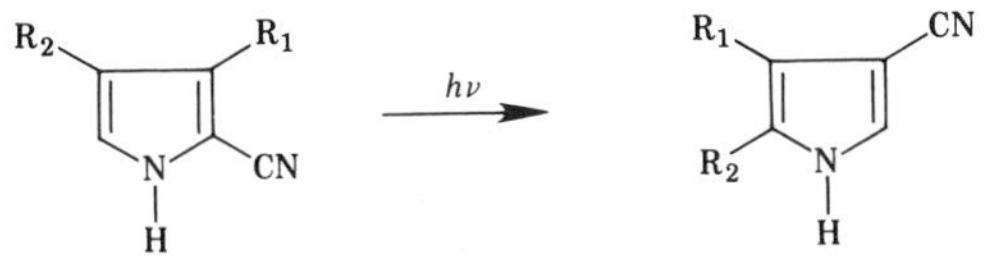

49 R_1 = CH$_3$; R_2 = H
50 R_1 = H; R_2 = CH$_3$

52 R_1 = CH$_3$; R_2 = H
53 R_1 = H; R_2 = CH$_3$

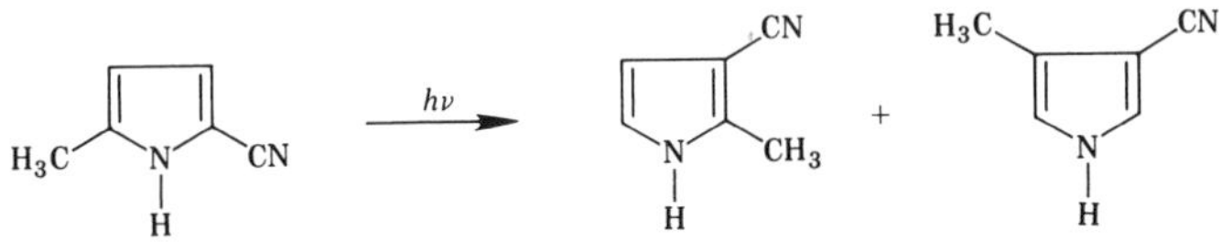

51

54(major)

55(minor)

transient intermediate, followed by a [1,3] sigmatropic shift of the nitrogen atom to give 57, which can then aromatize to pyrrole 54. The isolation of pyrrole **55** from the irradiation of **51** is readily accommodated by this mechanism if it is assumed that a small amount of **57** undergoes another [1,3] sigmatropic shift to **58** before aromatizing. The suggestion that 2,5 bonding in excited (π,π^*) pyrrole initiates the transposition is supported by a correlation diagram and has additional experimental support from the trapping of an azabicyclopentene intermediate with methanol. The initial work suggested **59** as the structure of the photoadduct (*30*). However,

subsequent studies (*33*) showed that azabicyclopentane **60** is the correct structure of the photoadduct. The genesis of adduct **60** is most simply understood as involving nucleophilic attack of methanol on the α,β-unsaturated nitrile function in the pyrrole valence tautomer **62**. Related trapping experiments with furan afforded additional evidence for the intermediacy of azabicyclopentene **62**; thus, irradiation of **47** in furan afforded Diels–Alder cycloadducts **63** and **64**.

The formation of azabicyclopentene **62** apparently involves a thermally activated step since irradiation of **47** at $-68°C$ yielded no detectable transposition product. If, as seems probable, the 2,5-bonded species **61** is the precursor of **62**, the temperature effect suggests that the thermal reversion of **61** to **47** has a lower activation energy than the isomerization to **62**. Further evidence regarding this point was obtained by studying the thermolysis of the furan photoadduct (**65**) derived from 2-cyano-5-methyl-pyrrole (**51**); cyanopyrroles **51**, **54**, **55**, and **49** were obtained in a ratio of 4:6:2:1. The results have been explained by assuming that the thermal retrogression of **65** yields **57**, which in turn gives access to the three isomeric azabicyclopentenes **56, 58,** and **66** that can be derived from **57** by one or more nitrogen "walk" steps. As the temperature is lowered, "walking" of the aziridine ring becomes progressively less favorable relative to aromatization. At 30°C, the formation of a photo-product requiring more than a single "walk" step is rare, and when such scrambling is observed (i.e., **51** → **55**) it is a relatively minor pathway.

Finally, it is interesting that the pyrrole ring system, which is very similar to furan in its ground state reactions, follows a distinctly different mechanism for ring transposition in the excited state.

C. Thiophenes

The photoisomerization of thiophenes has been studied in great detail (*16,34–40*). Probably the most extensively studied substrate is 2-phenylthiophene, which upon irradiation isomerizes to 3-phenylthiophene (*35*). Irradiation of deuterium-labeled 2-phenylthiophene (**67**) not only resulted in deuterium scrambling at all possible ring positions, but the recovered starting material was also found to have undergone deuterium scrambling (*36*). From these results it was obvious that a rather complex reaction had taken place. Carbon-14 labeling experiments showed that the phenyl group remains attached to the original carbon atom in the thiophene nucleus. These results led to the conclusion that the sequential order of the carbon atoms in the thiophene ring had changed during the rearrangement. A number of possible mechanisms have been proposed to rationalize the rearrangement patterns. One path involves the initial formation of a "valene" thiophene (**68**) followed by collapse to a symmetric Ladenburg structure (**69**). The observed specificity of the rearrangement, however, is inconsistent with the predicted symmetry of a valene intermediate.

A path (mechanism IV) has been proposed in which the sulfur 3d orbitals are allowed to interact with the neighboring double bond to give tricyclic zwitterion **70**, which subsequently collapses to the rearranged product (*16*).

Although this mechanism can account for the rearrangements that interchange an α- and β-carbon atom in the thiophene ring, the major aspects of the 3-phenylthiophene rearrangement are unexplained in terms of this pathway.

Instead, a third pathway (mechanism III) has been proposed (*11*) which would explain the majority of results encountered with the thiophene rearrangement if the following assumptions were made: (a) Dewar structures and cyclopropenylthiocarbonyls (71) are in equilibrium, and (b) in

the formation of a given cyclopropene, the ring contraction takes place in such a fashion as to place the phenyl group on the double bond of the cyclopropene. Although the requirements of the second assumption are not always adhered to, it does account for the major products of the photoreaction. Support for the contraction–expansion mechanism was found (27,41) in the formation of pyrroles from a series of thiophenes when the latter were irradiated in the presence of amines. The products were analogous to those formed under similar conditions in the irradiation of furans (27,28).

It should also be noted that a bicyclic species like that proposed in mechanism II has been isolated from the photolysis of tetra(trifluoromethyl)thiophene (73), additional support thus being provided for this pathway (42).

At present the mechanism of these interesting rearrangements has not been completely resolved. It seems highly likely that a crossover directly from the excited state hypersurface to the ground state hypersurface occurs. With certain systems ground state cyclopropenes or bicyclic species can be intermediates, whereas in other cases such species may not be involved. The phototranspositions appear to fall between furan and pyrrole photorearrangements: The irreversibility of rearrangement, retention of structural integrity of the migrating substituent, and failure to isolate intermediates are trademarks of the thiophene photorearrangement. The available data still do not allow a choice between intermediates **70** and **71**. As pointed out (*34*), however, the choice may be academic, since **70** and **71** could easily be two equivalent graphic representations of the same excited state intermediate.

Finally, it should be noted that a significant deviation in the photobehavior of the thiophene system was encountered on irradiation of dithienyl **75**. The rearrangement of 2,5′-dideuterio-2,3′-dithienyl (**75**) to chiefly 4,7-dideuteriobenzo[*b*]thiophene (**76**) must involve a complicated reorganization of atoms (40). A possible mechanism consistent with the dueterium labeling results is outlined below.

IV. FIVE-MEMBERED RING SYSTEMS WITH TWO HETEROATOMS

A. Isoxazoles

Many examples of the photorearrangement of isoxazoles have been reported in the literature, and much effort has been directed toward understanding the mechanism of this process. The occurrence of a ring contraction–ring expansion route in this heterocyclic system was first demonstrated for the photorearrangement of 3,5-diphenylisoxazole (77) to 2,5-diphenyloxazole (79) (4,43). The rearrangement was shown to pro-

ceed in two photochemical steps by way of an isolable 3-benzoyl-2-phenylazirine (78) intermediate. The photochemical behavior of the azirine was markedly dependent on the wavelength of the light used. With 313 nm or shorter-wavelength light, the azirine rearranged almost quantitatively to the oxazole ring, whereas 334 nm or longer-wavelength light caused nearly exclusive rearrangement back to the starting isoxazole. Sensitization data suggest the intermediacy of a triplet state of the azirine in the formation of the isoxazole ring. On the other hand, oxazole formation occurred from the electronically excited singlet state of the azirine. It was suggested that the two independent chromophores present in 78 are excited selectively with the different wavelengths of light used. Thus, the formation of isoxazole 77 may occur via the $^3(n,\pi^*)$ state of the carbonyl chromophore, which in turn may be excited selectively with 334 nm light. Irradiation with 313 nm or shorter-wavelength light causes selective excitation to the n,π^* level of the ketimine chromophore, which is known to induce C—C cleavage of the azirine ring (14). Formation of oxazole 79 can be readily rationalized by cyclization of the initially produced nitrile ylide 80.

A similar wavelength effect was encountered with the related 3-naphthoyl-2-phenylazirine system (44) and provides additional support for the contention that the higher energy state associated with the nitrogen

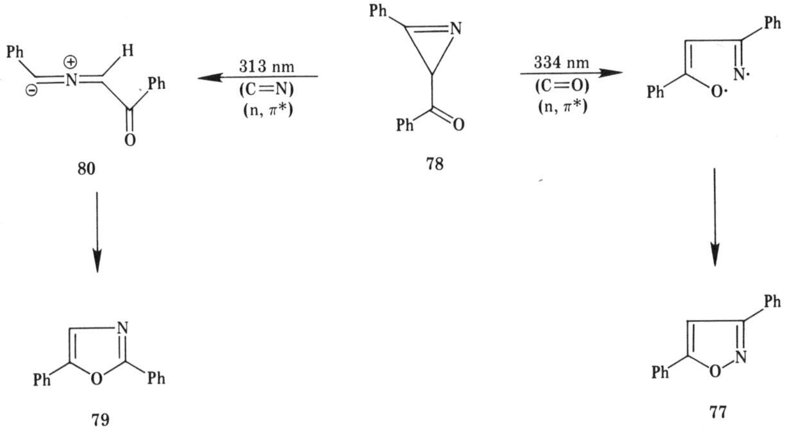

80   78

79   77

n, π^* transition leads to azirine C—C cleavage, whereas the lower energy state associated with the carbonyl n, π^* transition causes reorganization to the isoxazole ring.

A large variety of related isoxazoles have also been examined photochemically, and with few exceptions they undergo isomerization to an azirine. In many cases the azirines were stable enough to be isolated, although they frequently reacted further to give rearranged products. Thus, the photolysis of 3,4,5-triphenylisoxazole (**81**), besides forming azirine **82**, also gave oxazole **83** and ketenimine **84** (*45*).

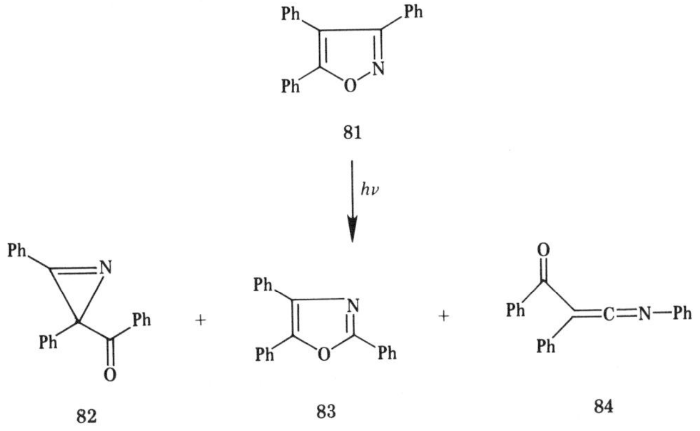

81

$h\nu$

82   83   84

Azirine formation was also observed in the irradiation of 3-aryl-5-aminoisoxazoles **85** (*46*) and **89** (*47*) and was suggested to be a transient species in the photorearrangements of isoxazoles **91** (*48*), **94** (*49*), and **97** (*50*).

3-Hydroxyisoxazoles (**100**) are converted to 2(3*H*)-oxazolones (**102**) upon irradiation, probably via the intermediacy of **101** (*51,52*).

The photorearrangement of 3,5-disubstituted 4-acetylisoxazoles was studied independently by two groups (*53,54*). Both found that the photolysis of **103** produced 2,5-dimethyl-4-acetyloxazole (**104**) as the exclusive photoproduct. Similar results were obtained with isoxazole **105**.

Irradiation of 4-trideuterioacetyl-5-methyl-3-phenylisoxazole (**107**) resulted in the scrambling of the deuteriomethyl group. In addition, a 1 : 1 mixture of oxazoles **109** and **110** was produced (*54*). The most probable mechanism for the photochemical transformation of this system is out-

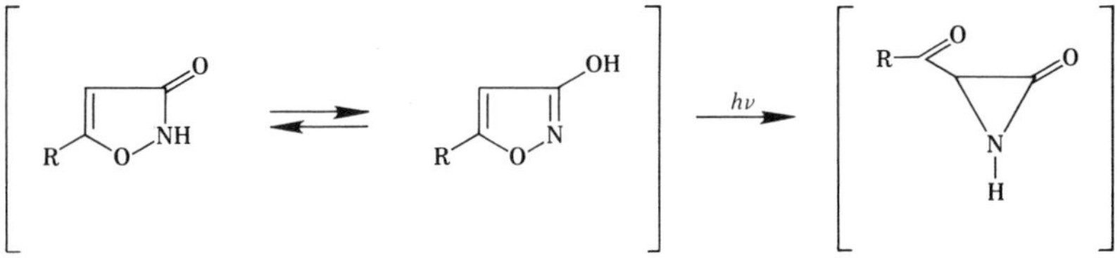

100   101

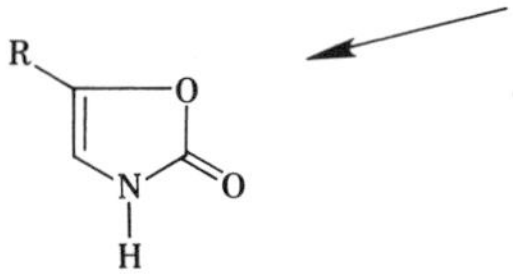

102

lined below. The key steps involve ring contraction to a 2*H*-azirine intermediate, followed by ring opening to a nitrile ylide (**111**), which subsequently cyclizes to produce the oxazole ring.

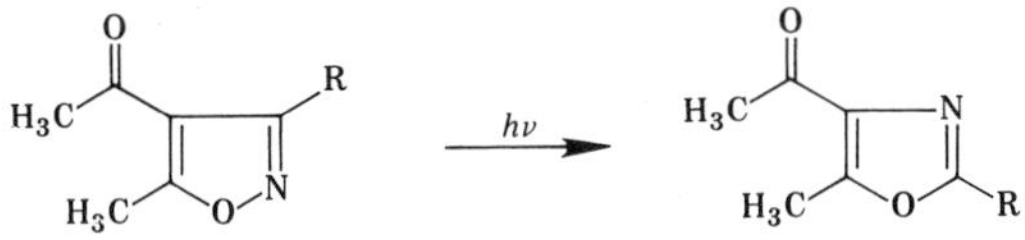

103 R = CH₃   104 R = CH₃
105 R = Ph   106 R = Ph

In contrast to the 5-methyl-substituted isoxazole system **107**, irradiation
of 3,5-diphenyl-4-acetylisoxazole (**112**) produced 3-phenyl-4-benzoyl-5-
methylisoxazole (**113**) as the only primary photoproduct. On further

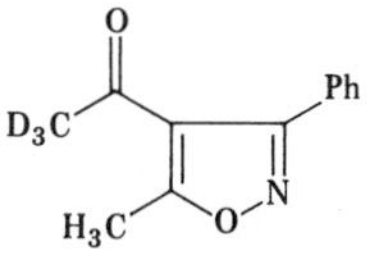

107

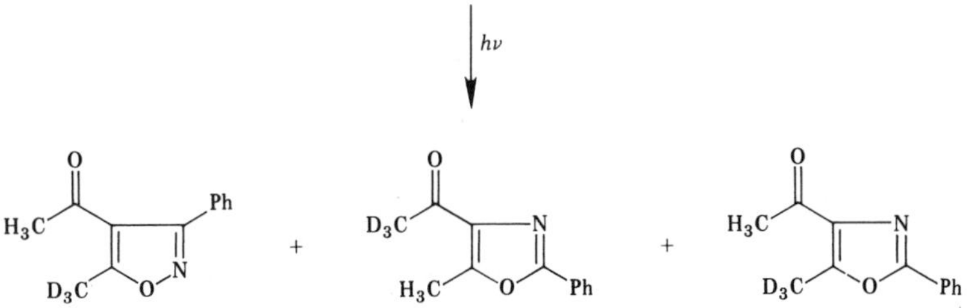

108   109   110

irradiation this material rearranged exclusively to 2,5-diphenyl-4-ace-
tyloxazole (114). The most striking aspect of this system is the product
specificity. One possible explanation for this result is to assume that
irradiation of 113 leads to azirine 115, which preferentially rearranges
to oxazole 114. This rationale would require a significant difference in
the activation energy of closure of the diradicals produced from the
azirine intermediate.

Subsequent work by this author showed that the exclusive formation of oxazole **114** could not be reconciled with a 2*H*-azirine intermediate (i.e., **115**). The results were rationalized in terms of a mechanism involving O—N bond cleavage, followed by a 1,2 carbon–nitrogen shift (*54*). In the π,π^* excited state, the isoxazole chromophore will have considerable charge-transfer character, as is represented by the valence-bond structure **117**. Cleavage of the O—N bond in this excited state will result in the formation of an electron-deficient nitrogen atom. A 1,2 carbon–nitrogen shift is the most obvious low-energy path available to the π,π^* state, and this will result in the formation of zwitterion **118**. Recombination of the two reactive centers in **118** affords oxazole **114**. Zwitterion **118** has the proper cisoid conformation of the oxygen atom and the electron-deficient carbon center to close to oxazole **114**. This mechanism avoids the necessity of having a symmetric intermediate (i.e., **115**) and can accommodate the product specificity since the dipolar species formed (**118**) on bond migration can readily collapse to the observed product before isomerization occurs. In order to form the isomeric oxazole **116**, rotation about the C—N bond of **118** would be necessary. This would require disruption of

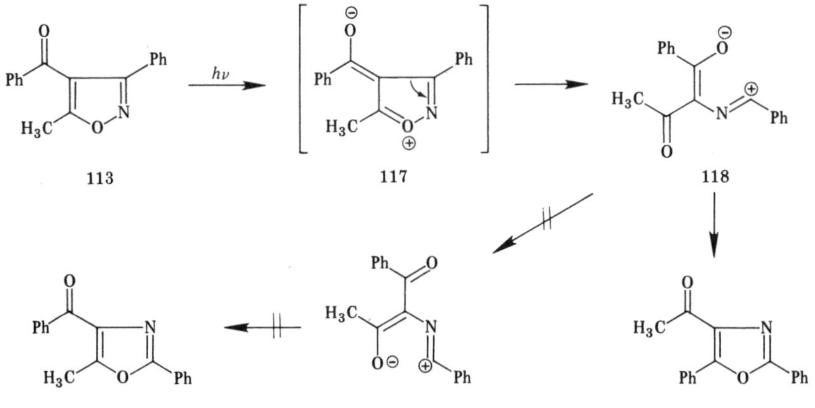

113 117 118

116 114

the coplanarity of the system and would have a significant activation energy barrier. It should be noted that the above mechanism does not explain the results encountered with isoxazole **107**. Clearly, further photochemical studies on related 4-carbonyl-substituted isoxazoles are necessary for a better understanding of the reaction mechanism.

The photochemical rearrangement of benzisoxazoles (**119**) to benzoxazoles (**122**) has been studied by a number of research groups (*55–58*). The following mechanism was proposed to rationalize the data (*58*):

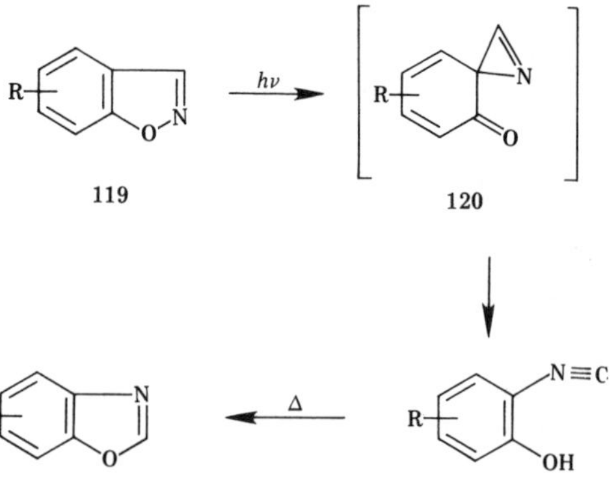

119 120

122 121

Evidence supporting this scheme was obtained by the detection of isonitrile **121** at −77°C. When this intermediate was allowed to warm to room temperature it cyclized quantitatively to oxazole **122**. The photoconversion of tetrahydrobenzisoxazole **123** to oxazole **126** proceeded via a similar set of intermediates, which could be detected spectroscopically (*59*). In contrast, no intermediates could be detected in the photoconversion of **127** to **128** (*59*).

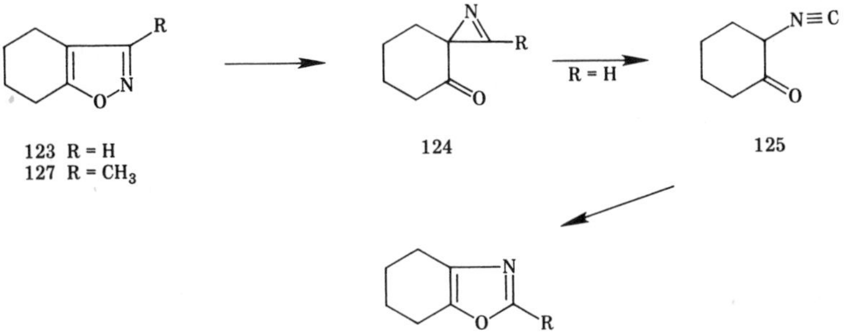

123 R = H
127 R = CH₃

124

125

126 R = H
128 R = CH₃

The photochemical isomerization of 3-hydroxy-1,2-benzisoxazole (**129**) to benzoxazolinone **130** has also been studied (*60*). The rearrangement was claimed to proceed via the keto tautomer **129b** since the photoisomerization of a number of *N*-alkyl-substituted benzisoxazolinones occurs under similar photolytic conditions. The extremely slow rate of isomerization of

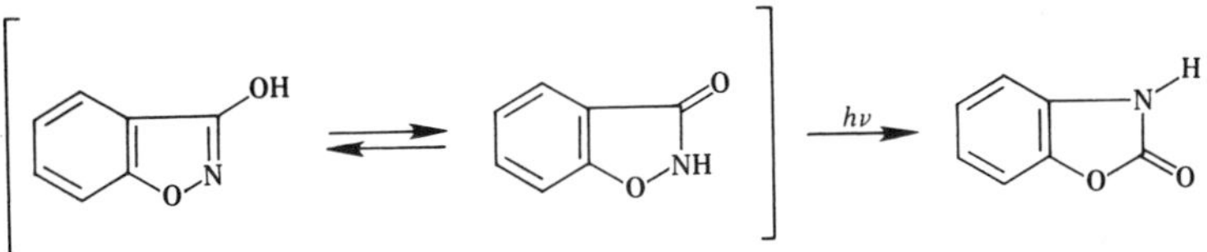

129a

129b

130

3-methoxy-1,2-benzisoxazole and the failure to detect an α-lactam intermediate at low temperature was interpreted as being inconsistent with a ring contraction–ring expansion sequence. Although an α-lactam intermediate had been suggested as an intermediate in the closely related transformation of 3-hydroxyisoxazole (**100**) to 2(3*H*)-oxazolone (**102**) (*51*), the authors favor the diradical mechanism shown below (*60*).

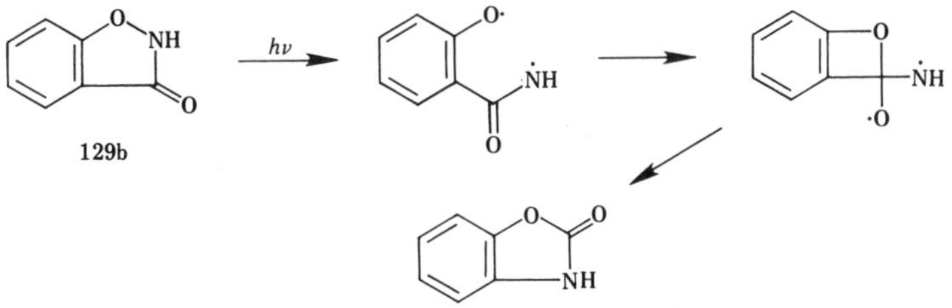

129b

130

B. Oxazoles

Investigations of the photochemistry of aryloxazoles have demonstrated that these species also undergo molecular reorganization under the influence of ultraviolet light (15,61). The light-induced reactions of this system were found to be considerably more complex than those of the related isoxazole system. For example, irradiation of 2,5-diphenyloxazole (79) in ethanol gave 4,5-diphenyloxazole (131) and 3,5-diphenylisoxazole (77) as major photoproducts (15). When the irradiation of 79 was conducted in benzene, 2,4-diphenyloxazole (132) was the only product obtained. Further irradiation of 132 in benzene produced 3,4-diphenylisoxazole (133) in good yield.

The above photorearrangements were divided into two basic sets. One set (type A) involves formal interchange of two adjacent ring atoms (e.g., 79 → 77) and is of some interest in relation to the reverse photorearrangement reported (4). The other set (type B) consists of a rearrangement involving the formal exchange of positions 2 and 4 (e.g., 79 → 131). Similar results were encountered with 4-methyl-2-phenyloxazole (134). In this case, however, azirine 137 was detected in the crude reaction mixture. It has been suggested that, in the rearrangement of oxazoles proceeding with formal interchange of adjacent ring atoms (type A), a 2*H*-azirine intermediate is involved which undergoes a subsequent rearrangement to the isoxazole ring (*15*).

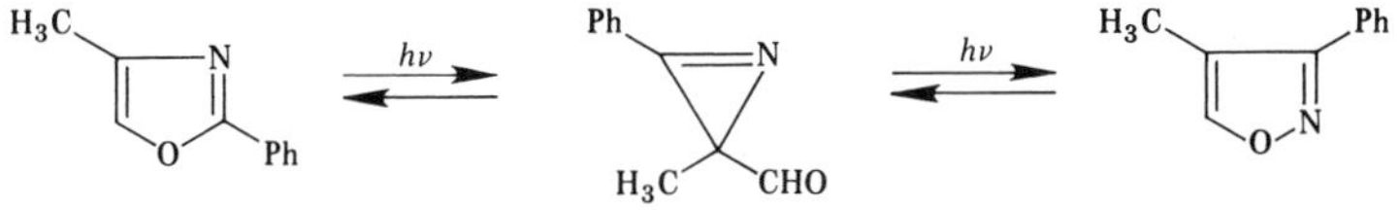

134   137   136

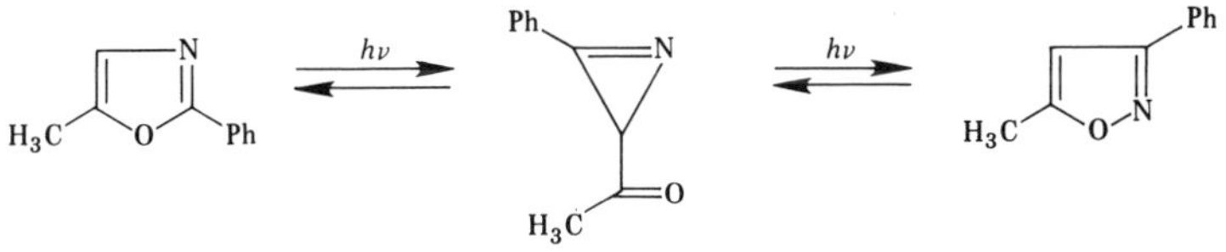

138   139   140

Although the majority of cases of formal interchange of two adjacent ring atoms have been observed with the C-2 and O atoms, two examples of interchange between the C-4 and C-5 atoms have been found (i.e.,

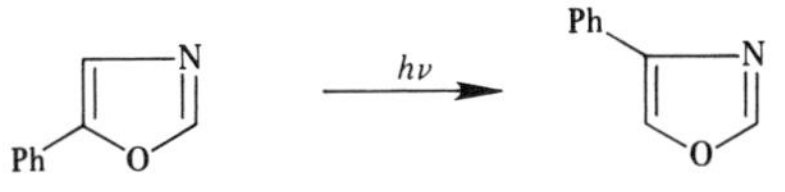

141   142

79 → **132** and **141** → **142**). These transformations can be explained in terms of a 1*H*-azirine intermediate (**143**) (*62,63*) derived by cleavage of the C-5—O bond (*15*).

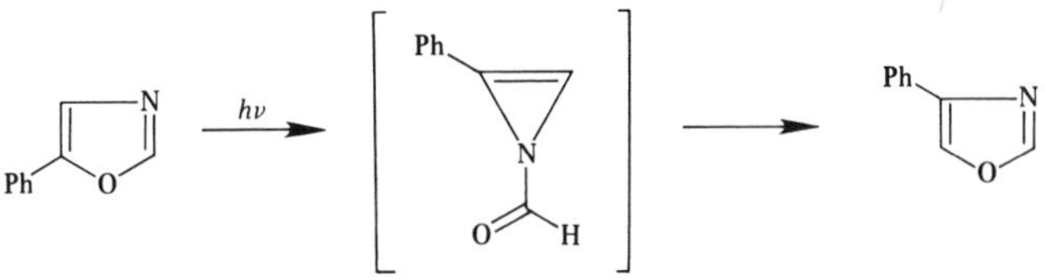

141   143   142

The type B rearrangement, however, cannot be rationalized by the ring contraction–ring expansion mechanism. Rather, this process seems to proceed via the internal cyclization–isomerization route (mechanism II). This is illustrated below for the conversion of **79** to **131** and **134** to **135**.

It is especially interesting that the photolysis of oxazole **144** was reported to give rise to isoxazole **145** and oxazole **146** (*15*). In this case the

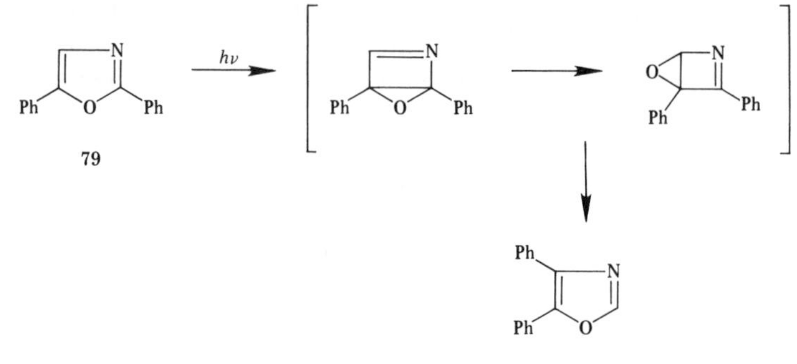

131

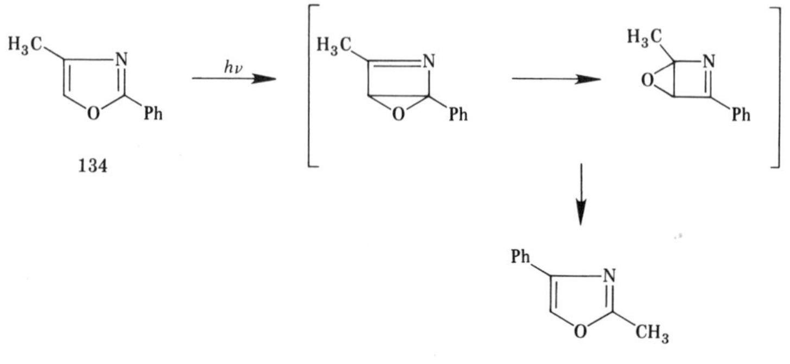

134

135

formation of isoxazole **145** can be explained by assuming that the initially formed bicyclic structure **147** prefers to reorganize to give the most stable bicyclic isomer (i.e., **148**). Thus, it would seem that, in the formation of a

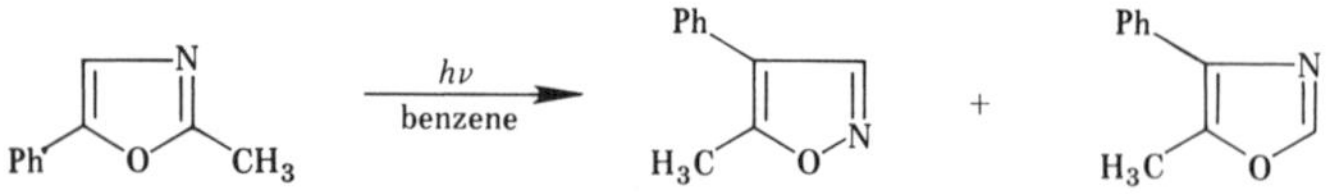

144   145   146

given bicyclic isomer, the 1,3-oxygen shift takes place in such a fashion as to place the aryl group on the double bond. The failure of oxazole **135** to undergo interchange of C-2 and C-4 or of C-5 and N (type B reaction) is consistent with this interpretation. The initially formed bicyclic isomer resulting from cyclization of **135** would give the starting material because its stability would be greater than that of the second bicyclic isomer resulting from a 1,3-oxygen migration. Finally, it should be noted that the conversion of oxazole **144** to **146** does not fit either mechanism I or II. The possibility does exist, however, that **146** is a secondary product derived

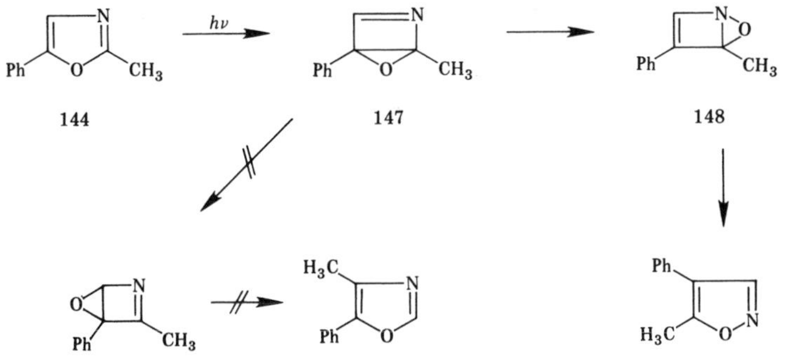

144   147   148

145

from **145** via a ring contraction–ring expansion route. Further work is necessary to verify this point.

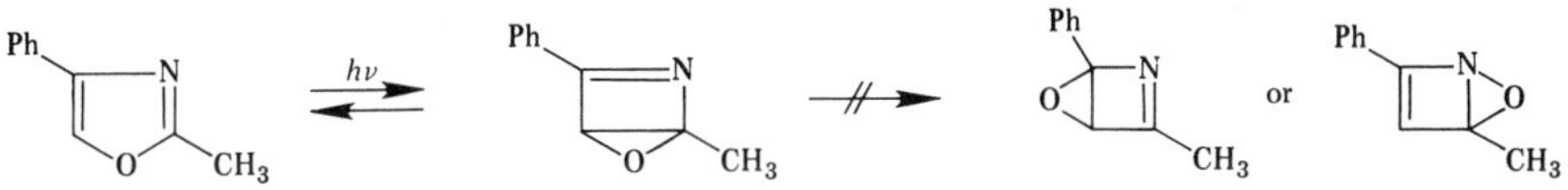

135

The rearrangements described above illustrate the complexity of oxazole photochemistry. Not only is there more than one available path, but structural changes in the oxazole ring play an important role in controlling the course of the rearrangement. In addition, the photobehavior of the system seems to be affected by the nature of the solvent employed.

C. Pyrazoles

A great deal of work has been done on the photorearrangement of pyrazoles to imidazoles (5,13,64–70). Some examples of this reaction involve the conversion of **149** to **150** and **151** to **152**:

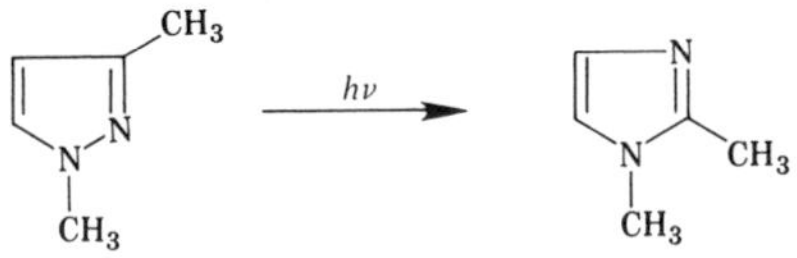

149   150

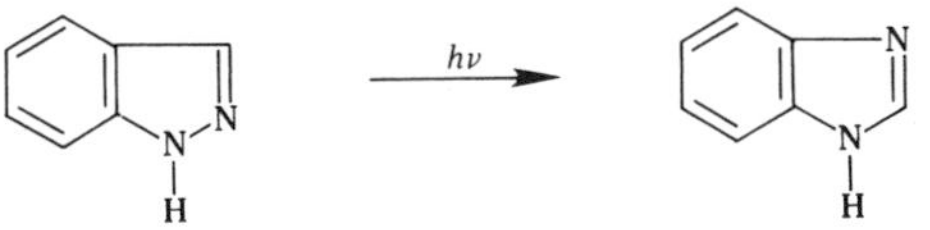

151   152

A related series of rearrangements was also encountered with pyrazolone **153** (*68*) and lactam **156** (*69,71*):

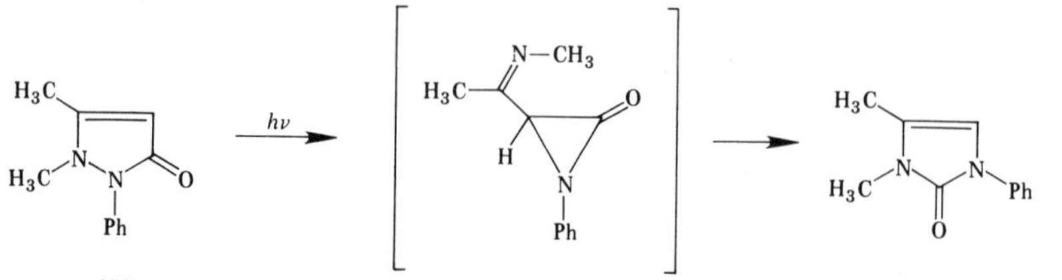

153 154 155

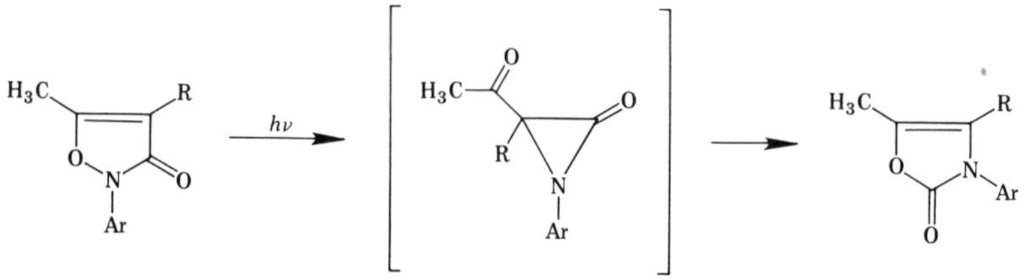

156 157 158

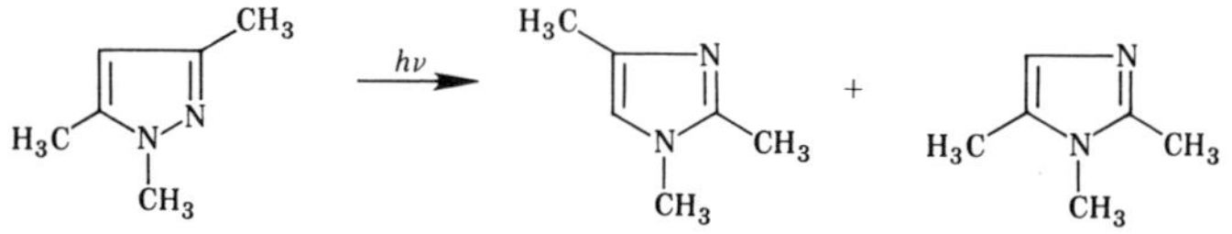

159 160 161

The early observations were rationalized by a ring contraction–ring expansion sequence (mechanism I) (*64*). The existence of other photoisomerization pathways for pyrazole derivatives was established by the photorearrangement of 1,3,5-trimethylpyrazole (**159**) to 1,2,4-trimethylimidazole (**160**) and 1,2,5-trimethylimidazole (**161**) (*5,67*) and by the photorearrangement of 2-methylindazole (**162**) to 1-methylbenzimidazole (**164**) (*64,72,73*).

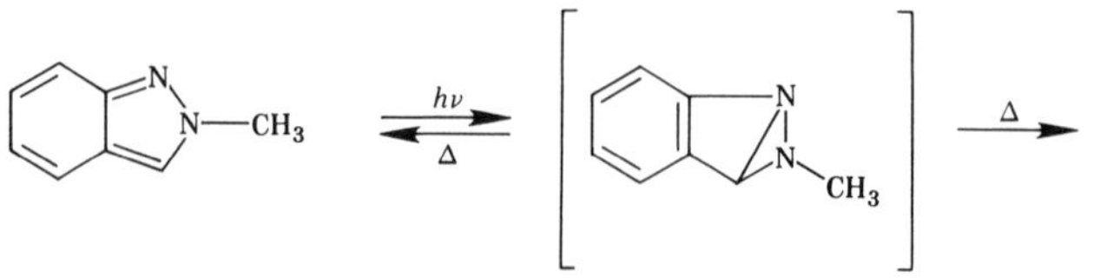

162 163 164

Although the formation of **161** from **159** is consistent with a ring contraction–ring expansion sequence, the formation of **160** requires a different process. This rearrangement has been suggested to proceed via the internal cyclization–isomerization route (mechanism II) (5,67).

With the 2-methylindazole system, the intermediate involved in a ring contraction–ring expansion sequence would be prohibitively strained. The mechanism of this reaction was subjected to considerable scrutiny (58,73–76) and was found to proceed via intermediate 163. This species can be produced in high concentrations by monochromatic irradiation of 162 at low temperatures and is transformed to 162 and 164 on warming in the dark (75).

The isolation of 3-anilino-2,3-diphenylacrylonitrile (166) as a product from the irradiation of 1,4,5-triphenylpyrazole (165) (77) allows one to speculate on the existence of a third route for the pyrazole–imidazole

rearrangement. Aminoacrylonitriles such as 169 give imidazoles (170) on irradiation, probably via four-membered ring intermediates (78,79). The possibility exists, therefore, that pyrazoles with only hydrogen in the 3 position may rearrange by the sequence pyrazole → aminoacryloni-trile → imidazole. A number of rearrangements of pyrazoles to imidazoles have been described (64) which could occur via an aminoacrylonitrile, and in the cases of pyrazole and 3-methylpyrazole it has been shown (79) that the appropriate aminoacrylonitrile does undergo photoconversion to the imidazole. Thus, photorearrangement of 5-methylpyrazole gives

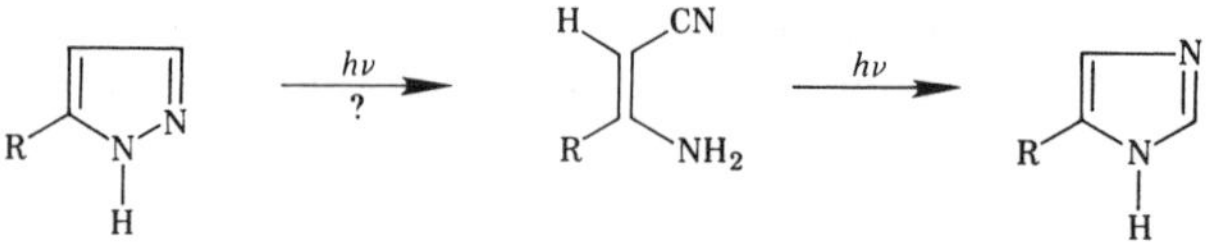

168   169   170

2-methylimidazole as well as 4-methylimidazole; the latter may arise via the aminocrotonitrile 169 (R = CH_3). It should be noted, however, that aminoacrylonitrile 166 did not afford imidazole 167 under either sensitized or unsensitized conditions (77). This could possibly be because compound 166 exists predominantly in the form with a trans arrangement of the nitrile and amino groups; molecular models indicate considerable strain in the cis form. Additional work is required before this mechanistic possibility can be accepted.

D. Imidazoles

Irradiation of a number of methyl-substituted imidazoles has been reported to result in the scrambling of the substituent groups (5,67). Some examples of this reaction are shown below. These photoreactions involve a formal interchange of the 1,5 or the 2,4 carbons of the imidazole ring.

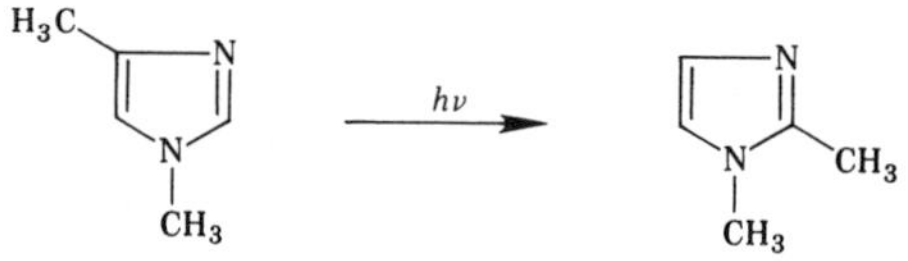

171   172

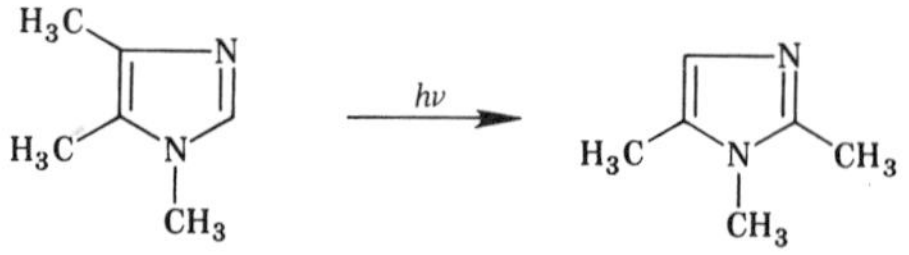

173   174

That these results cannot be accommodated by a ring contraction–ring expansion sequence, which allows interchange of only the 2,3 or 4,5 positions, is apparent. Two mechanisms have been suggested to explain these results. A difference between these two processes lies in the symmetry of 175, in which the original 2 and 5 positions become equivalent when groups A and C are equivalent. The intermediates in the internal cyclization–isomerization pathway (mechanism II) do not allow equiva-

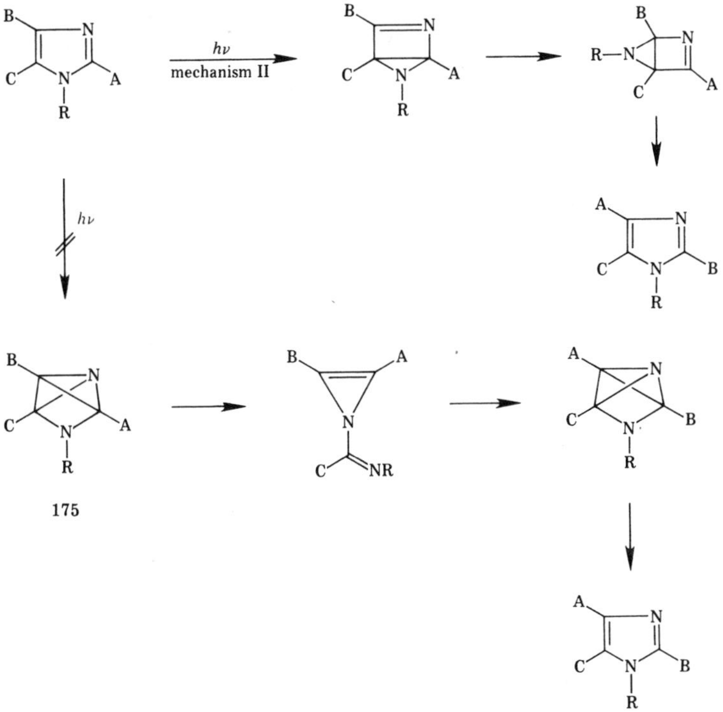

175

lence of the 2 and 5 positions. In order to distinguish between these two possibilities, Beak and Messer (5) irradiated 2-deuterio-1,4-dimethyl-imidazole (176). If mechanism II were followed, the expected product would be 1,2-dimethylimidazole-4d (177). The alternative path would be expected to produce an equal mixture of 177 and 1,2-dimethyl imidazole-5d (178). The results obtained led these workers to conclude that at least 90% of the rearrangement is in accord with mechanism II.

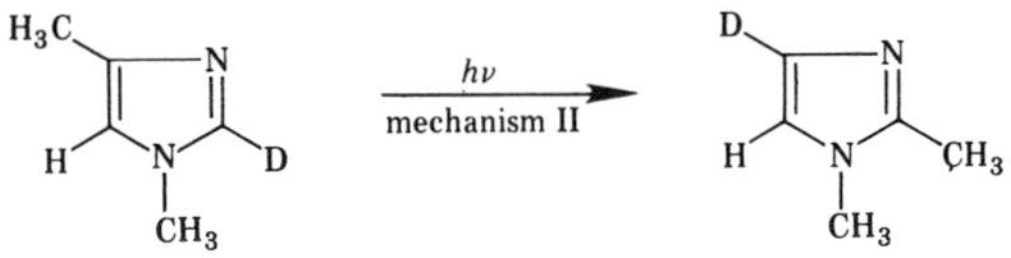

176   177

E. Isothiazoles and Thiazoles

Studies on the photochemical behavior of isothiazoles and thiazoles have been carried out (80–83). The main reaction observed involves photoisomerization, and several mechanistic possibilities have been put

forth. Since these mechanisms are closely related to those previously
discussed, this field will be reviewed briefly. Some of the typical systems
examined are exemplified below.

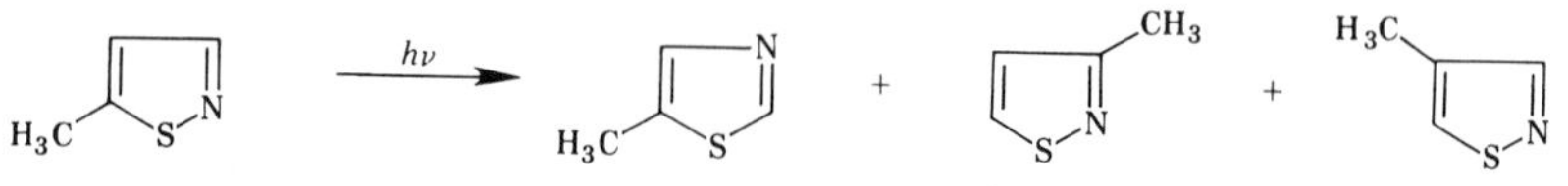

179 → 180 + 181 + 182

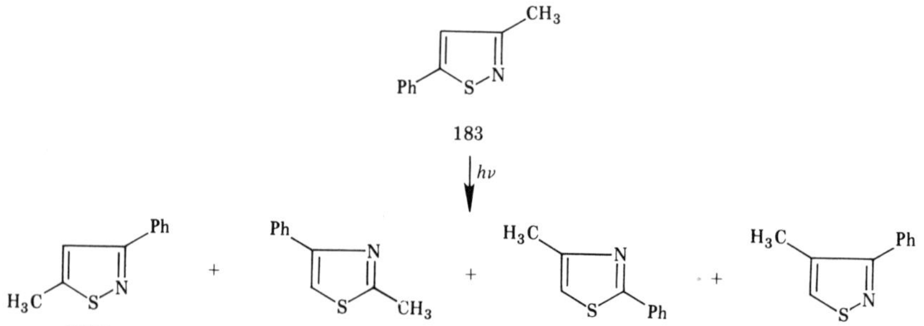

183

(65%) 184 + (25%) 185 + (trace) 186 + (trace) 187

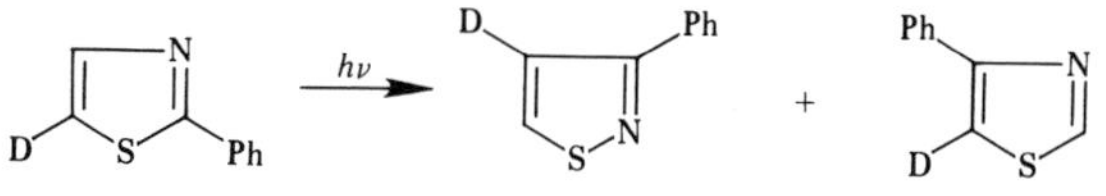

188 → 189 + 190

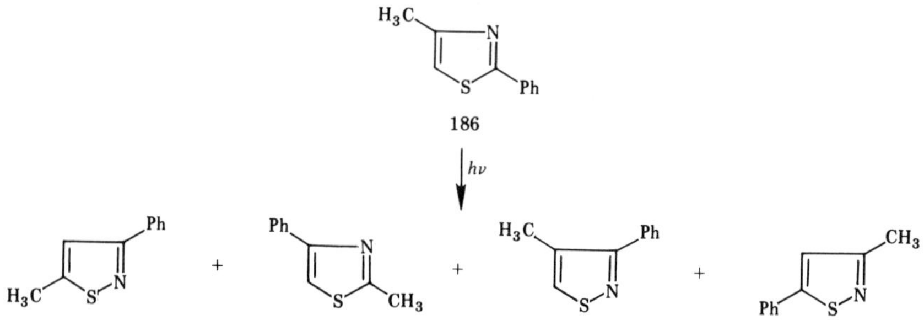

186

(64%) 184 + (31%) 185 + (4%) 187 + (1%) 183

Conflicting opinions have emerged in the study of the mechanism of
these photorearrangements. It was initially concluded that a pathway in-

volving valence isomerization with the formation of bicyclic intermediates (mechanism II) was compatible with the majority of the experimental results (80):

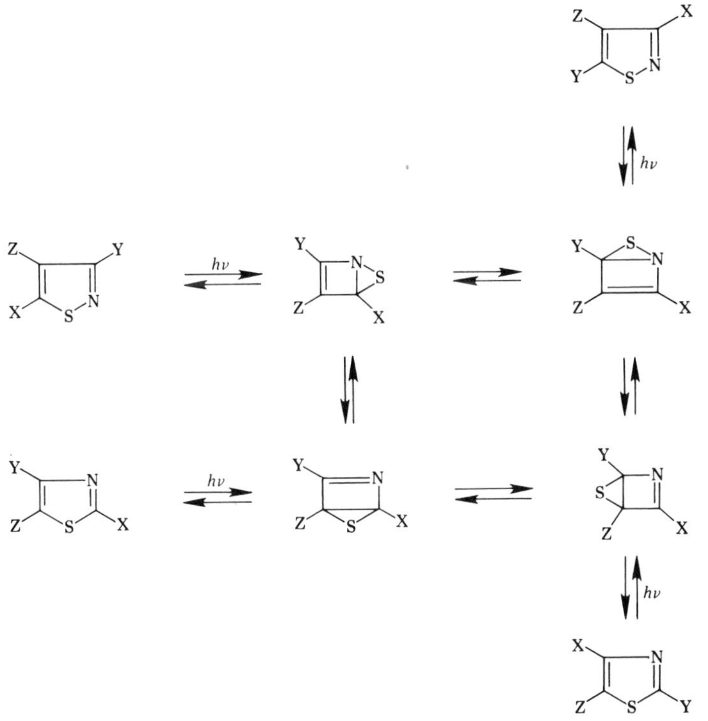

The results of other workers are at variance with this conclusion (83). Incorporation of deuterium was observed during the photorearrangement of 2-phenylthiazole and 4-phenylthiazole in benzene containing 2% D_2O (83). Thus, 2-phenylthiazole (191) was converted to a mixture of 4-phenylthiazole (192), 3-phenylisothiazole (193), and 3-phenyl-4-deuterio-isothiazole (194):

These observations appear to favor a tricyclic zwitterion intermediate in which deuterium incorporation is possible, rather than a valence-bond isomerization mechanism. The fact that the yield of rearranged products appears to increase with solvent polarity is also in agreement with this proposal (*81*). The zwitterion–tricyclic route (mechanism IV) readily accommodates the products obtained from the irradiation of 5-methylisothiazole (**179**). Mechanism II does not provide a satisfactory explanation for the formation of **180** and **182** with this system.

At present, more than 95% of the products of photorearrangements can be explained either by the valence-bond isomerization route (mechanism II) or by the zwitterion–tricyclic route (mechanism IV). Finally, it should be mentioned that sensitization and quenching experiments indicate that the reactive state in the case of 2-phenylthiazole is a singlet, whereas in the case of 3-phenylisothiazole it is a triplet (*80*).

F. Dihydro Heteroaromatic Compounds and Related Systems

Nonaromatic five-membered heterocycles have also been observed to undergo rearrangement on ultraviolet excitation (*20,21,84–88*). The photochemical isomerization reaction of a series of 2-isoxazolines can best be rationalized by the fragmentation–readdition route (mechanism V). Thus, on irradiation in acetonitrile, 3,5-diphenyl-2-isoxazoline (195) is converted to 4,5-diphenyl-3-oxazoline (198) in moderate yield (20,21). The available evidence indicates that the formation of 198 arises by cleavage of the starting material to benzaldehyde and phenylazirine (196). The three-membered heterocyclic ring undergoes a subsequent ring-opening reaction to give nitrile ylide 197, (89,90), which, in turn, cycloadds across the carbonyl group to give 3-oxazoline (198). Support for this mechanism was obtained by carrying out the irradiation of 195 in the presence of radioac-

tively labeled benzaldehyde and observing that the label is incorporated to a large extent in 198 (21). In fact, azirine 196 could be detected gas chromatographically when the irradiation of 195 was interrupted shortly after commencement (84). Subsequent studies showed that the irradiation of 2H-azirines in the presence of aldehydes produces 3-oxazolines in high yield (21,91,92).

Yet another rearrangement undoubtedly resulting from the fragmentation–readdition route is the formation of bicyclic 2-oxazoline (202) from the irradiation of tetrahydro-3aH-cyclopenta[d]isoxazole (199). Photochemical ring opening of 199 leads to azirine 200, which subsequently cycloadds across the neighboring carbonyl group. In this case it can be argued that steric strain is responsible for the reversal of the mode of cycloaddition of nitrile ylide 201 (88).

A comparable set of reactions appears to be responsible for the photochemical isomerization of bicyclic isoxazoline 203 to oxazabicyclo[3.2.0]-heptadiene (207) (87). A study of the reaction as a function of time showed that 2-phenyl-1,3-oxazepine (206) was the major product produced in the early stages of the photolysis. Further irradiation of this compound afforded 2-oxazoline (207). In this case, the initially formed nitrile ylide

(205) prefers to undergo an electrocyclization reaction to give 206 rather than add across the carbonyl group.

Another intriguing example of the fragmentation–readdition route involves the photoconversion of 3,4-diphenyl-1,2,5-oxadiazole (208) to 3,5-diphenyl-1,2,4-oxadiazole (209) (19). The fact that the irradiation of 208 in excess benzonitrile leads to an increase in the yield of 209 is evidence for the fragmentation–recombination pathway. When the irradiation of 208 is carried out in the presence of phenylacetylene, the 1,3-dipolar cycloadduct 210 is isolated in moderate yield (19).

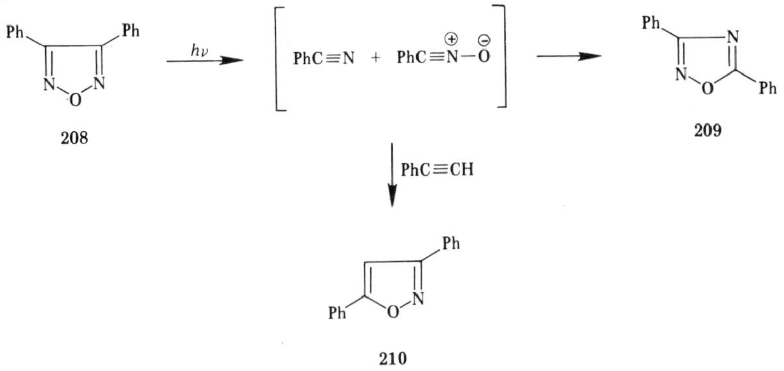

208 → [PhC≡N + PhC≡N⁺—O⁻] → 209

PhC≡CH

210

G. Mesoionic Compounds

The photochemistry of certain classes of five-membered mesoionic heterocycles has generally been rationalized in terms of a mechanism that involves a transient four-membered carbonyl-containing ring formed by a photolytically induced ring contraction (93–111). In fact, the UV spectrum of this transient species (i.e., **212**) has been recorded by low-temperature irradiation experiments (112). Although a wide variety of reactions have been reported, only a few examples exist in which an interchange of the ring atoms has occurred. The photoisomerization of 3-arylsydnones (**211**) to 3-aryloxa-3,4-diazolin-2-ones (**215**) was initially suggested to proceed via intermediate **212**, which undergoes a subsequent loss of carbon dioxide to give the diazirine derivative **212**; the latter would lead to ni-trilimine **214** through a ring-opening process (93–111). Evidence supporting

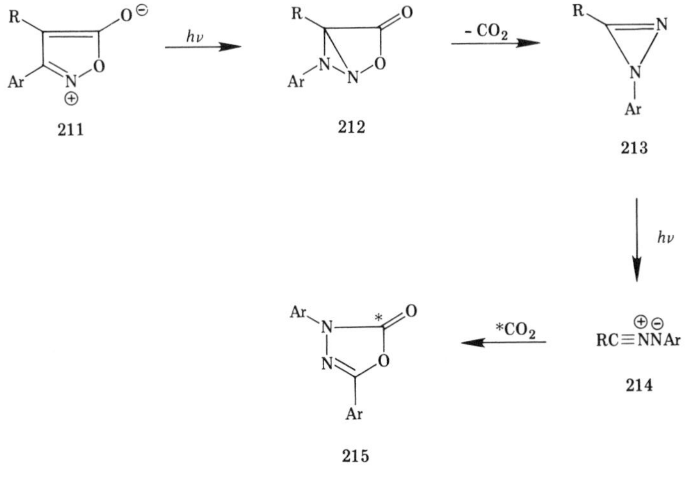

211 $\xrightarrow{h\nu}$ 212 $\xrightarrow{-CO_2}$ 213

$h\nu$

215 $\xleftarrow{*CO_2}$ $RC\equiv N\overset{\oplus}{N}\overset{\ominus}{Ar}$ 214

this pathway was obtained by the finding that the rearranged product could be rendered radioactive if the irradiation were carried out in the presence of radioactive carbon dioxide.

The rearrangement of the sydnone system has also been explained by assuming that the initially formed bicyclic tautomer **212** arranges to **216,** which then fragments to the nitrilimine **214,** thus bypassing the energy barrier to the antiaromatic diazirine intermediate (99,104). More recently, it has been suggested that the initially formed bicyclic intermediate **212**

                            R = H; Ar = m-pyridinyl

undergoes C—N bond fragmentation to give **217** as a transient species, which undergoes subsequent loss of carbon dioxide to afford nitrilimine **214** (112). In support of this suggestion the presence of a second transient species (λ_{max} 600 nm) was detected when **212** was allowed to warm in the dark in the rigid matrix (112).

Another group provided evidence for yet another photochemical isomerization reaction of sydnones, which probably involves a ketene derivative as an intermediate. The light-induced reaction of sydnone **218** in benzene afforded photoisomer **223** (*110*). Two possible reaction pathways were considered (*110*). The first involves the formation of the valence tautomer **219** by way of an electrocyclic ring opening of the sydnone. Intramolecular nucleophilic attack of the amino nitrogen on the carbonyl carbon of the ketene converts **219** to the four-membered ring **220,** which undergoes ring expansion to the spiro compound **223.** A second and more direct mechanism involves the previously postulated bicyclic intermedi-

ate (**221**) followed by ring opening to the ketene derivative **222,** which collapses to **223.**

N-Acylsydnone imine **224** rearranges upon irradiation to the mesoionic compound **225** (*113*), presumably by a path similar to that suggested to rationalize the photoreorganization of sydnones (*112*).

A similar sequence of reactions nicely accommodates the photorearrangement of **226** to **227**. In both of these cases the initially formed bicyclic intermediate undergoes ring fragmentation and subsequent reorganization to a new bicyclic species, which is the immediate precursor of the final product.

Irradiation of the mesoionic **228** gave an 80% yield of *N*-benzoyl-5-phenyl-1,2-dithiol-3-imine **(230)** (*102*). The formation of this compound was suggested to involve an initial photodisrotatory ring closure to give **229**, which undergoes a subsequent [1,3]sigmatropic rearrangement to **230**.

The irradiation of 3-methyl-2-methylthio-5-phenyl(1,3-thiazol-4-ylio) oxide **(231)** in ethanol solution resulted in a novel type of rearrangement for a mesoionic system, giving rise to the isomeric 3-methyl-4-methylthio-5-phenyl-1,3-thiazol-2-one **(233)** (*105*). The rearrangement was suggested to proceed via an unusual reactive intermediate (i.e., **232**). However, a more plausible scheme would involve photodisrotatory ring closure to **234**, followed by episulfide ring opening and reorganization of the resulting zwitterion **(235)** to the observed product.

An oxadiaziridine intermediate **(237)** has been proposed to account for the conversion of 1,2,3-thiadiazole 2-oxides **(236)** to the isomeric 3-oxides

(238) (*114*). The isolation of a low yield of 1,2,5-thiadiazole (239) from the diphenyl derivative (236, $R_1 = R_2 = Ph$) has been taken as evidence for an internal cyclization–isomerization route (mechanism II).

The latter reaction is somewhat related to the photochemical rearrangement of 4,4-dimethyl-3,5-diphenyl-4H-pyrazole 1-oxide (240) to 5,5-dimethyl-3,4-diphenyl-5H-pyrazole 1-oxide (241) (*115*). This conver-

sion has been proposed to proceed via a pathway involving valence isomerization with the formation of bicyclic intermediates (mechanism II) (*116*).

REFERENCES

1. P. Beak and W. Messer, *Org. Photochem.* **2**, 117 (1969).
2. A. Lablache-Combier and M. A. Remy, *Bull. Soc. Chim. Fr.* p. 679 (1971).

3. A. Lablache-Combier, *in* "Photochemistry of Heterocyclic Compounds" (O. Buchardt, ed.), p. 123. Wiley, New York, 1976.

4. E. F. Ullman and B. Singh, *J. Am. Chem. Soc.* **88**, 1844 (1966); **89**, 6911 (1967).

5. P. Beak and W. Messer, *Tetrahedron* **25**, 3287 (1969).

6. R. Hoffmann and R. B. Woodward, *Acc. Chem. Res.* **1**, 17 (1968).

7. K. E. Wilzbach, J. S. Ritscher, and L. Kaplan, *J. Am. Chem. Soc.* **89**, 1031 (1967); E. E. van Tamelen and S. P. Pappas, *ibid.* **85**, 3297 (1963).

8. G. L. Closs, W. A. Boll, H. Heyn, and V. Dev, *J. Am. Chem. Soc.* **90**, 173 (1968).

9. J. I. Brauman, L. E. Ellis, and E. E. van Tamelen, *J. Am. Chem. Soc.* **88**, 846 (1966); **89**, 5073 (1967); **93**, 6145 (1971); G. D. Andrew and J. E. Baldwin, *ibid.* **99**, 4851 (1971).

10. H. Morrison and F. J. Palensky, *J. Am. Chem. Soc.* **99**, 3507 (1977); A. Padwa, T. J. Blacklock, D. Getman, N. Hatanaka, and R. Loza, *J. Org. Chem.* **43**, 1481 (1978).

11. E. E. van Tamelen and T. Whitesides, *J. Am. Chem. Soc.* **93**, 6129 (1971).

12. R. Srinivasan, *J. Am. Chem. Soc.* **89**, 1758 and 4812 (1967).

13. H. Tiefenthaler, W. Dorscheln, H. Goth, and H. Schmid, *Tetrahedron Lett.* p. 2999 (1964).

14. A. Padwa, J. Smolanoff, and A. Tremper, *J. Am. Chem. Soc.* **97**, 4682 (1975).

15. M. Maeda and M. Kojima, *J. Chem. Soc., Trans. Perkin 1* p. 239 (1977).

16. H. Wynberg, R. M. Kellogg, H. V. Driel, and G. E. Beekhuis, *J. Am. Chem. Soc.* **89**, 3501 (1967).

17. M. Maeda and M. Kojima, *Tetrahedron Lett.* p. 3523 (1973).

18. R. M. Kellogg, *Tetrahedron Lett.* p. 1429 (1972).

19. T. S. Cantrell and W. S. Haller, *Chem. Commun.* p. 977 (1968); T. Mukai, T. Oine, and A. Matsubara, *Bull. Chem. Soc. Jpn.* **42**, 581 (1969).

20. T. Matsuura and Y. Ito, *Tetrahedron Lett.* p. 2283 (1973); *Tetrahedron* **31**, 1373 (1975).

21. H. Giezendanner, M. Marky, B. Jackson, H. J. Hansen, and H. Schmid, *Helv. Chim. Acta* **55**, 745 (1972).

22. H. Hiraoka and R. Srinivasan, *J. Am. Chem. Soc.* **90**, 2720 (1968); R. Srinivasan, *ibid.* **89**, 1758 and 4812 (1967); *Pure Appl. Chem.* **16**, 65 (1968); H. Hiraoka and R. Srinivasan, *J. Chem. Phys.* **48**, 2185 (1968); S. Bone and R. Srinivasan, *J. Am. Chem. Soc.* **92**, 1824 (1970).

23. E. E. van Tamelen and T. H. Whitesides, *J. Am. Chem. Soc.* **90**, 3894 (1968).

24. A. Padwa, T. Blacklock, D. Getman, and N. Hatanaka, *J. Am. Chem. Soc.* **99**, 2344 (1977).

25. A. Padwa, U. Chiacchio, and N. Hatanaka, *J. Am. Chem. Soc.* **100**, 3928 (1978).

26. H. Hiraoka, *J. Phys. Chem.* **74**, 574 (1970).

27. A. Couture and A. Lablache-Combier, *Chem. Commun.* p. 891 (1971).

28. A. Couture, A. Delevallee, A. Lablache-Combier, and C. Parhanyi, *Tetrahedron* **31**, 785 (1975).

29. T. Tsuchiya, H. Arai, and H. Igeta, *Chem. Commun.* p. 550 (1972); *Chem. Pharm. Bull.* **21**, 1516 (1973).

30. H. Hiraoka, *Chem. Commun.* p. 1610 (1971); *Tetrahedron* **29**, 2955 (1973).

31. H. Hiraoka, *Chem. Commun.* p. 1306 (1970).

32. J. Barltrop, A. C. Day, P. D. Moxon, and R. R. Ward, *Chem. Commun.* p. 786 (1975).

33. J. A. Barltrop, A. C. Day, and R. W. Ward, *Chem. Commun.* p. 131 (1978).

34. H. Wynberg, *Acc. Chem. Res.* **4**, 65 (1971).

35. H. Wynberg and H. van Driel, *J. Am. Chem. Soc.* **87**, 3998 (1965).

36. H. Wynberg, R. M. Kellogg, H. van Driel, and G. E. Beekhuis, *J. Am. Chem. Soc.* **88**, 5047 (1966).

37. H. Wynberg, G. E. Beekhuis, H. van Driel, and R. M. Kellogg, *J. Am. Chem. Soc.* **89**, 3498 (1967).
38. H. Wynberg, H. van Driel, R. M. Kellogg, and J. Buter, *J. Am. Chem. Soc.* **89**, 3487 (1967).
39. R. M. Kellogg and H. Wynberg, *Tetrahedron Lett.* p. 5895 (1968).
40. R. M. Kellogg, J. K. Dik, H. van Driel, and H. Wynberg, *J. Org. Chem.* **35**, 2737 (1970).
41. A. Couture and A. Lablache-Combier, *Tetrahedron* **27**, 1059 (1971).
42. H. Wiebe, S. Braslovsky, and J. Heicklen, *Can. J. Chem.* **50**, 2721 (1972); Y. Kobayashi, I. Kumadaki, A. Ohsawa, and Y. Sekine, *Tetrahedron Lett.* p. 2841 (1974); *Chem. Pharm. Bull.* **23**, 2773 (1975); *Heterocycles* **6**, 1587 (1977).
43. E. Ullman, *Acc. Chem. Res.* **1**, 353 (1968).
44. B. Singh, A. Zweig, and J. B. Gallivan, *J. Am. Chem. Soc.* **94**, 1199 (1972).
45. D. W. Kurtz and H. Shechter, *Chem. Commun.* p. 689 (1966).
46. T. Nishiwaki, A. Nakano, and H. Matsuoka, *J. Chem. Soc. C* p. 1825 (1970).
47. T. Nishiwaki and F. Fujiyama, *J. Chem. Soc., Trans. Perkin 1,* p. 1456 (1972).
48. H. Wamhoff, *Chem. Ber.* **105**, 748 (1972).
49. R. H. Good and G. Jones, *J. Chem. Soc. C* p. 1196 (1971).
50. T. Sato, K. Yamamoto, and K. Fukui, *Chem. Lett.* p. 111 (1973).
51. H. Göth, A. R. Gagneux, C. H. Eugster, and H. Schmid, *Helv. Chim. Acta* **50**, 137 (1967).
52. M. Nakagawa, T. Nakamura, and K. Tomita, *Agric. Biol. Chem.* **38**, 2205 (1974).
53. A. Padwa, E. Chen, and A. Ku, *J. Am. Chem. Soc.* **97**, 6484 (1975).
54. K. Dietliker, P. Gilgen, H. Heimgartner, and H. Schmid, *Helv. Chim. Acta* **59**, 2074 (1976).
55. H. Goth and H. Schmid, *Chimia* **20**, 148 (1966).
56. W. Heinzelmann and M. Marky, *Helv. Chim. Acta* **57**, 376 (1974).
57. J. P. Ferris, F. R. Antonucci, and R. W. Trimmer, *J. Am. Chem. Soc.* **95**, 919 (1973).
58. J. P. Ferris and F. R. Antonucci, *J. Am. Chem. Soc.* **96**, 2010 and 2014 (1974); *Chem. Commun.* p. 126 (1972).
59. J. P. Ferris and R. W. Trimmer, *J. Org. Chem.* **41**, 13 (1976).
60. L. J. Darlage, T. H. Kinstle, and C. L. McIntosh, *J. Org. Chem.* **36**, 1088 (1971).
61. M. Kojima and M. Maeda, *Tetrahedron Lett.* p. 2379 (1969); *J. Chem. Soc., Chem. Commun.* p. 539 (1973).
62. M. Ogata, M. Matsumoto, and H. Kano, *Tetrahedron* **25**, 5205 (1969).
63. T. L. Gilchrist, G. E. Gymer, and C. W. Rees, *J. Chem. Soc., Perkin Trans. 1* p. 555 (1973).
64. H. Tiefenthaler, W. Dorschelen, H. Goth, and H. Schmid, *Helv. Chim. Acta* **50**, 2244 (1967).
65. H. Goth, H. Tiefenthaler, and W. Dörscheln, *Chimia* **19**, 596 (1965).
66. J. P. Ferris and L. E. Orgel, *J. Am. Chem. Soc.* **88**, 1974 (1966).
67. P. Beak, J. L. Miesel, and W. R. Messer, *Tetrahedron Lett.* p. 5315 (1967).
68. S. N. Ege, *Chem. Commun.* p. 488 (1967); *J. Chem. Soc. C* p. 2624 (1969).
69. J. Reisch and A. Fitzek, *Tetrahedron Lett.* p. 4513 (1967); p. 271 (1969).
70. A. R. Gagneux and R. Göschke, *Tetrahedron Lett.* p. 5451 (1966).
71. J. Reisch and W. F. Ossenkop, *Chem. Ber.* **106**, 2070 (1973).
72. J. P. Dubois and H. Labhart, *Chimia* **23**, 109 (1969).
73. H. Labhart, W. Heinzelmann, and J. P. Dubois, *Pure Appl. Chem.* **24**, 495 (1970).
74. J. P. Ferris, K. V. Prabhu, and R. L. Strong, *J. Am. Chem. Soc.* **97**, 2835 (1975).

75. W. Heinzelmann, M. Marky, and P. Gilgen, *Helv. Chim. Acta* **59**, 1512, 1528, and 2362 (1976).
76. W. Heinzelmann, *Helv. Chim. Acta* **61**, 618 (1978).
77. J. Grimshaw and D. Mannus, *J. Chem. Soc., Perkin Trans. 1* p. 2096 (1977).
78. T. H. Koch and R. M. Rodehorst, *J. Am. Chem. Soc.* **96**, 6707 (1974).
79. J. P. Ferris and R. W. Trimmer, *J. Org. Chem.* **41**, 19 (1976); J. P. Ferris and J. E. Kuder, *J. Am. Chem. Soc.* **92**, 2527 (1970); J. P. Ferris, R. A. Sanchez, and L. E. Orgel, *J. Mol. Biol.* **33**, 693 (1968).
80. G. Vernin, J. C. Poite, J. Metzger, J. P. Aune, and H. J. M. Dou, *Bull. Soc. Chim. Fr.* p. 1103 (1971); G. Vernin, R. Jauffred, C. Richard, H. J. M. Dou, and J. Metzger, *J. Chem. Soc., Perkin Trans. 2* p. 1145 (1972); G. Vernin, C. Riou, H. J. M. Dou, L. Bouscasse, J. Metzger, and G. Loridan, *Bull. Soc. Chim. Fr.* p. 1743 (1973); C. Riou, J. C. Poite, G. Vernin, and J. Metzger, *Tetrahedron* **30**, 879 (1974); C. Riou, G. Vernin, H. J. M. Dou, and J. Metzger, *Bull. Soc. Chim. Fr.* p. 2673 (1972); G. Vernin, J. C. Poite, H. J. M. Dou, and J. Metzger, *ibid.* p. 3157; H. J. M. Dou, G. Vernin, and J. Metzger, *Chim. Acta Turc.* **2**, 82 (1974); G. Vernin H. J. M. Dou, and J. Metzger, *C. R. Hebd. Seances Acad. Sci., Ser. C* 1616 (1970).
81. J. P. Catteau, A. Lablache-Combier, and A. Pollet, *Chem. Commun.* p. 1018 (1969); *Tetrahedron* **28**, 3141 (1972).
82. M. Ohashi, A. Iio, and T. Yonezawa, *Chem. Commun.* p. 1148 (1970).
83. M. Kojima and M. Maeda, *Chem. Commun.* p. 386 (1970); *Tetrahedron Lett.* p. 3523 (1973); *Heterocycles* **3**, 389 (1975).
84. H. Giezendanner, H. J. Rosenkranz, H. J. Hansen, and H. Schmid, *Helv. Chim. Acta* **56**, 2588 (1973).
85. P. Claus, T. Doopler, N. Gakis, M. Georgarakis, H. Giezendanner, P. Gilgen, H. Heimgartner, B. Jackson, M. Marky, N. S. Narasimhan, H. J. Rosenkranz, A. Wunderli, H. J. Hansen, and H. Schmid, *Pure Appl. Chem.* **33**, 339 (1973).
86. T. Mukai and H. Sukawa, *Tetrahedron Lett.* p. 1835 (1973).
87. T. Mukai, T. Kumagi, and O. Seshimoto, *Pure Appl. Chem.* **49**, 287 (1977).
88. P. Claus, P. Gilgen, H. J. Hansen, H. Heimgartner, B. Jackson, and H. Schmid, *Helv. Chim. Acta* **57**, 2173 (1974).
89. A. Padwa, *Acc. Chem. Res.* **9**, 371 (1976).
90. P. Gilgen, H. Heimgartner, H. Schmid, and H. J. Hansen, *Heterocycles* **6**, 143 (1977).
91. A. Padwa, J. Smolanoff, and S. I. Wetmore, Jr., *J. Org. Chem.* **38**, 1333 (1973).
92. H. Giezendanner, H. Heimgartner, B. Jackson, T. Winkler, H. J. Hansen, and H. Schmid, *Helv. Chim. Acta* **56**, 2611 (1973).
93. C. H. Krauch, J. Kuhls, and H. J. Piek, *Tetrahedron Lett.* p. 4043 (1966).
94. M. Moriarty, R. Mukherjee, O. L. Chapman, and D. R. Eckroth, *Tetrahedron Lett.* p. 397 (1971).
95. C. S. Angadiyavar and M. V. George, *J. Org. Chem.* **36**, 1589 (1971).
96. H. Kato, M. Kawamura, and T. Shiba, *Chem. Commun.* p. 959 (1970).
97. H. Gotthardt, *Chem. Ber.* **105**, 188 (1972).
98. A. Holms, N. Harrit, K. Bechgaard, O. Buchardt, and S. E. Harnung, *J. Chem. Soc., Chem. Commun.* p. 1125 (1972).
99. H. Kato, T. Shiba, and Y. Miki, *J. Chem. Soc., Chem. Commun.* p. 498 (1972).
100. M. Marky, H. J. Hansen, and H. Schmid, *Helv. Chim. Acta* **54**, 1275 (1971).
101. Y. Huseya, A. Chinone, and M. Ohta, *Bull. Chem. Soc. Jpn.* **44**, 1667 (1971); **45**, 3203 (1972).
102. H. Kato, T. Shiba, H. Yoshida, and S. Fujimori, *Chem. Commun.* p. 1591 (1970).

103. I. R. Dunkin, M. Poliahoff, J. T. Turner, N. Harrit, and A. Holm, *Tetrahedron Lett.* p. 873 (1976).
104. H. Kato, T. Shiba, E. Kitajima, T. Kiyosawa, F. Yamada, and T. Nishiyama, *J. Chem. Soc., Perkin Trans. 1* p. 863 (1976).
105. O. Buchardt, J. Domanus, N. Harrit, A. Holm, G. Isaksson, and J. Sandstrom, *J. Chem. Soc., Chem. Commun.* p. 376 (1974).
106. D. H. R. Barton, E. Buschmann, J. Hausler, C. W. Holzapfel, T. Sheradsky, and D. A. Taylor, *J. Chem. Soc., Perkin Trans. 1* p. 1107 (1977).
107. A. Holm, N. H. Toubro, and N. Harrit, *Tetrahedron Lett.* p. 1909 (1976).
108. H. P. Braun, K. P. Zeller, and H. Meier, *Justus Liebigs Ann. Chem.* p. 1257 (1975).
109. R. Mukherjee and R. M. Moriarty, *Tetrahedron* **32,** 661 (1976).
110. H. Gotthardt, F. Reiter, A. Giesen, and V. Lamm, *Tetrahedron Lett.* p. 2331 (1978).
111. H. Gotthardt and F. Reiter, *Tetrahedron Lett.* p. 2749 (1976).
112. A. Trozzolo, unpublished results presented at the 7th IUPAC Symposium in Photochemistry, Leuven, Belgium, 1978.
113. A. Chinone and M. Ohta, *Chem. Lett.* p. 969 (1972).
114. H. P. Braun, K. P. Zeller, and H. Meier, *Chem.-Ztg.* **97,** 567 (1973); *Justus Liebigs Ann. Chem.* p. 1257 (1975).
115. W. R. Dolbier and W. M. Williams, *Chem. Commun.* p. 289 (1970).
116. The support of the National Science Foundation and the National Institutes of Health is gratefully acknowledged.

ESSAY **23** | # PHOTOCHEMICAL REARRANGEMENTS OF COORDINATION COMPOUNDS

FRANCO SCANDOLA

I. INTRODUCTION*

A. Scope and Limitations

The intent of this essay is to provide a survey and evaluation of recent developments in the photochemistry of coordination compounds with specific emphasis on the nature and mechanism of the geometric changes undergone by these compounds during the reaction process. Coverage is

* Abbreviations used in this chapter: acac, 2,4-pentanedionate; atc, 3-acetyl camphorate; bfa, 1,1,1-trifluoro-5,5-dimethylhexane-2,4-dionate; bipy, 2,2'-bipyridine; dpe, 1,2-bis-(diphenylphosphino)ethane; dpp, 1,3-bis(diphenylphosphino)propane; DTC, diethyl dithio-carbamate; en, ethylenediamine; Et_4dien, 1,1',7,7'-tetraethyldiethylenetriamine; gly, glyci-nate; mand, mandelate; NSSN, 1,8-bis(2-pyridyl)-3,6-dithiaoctane; ox, oxalate; $P(n\text{-}Bu)_3$, tri-n-butylphosphine; $P(n\text{-}Bu)_2$Ph, di-n-butylphenylphosphine; PEt_3, triethylphosphine; pfa, 1,1,1-trifluoro-5-methylhexane-2,4-dionate; phen, 1,10-phenanthroline; PMe_3, trimethyl-phosphine; $P(n\text{-}Pr)_2$Ph, di-n-propylphenylphosphine; py, pyridine; 2,3,2-tet, 1,4,8,11-tetra-azaudecane; tfa, 1,1,1-trifluoro-2,4-pentanedionate; tox, dithiooxalate.

REARRANGEMENTS IN GROUND AND EXCITED STATES, VOL. 3

restricted to the photochemistry of classical, Werner-type coordination compounds in fluid solution. The literature survey is intended to be selective rather than exhaustive. Two excellent books (*1,2*) and a number of reviews (*3–10*) provide a wide coverage of the literature.

In dealing with photochemical reactions of coordination compounds, we will designate as "rearrangements" a number of processes in which geometric changes play a substantial mechanistic role, regardless of the actual occurrence of an overall isomerization reaction.

B. Excited States of Coordination Compounds

In the photochemistry of coordination compounds, excited states are usually labeled according to their orbital parentage (*1,2*). A typical classification includes metal-centered (MC) states (also called ligand field or d–d states), ligand to metal charge-transfer (LMCT) states, metal to ligand charge-transfer (MLCT) states, and ligand-centered (LC) states (also called intraligand states). The one-electron transitions responsible for the various types of excited states are indicated in the simplified MO diagram for an octahedral complex shown in Fig. 1. As discussed in detail by Jørgensen (*11*), this classification based on preponderant one-electron

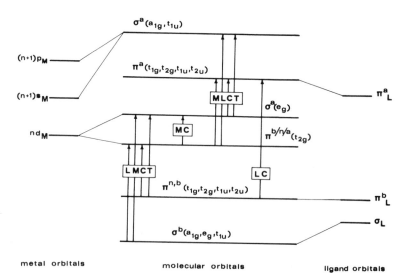

Fig. 1   Schematic MO diagram for an octahedral complex showing the principal types of electronic transitions classified according to their orbital parentage (symbols explained in the text). Molecular orbitals are connected with metal or ligand orbitals, from which they receive predominant contributions. Bonding, nonbonding, and antibonding orbitals are labeled b, n, and a, respectively.

configuration is meaningful for complexes containing metals in "normal" oxidation states and "innocent" ligands, i.e., for most of the classical complexes dealt with in this essay. The chemical reactivity of the various types of orbitally different excited states has been discussed in detail by several authors (1,2) and will not be further discussed here. Within this broad one-electron classification [which is reminiscent of the $\pi-\pi^*$ and $n-\pi^*$ classification of organic photochemistry (12–15)] the real excited state situation of coordination compounds is complicated by various factors.

The energy of the various types of excited states is determined by different and mutually quite independent factors. Actually, the energy of MC states is determined principally by interelectronic repulsion and ligand field parameters, whereas that of LMCT and MLCT states is influenced primarily by the relative redox properties of metal and ligands, and that of LC states depends on the spectroscopic characteristics of the ligand. As a consequence, the relative energy ordering of states of different orbital origin is not generally predictable and is expected to be a sensitive function of the composition of the complex. Often the energy balance may be so delicate that very subtle changes in structure are sufficient to change the orbital nature of the lowest excited state [e.g., methyl substitution in the 5,6 ligand positions of cis-dichlorobis(phenanthroline)-iridium(III) changes the lowest excited state from MLCT to LC (16)].

Owing to the variety of excited states of different orbital nature, Jablonski diagrams for coordination compounds are expected to be generally more complex than those of typical organic molecules (12–15). Another, more serious complication is represented by the fact that in coordination compounds each type of excited state does not generally appear as a pair of states of singlet/triplet multiplicity, as is the case of typical organic molecules. This fact is clearly seen for complexes having ground state open-shell configuration. An example of such a situation is represented by the low-energy portion of the state diagram for octahedral Cr(III) complexes shown in Fig. 2. Here, the difference from the organic case is not simply a matter of changing multiplicities (namely, doublet/quartet versus singlet/triplet). For example, it can be seen that (a) excited states may exist which belong to the same one-electron configuration as the ground state (intraconfigurational excited states), (b) spin-allowed states may be lower in energy than corresponding spin-forbidden states, and (c) the lowest excited state is not necessarily a spin-forbidden one.

The situation with ground state closed-shell systems, e.g., octahedral Co(III) complexes, is more similar to the organic case. However, it has been pointed out (17,18) that, even in this case, some types of excited states, e.g., LMCT states, may give rise to quite complex manifolds be-

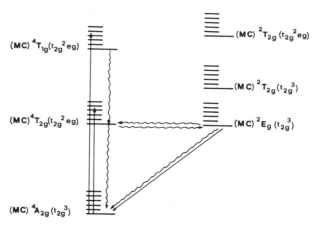

Fig. 2 Schematic Jablonski diagram for an octahedral Cr(III) complex. For the sake of clarity, only the most important photophysical and photochemical processes are indicated.

cause of the occurrence of high-spin and low-spin configurations at the metal which are of similar energy.

Another distinctive feature of the excited state situation of coordination compounds with respect to typical organic molecules is the usually high degree of spin–orbit coupling present in these compounds. This effect is especially important for second and third row transition metal complexes and may often lead to a situation in which discrete spin labels, although widely used in the literature, lose most of their meaning (19).

II. PHOTOCHEMICAL ISOMERIZATIONS OF COORDINATION COMPOUNDS

A. Cis–Trans Photoisomerization of Square Planar Complexes

In the field of square planar complexes, cis–trans photoisomerization reactions have essentially been studied only for Pt(II) compounds. The lack of corresponding interest in photoisomerization processes of Ni(II) and Pd(II) complexes stems, no doubt, from the much greater lability of the lighter-metal complexes. In these systems, fast ligand substitution and equilibria between different coordination geometries (see Section II,D for photochemical effects on these phenomena) are the dominant chemical features (20).

Cis–trans isomerizations of Pt(II) complexes have been known since the early times of inorganic photochemistry (21) and seem to be rather general phenomena in Pt(II) photochemistry, judging from the large number of

TABLE 1

Cis–Trans Photoisomerization of Platinum(II) Complexes

Complex	Type of isomeriza- tion	ϕ	Ref.
$Pt(PEt_3)_2Cl_2$	Cis → trans	0.13^a	27
	Trans → cis	1.00^a	27
$Pt(gly)_2$	Cis → trans	0.12^b	32
	Trans → cis	$\leq 0.001^b$	32
$Pt(py)_2Cl_2$	Cis → trans	0.038^c	34
	Trans → cis	$\sim 0.001^c$	34
$Pt(NH_3)_2(H_2O)_2^{2+}$	Cis → trans	0.13^d	35
	Trans → cis	$\leq 0.001^e$	35

[a] Methanol, 254 or 313 nm irradiation, degassed solution.
[b] Aqueous solution, 254 or 313 nm irradiation.
[c] $CHCl_3$, 313 nm irradiation, primary photoisomerization (34).
[d] Acidic (pH ≤ 1) aqueous solution, 365 nm irradiation.
[e] Estimated value; originally reported as not occurring (35).

systems involved in the pioneering qualitative work of Lifschitz and Froentjes (22). Nevertheless, few systems up to now have been the subject of quantitative studies capable of yielding mechanistic information. A number of these systems are listed in Table 1.

Cis–trans isomerization mechanisms are usually labeled as intramolecular or intermolecular, depending on the participation of species other than the complex (i.e., solvent or outer ligands) in the process. For the cis–trans photoisomerization of a complex of general formula PtA_2B_2, the plausible mechanisms can be summarized as follows:

1. *Twisting mechanism.* This strictly intramolecular mechanism involves the interconversion of cis and trans isomers through a pseudotetrahedral intermediate configuration, without bond breaking or bond formation [Eq. (1)]. In Eq. (1) the photochemical step is considered to be the

$$\tag{1}$$

formation of the tetrahedral intermediate. It may, however, be more correct to consider (*vide infra*) the whole process in terms of the evolution of the nuclear geometry during the radiationless deactivation of the excited state of the starting isomer.

2. *Dissociation–recombination mechanism.* In this mechanism, a ligand is photochemically dissociated from the starting isomer to give a trigonal tricoordinated intermediate, which may lead to the other isomer by prompt recoordination of the released ligand. This mechanism may be considered to be intramolecular inasmuch as it does not involve coordination to the metal of solvent molecules or free ligands in solution. For bis(chelate) complexes, the "released ligand" is one end of the bidentate ligand [Eq. (2)]. For monodentate ligands, this mechanism may work only

$$(2)$$

if some kind of interaction, e.g., ion pairing (*23*), makes geminate recombination of the released ligand more efficient than substitution of the intermediate by other potential ligands.

3. *Solvent-assisted paths.* These mechanisms are intermolecular and involve a primary photosolvation reaction producing an isomerized solvated intermediate, which, upon thermal anation, gives rise to the final isomer [Eq. (3)]. It should be noted that in order for this mechanism to work the

$$(3)$$

primary photosolvation reaction, whether associative or dissociative, must allow for stereomobility. This behavior would be contrary to the strong stereoretentivity characteristic of the thermal reactions of Pt(II) complexes (*20,24*).

4. *Ligand-assisted paths.* Intermolecular mechanisms of this type are believed to be responsible for the thermal cis–trans isomerizations of Pt(II) complexes (*1*). These mechanisms do not require stereomobility in the primary photochemical process. If one of the ligands A or B is present in solution as free ligand, a primary photosubstitution may occur, giving rise to PtA_3B or PtB_3A intermediates. The intermediates can be subsequently converted to the isomerized products by thermal substitution with the original ligand [Eqs. (4) and (5)]. It should be noted that the assisting free ligand and the direction of the photoisomerization are mutually de-

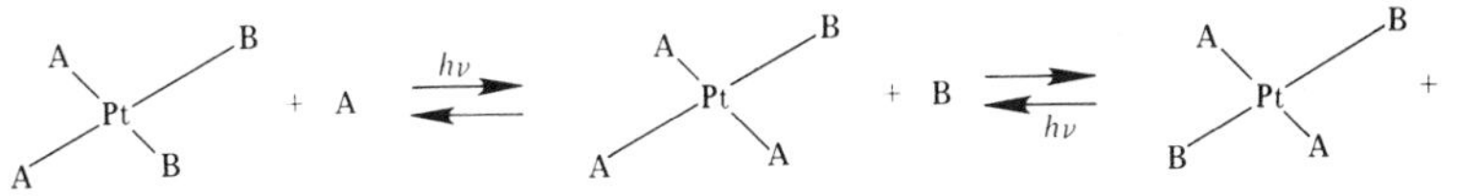

$$(4)$$

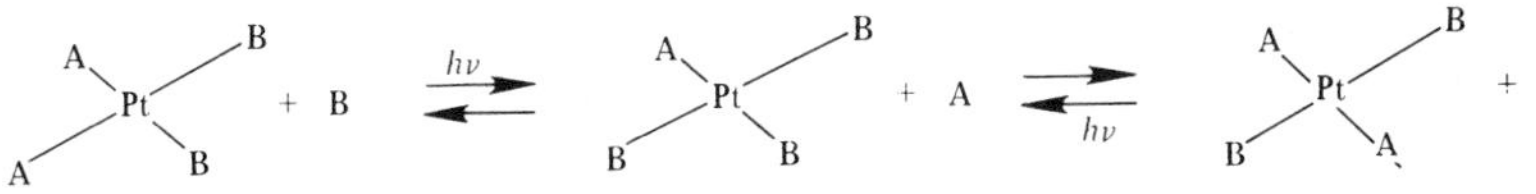

$$(5)$$

pendent in this mechanism. In particular, for efficient cis → trans isomerization the assisting ligand should be the one with lower trans effect (20,24), whereas the opposite holds for trans → cis isomerization. Otherwise, the secondary thermal substitution would lead back predominantly to the starting isomer.

Discriminating experimentally among the above-described mechanisms may often be difficult and require specifically designed experiments. A rather general test, however, is available which enables one to distinguish one mechanism from all the others. If the photoisomerization is carried out in the presence of high concentrations of labeled free ligands, it can easily be predicted that all except the "twisting" mechanism (mechanism 1) would lead to incorporation of the label either into the starting or into the resulting isomer. If no isotopic exchange occurs in such an experiment, the mechanism is almost certainly a "twisting" one.

The occurrence of the photoisomerization of *cis-* and *trans-*dichlorobis-(triethylphosphine)platinum(II), $Pt(PEt_3)_2Cl_2$, was first mentioned in the investigation of Lifschitz and Froentjes (22). This system was later characterized more fully by Haake and co-workers (25,26), who showed that both cis → trans and trans → cis photoisomerizations occurred upon ultraviolet irradiation [Eq. (6)] and led to photostationary states

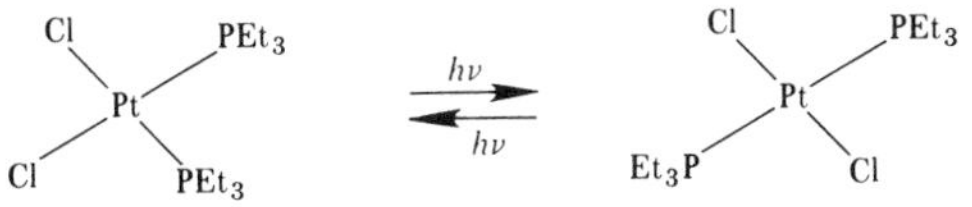

$$(6)$$

the isomer composition of which depended on the solvent, the polar cis isomer favored in more polar solvents. When using polychromatic light, they estimated the quantum yields of the two photoisomerization processes to be of the order of 10^{-2}. They also made, for the first time, the interesting suggestion that the isomerization processes could follow an intramolecular twisting mechanism involving triplet MC excited states (25).

A thorough investigation of the reaction mechanism of the $Pt(PEt_3)_2Cl_2$ system in ethanol solution was recently performed (27) and included quantum yield determinations, chloride exchange studies, and quenching experiments. The authors found essentially wavelength-independent (254–313 nm) quantum yields for both isomerization processes which were one order of magnitude higher than those estimated by others (25). For trans → cis isomerization, the quantum yield strongly depended on the concentration of dissolved oxygen, being 1.00 in deaerated solution and decreasing to 0.13 in aerated solution, without any further decrease caused by oxygen enrichment of the solution. On the other hand, no oxygen effect was observed for the cis → trans photoisomerization. These results were taken as an indication that (a) complete conversion to a reactive excited state occurs for each isomer following excitation to upper LC or CT excited states; (b) the principal reactive excited state for the trans → cis process is very long lived ($\tau \geq 10$ μsec) and is probably of triplet multiplicity (although a minor part of the photoisomerization comes from a shorter-lived state); (c) the cis → trans process originates in a short-lived excited state ($\tau \leq 0.1$ μsec) possibly of singlet multiplicity. Further experiments using 1,5-pentadiene [vertical triplet energy, 56.9–58.9 kcal/mol (28)] as quencher confirmed the quenchability of the trans → cis photoreaction, although the rate constants were lower than with oxygen (singlet energy 23 kcal/mol). Useful mechanistic information was obtained by studying the efficient trans → cis photoisomerization in the presence of labeled free chloride ions ($[Cl^-] \leq 1.92 \times 10^{-3} M$). The quantum yield was unaffected by the presence of Cl^- ions, and the isotope exchange was practically negligible as compared to the extent of isomerization. This is a strong indication that the photoisomerization of $Pt(PEt_3)_2Cl_2$ occurs by an intramolecular twisting mechanism. Details of the twisting mechanism are discussed below in the light of results obtained for other systems.

The photoisomerization of *cis*- and *trans*-bis(glycinato)platinum(II), $Pt(gly)_2$, has been studied in considerable detail (29–33). Although *cis*-$Pt(gly)_2$ undergoes a photodissociation reaction in acidic solution (pH ≤ 3) (32) [Eq. (7)], the only photoreaction observed in neutral solutions is the

$$\begin{array}{cc} \ce{cis-Pt(gly)_2} & \xrightarrow[H_3O^+]{h\nu} & \ce{product} \end{array} \tag{7}$$

cis → trans isomerization (29) [Eq. (8)]. The two photochemical processes

$$\begin{array}{cc} \ce{cis-Pt(gly)_2} & \xrightarrow{h\nu} & \ce{trans-Pt(gly)_2} \end{array} \tag{8}$$

are *not* mutually related through mechanism (2) or (3). In fact, the dissociated product does not convert thermally to the trans isomer upon neutralization of the solution (32). On the other hand, when the photo-isomerization in neutral solution is carried out in the presence of labeled free glycine, no isotopic scrambling occurs (30). This also shows that the mechanism of isomerization in neutral solutions is the intramolecular twisting mechanism 1. The quantum yield of the cis → trans photo-isomerization is 0.12 and is independent of wavelength of irradiation (254–313 nm) and of the concentration of dissolved oxygen (32). A sensiti-zation and quenching study (33) showed that the cis → trans photo-isomerization [Eq. (8)] can be sensitized by high-energy triplet sensitizers, such as pyrazine (triplet energy 74.7 kcal/mol) and xanthone (triplet energy 74.1 kcal/mol), and can be quenched by low-energy triplet quench-ers, such as Ni_{aq}^{2+} (triplet energy 25.4 kcal/mol). Intermediate sensitiz-ers and quenchers do not work, and this was taken as an indication that the quenchable excited state responsible for the reaction is strongly dis-torted, as expected on the basis of a twisting mechanism. From the quenching results, the lifetime of the reactive state was estimated to be $\geq 10^{-7}$ sec (33). The trans isomer appears to be definitely more photoinert than the cis; in fact, an upper limit of 0.001 was estimated for the trans → cis photoisomerization quantum yield (32).

The photoisomerization reaction of cis- and trans-dichlorobis(pyridine)-platinum(II), $Pt(py)_2Cl_2$, was studied in chloroform solution (34). It was found that 313 nm irradiation of the cis isomer causes simultaneous cis → trans isomerization [Eq. (9)] and detachment of one pyridine ligand [Eq. (10)]. By thermal secondary recoordination of the released pyridine, the latter process yields the trans isomer [Eq. (11)]. However, this step is

$$cis\text{-}Pt(py)_2Cl_2 \xrightarrow{h\nu} trans\text{-}Pt(py)_2Cl_2 \tag{9}$$

$$cis\text{-}Pt(py)_2Cl_2 + S \xrightarrow{h\nu} cis,trans\text{-}Pt(py)Cl_2S + py \tag{10}$$

$$trans\text{-}Pt(py)Cl_2S + py \xrightarrow{slow} trans\text{-}Pt(py)_2Cl_2 + S \tag{11}$$

slow (34) and cannot be used to account for the observed cis → trans photoisomerization in terms of mechanism 3. Therefore, the primary cis → trans photoisomerization was thought to occur via an intramolecular mechanism, presumably twisting mechanism 1. The quantum yields of the two primary processes are 0.038 [Eq. (9)] and 0.024 [Eq. (10)]. The trans isomer was found to undergo similar primary processes, i.e., isomeriza-tion and pyridine release, but with lower quantum yields ($\sim 10^{-3}$) (34).

The photochemistry of cis- and trans-diamminodiaquoplatinum(II), $Pt(NH_3)_2(H_2O)_2^{2+}$, was briefly investigated (35). In spite of the poor reso-lution of the spectra of the two isomers, an isomerization was detected spectrophotometrically when the cis isomer was irradiated in acidic solution at 363 nm. The quantum yield of the cis → trans isomerization was 0.13, but the trans isomer was practically unreactive. In the absence of water-exchange studies it is not possible to conclude anything about the mechanism of the photoisomerization.

In spite of the limited number of pertinent experimental data, the above survey suggests that cis–trans photoisomerization in square planar Pt(II) complexes occurs at least partially by the tetrahedral twisting mechanism. A brief discussion of some features of this mechanism seems to be appropriate at this point. The tetrahedral twisting mechanism implies that electronic excitation causes a square planar structure to undergo a facile rearrangement to one that is tetrahedral or pseudotetrahedral. Tetrahedral structures are relatively stable for Ni(II) complexes (in some cases these exhibit square planar/tetrahedral equilibria at room temperature) (36), and such structures should have increasing energies, relative to the square planar, in going to Pd(II) and to Pt(II); however, the energy difference is likely to be, in most cases, lower than the typical excitation energies of these complexes. Therefore, it is reasonable to consider a tetrahedral intermediate as energetically accessible from excited states of Pt(II) complexes.

Actually, there are a number of spectroscopic results and theoretical considerations which indicate that the tetrahedral structure may not simply be regarded as a chemical intermediate, but rather as the stable equilibrium geometry of some excited states of square planar complexes. Polarized crystal spectra of $Ni(CN)_4^{2-}$ and $PtCl_4^{2-}$ were interpreted (37–39) assuming tetrahedral equilibrium geometry for some of the excited states. The original suggestion (25) was developed from the photochemical standpoint by others (30,31), who proposed potential energy curves for the lowest excited state of $Pt(gly)_2$ having a minimum at a pseudotetrahedral "transoid" geometry. Subsequently, an extended Hückel MO calculation (40) for $Pt(gly)_2$ yielded two minima rather than one near the tetrahedral geometry, with the "transoid" one being somewhat deeper than the

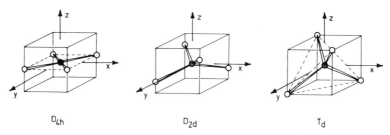

D_{4h} D_{2d} T_d

Fig. 3 Pictorial representation of the distortion coordinate leading from a square planar to a tetrahedral structure.

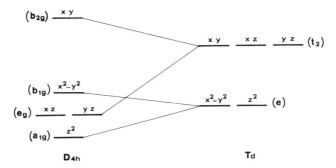

Fig. 4   Orbital correlation diagram for a square planar ↔ tetrahedral interconversion.

"cisoid." Similar results were obtained (41) with an angular overlap model for a general d^8 case.

The reasons for the appearance of minima at pseudotetrahedral geometries can be easily appreciated by considering correlation diagrams for square planar/tetrahedral structures of d^8 metal complexes. Orbital and/or state correlation diagrams for these systems have been proposed by others (37–39,42,43) for different purposes and with various degrees of sophistication. Our initial approach will be similar to that of Whitesides (43). Let us consider a square planar to tetrahedral rearrangement of a PtA$_4$ complex involving D_{4h}, D_{2d}, and T_d symmetries, as shown in Fig. 3. The d-orbital ordering in D_{4h} and T_d symmetries and the appropriate orbital correlation diagram are shown in Fig. 4. In working out a state correlation diagram for a d^8 complex, several steps are followed. First, the one-electron configurations in both geometries, the corresponding states, and their components in D_{2d} symmetry are derived, as shown in Tables 2 and 3. When one is correlating square planar and tetrahedral states of the same D_{2d} symmetry type, it is more informative to follow first the correlation between the one-electron configurations dictated by Fig. 4, and then to

TABLE 2

Electronic States for a d^8 System in D_{4h} and D_{2d} Symmetry

One-electron configuration, D_{4h}	States	
	D_{4h}	D_{2d}
$(a_{1g})(e_g)^4(b_{1g})^2(b_{2g})$	$^1B_{2g}$, $^3B_{2g}$	$^1B_2$, $^3B_2$
$(a_{1g})^2(e_g)^3(b_{1g})^2(b_{2g})$	^1E_g, ^3E_g	^1E, ^3E
$(a_{1g})^2(e_g)^4(b_{1g})(b_{2g})$	$^1A_{2g}$, $^3A_{2g}$	$^1A_2$, $^3A_2$
$(a_{1g})^2(e_g)^4(b_{1g})^2$	$^1A_{1g}$	$^1A_1$

TABLE 3

Electronic States for a d^8 System in T_d
and D_{2d} Symmetry

One-electron configuration, T_d	States	
	T_d	D_{2d}
$(e)^3(t_2)^5$	$^1T_1$	^1E, $^1A_2$
	$^1T_2$	^1E, $^1B_2$
	$^3T_1$	^3E, $^3A_2$
	$^3T_2$	^3E, $^3B_2$
$(e)^4(t_2)^4$	$^1A_1$	$^1A_1$
	$^1T_2$	^1E, $^1B_2$
	^1E	$^1A_1$, $^1B_1$
	$^3T_1$	^3E, $^3A_2$

allow for configuration interaction, than simply to use the noncrossing rule. In particular, states deriving from the ground $(a_{1g})^2(e_g)^4(b_{1g})^2$ and excited $(a_{1g})^2(e_g)^3(b_{1g})^2(b_{2g})$ configurations tend to correlate with states deriving from the ground $(e)^4(t_2)^4$ configuration, whereas the other square planar one-electron excited states tend to correlate with states from the excited $(e)^3(t_2)^5$ tetrahedral configuration. The resulting state correlation diagram is shown in Fig. 5. The diagram shows a number of interesting features. The square planar ground state correlates with an intraconfigura-

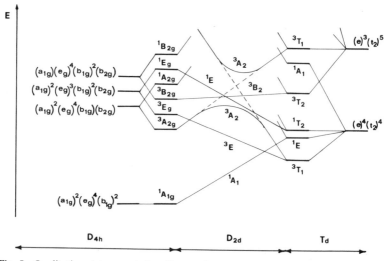

Fig. 5 Qualitative state correlation diagram for square planar ↔ tetrahedral interconversion of a d^8 metal complex.

tional excited state of tetrahedral structure. On the other hand, there are two low-lying excited states of the square planar structure, namely, ^3E_g and $^3A_{2g}$, which correlate with the ground state of the tetrahedral geometry. Among these, ^3E_g goes smoothly downhill to the tetrahedral ground state, whereas $^3A_{2g}$ correlates to the tetrahedral ground state through an energy barrier that originates from the "avoided crossing" (44) between the two $^3A_2$ states. According to this picture, therefore, the ^3E_g state is unstable in D_{4h} symmetry and must have a minimum in T_d geometry, whereas the ground state and the other LF states (except, possibly, for ^1E_g) have minima at square planar geometry.

The description presented thus far has completely neglected spin–orbit coupling. Actually, spin–orbit coupling is extremely important for platinum compounds (spin–orbit coupling parameters for $PtCl_4{}^{2-}$, 2600–3400 cm^{-1}) (39). It causes "singlet" and "triplet" states of the same spin–orbit representation to mix, giving rise to splitting of the formally triplet states. A complete ligand field treatment of $PtCl_4{}^{2-}$ in D_{4h} symmetry, including spin–orbit coupling, has been given (38). It can be easily demonstrated that the ground state $^1A_{1g}$ has the spin–orbit representation Γ_1 and that both ^3E_g and $^3A_{2g}$ split into manifolds that contain Γ_1 states. The same is true in D_{2d} symmetry. As a consequence, the formally singlet A_1 and the formally triplet E and A_2 states are now allowed to interact via a spin–orbit-induced perturbation (45). The result may be the avoidance of the crossing of surfaces shown in Fig. 5, giving rise to a situation of the type shown in Fig. 6.

Thus, it seems likely that in PtA_4 complexes the square planar ground state has a minimum at a geometry that is close but not identical to the

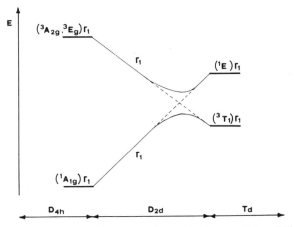

Fig. 6 Effect of spin–orbit perturbation on the lowest states of Fig. 5.

tetrahedral. The same should be true for a PtA_2B_2 complex, for which most of the above reasoning could be repeated, albeit in lower symmetries. Now, if we think of a cis–trans isomerization reaction as involving a square planar to tetrahedral to square planar rearrangement, the potential energy diagram along the whole reaction coordinate would be made up of two halves similar to that shown in Fig. 6 and roughly symmetric about the tetrahedral structure. Actually, differences between the two isomeric square planar forms are expected for both the energy position of the ground state (which depends on the thermodynamic stability of the isomers) and the excitation energies. These differences are expected to affect markedly the position of minima and maxima around the tetrahedral arrangement as well as the heights of the corresponding potential energy barriers, although it may not be possible to predict this influence in a straightforward manner.

A number of experimental results are, however, closely dependent on shape, position, and barrier height of the maxima and minima at quasi-tetrahedral geometries. First of all, the ratio between quantum yields of the cis $\rightarrow$ trans and trans $\rightarrow$ cis photoreactions should be highly dependent on these features, if wavelength independence of quantum yields is taken as an indication that relaxation to the lowest triplet precedes the rearrangement in both cases. For example, the "transoid" minimum being deeper than the "cisoid" and/or the ground state "transoid" barrier being lower than the "cisoid" would favor the occurrence of cis $\rightarrow$ trans over trans $\rightarrow$ cis photoisomerization, and vice versa (Fig. 7). As Table 1 shows, in all of the well-characterized systems, one isomerization is strongly favored over the other, indicating that such an asymmetry generally plays an important role. Another experimental result of considerable interest in connection with the shape of the potential energy curves near tetrahedral geometries is the possibility that the main isomerization reaction is quenched, presumably by energy transfer, if suitable low-energy quenchers are used (27,33). As briefly remarked (33), the reactive excited state must be intercepted by the quencher in a minimum which lies *before* the tetrahedral geometry and which is different from that minimum whose deactivation to the ground state leads to isomerization. This, again, is consistent with the picture described above but would be incompatible with any model with a single minimum on the excited state potential surfaces.

In conclusion, some of the gross features of observed cis–trans photo-isomerization reactions are consistent with the above crude model of tetrahedral twist. Nonetheless, several features of certain specific systems cannot be easily explained. For example, the remarkably long lifetime exhibited by the quenchable excited state is particularly puzzling (27,33);

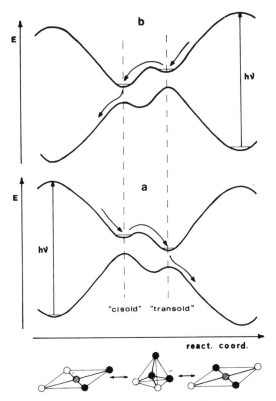

Fig. 7 Representation of two possible energy profiles favoring cis → trans (a) and trans → cis (b) photoisomerization of square planar complexes.

this would imply poor dynamic linkage (46) between excited and ground state surfaces and also relatively high barriers in the excited state between the quenchable minimum and that responsible for the isomerization. It is apparent that more experimental studies are needed before the photoisomerization mechanism can be completely elucidated. It seems likely that both temperature dependence studies and flash photolysis investigations would help considerably in clarifying many issues of these intriguing systems.

B. Cis–Trans Photoisomerization of Octahedral Complexes

The two most important types of geometric isomerizations of octahedral complexes are the cis–trans isomerization of MA_4B_2 complexes [Eq.

$$\text{Cis} \rightleftharpoons \text{Trans} \tag{12}$$

Cis   Trans

$$\text{Cis} \rightleftharpoons \text{Trans} \tag{13}$$

Cis   Trans

(12)] and that of MA_3B_3 complexes [Eq. (13)]. In these systems, A and B may be unidentate ligands or ends of AA, BB, or AB chelating ligands. In some cases, notably in the cis–trans isomerization of tris(chelate) $M(AB)_3$ complexes, the geometric isomerization is intimately related to enantiomerization. Thermal isomerization mechanisms of octahedral complexes have been reviewed and discussed (20,47). From the photochemical viewpoint, the possible isomerization mechanisms are essentially the same as the thermal ones, namely, bond rupture or twisting mechanisms (20,47), with the principal reaction intermediate being reached by an excited state photochemical process rather than by a ground state thermally activated process. Photochemical isomerization processes are predicted to occur rather easily, since excited states of coordination compounds, especially MC states, are expected on general grounds to be both more substitution labile and less rigid than the corresponding ground states.

In fact, reports of cis–trans photoisomerization of octahedral complexes are not very common in the literature. A number of systems for which such processes have been reported are shown in Table 4. Other systems exhibiting cis–trans photoisomerization in conjunction with enantiomerization are dealt with in Section II,E. As shown in Table 4, the reports concern Cr(III), Co(III), and Ir(III) complexes containing unidentate ligands usually irradiated in the MC spectral region. In no case have ligand-exchange studies been performed, so that conclusive evidence for or against bond rupture mechanisms (20,47) is lacking. However, it should be noted that (a) most of the systems shown in Table 4 are aquo complexes in aqueous solution; (b) other systems, namely, the $Ir(en)_2Cl_2{}^+$ complexes, were studied in aqueous solution containing free Cl^- ligands; (c) the remaining systems, namely, the IrL_3X_3 complexes, were studied in organic

TABLE 4

Cis–Trans Photoisomerization of Octahedral Complexes

Complex	Type of isomerization	ϕ	Remarks[a]	Ref.
$Cr(NH_3)_4(H_2O)_2^{3+}$	Trans → cis	0.35		49
$Cr(en)_2(H_2O)_2^{3+}$	Cis → trans	0.15	Simultaneous en aquation	50
$Cr(en)_2(H_2O)(OH)^{2+}$	Cis → trans	0.05	Simultaneous en aquation	50
	Trans → cis	0.30		50
$Cr(en)_2(OH)_2^{+}$	Cis → trans	0.15–0.065	Simultaneous en aquation, added en	50
	Trans → cis	0.01	Added en	50
$Cr(en)_2(H_2O)Cl^{2+}$	Trans → cis	0.40		49
$Cr(en)_2(H_2O)NCS^{2+}$	Trans → cis	0.42		49
$Co(CN)_4(H_2O)_2^{-}$	Cis → trans	0.34		53
	Trans → cis	0.04–0.004		53
$Co(CN)_4(OH)_2^{3-}$	Cis → trans	0.045		53
$Co(en)_2(H_2O)Cl^{2+}$	Cis → trans	0.0042		54
$Ir(en)_2Cl_2^{+}$	Cis → trans	—[c]	Added Cl^-	55
	Trans → cis	—[c]	Added Cl^-	55
$IrL_3X_3^{b}$	Trans → cis	—[c]	Benzene, acetone, chloroform	56

[a] Unless otherwise noted, aqueous solution of appropriate pH, room temperature, wavelength of irradiation in the MC region.

[b] $X = Cl, Br, I; L = PMe_3, PEt_3, P(n\text{-}Bu)_3, P(n\text{-}Pr)_2Ph, P(n\text{-}Bu)_2Ph$.

[c] Not reported.

noncoordinating solvents which would allow fast recoordination of any released ligand. The above observations indicate that the experimental conditions of all of the systems in Table 4 are suitable for isomerization by dissociation–recoordination mechanisms (20,47). Similar systems not fulfilling the same conditions, e.g., containing other ligands instead of water, in the absence of external free ligands, or in coordinating solvents, generally exhibit photosolvation reactions rather than isomerization (1,48). Thus, it seems highly probable that the geometric photoisomerization reactions of the octahedral complexes in Table 4 occur via ligand photosubstitution. Considerations about the mechanisms of these processes, therefore, are strongly dependent on the stereochemistry of ligand photosubstitution in these complexes.

For the Cr(III) complexes, the trans → cis photoisomerizations (49,50) can be well accounted for by the stereospecific photoaquation mechanism of these complexes (Section III), assuming that photoexchange of water occurs. As shown by Eq. (14), the strongest field ligand on the tetragonal

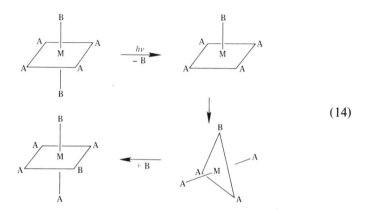

$$(14)$$

axis (which in the cases shown in Table 4 is water or OH$^-$) is released in the primary photochemical process, the square pyramidal excited intermediate then rearranges to a trigonal bipyramid containing the ligand trans to that released in the equatorial plane, and the resultant trigonal bipyramidal intermediate undergoes selective cis attack by the solvent (*51*), giving rise to the cis isomer of the starting complex.

For the cis → trans photoisomerizations (*50*), all involving $Cr(en)_2X_2^{n+}$ complexes, the mechanistic pattern is not as straightforward as that described above. It can be easily shown that a dissociative water-exchange mechanism cannot lead from the cis to the trans isomer. In fact, two trigonal bipyramidal intermediates can be formed from a *cis*-CrA_4B_2 upon release of B, one having B in the axial position (which can only lead back to the starting cis isomer) and one that is identical to that of the trans → cis isomerization [Eq. (14)]. Therefore, in these cases, it seems necessary to invoke either an intramolecular twisting mechanism or a one-ended dissociation–recombination mechanism involving the en ligand. Incidentally, photodetachment of one en ligand end trans to H_2O is in these cases the primary photoprocess predicted by Adamson's first rule (*52*). Also, the fact that an efficient photoaquation reaction always accompanies the isomerization strongly supports one-ended en detachment. A mechanism of this type is shown in Eq. (15), where A—A is en and B is H_2O or OH$^-$. Note that in this case the final attack on the trigonal bipyramidal intermediate occurs trans to the nitrogen ligand, as predicted by the symmetry selection rules for this process (*51*).

For the d^6 systems, photosubstitution mechanisms and stereochemistry are much less understood than for Cr(III) complexes (*48*). In the aquo- and hydroxotetracyanocobaltate(III) cases, a water-exchange mechanism was proposed (*53*) which was similar to that shown in Eq. (14) for the trans → cis thermal and photochemical isomerization of these complexes. Since it

(15)

was assumed that the trigonal bipyramidal intermediate, as in the Cr(III) case, undergoes only cis attack, it was necessary to postulate a twisting mechanism for the efficient cis → trans photoisomerization. It should be noted, however, that the cis → trans photoisomerization (quantum yield significantly lower than unity) is highly compatible with a water-exchange mechanism, provided that the trigonal bipyramidal intermediate is allowed to undergo both cis- and trans attack, leading to a mixture of the two isomers. The potential energy profiles for a twisting mechanism in this system have been discussed (41).

For the $Co(en)_2(H_2O)Cl^{2+}$ case, a bond rupture mechanism involving the en ligand was proposed (54), although a water-exchange mechanism via a trigonal bipyramidal intermediate could not be ruled out. As far as the Ir(III) complexes are concerned, the systems reported in Table 4 have been studied only qualitatively (55,56). For IrL_3X_3 complexes, the fact that the presence of external free ligands leads to the incorporation of these species into the isomerized complex (56) is a strong indication of the occurrence of dissociation–recombination mechanisms, which in these systems should be further facilitated by the use of noncoordinating solvents.

C. Linkage Photoisomerization

The most common ambidentate ligands giving rise to linkage isomerization processes are NO_2^- and SCN^- (57). Although one of two possible forms is always more stable than the other (usually the N-bonded "nitro" isomer for the NO_2^- complexes, and either S-bonded "thiocyanato" or N-bonded "isothiocyanato" isomers for SCN^- complexes, depending on the metal, oxidation state, other ligands, and solvent), with these ligands both linkage isomers can often be chemically isolated. With other ambidentate ligands, e.g., CN^-, one of the isomers is generally so unstable as to be detectable only by fast techniques. A method for obtaining such wrong-bonded isomers in solution is that which makes use of inner-sphere electron-transfer processes of the type shown in Eq. (16) (58).

$$Co(CN)_5^{3-} + Co(NH_3)_5CN^{2+} \rightarrow Co(CN)_5NC^{3-} + Co^{2+} + 5NH_3 \qquad (16)$$

Thermal linkage isomerization rates span several orders of magnitude [half-life for $Co(NH_3)_5ONO^{2+}$ and $Co(CN)_5NC^{3-}$, 16 hr and 1.6 sec, respectively]. For octahedral complexes, the known thermal isomerization mechanisms are intramolecular (20). Whether the intramolecular mechanism involves a transition state with residual covalent bonding [Eq. (17)] (20) or a dissociated intermediate of ion pair type [Eq. (18)] (59), it must be remarked that these thermal reactions always involve substantial *hetero-lytic* bond cleavage in the activation process.

$$Co(NH_3)_5NO_2^{2+} \rightarrow \left[Co(NH_3)_5 \cdots \begin{array}{c} \cdot\cdot O \\ \mid \\ N-O \end{array} \right]^{2+} \rightarrow Co(NH_3)_5ONO^{2+} \qquad (17)$$

$$Cr(H_2O)_5SCN^{2+} \rightarrow [Cr(H_2O)_5^{3+}, SCN^-] \rightarrow Cr(H_2O)_5NCS^{2+} \qquad (18)$$

A number of systems have been reported to undergo photochemical linkage isomerization (Table 5). All of these systems are d^6 metal complexes. Contrary to what happens in thermal reactions, the linkage isomerizations can be photochemically driven against a thermodynamic gradient. In fact, the stable N-bonded "nitro" complexes are converted to unstable O-bonded "nitrito" isomers, and the stable O-bonded formato complex is transformed to a transient product identified as a C-bonded isomer of the starting complex. A second, and more important, observation is that the photochemical linkage isomerization is usually promoted by LMCT irradiation and is accompanied in fluid solutions by [and apparently strongly coupled to (*vide infra*)] a redox decomposition process. Thus, it appears that, unlike thermal processes, the photochemical linkage isomerizations of Table 5 are promoted by excited state *homolytic* metal–ligand bond splitting.

The results obtained (60,61) on the formatopentamminecobalt(III) complex, $Co(NH_3)_5O_2CH^{2+}$, and their mechanistic interpretation are sufficiently different from those for the other systems in Table 5 to warrant separate discussion. Kantrowitz *et al.* (61) performed a thorough study of the 254 nm photochemistry of this complex, consisting of a redox decomposition reaction producing Co^{2+}, CO_2, and H_2 in nonstoichiometric yields. The quantum yields of formation of these products were measured in the presence of various free-radical scavengers, indicating that Co^{2+} and CO_2 arise from both scavengeable and nonscavengeable sources, whereas H_2 is completely scavengeable. A flash photolysis investigation

TABLE 5

Linkage Photoisomerization of d^6 Metal Complexes

Complex	λ (nm)	$\phi_{isomer.}$	ϕ_{redox}	Medium	Type of irradiation	Ref.
$Co(NH_3)_5(NO_2)^{2+}$	254	0.13	0.51	H_2O	LMCT	63
	313	0.11	0.41	H_2O	LMCT	63
	365	0.055	0.31	H_2O	LMCT	63
	442	0.035	0.12	H_2O	MC	63
	365	0.21	0.11	70% glycerol	LMCT	64
	254–442	a	b	Solid state	LMCT, MC	63
$Co(NH_3)_5SCN^{2+}$	250	0.17	0.35	H_2O	LMCT	67
	288	0.19	0.29	H_2O	LMCT	67
	333	0.15	0.24	H_2O	LMCT	67
	470	0.012	0.015	H_2O	MC	67
	288	0.15	0.057	70% glycerol	LMCT	67
$Co(NH_3)_5O_2CH^{2+}$	254	c	0.55^d	H_2O	LMCT	61
$Co(acac)_2pyNO_2$	231–365	a	b	Solid state	LMCT	95
	>450	b	b	Solid state	MC	95
$Pt(NH_3)_4(NH_2)(NO_2)^{2+}$	254	0.11	0.54	H_2O	LMCT	96
	313	0.29	0.23	H_2O	LMCT	96

a Efficient isomerization observed.

b Not observed.

c Transient absorption attributed to $Co(NH_3)_5CO_2H^{2+}$ in flash photolysis, which decays to redox products.

d Overall redox quantum yield (see text).

of this system (60) revealed the presence of a relatively long lived intermediate decaying with first-order kinetics ($\tau = 0.1$ sec at pH 2) to Co^{2+} and CO_2. The intermediate had a pK_a value of 2.6, with the protonated form decaying more slowly than the unprotonated. In view of the identity of this intermediate with that generated from a similar complex containing monodentate oxalate, $Co(NH_3)_5O_2CCO_2H^{2+}$, the authors proposed (61) that the observed intermediate is a C-bonded isomer of the formato starting complex, namely, $Co(NH_3)_5CO_2H^{2+}$. The proposed photoreaction mechanism is rather complex (61), but the essential features can be summarized as follows [Eqs. (19)–(22)]. The observed H_2 and CO_2 arise from

$$Co(NH_3)_5O_2CH^{2+} \xrightarrow{h\nu} {}^1(LMCT)Co(NH_3)_5O_2CH^{2+} \qquad (19)$$

$$
{}^1(LMCT)Co(NH_3)_5O_2CH^{2+} \left\{
\begin{array}{l}
\rightarrow {}^3(LMCT)Co(NH_3)_5O_2CH^{2+} \\
\\
\rightarrow (LC)Co(NH_3)_5O_2CH^{2+}
\end{array}
\right. \qquad (20)
$$

$$^3(LMCT)Co(NH_3)_5O_2CH^{2+} \longrightarrow Co^{2+} + HCO_2\cdot + 5NH_3 \qquad (21)$$

$$(LC)Co(NH_3)_5O_2CH^{2+} \longrightarrow Co(NH_3)_5CO_2H^{2+} \rightarrow Co^{2+} + \cdot CO_2H + 5NH_3 \quad (22)$$

secondary reactions of the $HCO_2\cdot$ and $\cdot CO_2H$ radicals. The key feature of this mechanism is that the two observed photoprocesses, redox decomposition and linkage isomerization, are supposed to arise from different excited states, namely, LMCT and LC states, respectively. In the LC excited state, the isomerization is assumed (60) to occur via deprotonation of the carbon atom, concomitant with rotation of the group, coordination of the "carbene-like" carbon, and transfer of the proton to one oxygen.

An important requirement of the proposed mechanism for linkage isomerization of $Co(NH_3)_5O_2CH^{2+}$ is that the acidity of the hydrogen atom bound to carbon must be greatly increased in the reactive LC excited state with respect to the ground state (notice that the transient isomer is formed efficiently even at pH 0) (61). This point is not obvious and may cause some difficulty. Actually, low-lying excited states of a coordinated formato ligand should be of the $n-\pi^*$ type involving the carbonyl group. It is known that such excited states of carbonyl compounds either behave as diradicals (if they are of triplet multiplicity) or show enhanced nucleophilic behavior at carbon (if they are singlets) (62). Neither of these features is consistent with the carbon hydrogen becoming extremely acidic in the excited state. It would perhaps be more easy to account for a strongly enhanced acidity of the hydrogen atom if the reactive excited state for isomerization were a LMCT excited state, i.e., a state in which substantial electron density has been withdrawn from the formato ligand. According to this hypothesis, both the redox decomposition and the linkage isomerization would have as a common precursor a LMCT state. This possibility, of course, does not imply that a simple radical pair mechanism operates, such as that proposed for the other systems in Table 5 (vide infra).

The results obtained with the other systems in Table 5 are rather consistent, and the interpretations proposed by the authors all fit into a general mechanistic scheme. These systems, therefore, will be discussed together; the $Co(NH_3)_5NO_2^{2+}$ and $Co(NH_3)_5SCN^{2+}$ cases, for which very detailed experimental information is available (18,63–67), will be taken into particular consideration. For these complexes, the results can be summarized as follows:

1. The photochemical behavior consists (63,66,67) of two simultaneous photoreactions, i.e., a redox decomposition [Eq. (23)] and a linkage

$$Co(NH_3)_5L^{2+} \rightarrow Co^{2+} + 5NH_3 + L \quad (23)$$

$$L = NO_2, SCN$$

isomerization [N-bonded to O-bonded for $Co(NH_3)NO_2^{2+}$, and S-bonded to N-bonded for $Co(NH_3)_5SCN^{2+}$].

2. The ratio of the quantum yields for redox decomposition and isomerization is practically constant and is independent of the wavelength of irradiation (*63,64,67*) (Table 5).

3. The quantum yields decrease markedly with increasing wavelength of irradiation. Although most of the photochemistry follows LMCT excitation, the onset of the photoredox behavior occurs definitely in the MC spectral region (*63,64,67*) (Fig. 8).

4. The quantum yields of redox decomposition are strongly quenched in going from aqueous solution to viscous water/glycerol solvent mixtures (*65,67*). The quantum yield for linkage isomerization is either increased (*65*) [$Co(NH_3)_5NO_2^{2+}$] or almost unaffected (*67*) [$Co(NH_3)_5SCN^{2+}$] by such a solvent change. In the solid state, no redox decomposition is observed, but linkage isomerization is efficient (Table 5).

The results have led several authors (*63,64,67*) to formulate a general radical pair mechanism, which can be represented schematically as follows. In Eqs. (24)–(30), XY^- denotes an ambidentate ligand. For the $Co(NH_3)_5NO_2^{2+}$ and $Co(NH_3)_5SCN^{2+}$ cases, the two coordinating positions X and Y represent N and O or S and N, respectively.

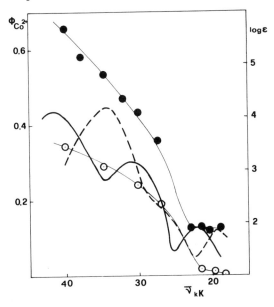

Fig. 8 Absorption spectra (right scale) and redox quantum yields (left scale) of $Co(NH_3)_5NO_2^{2+}$ (——, ●) and of $Co(NH_3)_5SCN^{2+}$ (----, ○).

$$Co(NH_3)_5XY^{2+} \xrightarrow{h\nu} (LMCT)Co(NH_3)_5XY^{2+} \tag{24}$$

$$(LMCT)Co(NH_3)_5XY^{2+} \longrightarrow [Co(NH_3)_5^{2+},XY^{\cdot}]_{solv.\ cage} \tag{25}$$

$$[Co(NH_3)_5^{2+},XY^{\cdot}]_{solv.\ cage} \begin{cases} \longrightarrow Co(NH_3)_5XY^{2+} \tag{26} \\ \\ \longrightarrow Co(NH_3)_5^{2+},XY^{\cdot} \tag{27} \end{cases}$$

$$Co(NH_3)_5^{2+},XY^{\cdot} \begin{cases} \longrightarrow Co(NH_3)_5YX^{2+} \tag{28} \\ \\ \longrightarrow Co(NH_3)_5^{2+} + XY^{\cdot} \tag{29} \end{cases}$$

$$Co(NH_3)_5^{2+} \longrightarrow Co^{2+} + 5NH_3 \tag{30}$$

Following excitation [Eq. (24)], a LMCT excited state is populated. This excited state is essentially dissociative and produces quantitatively, by homolytic Co—X bond splitting, a caged or "primary" radical pair [Eq. (25)]. This primary radical pair can either recombine to give the starting complex [Eq. (26)] or undergo a diffusive displacement, producing a solvent-separated or "secondary" radical pair [Eq. (27)]. The secondary radical pair can either undergo recombination to the isomerized complex [Eq. (28)] or diffuse into bulk solvent [Eq. (29)] to give kinetically free radicals which suffer their own fate; that of $Co(NH_3)_5^{2+}$ is to decompose to Co^{2+} and ammonia [Eq. (30)].

According to this mechanism, the overall reaction quantum yield is governed by the competition between processes (26) and (27) in the primary caged radical pair, a competition that depends primarily on the energy of the irradiation wavelength that is converted to kinetic energy of the radicals in the relaxation of the dissociative excited state. The partitioning of the overall photoreaction between linkage isomerization and redox decomposition is governed by the competition between processes (28) and (29) in the secondary radical pair, a competition that is strongly influenced by the rigidity of the solvent structure surrounding the radical pair.

This mechanism accounts well for experimental observations 1–4. The mechanism has been criticized (68,69) on the basis of some results on the solvent dependence of the photochemistry of $Co(NH_3)_5NO_2^{2+}$ and the somewhat related $Co(NH_3)_5N_3^{2+}$ complex: In spite of the sharp decreases in redox quantum yields observed in going from water to water/glycerol or water/ethylene glycol mixtures, no appreciable quantum yield reduction was obtained when the same macroscopic viscosities were made up with aqueous solutions of viscous polymers or water/cyclohexanol solutions. Although these results emphasize the point that macroscopic viscosity may often have nothing to do with the microscopic viscosity around the complex, they do not seem to invalidate the radical pair model for these photoreactions. As admitted (69), aqueous solutions of synthetic polymers are presumably extremely inhomogeneous, with all of the charged complex ions in regions of practically pure water. Similar arguments may be made to some extent for water/cyclohexanol mixtures, in view of the poor miscibility of cyclohexanol with water and the need to add ethanol to keep the mixture "homogeneous" (69).

Johnson and Pashman (70) have reported the observation of a transient infrared absorption that can be trapped at 77 K in the 365 nm solid-state photolysis of $[Co(NH_3)_5NO_2]Cl_2$. Since this absorption is different from that of both linkage isomers as well as from that of free NO_2 radical, the authors tentatively assigned this transient as a bidentate NO_2 adduct similar to the proposed transition state of the thermal isomerization reaction [Eq. (17)]. Owing to the very peculiar conditions of this experiment, this result does not seem to be crucial for the evaluation of the radical pair model of the photoisomerization in solution.

There are two important requirements of the radical pair mechanism [Eqs. (24)–(30)] that deserve some comment. First, the reactive LMCT state is assumed to be dissociative, i.e., a state without any energy minimum between the Franck–Condon levels reached by excitation and the caged radical pair products. Interestingly, $Co(NH_3)_5NO_2^{2+}$ and $Co(NH_3)_5SCN^{2+}$ are among the few cobalt–pentammine complexes for which the threshold energy for appreciable photoredox behavior E_{th} is substantially lower than the extrapolated threshold energy for LMCT absorption $E_{th'}$ (Fig. 8). For most $Co(NH_3)_5L^{2+}$ complexes (including L = NCS; no data for L = ONO) $E_{th'} - E_{th} \leq 5.7$ kcal/mole (71). Since $E_{th'}$ is a measure of the energy of the thermally equilibrated LMCT state (71,72), the fact that $E_{th'} > E_{th}$ for $Co(NH_3)_5NO_2^{2+}$ and $Co(NH_3)_5SCN^{2+}$ is consistent with the interpretation that the LMCT states of these complexes are dissociative. Obviously, the photoredox behavior observed in these systems in the MC spectral region is thought to arise from the conversion of MC excited states to "nonspectroscopic" levels of the dissociative LMCT state (64).

A second, and perhaps more puzzling, requirement of the radical pair mechanism [Eqs. (24)–(30)] is that, whereas primary recombination inside the cage must occur only with the X atom of the XY ligand (N for NO_2 and S for SCN), the secondary recombination of the solvent-separated radical pair must occur only through the Y atom (O for NO_2 and N for SCN). The stereoretentive behavior of the primary recombination is required by the strong wavelength dependence of the overall quantum yield coupled with the constant ratio of the two reaction modes. The reason for the stereoretentivity of the primary recombination lies most likely in the lack of rotational relaxation of the XY radical during the short lifetime of the primary solvent cage. Stereoretentive behavior has been observed in a number of organic systems in which cage effects are important (73). In the $Co(NH_3)_5NO_2^{2+}$ and $Co(NH_3)_5SCN^{2+}$ cases, in which interaction between the ligand radicals and the solvent water should be strong, it seems likely that no rotation can occur without molecules of the primary solvent cage being involved in the process. The opposite specificity in the secondary recombination is strongly demanded by the experimental finding that no isomerization is obtained upon LMCT excitation of $Co(NH_3)_5NCS^{2+}$ (74–76) and $Co(NH_3)_5ONO^{2+}$ (63), which should give rise to secondary radical pairs that are indistinguishable from those originating from their linkage isomers. Thus, a strong stereospecificity is indicated in the secondary recombination, favoring O coordination of NO_2 and S coordination of SCN. An attempt to explain this behavior for the $Co(NH_3)_5NO_2^{2+}$ case has been presented by Endicott (72) on the basis of a dynamic model for recombination in which energy barriers are considered to result from both bond compression and solvent repolarization. Although calculations based on this model require a number of debatable (67) assumptions, they predict substantially higher barriers for recombination through N than through O of the NO_2 radical (72). An interesting and conceptually simple argument has been advanced in this regard (67): The secondary recombination is considered to be an ''ordinary'' inner-sphere electron-transfer process (20,77,78). According to this suggestion, the rate-determining step in the secondary recombination should be the formation of a precursor complex by coordination of the oxidized ligand radical to the Co(II) center [Eq. (31)] before the electron-transfer step [Eq. (32)]. Of the two possible

$$Co(II)(NH_3)_5XY \cdot \qquad (31a)$$

$$Co(NH_3)_5{}^{2+}, XY \cdot$$

$$Co(II)(NH_3)_5YX \cdot \qquad (31b)$$

$$Co(II)(NH_3)_5XY \cdot \longrightarrow Co(III)(NH_3)_5XY^{2+} \qquad (32a)$$

$$Co(II)(NH_3)_5YX \cdot \longrightarrow Co(III)(NH_3)_5YX^{2+} \qquad (32b)$$

recombination paths, that going through the more stable precursor complex will be favored. Orhanovic and Sutin (67) point out that the precursor complexes in Eqs. (31) are identical with the thermally equilibrated LMCT states of the two isomers. Now, as discussed above, the LMCT states for both $Co(NH_3)_5NO_2^{2+}$ and $Co(NH_3)_5SCN^{2+}$ are dissociative unbound states, so that the precursor complexes for recombination of NO_2 via N or of SCN via S would have no appreciable stability. On the other hand, the LMCT state of $Co(NH_3)_5NCS^{2+}$ is a ''normal'' bound state (E_{th}

$\approx E_{th'}$) and would constitute a stable precursor complex for recombination of SCN via N. Similar information is not available for $Co(NH_3)_5ONO^{2+}$ (E_{th} not accurately known), but it seems likely that similar arguments may also apply in this case.

In conclusion, the stereospecificity in the secondary recombination of the radical pair is determined, according to this model, by the bonding properties of the LMCT states of the two linkage isomers. It is worth pointing out that the stereoretentive primary recombination of the caged radical pair [Eq. (26)] cannot be viewed in the same way, but rather as an outer-sphere (20,78) (presumably nonadiabatic) electron-transfer process leading directly to the ground state products. This process may in many aspects be likened to a radiationless deactivation of the relaxed LMCT state, although the wavelength dependence of the quantum yields is definitely more consistent with a cage recombination process.

An important question about the radical pair mechanism for redox decomposition and linkage isomerization is that concerning the multiplicity of the reactive LMCT state. This point has been discussed by several authors in the context of the redox photochemistry of Co(III) complexes (1,79). However, very little real progress toward reaching an answer to this question has been made. Two factors may account for this situation. First, attempts to sensitize the redox decomposition of Co(III) complexes with triplet energy donors (80–92) have often been plagued by the possibility of chemical sensitization occurring in the systems studied (mainly by electron transfer) (86,92–94). Second, much confusion in the discussion of experimental results has arisen because of the use of incorrect or incomplete descriptions of the LMCT manifolds. In fact, many discussions have been made in terms of "organic-like" pairs of LMCT states of singlet/triplet multiplicity. That the situation is more complex has only recently been recognized (17,18). The main complication consists of the presence of LMCT states corresponding to $(t_{2g}^6 e_g)$ low-spin or $(t_{2g}^5 e_g^2)$ high-spin Co(II). States of the first type exist as singlet/triplet pairs, whereas those of the second have triplet/quintet multiplicity. Whereas the high-spin states are higher in energy than the low-spin states in the Franck–Condon geometry of a Co(III) complex, the situation is reversed in the relaxed geometry of a $Co(NH_3)_5^{2+}$, L· radical pair. This implies crossing of the high-spin and low-spin states along the reaction coordinate, with the possibility of avoidance (44) of the crossing for the triplet states yielding a path for adiabatic transition from the initially populated low-spin configuration to high-spin products. The LMCT excited state situation for Co(III) complexes and the problems involved have been discussed in detail (17,18).

D. Photoinduced Changes in Coordination Geometry

The various types of photoisomerization processes discussed so far do not involve net changes in the coordination structure of the complexes. This section deals with those photochemical processes in which the coordination structure of the complex is changed. Strictly speaking, only some of these can be classified as photoisomerizations, namely, the square planar/tetrahedral isomerizations of Ni(II) complexes, whereas in other cases changes in coordination number and/or oxidation state accompany the change in coordination structure.

Nickel(II) complexes exhibit a great variety of coordination numbers and structures among transition metal complexes (97). In solution, complex equilibria are often established between different species (20), as shown schematically in Eq. (33). Because of the general lability of Ni(II)

$$(33)$$

complexes, these equilibria are very rapid, and the rates of interconversion can usually be measured only by fast relaxation techniques. Some very interesting studies have been performed on photochemical effects on these equilibria (Table 6). Incidentally, these studies provide the first clear example of photochemical reactions of coordination compounds induced by infrared radiation.

The behavior of the Ni(II) complex of 1,4,8,11-tetraazaundecane (2,3,2-tet) in aqueous solution under irradiation with the 1.06 μm pulse of a Q-switched Nd laser was studied (98). The complex exists as an equilibrium mixture of the yellow (λ_{max} 440 nm) square planar configuration and the blue diaquo pseudooctahedral form [Eq. (34)]. During the time of the

$$Ni(2,3,2\text{-tet})_2^{2+} + 2H_2O \rightleftarrows Ni(2,3,2\text{-tet})_2(H_2O)_2^{2+} \qquad (34)$$

irradiation pulse, an increase in absorbance at 440 nm was observed, which decayed almost to the original level with a lifetime of 0.3 μsec. This

TABLE 6

Photoinduced Changes in Coordination Geometry of Ni(II) Complexes

Photochemical reaction	λ (nm)	Re-marks	Ref.
$Ni(2,3,2\text{-tet})(H_2O)_2^{2+} \rightarrow Ni(2,3,2\text{-tet})^{2+} + 2H_2O$	1060	[a]	98
$[NiNSSN(H_2O)_2](ClO_4)_2 \rightarrow [NiNSSN(ClO_4)](ClO_4) + 2H_2O$	900–1800	[b]	100
$Ni(Et_4\text{dien})Cl_2 \rightarrow Ni(Et_4\text{dien})Cl^+ + Cl^-$	1060	[c]	101
$Ni(Et_4\text{dien})Cl^+ + Cl^- \rightarrow Ni(Et_4\text{dien})Cl_2$	530	[c]	101
$Ni(dpp)Cl_2$ (planar) $\rightarrow Ni(dpp)Cl_2$ (tetrahedral)	530	[d]	102
$Ni(dpp)Cl_2$ (tetrahedral) $\rightarrow Ni(dpp)Cl_2$ (planar)	1060	[d]	102
$Ni(dpe)Cl_2$ (planar) $\rightarrow Ni(dpe)Cl_2$ (tetrahedral)	530	[e]	102

[a] Aqueous solution, Q-switched Nd laser irradiation, thermal equilibrium reestablished with $\tau = 0.3$ μsec.

[b] Solid state, continuous irradiation, thermally inefficient reaction.

[c] Acetonitrile solution, Q-switched Nd laser irradiation, thermal equilibrium reestablished with $\tau \sim 1$ μsec.

[d] Acetonitrile solution, Q-switched Nd laser irradiation, thermal equilibrium reestablished with $\tau = 0.95$ μsec.

[e] Acetonitrile solution, Q-switched Nd laser irradiation, thermally reversible reaction.

result was interpreted as a perturbation of the equilibrium [Eq. (34)] toward the left caused by the laser pulse. Both the blue octahedral diaquo complex and the solvent water absorb at 1.06 μm. That the perturbation of the equilibrium was caused by a photochemical reaction of the complex and not by light absorption by the solvent was demonstrated by observing the same results in nonabsorbing D_2O solvent. Thus, 1.06 μm light absorption in the lowest MC band of $Ni(2,3,2\text{-tet})_2(H_2O)_2^{2+}$ causes fast (although presumably stepwise) release of the two axial water molecules, yielding the square planar form. The decay of the 440 nm transient absorption is attributed to the relaxation of the thermal equilibrium [Eq. (34)]. The correctness of this assumption was further demonstrated by subsequent work of Creutz and Sutin (99). They confirmed the findings of Ivin *et al.* (98) and were able to observe the same relaxation kinetics by using a Raman-shifted frequency of the Nd laser, namely, 1.41 μm, which is absorbed only by solvent water and causes a substantial temperature jump in the system. A quantum yield for the primary octahedral to square planar conversion of about 0.2 was calculated.

A substantially similar process is the conversion, by continuous infrared irradiation, of the blue dihydrate form of an Ni(II) complex of 1,8-bis(2-pyridyl)-3,6-dithiaoctane (NSSN) to an anhydrous form [Eq. (35)] which occurs in the solid state (100). The reaction does not proceed

$$\left[\begin{array}{c} H_2O \\ S \diagdown Ni \diagup N \\ S \diagup \quad \diagdown N \\ H_2O \end{array} \right] (ClO_4)_2 \xrightarrow{h\nu \ (IR)} \left[\begin{array}{c} ClO_4 \\ S \diagdown Ni \diagup N \\ S \diagup \quad \diagdown N \end{array} \right] ClO_4 + 2H_2O \qquad (35)$$

upon heating and is thus a true photochemical process. Again, the effect of low-energy electronic excitation is to cause the expulsion of axial-coordinated water. In this system, the reactant and product structures are trapped in the solid state and no fast reequilibration occurs.

Very interestingly, a recent study (*101*) has provided evidence for the occurrence of photochemical reactions of Ni(II) complexes that are essentially the reverse of the axial dissociations discussed above. The chloro(1,1′,7,7′-tetraethyldiethylenetriamine)nickel(II) chloride complex salt, [Ni(Et$_4$dien)Cl]Cl, dissolved in acetonitrile exists as an equilibrium mixture of a square planar form, a solvent-separated ion pair, and a pentacoordinated form, according to Eq. (36). If such solutions are

$$Ni(Et_4dien)Cl^+ + Cl^- \rightleftarrows Ni(Et_4dien)Cl^+//Cl^- \rightleftarrows Ni(Et_4dien)Cl_2 \qquad (36)$$

irradiated with 1.06 μm from a Nd laser, transient conductivity changes indicate that the absorbing pentacoordinated Ni(Et$_4$dien)Cl$_2$ form is converted photochemically to four-coordinated Ni(Et$_4$dien)Cl$^+$//Cl$^-$. This process is similar to the dissociation processes discussed above. If, however, the laser wavelength is changed by frequency doubling to 530 nm, so that the square planar form is the principal absorbing species, the conductivity changes clearly indicate the occurrence of a photoassociation reaction leading from Ni(Et$_4$dien)Cl$^+$//Cl$^-$ to Ni(Et$_4$dien)Cl$_2$. Thus, depending on the absorbing species, both axial photodissociation and axial photoassociation processes are possible in these systems.

The induction by light of two opposite processes, in this case octahedral to square planar (or square pyramidal) and square planar (or square pyramidal) to octahedral, although not very common, is not unexpected from a photochemical standpoint. Actually, this is just the behavior expected when the systems are such that ground state reactants correlate with excited state products and vice versa. As far as these Ni(II) systems are concerned, it should be remarked that, whereas the square planar forms are diamagnetic, the octahedral and the pentacoordinated forms are paramagnetic in their ground states. Therefore, singlet excited states of octahedral and pentacoordinate forms can relax smoothly to square planar ground states, whereas triplet excited states of square planar complexes should tend to associate axial ligands to yield adiabatically ground state octahedral or pentacoordinated products.

Another interesting example of photochemical effects on structural equilibria of Ni(II) complexes is represented by a study carried out on dichloro-1,3-bis(diphenylphosphino)propanenickel(II), Ni(ddp)Cl$_2$ (102). In acetonitrile solution, this complex is present as an equilibrium mixture of tetrahedral and square planar forms [Eq. (37)]. When these solutions

$$\text{Ni(ddp)Cl}_2 \text{ (tetrahedral)} \rightleftarrows \text{Ni(ddp)Cl}_2 \text{ (square planar)} \qquad (37)$$

are irradiated with 1.06 μm pulses from a Nd laser, which are absorbed by the tetrahedral isomer, a displacement of the equilibrium [Eq. (37)] toward the right takes place. If by frequency doubling the absorbing species becomes the square planar isomer, a dispacement of the equilibrium toward the left is observed. The relaxation times (0.95 μsec at 24°C) are the same for both reequilibration processes (102). Again, this two-way behavior is that expected for a ground state–excited state correlation between reactants and products. The state correlation diagram is, in this case, qualitatively the same as that constructed in Section II,A for Pt(II) complexes neglecting spin–orbit coupling (Fig. 5), in which ^3E_g and $^3A_{2g}$ square planar excited states correlate with the tetrahedral $^3T_1$ ground state, and the ^1E tetrahedral excited state correlates with the $^1A_{1g}$ square planar ground state.

There are a number of reports on photochemically induced changes in coordination structure which, although formally similar to those discussed above, differ from the Ni(II) cases in that they involve changes in the oxidation state of the metal. Examples of this type of behavior are the redox photoreactions of tris(acetylacetonato)cobalt(III), Co(acac)$_3$ [Eq. (38)] (103), and of tris(trifluoroacetylacetonate)manganese(III), Mn(tfa)$_3$ [Eq. (39)] (104). Clearly, in these systems the change in geometry is dictated by the coordinating properties of the metal in the new oxidation state obtained by LMCT photochemistry.

$$\text{Co(III)(acac)}_3 \xrightarrow{h\nu} \text{Co(II)(acac)}_2 + \text{acac} \cdot \qquad (38)$$

$$\text{Mn(tfa)}_3 \xrightarrow[\text{ROH}]{h\nu} \text{Mn(tfa)}_2 + \text{H(tfa)} \qquad (39)$$

E. Optical Photoisomerization

The most common types of complexes existing as D–L enantiomers are octahedral tris(chelate), M(chel)$_3$, and cis-bis(chelate), M(chel)$_2$X$_2$, complexes. When the chelating ligands are unsymmetric, an additional cis–trans isomerism is possible for M(μ-chel)$_3$ complexes. The nomenclature and the general mechanisms for the interconversion of optical and geometric isomers of these complexes have been thoroughly reviewed (47). For the sake of convenience, the isomerization mechanisms can be divided into "twisting" and "bond rupture" mechanisms, with the bond rupture mechanisms being further labeled as intermolecular or intramolecular, depending on whether there is complete or incomplete dissociation of one ligand from the coordination sphere.

Optical photoisomerization, photoenantiomerization, is simply a process whereby enantiomers are photochemically converted to one another [Eq. (40)]. Observable processes that are related to photoenantiomeriza-

$$D \underset{h\nu}{\overset{h\nu}{\rightleftharpoons}} L \tag{40}$$

tion are *photoracemization* and (partial) *photoresolution*. Photoracemization is usually observed with nonpolarized (or plane-polarized) light, starting with one resolved enantiomer that is photochemically converted to a racemic mixture. Partial photoresolution of a racemic mixture can be obtained by irradiation with circularly polarized light, provided that the wavelength used falls within a circular dichroism band. Since the quantum yields for $D \rightarrow L$ and $L \rightarrow D$ conversion must be the same by symmetry, the amount of photoresolution is a direct function of the circular dichroism or, more precisely, of the dissymmetry factor $g = (\epsilon_l - \epsilon_d)/\epsilon_{av}$, where ϵ_l, ϵ_d, and ϵ_{av} are molar extinction coefficients for left- and right-handed circularly polarized light and unpolarized light, respectively. Since g is usually of the order of a few percent, only small degrees of photoresolution can be obtained. The kinetic principles of photoresolution, including the effect of simultaneous thermal racemization, have been lucidly discussed (*105*).

Experimental studies of photoenantiomerization and related processes, which were very rare in the photochemistry of coordination compounds until a few years ago (*1*), have experienced a considerable expansion in recent years. A number of systems on which enantiomerization studies have been performed are listed in Table 7.

By far the best studied photoenantiomerization reaction is that of trioxalatochromium(III), $Cr(ox)_3{}^{3-}$, the photoracemization of which was first examined in detail in 1962 (*106*). The authors compared thermal racemization rates and photoracemization quantum yields obtained upon MC irradiation as a function of temperature and solvent composition (water, D_2O, water/organic solvent mixtures). They also compared thermal rates and photochemical quantum yields of ^{18}O exchange with corresponding racemization data. The results obtained led the authors to propose similar bond rupture mechanisms for the thermal and photochemical racemization of $Cr(ox)_3{}^{3-}$ consisting of one-end dechelation of oxalate with concomitant coordination of water, followed by an intramolecular displacement of oxalate by the dangling ligand [Eq. (41)]. According to this proposal, the observed retarding effect of nonaqueous solvents is attributed to these solvents being less efficient than water, both as nucle-

TABLE 7

Optical Photoisomerization and Related Reactions of Octahedral Complexes

Complex	Observed process[a]	Type of irradiation[b]	Remarks[c]	Ref.
$Cr(ox)_3^{3+}$	Rac	420	$\phi = 0.11,$ $\phi_{DMSO} = 5 \times 10^{-4}$	107
	Res	CP 546	1.4°C	105
$Cr(tox)_3^{3+}$	Res	CP 579	1.4°C	105
$\mu\text{-}[Cr(ox)_2OH]_2^{4-}$	Res	CP 546	1.4°C	105
$cis\text{-}Cr(ox)_2(H_2O)_2^-$	Geom	CP 546	1.4°C	105
$Cr(phen)_3^{3+}$	Rac	350	$\phi = 0.016$	109
	Res	546	D-Tartrate present	110
$Cr(ox)(phen)_2^+$	Rac	496.5	15°C, $\phi = 0.21$	111
	Res	CP 496.5	15°C, 1.6% resolution	111
$Cr(ox)_2phen^-$	Res	CP 514.5	15°C, 2.0% resolution	111
$Cr(bipy)_3^{3+}$	Res	CP 488.0	15°C	111
$Cr(mand)_3^{3+}$	Poa	CP 514.5	No photostationary state	121
$Cr(DTC)_3$	Poa	CP 623.8	No photostationary state	121
$Cr(acac)_3$	Rac	546.1	$\phi_{C_6H_5Cl} = 0.0055$	113
	Res	CP 546.1	Chlorobenzene	113
$cis\text{-}Cr(tfa)_3$	Res[d]	CP 546.1	34°C, chlorobenzene	114
	Rac[d]	CP 546.1	34°C, $\phi_{C_6H_5Cl} = 0.0024$	114
	Geom[d]	CP 546.1	34°C, $\phi_{C_6H_5Cl} = 0.0048$	114
$trans\text{-}Cr(tfa)_3$	Res[e]	CP 546.1	34°C, chlorobenzene	114
	Rac[e]	CP 546.1	34°C, $\phi_{C_6H_5Cl} = 0.0038$	114
	Geom[e]	CP 546.1	34°C, $\phi_{C_6H_5Cl} = 0.0095$	114
$cis\text{-}Cr(atc)_3$	Rac[d]	254, 350, 577	35°C, n-hexane	116
	Geom[d]	254, 350, 577	35°C, n-hexane	116
$trans\text{-}Cr(atc)_3$	Rac[e]	254, 350, 577	35°C, n-hexane	116
	Geom[e]	254, 350, 577	35°C, n-hexane	116
$cis\text{-}Cr(pfa)_3$	Geom[d]	577	$\phi_{n-hexane} = 0.0093$	120
$trans\text{-}Cr(pfa)_3$	Geom[e]	577	$\phi_{n-hexane} \geq 5 \times 10^{-5}$	120
$cis\text{-}Cr(bfa)_3$	Geom[d]	577	n-hexane	120
$Co(ox)_3^{3-}$	Res	CP 632.8	—	121
$\mu\text{-}[Co(ox)_2OH]_2^{4-}$	Res	CP 632.8	—	121
$trans\text{-}Rh(tfa)_3$	Geom[e]	254	$\phi_{cyclohexane} = 9.2 \times 10^{-5}$	122

[a] Abbreviations: Rac, photoracemization; Res, photoresolution; Geom, cis–trans photoisomerization; Poa, photoinduced optical activity.

[b] Unless otherwise noted, wavelength (nanometers) of unpolarized light used; CP indicates the use of circularly polarized light.

[c] Unless otherwise noted, aqueous solution and room temperature.

[d] System exhibiting simultaneous enantiomerization and cis–trans isomerization; quantum yield of Rac corresponds to $\phi_1 + \phi_5$ in Eq. (43); quantum yield of Geom corresponds to $\phi_2 + \phi_5$ in Eq. (43).

[e] System exhibiting simultaneous enantiomerization and cis–trans isomerization; quantum yield of Rac corresponds to $\phi_4 + \phi_6$ in Eq. (43); quantum yield of Geom corresponds to $\phi_3 + \phi_6$ in Eq. (43).

(41)

ophiles toward Cr(III) and in favoring charge separation in the bond rupture process (106). In subsequent work (107) on $Cr(ox)_3^{3-}$ in water/DMSO mixtures, the observed solvent effects were compared with the composition of the complex solvation shell as determined by NMR techniques. It was found that DMSO causes a pronounced retardation of both thermal and photochemical racemizations, in spite of its good coordinating ability toward Cr(III) and its preferential solvation of the complex in the solvent mixtures. This result requires a role for the solvent that is different from that previously proposed (106). On the basis of this solvent effect and an observed [H⁺] dependence of the photoracemization reaction, a model was envisioned in which the role of water is that of facilitating the metal–ligand bond rupture via hydrogen bonding to the carboxylic oxygen (107). This picture is consistent with an essentially dissociative mechanism for Cr(III) photosubstitutions (see Section III,A for a discussion of this point), which in this case would proceed through a trigonal bipyramidal intermediate with an axial dangling ligand (47), as in Eq. (42).

(42)

Partial photoresolution of $Cr(ox)_3^{3-}$ racemic mixtures with circularly polarized light was studied independently by two groups (105,108). In both cases the results were consistent with the expectations based on known photoracemization quantum yields and thermal racemization rates. Similar photoresolution results were obtained (105) for tris(dithiooxalato)-chromate(III), $Cr(tox)_3^{3-}$, and di-μ-hydroxytetraoxalatodichromate(III), μ-$[Cr(ox)_2OH]_2^{4-}$. cis-Diaquodioxalatochromate(III), cis-$Cr(ox)_2$-$(H_2O)_2^-$, was rather exceptional in that it could not be resolved into enantiomers and only underwent reversible cis–trans isomerization.

A number of investigations have been performed (109–112) on Cr(III) complexes containing 1,10-phenanthroline (phen) and 2,2'-bipyridine (bipy) ligands. Quantum yields of photoracemization have been measured for $Cr(phen)_3^{3+}$ (109) and $Cr(ox)(phen)_2^+$ (111). Photoresolution with circularly polarized light has been achieved for $Cr(ox)(phen)_2^+$, $Cr(ox)_2phen^-$, and $Cr(bipy)_3^{3+}$. An interesting case of photoresolution with *unpolarized* light occurs when $Cr(phen)_3^{3+}$ is irradiated in the presence of antimony D-tartrate (*110*). This photochemical analogue of the Pfeiffer effect indicates that selective interactions between the optically active counterion and the excited enantiomeric complexes occur, causing differences in the quantum yields of the two enantiomerization processes [Eq. (40)]. The same authors (*109,112*) have also studied the effect of selective doublet quenchers (I^-, OH^-, SCN^-, O_2) on the photoracemization quantum yields of $Cr(phen)_3^{3+}$ in order to identify the reactive state of the enantiomerization process. The results, with the exception of the puzzling behavior observed with OH^- (enhancement of the photoracemization upon doublet quenching), are in agreement with the generally accepted (*48*) view that MC photochemistry of Cr(III) complexes arises principally from the lowest quartet excited state ($^4T_{2g}$), often in thermal equilibrium with the lowest doublet state (^2E_g). As far as the chemical mechanism of these enantiomerization processes is concerned, both twisting and one-end dissociation mechanism seem plausible (*112*).

Another group of complexes the photoenantiomerization reactions of which have been studied in detail includes tris(2,4-pentanedionato)-chromium(III), $Cr(acac)_3$, and several analogues containing unsymmetric β-diketonato ligands. Photoresolution experiments in which solutions of $Cr(acac)_3$ in organic solvents are irradiated with circularly polarized light in the MC spectral region, have been performed (*113*). The photoresolution results agree with theory (*105*) and give wavelength-independent quantum yields of inversion. As far as the chemical mechanism of inversion is concerned, the noncoordinating nature of the solvents used suggests (*113*) either a twisting or a unimolecular one-ended dissociation mechanism of the type shown in Eq. (42).

Studies of complexes containing unsymmetric acac derivatives are complicated by the superposition of optical and geometric isomerization characteristic of these systems (*47*). In these cases, the complete reaction scheme involves as many as 12 interconversion processes [Eq. (43)].

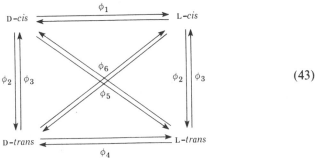

$$(43)$$

Since processes for any D → L and L → D conversion must have, by symmetry, the same quantum yield, a total of six quantum yields [Eq. (43)] is needed to describe fully a photochemical system of this kind. This photokinetic information was obtained (*114*) for tris(1,1,1-trifluoro-2,4-pentanedionato)chromium(III), Cr(tfa)$_3$, in chlorobenzene by partial photoresolution of a racemic mixture with circularly polarized light and subsequent separation of cis and trans isomers by thin-layer chromatography. All six quantum yields were found to have sizable values. Since a twisting mechanism excludes paths 2 and 3, and a bond rupture mechanism via a trigonal bipyramidal intermediate prohibits path 1, whereas a bond rupture mechanism via a square pyramidal intermediate allows all six paths (*115*), the authors conclude that "both a bond rupture mechanism and a twisting mechanism are operative" (*114*). Kinetic information of the same type was obtained (*116*) on tris [(+)-3-acetyl-camphorato]chromium(III), Cr(atc)$_3$, from photoisomerization of the four individual starting isomers, followed by product separation by means of high-pressure liquid chromatography. A comparison of experimental ratios of quantum yields for the various paths with theoretical expectations (*115,117,118*) led the authors to suggest, at least for the cis isomers, a bond-breaking mechanism with a square pyramidal intermediate having an axial dangling ligand (*116*). An earlier report (*119*) claiming that no cis–trans isomerization of tris(1,1,1-trifluoro-5,5-dimethylhexane-2,4-dionato)chromium(III), Cr(bfa)$_3$, occurred upon MC irradiation in hexane solution was subsequently shown to be incorrect (*120*): Cis–trans isomerization was obtained following MC irradiation of this complex and of the similar tris(1,1,1-trifluoro-5-methylhexane-2,4-dionato)chromium(III), Cr(pfa)$_3$.

Two Cr(III) complexes, namely, tris(mandelato)chromium(III), Cr(mand)$_3$, and tris(diethyl dithiocarbamate)chromium(III), Cr(DTC)$_3$, in racemic mixtures were found to exhibit optical activity upon irradiation with circularly polarized light (*121*). Since no photostationary state was attained, the photoinduced optical activity must be the consequence of some type of photochemical decomposition.

Besides the Cr(III) complexes discussed above, a few d^6 metal complexes have been photoresolved with circularly polarized light (*121*). An interesting and somewhat puzzling result is the strong solvent dependence found (*122*) for the trans → cis isomerization of Rh(tfa)$_3$; this substance in cyclohexane undergoes clean isomerization, whereas in 2-propanol irradiation gives rise only to decomposition. This result, obtained upon ultraviolet irradiation, is strongly suggestive of a primary photochemical process quite different from those operative in the Cr(III) cases, namely, one of homolytic metal–ligand bond breaking, followed by intramolecular radical recombination in competition with bimolecular radical scavenging.

III. STEREOCHEMICAL CHANGES DURING LIGAND PHOTOSUBSTITUTION: CHROMIUM(III) COMPLEXES

The photochemical reactions discussed in Section II, with the exception of some of the processes described in Section II,D, can strictly be classified as photoisomerizations. Photochemical rearrangements can also occur as steps in the mechanisms of photoreactions of coordination compounds other than photoisomerization. Common photoreactions of coordination compounds are ligand photosubstitution following MC irradiation and redox photochemistry induced by LMCT irradiation (1,2). Stereochemical changes accompanying redox photochemistry are often difficult to define, since the reduced metallo fragment generally has an extremely different coordination chemistry relative to that of the original complex (79). In ligand photosubstitution, on the contrary, stereochemical problems are clear-cut since the coordination geometry is unchanged in going from reactants to products. In particular, for octahedral complexes the point of interest is the degree to which the configuration (cis or trans) of the reactant is maintained in the photosubstituted products. Photosubstitution reactions of octahedral complexes have been studied principally for Cr(III) complexes and, to a more limited extent, for Co(III) and some heavier-metal complexes (1,2). Thus far, general stereochemical trends have emerged only for the Cr(III) complexes. In this section some of the mechanistic implications of the stereochemistry of Cr(III) photosubstitution reactions are discussed.

The ligand photosubstitution reactions of chromium(III) complexes constitute perhaps the most extensively studied field of inorganic photochemistry. Work in this area has been thoroughly reviewed (1,48). The photochemical behavior of truly octahedral (O_h microsymmetry) Cr(III) complexes in aqueous solution is relatively simple: Irradiation in the MC region gives rise to photoaquation reactions [Eq. (44)] with high quantum

$$CrA_6 + H_2O \xrightarrow{h\nu} CrA_5(H_2O) + A \qquad (44)$$

yields independent of the irradiation wavelength. The behavior is more complex for mixed-ligand complexes for which two or more photoaquation modes are possible depending on the released ligand. Equation (45) shows the possibilities for a monosubstituted octahedral complex. In these cases, it is generally found that one of the pathways has much

$$CrA_5X + H_2O \xrightarrow{h\nu} \begin{cases} \rightarrow CrA_5(H_2O) + X \\ \rightarrow CrA_4X(H_2O) + A \end{cases} \tag{45}$$

greater quantum yields than the others and that often the quantum yield ratios are dependent on wavelength.

In 1967, Adamson (52) proposed some empirical rules for predicting the type of released ligand in the photosubstitution reactions of mixed-ligand Cr(III) complexes. Briefly, the rules state that the strongest field ligand on the weakest field axis of the octahedron is the labilized one. Adamson's rules have been criticized on the basis of certain restrictive interpretations implying stereochemical consequences (123), but their predictive value is now generally recognized.

As far as the identification of the reactive excited state in the photochemistry of Cr(III) complexes is concerned, reference can be made to the energy-level diagram of Fig. 2. The most likely candidates are obviously the lowest spin-allowed and the lowest spin-forbidden excited states ($^4T_{2g}$ and ^2E_g in O_h symmetry, respectively). A great deal of information has accumulated, mainly from sensitization and quenching studies, which indicates that in most cases it is the lowest quartet excited state that reacts (48). Often, the quartet and the doublet may be in thermal equilibrium at room temperature, so that the quartet photosubstitution reaction consists of a prompt component and a delayed component (which may be quenched by suitable doublet quenchers) arising from back intersystem crossing from the doublet. The quartet state, according to recent fast laser photolysis measurements (124), undergoes intersystem crossing to the doublet in a few picoseconds, which means that the specific rate for ligand substitution in the quartet state must be extremely high.

A number of more or less sophisticated theoretical models have been proposed (125–129) in order to rationalize Adamson's rules in terms of the quartet hypothesis. Currently the most convincing one seems to be that proposed by Vanquickenborne and Ceulemans (129). This model predicts the labilized ligand by estimating absolute energies of individual bonds in the excited state (rather than differences in bond energies between ground and excited state, as done by most other models) in terms of σ- and π-bonding contributions of the ligands. This model is remarkably successful in predicting the released ligand in photosubstitutions of a wide variety of first row transition metal complexes, including some Cr(III) complexes not obeying Adamson's rules and several Co(III) complexes.

A point that has been the subject of considerable debate in the photochemistry of Cr(III) complexes is the "chemical" mechanism of the photosubstitution reaction in the lowest quartet excited state (9,48). As we shall see, this point is closely related to the stereochemistry of these photosubstitutions. Both dissociative and associative limiting mechanisms (20,24) can be considered for ligand substitution in the quartet state, although labels related to modes of activation should be extrapolated with great caution to extremely fast, practically nonactivated, excited state processes. It should be noted that all of the theoretical models proposed to account for Adamson's rules rely on estimates of bond labilization in the excited state and more or less explicitly assume dissociative-type mechanisms for the process. Unfortunately, kinetic effects of the entering ligand can hardly be experimentally investigated, since the short lifetime of the excited state (124) prevents substitution by ligands other than the solvent, except at extremely high ligand concentrations. A recent report (130), in which $Cr(NH_3)_6^{3+}$ in aqueous solution containing 0–8 M Cl^- is shown to undergo competitive aquation and chloride substitution with constant total quantum yield, is definitely in line with a dissociative mechanism followed by competitive scavenging of a pentacoordinated intermediate [although the mechanism proposed by the authors is somewhat different (130)]. Langford and Tong (131), on the other hand, interpreted as evidence in favor of an associative mechanism the higher quantum yields for N_3^- relative to SCN^- photoanation of $Cr(DMSO)_6^{3+}$. An approach to this problem has been taken by various authors (132–135) by studying the effects of solvent on photosubstitution reactions of Cr(III) complexes. However, the results are complex, and no general pattern of diagnostic value seems to have emerged from these studies.

Up to now, the strongest arguments in favor of an associative mechanism have been based on the stereochemistry of these photosubstitution reactions. These processes have been found (9,48,49) to be extremely stereospecific, in that usually 100% cis products are obtained upon photosubstitution of trans reactants [Eq. (46)]. This behavior has been sum-

$$trans\text{-}CrA_4XY + H_2O \xrightarrow{h\nu} cis\text{-}CrA_4X(H_2O) + Y \qquad (46)$$

marized (9) in the proposition that "the entering ligand will stereospecifically occupy a position corresponding to entry in the coordination sphere trans to the leaving ligand." Since a pentacoordinated intermediate would yield upon substitution a mixture of isomers (two-thirds cis and one-third trans, if statistical), the strong stereospecificity for the cis configuration has been taken as evidence for an associative mechanism (9). Also, the very low quantum yields observed for "stereorigid" complexes containing macrocyclic ligands (136) have been taken as evidence for the need for distortion in order to achieve seven-coordination in an associative mechanism.

This type of argument based on the stereochemistry of the photo-

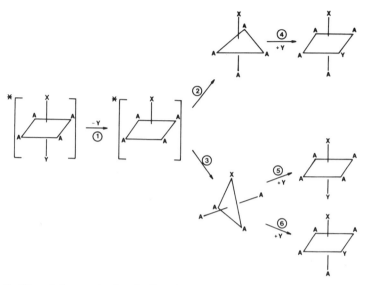

Fig. 9 Dissociative mechanism for ligand substitution in excited tetragonal Cr(III) complexes. Asterisk denotes electronically excited species.

substitution reactions should be revised in the light of a recent article (51) which represents an elegant application of symmetry-based selection rules to a complex photochemical problem. The approach used by the authors is that of considering the photosolvation reaction of a tetragonal *trans*-CrA_4XY complex as made up of several distinct steps, as shown in Fig. 9. In the lowest quartet excited state (in most practical cases the tetragonal ^4E_g component of the octahedral $^4T_{2g}$ state) reached following irradiation, the weakest bond dissociates heterolytically (step 1), as predicted by any one of the models or empirical rules for the photoreactions. The initially formed excited square pyramidal CrA_4X fragment relaxes by distortion to a ground state trigonal bipyramidal intermediate in one of two possible ways, i.e., with axial X (step 2) or with equatorial X (step 3). Upon equatorial coordination of solvent, the axial intermediate can only yield cis solvated product (step 4), whereas the equatorial intermediate can give both trans (step 5) and cis (step 6) products depending on the trans or cis site of attack. State correlation diagrams for all individual steps 2 to 6 have been calculated (51) in order to determine the predictions of symmetry-based selection rules for this process. The results are as follows. Of the two paths leading from the excited square pyramid to ground state pentagonal bipyramid, that with axial X (step 2) is symmetry forbidden (uphill excited state to excited state correlation), whereas that with equatorial X (step 3) is allowed (excited to ground state correlation). Of the two possible modes of solvent attack on the equatorial trigonal bipyramid, the trans mode (step 5) is forbidden (ground to excited state correlation), whereas the cis one (step 6) is allowed (downhill ground state to ground state correlation). The last result holds if, as is usually the case, X has a lower ligand field strength than does A. These results show that, if a dissociative mechanism such as that shown in Fig. 9. is operative, the strong stereospecificity of the overall process is imposed by the symmetry selection rules allowing only the 1, 3, 6 single-step sequence.

This conclusion considerably weakens any argument in favor of associative mechanisms based on the need to explain the stereospecific trans → cis behavior of the photosubstitution reactions of Cr(III) complexes. Also, the need for flexibility of the equatorial framework does not support association, since it is a built-in feature of a dissociative mechanism of the type shown in Fig. 9. In conclusion, it now seems that theoretical models based on essentially dissociative mechanisms are capable of accounting for the type of substituted ligand, the stereochemistry of the process, and the effect of equatorial rigidity on photosubstitution quantum yields.

A question that has been generally overlooked or, at best, understated in the discussion of photosubstitution mechanisms is the following: What portion of the overall photosubstitution process actually occurs on excited state potential energy surfaces? Whereas there is little doubt that the final photosubstitution products are not formed in electronically excited states, the question is open as to whether the primary photoreaction intermediate is formed in an excited or a ground state. From a general viewpoint, in spite of the considerable bond weakening occurring in the reactive MC excited state (125–129), it seems likely that a substantial activation energy would still be required if the primary step of a dissociative mechanism were to occur entirely in the excited state energy surface (i.e., with production of an MC excited state of the square pyramidal intermediate as in Fig. 9). As suggested for some d^6 systems (137), it seems more likely that the bond dissociation initiates in the "reactive" excited state and terminates on a ground state potential energy surface via dynamic coupling between the two states. A way of looking at this process in terms of the mechanism of Fig. 9 is to consider the formally consecutive bond-breaking (step 1) and deactivation–distortion (step 3) processes as a single concerted step. According to this picture, distortion of the other bonds simultaneous to bond breaking affords a low-energy pathway for excited to ground state dissociation. Blocking this possibility with rigid equatorial ligands would leave the complex only with the possibility of a substantially activated, fully excited state bond rupture process (138).

REFERENCES

1. V. Balzani and V. Carassiti, "Photochemistry of Coordination Compounds." Academic Press, New York, 1970.
2. A. W. Adamson and P. D. Fleischauer, eds., "Concepts of Inorganic Photochemistry." Wiley, New York, 1975.
3. E. L. Wehry, *Q. Rev., Chem. Soc.* **21**, 213 (1967).
4. V. Balzani, L. Moggi, F. Scandola, and V. Carassiti, *Inorg. Chim. Acta, Rev.* **1**, 7 (1967).
5. A. W. Adamson, W. L. Waltz, E. Zinato, D. W. Watts, P. D. Fleischauer, and R. D. Lindholm, *Chem. Rev.* **68**, 541 (1968).
6. A. W. Adamson, *Coord. Chem. Rev.* **3**, 169 (1968).
7. D. Valentine, Jr., *Adv. Photochem.* **6**, 123 (1968).
8. P. D. Fleischauer, A. W. Adamson, and G. Sartori, *Prog. Inorg. Chem.* **17**, 1 (1972).
9. A. D. Kirk, *Mol. Photochem.* **5**, 127 (1973).
10. C. R. Bock and E. A. Koerner von Gustorf, *Adv. Photochem.* **10**, 221 (1977).
11. C. K. Jørgensen, *Struct. Bonding (Berlin)* **1**, 234 (1966).
12. N. J. Turro, "Molecular Photochemistry." Benjamin, New York, 1965.
13. J. G. Calvert and J. N. Pitts, Jr., "Photochemistry." Wiley, New York, 1966.
14. R. P. Wayne, "Photochemistry." Butterworth, London, 1970.
15. J. P. Simons, "Photochemistry and Spectroscopy." Wiley, New York, 1971.
16. R. J. Watts, G. A. Crosby, and J. L. Sansregret, *Inorg. Chem.* **11**, 1474 (1972).
17. J. F. Endicott and G. J. Ferraudi, *Inorg. Chem.* **14**, 3133 (1975).
18. M. A. Scandola, C. Bartocci, F. Scandola, and V. Carassiti, *Inorg. Chim. Acta* **28**, 151 (1978).
19. G. A. Crosby, *Adv. Chem. Ser.* **150**, 149 (1976).
20. F. Basolo and R. G. Pearson, "Mechanism of Inorganic Reactions," 2nd ed. Wiley, New York, 1967.
21. L. Ramberg, *Ber. Dtsch. Chem. Ges.* **43**, 580 (1910).
22. I. Lifschitz and W. Froentjes, *Z. Anorg. Allg. Chem.* **224**, 173 (1935); **223**, 1 (1937).
23. C. Bartocci, F. Scandola, and V. Carassiti, *J. Phys. Chem.* **78**, 2349 (1974).
24. C. H. Langford and H. B. Gray, "Ligand Substitution Mechanisms." Benjamin, New York, 1966.
25. P. Haake and T. A. Hylton, *J. Am. Chem. Soc.* **84**, 3774 (1962).
26. S. H. Mastin and P. Haake, *J. Chem. Soc., Chem. Commun.* p. 202 (1970).
27. S. H. Goh and C. Y. Mok, *J. Inorg. Nucl. Chem.* **39**, 531 (1977).
28. A. A. Lamola, *in* "Energy Transfer and Organic Photochemistry" (A. A. Lamola and N. J. Turro, eds.), p. 102. Wiley (Interscience) New York, 1969.
29. V. Balzani, V. Carassiti, L. Moggi, and F. Scandola, *Inorg. Chem.* **4**, 1243 (1965).
30. F. Scandola, O. Traverso, V. Balzani, G. L. Zucchini, and V. Carassiti, *Inorg. Chim. Acta* **1**, 76 (1967).
31. V. Balzani and V. Carassiti, *J. Phys. Chem.* **72**, 383 (1968).
32. F. Bolletta, M. Gleria, and V. Balzani, *Mol. Photochem.* **4**, 205 (1972).
33. F. Bolletta, M. Gleria, and V. Balzani, *J. Phys. Chem.* **76**, 3934 (1972).
34. L. Moggi, G. Varani, N. Sabbatini, and V. Balzani, *Mol. Photochem.* **3**, 141 (1971).
35. J. R. Perumareddi and A. W. Adamson, *J. Phys. Chem.* **72**, 414 (1968).
36. G. N. La Mar and E. O. Sherman, *J. Am. Chem. Soc.* **92**, 2691 (1970), and references therein.
37. C. J. Ballhausen, N. Bjerrum, R. Dingle, K. Eriks, and C. R. Hare, *Inorg. Chem.* **4**, 514 (1965).

38. D. S. Martin, M. A. Tucker, and A. J. Kassman, *Inorg. Chem.* **4,** 1682 (1965).
39. D. S. Martin, M. A. Tucker, and A. J. Kassman, *Inorg. Chem.* **5,** 1298 (1966).
40. F. S. Richardson, D. D. Shillady, and A. Waldrop, *Inorg. Chim. Acta* **5,** 279 (1971).
41. J. K. Burdett, *Inorg. Chem.* **15,** 212 (1976).
42. D. R. Eaton, *J. Am. Chem. Soc.* **90,** 4272 (1968).
43. T. H. Whitesides, *J. Am. Chem. Soc.* **91,** 2395 (1969).
44. L. Salem, C. Leforestier, G. Segal, and R. Wetmore, *J. Am. Chem. Soc.* **97,** 479 (1975).
45. G. Herzberg, "Electronic Spectra and Electronic Structure of Polyatomic Molecules," p. 19. Van Nostrand-Reinhold, Princeton, New Jersey, 1966.
46. W. G. Dauben, L. Salem, and N. J. Turro, *Acc. Chem. Res.* **8,** 41 (1975).
47. N. Serpone and D. G. Bickley, *Prog. Inorg. Chem.* **17,** 391 (1972).
48. E. Zinato, *in* "Concepts of Inorganic Photochemistry" (A. W. Adamson and P. D. Fleischauer, eds.), p. 143. Wiley, New York, 1975.
49. P. Riccieri and E. Zinato, *J. Am. Chem. Soc.* **97,** 6071 (1975).
50. A. W. Adamson, *Adv. Chem. Ser.* **49,** 237 (1965).
51. L. G. Vanquickenborne and A. Ceulemans, *J. Am. Chem. Soc.* **100,** 475 (1978).
52. A. W. Adamson, *J. Phys. Chem.* **71,** 798 (1967).
53. L. Viaene, J. D'Olieslager, and S. De Jaegere, *Inorg. Chem.* **14,** 2736 (1975).
54. P. Sheridan and A. W. Adamson, *J. Am. Chem. Soc.* **96,** 3032 (1974).
55. G. S. Kovalenko, I. B. Baranovskii, and A. V. Babaeva, *Russ. J. Inorg. Chem. (Engl. Transl.)* **16,** 148 (1971).
56. P. R. Brooks, C. Masters, and B. L. Show, *J. Chem. Soc. A* p. 3756 (1971).
57. J. L. Burmeister, *Coord. Chem. Rev.* **3,** 225 (1968); R. J. Balahura and N. A. Lewis, *Coord. Chem. Rev.* **20,** 109 (1976).
58. J. Halpern and S. Nakamura, *J. Am. Chem. Soc.* **87,** 3002 (1965).
59. A. Haim and N. Sutin, *J. Am. Chem. Soc.* **87,** 4210 (1965); **88,** 434 (1966).
60. A. F. Vaudo, E. R. Kantrowitz, and M. Z. Hoffman, *J. Am. Chem. Soc.* **93,** 6698 (1971).
61. E. R. Kantrowitz, M. Z. Hoffman, and K. M. Schilling, *J. Phys. Chem.* **76,** 2492 (1972).
62. P. J. Wagner, *Top. Curr. Chem.* **66,** 1 (1976).
63. V. Balzani, R. Ballardini, N. Sabbatini, and L. Moggi, *Inorg. Chem.* **7,** 1398 (1968).
64. F. Scandola, C. Bartocci, and M. A. Scandola, *J. Phys. Chem.* **78,** 572 (1974).
65. F. Scandola, C. Bartocci, and M. A. Scandola, *J. Am. Chem. Soc.* **95,** 7898 (1973).
66. A. Vogler and H. Kunkely, *Inorg. Chim. Acta* **14,** 247 (1975).
67. M. Orhanovic and N. Sutin, *Inorg. Chem.* **16,** 550 (1977).
68. P. Natarajan, *J. Chem. Soc., Chem. Commun.* p. 26 (1975).
69. P. Natarajan, *J. Chem. Soc., Dalton Trans.* p. 1400 (1976).
70. D. A. Johnson and K. A. Pashman, *Inorg. Nucl. Chem. Lett.* **2,** 23 (1975).
71. J. F. Endicott, G. J. Ferraudi, and J. R. Barber, *J. Phys. Chem.* **79,** 630 (1975).
72. J. F. Endicott, *Inorg. Chem.* **14,** 448 (1975).
73. J. P. Lorand, *Prog. Inorg. Chem.* **17,** 207 (1972).
74. A. W. Adamson and A. M. Sporer, *J. Am. Chem. Soc.* **80,** 3865 (1958).
75. A. W. Adamson and A. M. Sporer, *J. Inorg. Nucl. Chem.* **8,** 209 (1958).
76. A. W. Adamson, *Discuss. Faraday Soc.* **29,** 163 (1960).
77. H. Taube, *Adv. Inorg. Chem. Radiochem.* **1,** 1 (1959).
78. N. Sutin, *in* "Inorganic Biochemistry" (G. L. Eichorn, ed.), p. 611. Elsevier, Amsterdam, 1973.
79. J. F. Endicott, *in* "Concepts of Inorganic Photochemistry" (A. W. Adamson and P. D. Fleischauer, eds.), p. 81. Wiley, New York, 1975.
80. A. Vogler and A. W. Adamson, *J. Am. Chem. Soc.* **90,** 5943 (1968).

81. M. A. Scandola, F. Scandola, and V. Carassiti, *Mol. Photochem.* **1**, 403 (1969).
82. M. A. Scandola and F. Scandola, *J. Am. Chem. Soc.* **92**, 7278 (1970).
83. H. D. Gafney and A. W. Adamson, *J. Phys. Chem.* **76**, 1105 (1972).
84. P. Natarajan and J. F. Endicott, *J. Phys. Chem.* **77**, 971 (1973).
85. P. Natarajan and J. F. Endicott, *J. Am. Chem. Soc.* **94**, 3635 (1972).
86. H. D. Gafney and A. W. Adamson, *J. Am. Chem. Soc.* **94**, 8283 (1972).
87. P. Natarajan and J. F. Endicott, *J. Am. Chem. Soc.* **95**, 2470 (1973).
88. P. Natarajan and J. F. Endicott, *J. Phys. Chem.* **77**, 1823 (1973).
89. J. N. Demas and A. W. Adamson, *J. Am. Chem. Soc.* **95**, 5159 (1973).
90. P. Natarajan and J. F. Endicott, *J. Phys. Chem.* **77**, 2049 (1973).
91. L. Moggi, N. Sabbatini, and O. Traverso, *Mol. Photochem.* **5**, 11 (1973).
92. H. D. Gafney and A. W. Adamson, *Coord. Chem. Rev.* **16**, 171 (1975).
93. V. Balzani, L. Moggi, M. F. Manfrin, F. Bolletta, and G. S. Laurence, *Coord. Chem. Rev.* **15**, 321 (1975).
94. G. Navon and N. Sutin, *Inorg. Chem.* **13**, 2159 (1974).
95. D. A. Johnson and J. E. Martin, *Inorg. Chem.* **8**, 2509 (1969).
96. N. Sabbatini, L. Moggi, and G. Varani, *Inorg. Chim. Acta* **5**, 469 (1971).
97. F. A. Cotton and G. Wilkinson, "Advanced Inorganic Chemistry," 3rd ed. Wiley (Interscience), New York, 1972.
98. K. J. Ivin, R. Jamison, and J. J. McGarvey, *J. Am. Chem. Soc.* **94**, 1763 (1972).
99. C. Creutz and N. Sutin, *J. Am. Chem. Soc.* **95**, 7177 (1973).
100. J. H. Worrel and J. J. Genova, *J. Am. Chem. Soc.* **92**, 5282 (1970).
101. L. Campbell and J. J. McGarvey, *J. Am. Chem. Soc.* **99**, 5809 (1977).
102. J. J. McGarvey and J. Wilson, *J. Am. Chem. Soc.* **97**, 2531 (1975).
103. N. Filipescu and H. Way, *Inorg. Chem.* **8**, 1863 (1969).
104. H. D. Gafney, Ph.D. Thesis, Wayne State University, Detroit, Michigan (1970).
105. K. L. Stevenson and J. F. Verdieck, *Mol. Photochem.* **1**, 271 (1969).
106. S. T. Spees and A. W. Adamson, *Inorg. Chem.* **1**, 531 (1962).
107. V. Sastri and C. H. Langford, *J. Phys. Chem.* **74**, 3945 (1970).
108. B. Nordén, *Acta Chem. Scand.* **24**, 349 (1970).
109. N. A. P. Kane-Maguire and C. H. Langford, *J. Am. Chem. Soc.* **94**, 2125 (1972).
110. N. A. P. Kane-Maguire, B. Dunlop, and C. H. Langford, *J. Am. Chem. Soc.* **93**, 6293 (1971).
111. N. A. P. Kane-Maguire and C. H. Langford, *Can. J. Chem.* **50**, 3381 (1972).
112. N. A. P. Kane-Maguire and C. H. Langford, *Inorg. Chem.* **15**, 464 (1976).
113. K. L. Stevenson, *J. Am. Chem. Soc.* **94**, 6652 (1972).
114. K. L. Stevenson and T. P. Vanden Driesche, *J. Am. Chem. Soc.* **96**, 7964 (1974).
115. J. G. Gordon and R. H. Holm, *J. Am. Chem. Soc.* **92**, 5319 (1970).
116. S. S. Minor and G. W. Everett, Jr., *Inorg. Chem.* **15**, 1526 (1976).
117. C. Kutal and R. E. Sievers, *Inorg. Chem.* **13**, 897 (1974).
118. G. W. Everett, Jr. and R. R. Horn, *J. Am. Chem. Soc.* **96**, 2087 (1974).
119. R. D. Koob, J. Beusen, S. Anderson, D. Gerber, S. P. Pappas, and M. L. Morris, *J. Chem. Soc., Chem. Commun.* p. 966 (1972).
120. S. S. Minor and G. W. Everett, Jr., *Inorg. Chim. Acta* **20**, L51 (1976).
121. V. S. Sastri, *Inorg. Chim. Acta* **7**, 381 (1973).
122. P. A. Grutsch and C. Kutal, *J. Am. Chem. Soc.* **99**, 7397 (1977).
123. M. F. Manfrin, L. Moggi, and V. Balzani, *Inorg. Chem.* **10**, 207 (1971).
124. A. D. Kirk, P. E. Hoggard, G. B. Porter, M. C. Rockley, and M. M. Windsor, *Chem. Phys. Lett.* **37**, 193 (1976).
125. J. I. Zink, *J. Am. Chem. Soc.* **94**, 8039 (1972).

126. J. I. Zink, *Inorg. Chem.* **12,** 1957 (1973).
127. J. I. Zink, *J. Am. Chem. Soc.* **96,** 4464 (1974).
128. M. Wrighton, H. B. Gray, and G. S. Hammond, *Mol. Photochem.* **5,** 164 (1973).
129. L. G. Vanquickenborne and A. Ceulemans, *J. Am. Chem. Soc.* **99,** 2208 (1977).
130. H. H. Krause and F. Wasgestian, *Inorg. Chim. Acta* **29,** 231 (1978).
131. C. H. Langford and J. P. Tong, *J. Chem. Soc., Chem. Commun.* p. 138 (1977).
132. S. Behrendt, C. H. Langford, and L. S. Frankel, *J. Am. Chem. Soc.* **91,** 1236 (1969).
133. V. S. Sastri, R. W. Henwood, S. Behrendt, and C. H. Langford, *J. Am. Chem. Soc.* **94,** 753 (1972).
134. C. F. C. Wong and A. D. Kirk, *Can. J. Chem.* **53,** 419 (1975).
135. C. F. C. Wong and A. D. Kirk, *Can. J. Chem.* **54,** 3794 (1976).
136. C. Kutal and A. W. Adamson, *J. Am. Chem. Soc.* **93,** 5581 (1971); *Inorg. Chem.* **12,** 1990 (1973).
137. J. F. Endicott and G. J. Ferraudi, *J. Phys. Chem.* **80,** 949 (1976).
138. The author wishes to thank Dr. C. Bartocci, Dr. C. A. Bignozzi, Dr. C. Chiorboli, Dr. M. T. Indelli, Dr. A. Maldotti, and Mr. L. Righetti for their help in the preparation of the manuscript.

INDEX

ORGANIC CHEMISTRY

A SERIES OF MONOGRAPHS

EDITOR

HARRY H. WASSERMAN

Department of Chemistry
Yale University
New Haven, Connecticut

1. Wolfgang Kirmse. CARBENE CHEMISTRY, 1964; 2nd Edition, 1971

2. Brandes H. Smith. BRIDGED AROMATIC COMPOUNDS, 1964

3. Michael Hanack. CONFORMATION THEORY, 1965

4. Donald J. Cram. FUNDAMENTALS OF CARBANION CHEMISTRY, 1965

5. Kenneth B. Wiberg (Editor). OXIDATION IN ORGANIC CHEMISTRY, PART A, 1965; Walter S. Trahanovsky (Editor). OXIDATION IN ORGANIC CHEMISTRY, PART B, 1973; PART C, 1978

6. R. F. Hudson. STRUCTURE AND MECHANISM IN ORGANO-PHOSPHORUS CHEMISTRY, 1965

7. A. William Johnson. YLID CHEMISTRY, 1966

8. Jan Hamer (Editor). 1,4-CYCLOADDITION REACTIONS, 1967

9. Henri Ulrich. CYCLOADDITION REACTIONS OF HETEROCUMULENES, 1967

10. M. P. Cava and M. J. Mitchell. CYCLOBUTADIENE AND RELATED COMPOUNDS, 1967

11. Reinhard W. Hoffmann. DEHYDROBENZENE AND CYCLOALKYNES, 1967

12. Stanley R. Sandler and Wolf Karo. ORGANIC FUNCTIONAL GROUP PREPARATIONS, VOLUME I, 1968; VOLUME II, 1971; VOLUME III, 1972

13. Robert J. Cotter and Markus Matzner. RING-FORMING POLYMERIZATIONS, PART A, 1969; PART B, 1; B, 2, 1972

14. R. H. DeWolfe, CARBOXYLIC ORTHO ACID DERIVATIVES, 1970

15. R. Foster. ORGANIC CHARGE-TRANSFER COMPLEXES, 1969

16. James P. Snyder (Editor). NONBENZENOID AROMATICS, VOLUME I, 1969; VOLUME II, 1971

17. C. H. Rochester. ACIDITY FUNCTIONS, 1970

18. Richard J. Sundberg. THE CHEMISTRY OF INDOLES, 1970

19. A. R. Katritzky and J. M. Lagowski. CHEMISTRY OF THE HETEROCYCLIC N-OXIDES, 1970

20. Ivar Ugi (Editor). ISONITRILE CHEMISTRY, 1971